PREFACE TO THE SECOND EDITION

SINCE the publication of our first edition in 1951, the literature of surface activity has been enriched by a large number of papers in the scientific and technological journals, as well as by several valuable books on the subject. Perhaps the most significant developments have been in the physical chemistry of interfacial processes, and in the technical applications of surface-active materials, and this fact has seemed to us to re-emphasise the desirability of approaching the whole subject from the physico-chemical point of view, *i.e.*, in terms of the unifying "scientific discipline" of colloid science. Such an approach seems more than ever to offer the best basis for examining the applications of surface-active agents, and for trying to relate surface active properties to the chemical structures of the agents themselves, especially as the technological scope of surface activity continues to expand. We have therefore adhered to the general plan of our first edition, and have found that the considerable amount of new material has fitted in quite readily.

A great deal of the newer patent literature on the preparation and uses of surface-active agents is concerned with process improvements, or with the elaboration or modification of chemical types which had already been described. It is therefore important to note again that we have considered patent specifications purely as *literature*, without regard to their possible validity or value as monopoly instruments.

Our thanks are due to several colleagues for kindly reading portions of the new material in this edition, especially Mr. S. Horrobin, Dr. W. Baird, Mr. C. A. Norris, Mr. G. Boardman, and Dr. A. K. Gupta, to the Elsevier Publishing Company for permission to reproduce Figure 22, and to Dr. C. M. Blair, Mr. E. J. Pryor, and the Editor of *Chemistry and Industry* for access to the manuscripts of two papers which were still in the press at the time of writing. Our thanks are also due to Messrs. Imperial Chemical Industries Limited, Dyestuffs Division, and to I.C.I. (Hyde) Limited, for the provision of valuable library facilities.

J. L. MOILLIET
B. COLLIE
W. BLACK

Research Laboratories,
Imperial Chemical Industries Ltd.,
Hexagon House,
Blackley, Manchester
          and
Research Department,
I.C.I. (Hyde) Ltd.
1960

PREFACE TO THE FIRST EDITION

THE technological and scientific importance of synthetic surface-active agents, and of the effects which they make possible, are too well known to require any explanation. Our object in adding another book to the literature on the subject is to attempt an approach from the physico-chemical point of view, in which technical processes are considered in terms of their component physical chemical phenomena and the relation of both to the chemistry of surface-active agents is indicated. Such an approach is convenient in that it gives some coherence and unity to a discussion which must necessarily cover a wide range of processes and substances; we believe that it will also prove to be a useful one if it leads to a fuller understanding of the relation between chemical constitution and surface activity, and of the mode of action of surface-active agents, both of which are essentially physical chemical problems. The fact that neither problem has yet been fully solved, in spite of the large amount of excellent technological and fundamental work which has been done, in no way diminishes the force of this argument, and we hope that the present book will in fact help to draw attention to some of the gaps in present-day knowledge on these topics.

No attempt has been made in the third part of the book, which deals with the chemical constitution of surface-active agents, to compile lists of commercial products. Useful lists of this type are periodically published in the technical journals, but we feel that they become too quickly out of date to be worth including in the present monograph, and that it is impossible to prepare lists which give accurately the compositions of all commercial products. Our advice to the reader who wishes to obtain commercial surface-active products for general or specific uses is to write directly to the manufacturers who are listed in directories such as the *F.B.I. Register of British Manufacturers* (published by the Federation of British Industries, 21 Tothill Street, Westminster, London, W.C.2), or the "Buyers Guide Sections" of *Chemical Industries* (published at 1309 Noble Street, Philadelphia, Pa.).

A word of explanation is needed about two sources of information on which we have drawn heavily, *viz.*, patent specifications, and the reports ("B.I.O.S.," "F.I.A.T.," etc.) of the Allied Missions to Germany at the end of the Second World War. The former have been considered purely as literature; *i.e.*, no attempt has been made to ascertain whether or not patents are still in force, or to cover all equivalent specifications in different countries, and we have tried to avoid making observations concerning the validity of particular patents as legal monopoly instruments. We have also tended to choose British and United States Specifications for illustrating

vii

different types of surface-active agents, on the grounds that the originals would be more readily available to most of our readers. As regards reports by the Allied Missions, it is perhaps pertinent to point out that, in the nature of things, their availability tends to exaggerate the unquestionably major part which German chemical industry has played in the discovery of synthetic surface-active agents. The fact that a product or process is illustrated by reference to information obtained from a particular German firm does not mean that the concern in question is necessarily the only (or even the original) manufacturer.

Major portions of the manuscript have been read by Professor E. A. Guggenheim, Sc.D., F.R.S., Dr. G. S. Hartley, Mr. S. Horrobin, and Dr. W. Baird, to whom the authors' thanks are due for valuable constructive criticisms, and for pointing out a number of inaccuracies and inconsistencies. We are also indebted to the following colleagues for useful textual criticisms: Mr. G. E. Davies, Mr. P. T. Gale, Dr. A. S. Gomm, Mr. A. MacArthur, Dr. A. R. Martin, Dr. S. H. Oakeshott, Dr. C. Preston, Dr. F. S. Statham, and Dr. Arthur T. Williamson. A number of private communications are acknowledged in the text. Our thanks are also due to Messrs. Williams and Wilkins, Baltimore, Maryland, for permission to reproduce Figure 2, to the American Institute of Physics, New York, for permission to reproduce Figure 13, and to Messrs. Imperial Chemical Industries Limited, Dyestuffs Division, for the use of library facilities, which have been invaluable.

J. L. MOILLIET

B. COLLIE

Research Laboratories,
Imperial Chemical Industries Ltd.,
Hexagon House,
Blackley,
Manchester.

1950

CONTENTS

	Page
Preface to 2nd edition	v
Preface to 1st edition	vii
Literature abbreviations	xi
List of illustrations	xv

PART I

The Physical Chemistry of Surface-Active Agents and Interfacial Processes

Chapter

1. INTRODUCTION: SURFACE-ACTIVE AGENTS, SURFACE ACTIVITY, AND INTERFACIAL PROCESSES   3

2. THE STATES OF SOLUTION OF SURFACE-ACTIVE AGENTS   12

Physical properties of paraffin-chain salts, micellar theories, and critical concentration. Non-paraffin-chain amphipathic electrolytes. Non-ionogenic surface-active agents. Solubilisation by amphipathic electrolytes. Critical concentration: determination and factors influencing it.

3. THE ADSORPTION OF SURFACE-ACTIVE AGENTS AT INTERFACES   64

Thermodynamics of adsorption of surface-active agents: Gibbs's equation; surface-active electrolytes; micelle formation; surface tension minima; direct determination of surface excesses; effect of interfacial complexes; "Traube's rule"; Gibbs's equation and solid-liquid interfaces; adsorption maxima at solid-liquid interfaces; interfacial equations of state; adsorption of surface-active macromolecules. Kinetics of adsorption of surface-active agents: rapid and slow surface-ageing phenomena.

4. FUNDAMENTAL INTERFACIAL PROCESSES   132

Wetting phenomena: thermodynamics and kinetics; effect of surface roughness, geometric structure, and adsorption of surface-active agents. Deflocculation and flocculation. Protective colloid action. Mechanical phase-subdivision processes: emulsification; dispersion of solid particles. Precipitation processes. Foam formation and destruction.

PART II

Technical Applications of Synthetic Surface-Active Agents

5. TECHNICAL WETTING-OUT AND WATER-PROOFING PROCESSES   211

Wetting-out of isolated surfaces: spreading of bulk liquid phases; adhesion of liquid droplets to solid surfaces; wetting-out of dust particles on liquids. Wetting-out of porous masses: textiles, powders, etc. Re-wetting processes. Water-proofing.

6. THE PREPARATION OF EMULSIONS: DEMULSIFICATION   248

Emulsion techniques: general methods; self-emulsifying oils; interfacial complexes. Emulsifying machinery: high speed stirrers, colloid mills, etc. Water-in-oil emulsions. Demulsification.

x   *Contents*

Chapter   *Page*

7. THE DISPERSION OF SOLIDS IN LIQUID MEDIA   269

   Introduction. Mechanical methods for producing dispersions: ball-milling,
   "colloid"-milling, plastic milling, dry pulverisation, intensive mixing. Dispersion by controlled precipitation (condensation). Stabilisation of dispersions.
   Preparation of dispersions in non-aqueous media.

8. DETERGENT PROCESSES   285

   Introduction. Fundamental phenomena: initial wetting-out, displacement of
   liquid dirt, detachment of solid dirt. Favourable ancillary phenomena:
   emulsification and deflocculation, solubilisation, foaming. Unfavourable
   ancillary phenomena: exhaustion of detergent, re-deposition of dirt. Evaluation of detergents. "Detergent builders." Public health aspects of the use of
   synthetic detergents. Correlation between detergent action and states of
   solution of surface-active agents.

9. SOME OTHER APPLICATIONS OF SURFACE-ACTIVE AGENTS   318

   Dyeing assistants: levelling, restraining, fixing, stripping, and pigment-pad-
   dyeing agents. Bactericides. Flotation of ores. Emulsion polymerisation.
   Some less common uses.

                                PART III

The Chemical Constitution of Synthetic Surface-Active Agents

10. ANIONIC SURFACE-ACTIVE AGENTS: SULPHONIC ACIDS AND THEIR
    SALTS   355

    Historical. Classification of types. Aliphatic sulphonates. Sulphonates of
    aliphatic-aromatic hydrocarbons: alkylated naphthalene, alkylated benzene,
    aralkyl aromatic, etc. Ester sulphonates: sulphoester and sulphoacyl com-
    pounds. Amide sulphonates: sulphoamide and sulphoacylamide compounds,
    sulphonamide sulphonates. Miscellaneous: sulphonates containing ether,
    amino, keto, and sulphone groups.

11. ANIONIC SURFACE-ACTIVE AGENTS: THE ALIPHATIC SULPHATES   402

    Introduction. Sulphated fatty alcohols: straight-chain, secondary, tertiary,
    and branched-chain fatty alcohol sulphates, sulphated olefins, etc. Sulphated
    fatty condensation products. Sulphated fatty glycerides, acids, and esters:
    "sulphonated oils." Technical applications.

12. OTHER ANIONIC SURFACE-ACTIVE AGENTS   437

    Carboxylates, sulphinates, phosphates, and other types.

13. CATIONIC SURFACE-ACTIVE AGENTS   445

    Amine salts. Quaternary ammonium compounds. Pyridinium compounds.
    Other quaternary and ternary cationic agents. Special uses.

14. NON-IONIC SURFACE-ACTIVE AGENTS   465

    Polyethenoxy compounds. Derivatives of polyglycerols. Other types: fatty
    esters of glycol, sorbitol, and mannitol; polymerised dioxolanes, substituted
    betaines, sugar detergents, etc.

15. OTHER TYPES OF SURFACE-ACTIVE MATERIALS   487

    Macromolecules and polymers. Lignin sulphonic acids. Salts of organic bases
    and anionic surface-active agents. Special mixtures.

Author index   497

Subject index   507

LITERATURE ABBREVIATIONS

Acta Chem. Scand.	Acta Chemica Scandinavica
Amer. Dyes. Reporter	American Dyestuffs Reporter
Amer. J. Pub. Health	American Journal of Public Health
Angew. Chem.	Angewandte Chemie
Ann. der Physik	Annalen der Physik
Ann. N.Y. Acad. Sci.	Annals of the New York Academy of Sciences
Ann. Rev. Microbiol.	Annual Review of Microbiology
Biochem. J.	The Biochemical Journal
B.I.O.S.	British Intelligence Objectives Sub-Committee reports
B.P.	British Patent Specification
Bact. Rev.	Bacteriological Reviews
Ber.	Berichte der deutschen chemischen Gesellschaft, or Chemische Berichte
Biochem. Z.	Biochemische Zeitschrift
Brit. Med. J.	British Medical Journal
Bull. Acad. Sci. U.R.S.S.	Bulletin de l'académie des sciences de l'Union des Républiques Soviétiques Socialistes
Bull. soc. chim.	Bulletin de la Société Chimique de France
Bull. soc. chim. Belg.	Bulletin de la Société Chimique de Belgique
Compt. rend.	Comptes rendus hebdomadaires des séances de l'Académie des Sciences
C.R. Acad. Sci. U.R.S.S.	Comptes rendus (Doklady) de l'Académie des Sciences de l'U.R.S.S.
Chem. Abs.	Chemical Abstracts
Chem. and Ind.	Chemistry and Industry
Chem. Met. Engineering	Chemical and Metallurgical Engineering or (since 1946) Chemical Engineering
Chem. Zentr.	Chemisches Zentralblatt
Chem. Ztg.	Chemiker-Zeitung
Deutsche med. Wochschr.	Deutsche medizinische Wochenschrift
D.R.P.	German Patent Specification
Fette u. Seifen	Fette und Seifen, einschliesslich der Anstrichmittel
First Congress	Premier Congrès Mondial de la Détergence
F.P.	French Patent Specification
F.I.A.T.	Field Information Agency, Technical (reports)
Ind. Eng. Chem.	Industrial and Engineering Chemistry
Ind. Eng. Chem. (Anal.)	do., Analytical Edition
J. Amer. Chem. Soc.	Journal of the American Chemical Society

J. Amer. Oil Chem. Soc.	Journal of the American Oil Chemists' Society
J. Amer. Pharm. Ass.	Journal of the American Pharmaceutical Association (Scientific Edition)
J. Amer. Vet. Med. Ass.	Journal of the American Veterinary Medical Association
J. Appl. Chem.	Journal of Applied Chemistry
J. Bact.	Journal of Bacteriology
J. Chem. Phys.	Journal of Chemical Physics
J. Chem. Soc.	Journal of the Chemical Society
J. chim. phys.	Journal de chimie physique
J. Coll. Sci.	Journal of Colloid Science
J. Exptl. Med.	Journal of Experimental Medicine
J. Gen. Microbiol.	Journal of General Microbiology
J. Hygiene	Journal of Hygiene
J. Inst. Petroleum	Journal of the Institute of Petroleum
J. Oil Colour Chem. Ass.	Journal of the Oil and Colour Chemists' Association
J. Phys. Chem.	Journal of Physical Chemistry
J. Phys. Chem. U.S.S.R.	Journal of Physical Chemistry of the U.S.S.R.
J. Phys. Coll. Chem.	Journal of Physical and Colloid Chemistry
J. Polymer Sci.	Journal of Polymer Science
J. Pomology	Journal of Pomology
J. Soc. Chem. Ind.	Journal of the Society of Chemical Industry
J. Soc. Cosmetic Chem.	Journal of the Society of Cosmetic Chemists
J. Soc. Dyers Colourists	Journal of the Society of Dyers and Colourists
J. Soc. Leather Trades Chem.	Journal of the Society of Leather Trades Chemists
J. Textile Inst.	Journal of the Textile Institute
Koll. Beih.	Kolloid-Beihefte, Kolloidchemische Beihefte
Koll. Z.	Kolloid-Zeitschrift
Koll. Zhur.	Kolloidnyi Zhurnal
Lieb. Ann.	Liebigs Annalen der Chemie
Phil. Mag.	Philosophical Magazine
Phil. Trans.	Philosophical Transactions of the Royal Society
Phys. Rev.	Physical Review
Proc. Nat. Acad. Sci.	Proceedings of the National Academy of Sciences of the U.S.A.
Proc. Roy. Soc.	Proceedings of the Royal Society
Proc. Soc. Exptl. Bio. Med.	Proceedings of the Society of Experimental Biology and Medicine
Quart. Rev.	Quarterly Reviews of the Chemical Society
Rec. trav. chim.	Recueil des travaux chimiques des Pays-Bas et de la Belgique

Second Congress	Proceedings of the Second International Congress of Surface Activity
Seifensieder Ztg.	Seifensieder-Zeitung
Soap Sanit. Chemicals	Soap and Sanitary Chemicals
Surg. Gynec. Obstet.	Surgery, Gynecology, and Obstetrics
Sw. P.	Swiss Patent Specification
Textilber.	Melliands Textilberichte
Text. Res. J.	Textile Research Journal
Trans. Faraday Soc.	Transactions of the Faraday Society
Trans. Inst. Mining Engineers	Transactions of the Institution of Mining Engineers
U.S.P.	United States Patent Specification
Z. angew. Chem.	Zeitschrift für angewandte Chemie
Z. Elektrochem.	Zeitschrift für Elektrochemie
Z. Physik	Zeitschrift für Physik
Z. physik. Chem.	Zeitschrift für Physikalische Chemie
Z. physik. Chem. (Leipzig)	Zeitschrift für physikalische Chemie (Leipzig Edition)
Zh. Eks. Teor. Fiz.	Zhurnal Eksperimental'noi i teoreticheskoi Fiziki

ILLUSTRATIONS

Figure   *Page*

1. Partial specific volumes of water and butyric acid at 0° c.   13

2. Physical property curves for aqueous sodium dodecyl sulphate   15

3. Variation of the concentration of micelles (c_m); the ratio of the micelle concentration to total concentration (c_m/c): and the rate of change of micelle concentration (dc_m/dc) for a micelle consisting of 20 molecules (m = 20)   17

4. Density of solution and apparent and partial specific volumes of butyric acid in water at 0° c.   17

5. Osmotic activity of butyric acid solutions   18

6. Conductivity of aqueous solutions of cetyltrimethylammonium bromide at 35° c.   19

7. Conductivities of aqueous solutions of amphipathic electrolytes   20

8. "Lamellar Micelle" in 15% potassium laurate solution—highly-idealised cross-section   23

9. Equivalent conductivity of dodecane and tetradecane sulphonic acids   25

10. Solubilities of amphipathic electrolytes in water   27

11. Transport numbers of positive and negative radicals of amphipathic electrolytes   29

12. Transport number and conductivity of cetyltrimethylammonium bromide at 35° c.   30

13. Resolved M-band and I-band from aqueous solutions of potassium laurate and potassium myristate   34

14. Solubilisation by amphipathic electrolytes   46

15. Differential solubilisation by amphipathic electrolytes   49

16. Equivalent conductivities of alkylamine hydrochlorides at 60° c.   57

17. Conductivities of hexadecyl and octadecyl pyridinium iodates   58

18. Equilibrium state corresponding to finite contact angle (θ)   134

19. Thermodynamical derivation of Young's equation   135

20. Capillary rise in inwardly and outwardly tapering capillaries   149

21. Total potential energy curves of interaction between two spherical particles   164

22. The effect of the surface potential (ψ_0) on the total potential energy of interaction   165

Figure   *Page*

23. Effect of Born repulsion on potential energy curves: flocculation
    (F) and deflocculation (D). Also shown, curve with secondary
    minimum   166

24. Equilibrium sedimentation volume of 1 gm. Prussian Blue as
    function of amount of cetyltrimethylammonium bromide   175

25. Effect of oleic acid on yield value of tin crystal in pure hydro-
    carbon oil   182

26. Equilibrium crystal shape: generalised case of a parallelepiped   190

SURFACE ACTIVITY

PART I

THE PHYSICAL CHEMISTRY OF SURFACE-ACTIVE AGENTS AND INTERFACIAL PROCESSES

CHAPTER 1

INTRODUCTION: SURFACE-ACTIVE AGENTS, SURFACE ACTIVITY, AND INTERFACIAL PROCESSES

SURFACE-active agents—substances which alter the conditions prevailing at interfaces—have been obtained from natural products by extraction or modification since prehistoric times. Examples which come immediately to mind are cleansing materials such as the soaps, water-proofing agents such as greases and tallows, and dispersing or emulsifying agents such as glue, egg white, the natural gums, and the various organic substances used by primitive peoples in the puddling of clay. Many such agents, which are derived by relatively simple treatments of natural products, have been the subject of technical and scientific research for many years, as the result of which, as is well known, very great improvements have been made in their variety, purity, and performance. *Synthetic surface-active agents*, on the other hand—and by this term we understand substances which have been specially synthesised in order to obtain surface-active effects—represent a relatively modern development, which may be said to have evolved from the "sulphonated oils" of the last century, and to have reached its most active phase in the period between the two World Wars. The scope of the present book will be limited to these synthetic agents, partly because they constitute a coherent theme, but principally in order to reduce the subject matter of a single monograph to manageable proportions.

The applications of surface-active agents are very widely distributed throughout science, technology, and everyday life. Examples which at once come to mind are the washing, wetting-out, or water-proofing of textile materials, the preparation of dispersions and emulsions, the application of agricultural and horticultural sprays, and a wide variety of special uses the number of which is continually increasing. It is this great diversity in the applications of surface-active agents which makes it so important, when we try to examine how they function, to look for fundamental concepts which will give some unity or "scientific discipline" to the whole picture.

It seems clear that the most suitable basis on which to construct a picture of the action of surface-active agents is in the first place to recall that the fundamental phenomenon is *adsorption* and that this adsorption can lead to one or both of two quite distinct types of effects:

(*a*) *lowerings of one or more of the boundary tensions* prevailing at the interfaces in the system in question, and/or

(*b*) *stabilisation of one or more of the interfaces* by the formation of adsorbed layers which mechanically oppose any tendency for these interfaces to be diminished in area or destroyed.

Practically all the examples of surface activity which we shall consider in the present book can be shown to be due to one or both of these two types of effects, sometimes acting alone and sometimes in combination, sometimes at a single interface and sometimes at several. (The only possible exceptions to this generalisation are the phenomena of solubilisation by certain surface-active materials, which are discussed in Chapter 2.)

The physical significance of the interfacial tension and the manner in which it is lowered by surface-active agents are considered more fully in Chapter 3. It will suffice here to point out that an interfacial tension is always present at the interface between any two incompletely miscible phases, and that it arises from a dissymmetry among the forces acting on the molecules or atoms at or near the interface. The interfacial tension, the effect of which is always a tendency to reduce the area of the interface to a minimum, may be quite properly treated as a tension (usually expressed in dynes/cm.) acting parallel to the interface.* It is numerically equal to the amount of work (usually in ergs/cm.²) which must be done in reversibly increasing the interface by unit area. Neither of these conventions, nor the fact that the interfacial tension is "real," means however that a contractile skin is necessarily present in the interface.[1] This point is important when we come to consider the effect of adsorbed surface-active agents.

Lowerings in the interfacial tension between incompletely miscible phases can contribute usefully to technical processes in several ways. Thus a lowering of the interfacial tension between a liquid and another phase (gaseous, liquid, or solid) may promote the dispersion of one phase in another. Examples are furnished by emulsification and spraying processes, and by the dispersion of solids in liquid media, all such processes being characterised by the fact that the area of the interface between the two phases is greatly increased. Alternatively, the displacement of one fluid phase (liquid or gaseous) from the surface of a solid substrate by a second fluid phase which is not miscible with the first, may be helped (or even made possible) by the fact that a surface-active agent decreases certain interfacial tensions relatively more than others. Such displacement phenomena, which are the basis of such technical processes as wetting, waterproofing, and detergent action, are characterised by the fact that certain types of interfaces (*e.g.*, liquid-solid or air-solid) tend to increase in area at the expense of other interfaces of the same or different types. In all the processes just mentioned, the change in the total free energy of the system which is due to the extensions or contractions of the various interfaces,

---

* This conception becomes less simple when we are dealing with an interface at which one phase is a crystalline solid. This point is referred to again in Chapter 3.

[1] See Adam, *Physics and Chemistry of Surfaces*, Oxford University Press, 3rd Edition, 1941, p. 3.

depends on the magnitudes of the interfacial tensions involved; consequently the effect of a surface-active agent can often be usefully analysed *thermodynamically* in terms of its effect on *the change in the total free energy residing in the interfaces* of the system, *i.e.*, the change in the *total interfacial free energy** of the system.

In making such a thermodynamical analysis, however, it is important to note that a surface-active agent is not simply a "fuel economiser"—*i.e.*, its value cannot be judged directly from the number of calories (usually extremely small) which it makes available by decreasing the total free energy of a system. The rôle of a surface-active agent is rather to alter the *equilibrium state towards which the system is striving, and its technical value is to be judged by how far this alteration in the equilibrium state is favourable to the desired technical effect.*

Let us suppose, to take one familiar example, that we are attempting to "wet out" a porous solid mass (such as a piece of cloth) in an aqueous solution, *i.e.*, to expel the air from the mass and to replace it completely by the aqueous solution. If the interfacial tensions solid-liquid, liquid-air, and solid-air have certain values, we may find that the equilibrium state, towards which the system continually strives, is such that the air is displaced only slightly by the solution. If we now forcibly immerse the porous mass in order to exploit the effect of the buoyancy of the air, and agitate it vigorously, we may find that most of the mechanical work, if not substantially all of it, will be wasted, because (*i*) the effect of the "tensions" set up by the mechanical work and/or the force of gravity is continually being opposed by the net effect of the interfacial tensions, (*ii*) the tensions set up mechanically may be so widely or inefficiently applied inside the porous mass that they are insufficient to overcome the resultant of the interfacial tensions except at a very few places, and (*iii*) the effect of mechanical work may be intermittent, so that a local advance by the liquid may be nullified as soon as the mechanical tension is relaxed, even momentarily. If, however, we now add a so-called "wetting agent," which so changes the interfacial tensions that the equilibrium state corresponds to a complete or partial displacement of the air, then the interfacial tensions will offer less resistance to the wetting process, or they may even cause it to occur spontaneously: in either event the wetting process may well be enormously helped by the wetting agent—and the saving of energy may be immeasurably greater than the actual reduction in total interfacial free energy. This and other examples are more fully discussed in later chapters.

The tendency for surface-active agents to be adsorbed at interfaces is most frequently due to a property for which G. S. Hartley has coined the name "*amphipathy*": *i.e.*, the occurrence in a single molecule or ion, with a suitable degree of separation, of one or more groups which have an

---

* The definition of "interfacial free energy," or "free energy of the interface," is considered more fully on p. 64; we do not use it as a synonym for the interfacial tension.

affinity ("sympathy") for the phase in which the molecule or ion is dissolved, together with one or more groups which are antipathetic to the
medium (*i.e.*, which tend to be expelled by it). It is convenient to refer to
these two types of groups as "lyophilic" and "lyophobic," respectively (or
"hydrophilic" and "hydrophobic" if the solvent is water). Winsor[1] prefers
the word "amphiphilic" to describe these compounds, since he considers
that it is the attractions of like for like rather than the repulsive forces
between like and unlike which are more frequently the dominant ones,
and which are responsible for their special properties. Since, however, we
shall be dealing almost entirely with aqueous solutions we prefer to refer
to these substances as "amphipathic." Examples of amphipathic surface-
active agents for use in aqueous media are:

$C_{17}H_{35}COO^-$ Na^+ (sodium stearate),

$C_{16}H_{33}OSO_3^-$ Na^+ (sodium cetyl sulphate),

$C_{17}H_{33}CON(CH_3)CH_2CH_2SO_3^-$ Na^+ (sodium salt of oleyl-N-
   methyltaurine),

$C_{16}H_{33}N(CH_3)_3^+$ Br^- (cetyltrimethylammonium bromide),

$C_{16}H_{33}[OCH_2CH_2]_nOH$ (cetyl polyglycol ether, where n may
   for example lie between 15 and 30),

$(C_3H_7)_2C_{10}H_5SO_3^-$ Na^+ (sodium diisopropylnaphthalene sulphonate),

$C_8H_{17}OOC\!\!-\!\!CH\!\!-\!\!SO_3^-$ Na^+ (sodium dioctyl sulphosuccinate).
$C_8H_{17}OOC\!\!-\!\!CH_2$

The presence of the hydrophilic group (*e.g.*, an ionising group or a polyglycol chain) renders each of these substances soluble in water at an
appropriate temperature, but in each case the water strives in effect to
expel the hydrocarbon grouping, which may be considered to be water-
insoluble. As a result of these two opposing tendencies, the ions or molecules
of the surface-active agent tend to become concentrated at the interface
between the aqueous solution and an external phase, provided that this
external phase is sufficiently "sympathetic" to the hydrocarbon grouping
in the surface-active agent. (If, of course, the hydrocarbon grouping is
actually "soluble" in the external phase—as will be true, for example, at
many oil-water interfaces—or has some other special affinity for it, this
tendency will be encouraged.) In other words, in the absence of special
directive forces acting in the opposite sense, the ions or molecules of the
agent will be adsorbed in the interface and will be so orientated that, on
the whole, they turn a majority of their hydrophilic groups towards the
aqueous phase and a majority of their hydrophobic groups away from the
water and perhaps even into the non-aqueous medium. Such a phenomenon
we can conveniently call an *amphipathic* or *non-specific adsorption*; it causes

[1] Winsor, *Solvent Properties of Amphiphilic Compounds*, Butterworth, 1954.

a reduction in the interfacial tension, because the dissymmetry in the forces on the molecules near the interface is now diminished. The surface-active molecule or ion can be looked on as a sort of bridge between the two phases, which makes the transition between them less abrupt. The adsorbed ions or molecules may also, if they form a sufficiently compact interfacial layer, *stabilise* the interface in the sense discussed above, *i.e.*, make it more difficult for the interface to be destroyed or diminished in area.

The precise structure of interfacial films of surface-active agents cannot be described in many cases, but the orientation to which we have just referred does not imply that the molecules are necessarily closely packed in a solid film. The structure of interfacial films, usually of insoluble sub-stances, is the subject of an extensive literature, of which the best review is undoubtedly Adam's book. Fortunately, a complete picture of the struc-ture of the interfaces involved is not usually necessary for analysing the processes in which surface-active agents are used. It is probably a fair generalisation to make, however, that most films of soluble surface-active agents at liquid-air interfaces are of the gaseous type, in which the mole-cules are free to move laterally on the surface, with a fairly labile equil-ibrium between the molecules in the interface and those in the solution below, especially when appreciable concentrations of other electrolytes are also present. Exceptions to this are provided by the interfaces in foams, which may contain liquid or even solid films. Many interfacial films at liquid-liquid interfaces will also be gaseous, though efficient emulsifying agents are usually characterised by their tendency to form films of a more condensed type. The state of adsorbed surface-active molecules at solid-liquid or solid-gas interfaces is more a matter for conjecture. We would suggest, however, that the following general rule may be of some use in con-sidering what type of interfacial film(s) is (are) most likely to be present, or most to be desired, in all types of technical interfacial processes: where the function of the surface-active agent is a dynamic one (*i.e.*, where it is in-tended to help a process in which fresh interfaces are being created), then it should form films of the gaseous type at the interfaces in question; where a surface-active agent is added in order to stabilise a particular state of extension of one or more interfaces, it should tend to form films of a more condensed type (liquid, condensed liquid, or solid). This principle means of course that the presence of lateral forces between adsorbed molecules or ions may sometimes be nearly as important as their behaviour with respect to the two media which meet at the interface.

The picture given, in the penultimate paragraph, of the orientation of amphipathetically adsorbed surface-active molecules or ions was subject to the *proviso* that there were no special directive forces of a more powerful nature acting in the opposite sense. This qualification is important, because many instances are known of adsorption with orientation in the reverse sense, in which it is the hydrophilic group which is bound to the surface of a solid external phase, and the hydrophobic groups are orientated towards the aqueous phase. (These cases are frequently "chemisorptions," in which the polar group is bound to certain groups in the surface of the solid by chemical linkages.) The result of such a specific adsorption will often be that the surface of the solid becomes more rather than less hydrophobic, so that it is more difficult to wet by aqueous media. Among technical applications of this effect may be mentioned the action of flotation agents on minerals, or of certain paraffin chain salts on certain pigments. As we shall see in Chapters 3 and 4, however, this decreased "affinity" between the surface of the solid and the liquid medium does not mean that the solid-liquid interfacial tension is actually increased by the occurrence of a specific adsorption. This is in fact improbable (and usually impossible), and the decrease in ease of wetting is due to a decrease in the work of adhesion liquid-solid, the magnitude of which is determined by all three of the interfacial tensions, solid-liquid, solid-air, and liquid-air.

The term specific adsorption can also be used in a wider sense to cover all cases in which adsorption is due to a positive attraction, or an actual linkage, between specific polar groups in the adsorbent and in the surface-active molecule or ion; *i.e.*, it does not necessarily imply that the surface-active agent is amphipathic. A considerable number of technically important surface-active agents cannot in fact be considered to be amphipathic; *i.e.*, their ultimate particles (molecules, macromolecules, or colloidal aggregates) do not have well-defined, separate lyophobic and lyophilic regions. The lyophobic groups may even be absent. In many such cases it seems reasonable to postulate that certain of the lyophilic groups are adsorbed by virtue of attractive forces or specific bonds between them and groups in the interface, especially if the external phase is a solid. Many such agents can be designated, perhaps as a concession to our present lack of knowledge, as *specific* surface-active agents. Many of the water-soluble agents whose surface activity cannot readily be interpreted in terms of simple amphipathy are *macromolecular*, and here a contributory factor in surface activity may be a sort of configurational entropy, the most "probable" position of many dissolved macromolecules being at or near the interface. Examples of such agents, which are used, for example, as protective colloids for dispersions and emulsions in aqueous media, are:

$$HOC_2H_4[OCH_2CH_2]_nOH \text{ (polyethylene glycol),}$$
$$\ldots CH_2CHOHCH_2CHOH \ldots \text{ (polyvinyl alcohol),}$$

and water-soluble cellulose ethers, water-soluble cellulose glycollates, and (for certain purposes) water-soluble dyestuffs. In all these cases the hydrophobic groups are so small and so scattered among the hydrophilic groups, that the molecule is negligibly amphipathic.

It will be clear that there must be many "border-line" cases between amphipathic and specific surface-active agents. Thus polyvinyl alcohol can be considered to be amphipathic in the sense of having a hydrophilic and a hydrophobic "side" when its formula is written

$$\ldots CH_2\!-\!CH\!-\!CH_2\!-\!CH \ldots$$
$$OHOH$$

and the same argument applies to the important deflocculating agents obtained by condensing aromatic sulphonic acids with formaldehyde, *e.g.*,

$$Na^+\ ^-O_3S \text{\Large (aromatic structure)} SO_3^-\ Na^+.$$

The essential distinction which we should like to make between amphipathic and specific adsorption is that the former is determined by a quite general tendency for the medium to expel one part of the molecule (or ion) while retaining the other, *and that it therefore frequently lends itself to predictions*. A specific adsorption, on the other hand, being due to positive attractions or interactions between specific groups, is usually more unpredictable in its occurrence, and often gives results which appear at first sight to be "anomalous" from a simple application of the rules of amphipathy.

So far we have been considering the applications of surface-active agents chiefly in thermodynamical terms. Such an approach is often of great value, because (a) we are principally concerned in many cases with whether or not a process is possible, and (b) in many technical interfacial processes there appears to be a good correlation—at least qualitatively—between the surface free energy change accompanying the process and the speed with which it takes place. (In other words, we can often treat interfacial tensions, or the pressure differences which they set up across curved menisci, as if they were mechanical tensions acting directly in dynamic processes.) It should be noted, however, that in such a treatment it is necessary to use the interfacial tension obtaining at the appropriate age of the surface, *i.e.*, consideration must be given to the *kinetics of the adsorption of surface-active agents at interfaces*, which determine the speed with which interfacial tensions are lowered by surface-active agents in the course of dynamic processes. Unfortunately, the exact information which is available on the kinetics of adsorption of surface-active compounds is restricted in scope, and we shall therefore generally have to content ourselves with qualitative arguments, often in the form of *caveats*.

The criterion of the change in interfacial free energy becomes of quite minor importance when we consider phenomena in which the function of surface-active agents is to preserve the metastable state of certain systems: for example, to prevent flocculation, aggregation, or coalescence in dispersions and emulsions. The action of surface-active agents as protective colloids or emulsion stabilisers can in fact be regarded as being for the most part the prevention of the establishment of a state in which the total interfacial free-energy is at a minimum, this state being characterised *inter alia* by the fact that the total area of each type of interface is at a minimum. (Even here, however, any agent which reduces the interfacial tension, and hence the total interfacial free energy, will tend to stabilise the state of the system, other things being equal.) The application of surface-active agents as protective colloids and emulsion stabilisers can therefore best be examined by reference to physical pictures of the interfaces concerned, these physical pictures being taken from the generally accepted theory of the stabilisation of disperse systems. This entails examining how surface-active agents may affect stabilising electrokinetic potentials, the hydration of dispersed particles, or the mechanical strength of interfacial films. Here it becomes necessary to consider how the presence of adsorbed surface-active agents fits into the picture of the stabilisation of disperse systems which has been developed by the Kruyt-Overbeek school in Holland, the Derjaguin school in Russia, and other workers. Surface-active agents have a considerable effect on this picture, and in many cases we can usefully treat them as forming an interfacial phase, which is capable of converting many "lyophobic" sols into what are effectively lyophilic dispersions.

It will have been noticed that the typical surface-active agents listed earlier in the present chapter fall naturally into three types on an electrochemical basis, according to whether the surface-active unit (in aqueous solution) is an unionised molecule, an anion, or a cation. This useful classification, which corresponds to many of the properties of surface-active agents, is well established,[1] and requires no further explanation, except to note that some surface-active agents may belong to more than one class: *e.g.*, they may contain both cationic and anionic groups (as in the "betaine" structures), or both ionising and non-ionic hydrophilic groups, as in structures of the types

$$R—[OC_2H_4]_nOSO_3{}^-, Na^+$$

or
$$R—N\begin{array}{l} [C_2H_4O]_nH \\ \\ [C_2H_4O]_mH \end{array} \qquad \text{(in acid media)}.$$

An important factor in determining the behaviour of a surface-active agent is its state of solution in the medium in which it is used. The available information, most of which relates to aqueous solutions, is reviewed in Chapter 2, in which it is pointed out that the very characteristics which confer surface-activity on a molecule or ion (notably the property of amphipathy), may also cause the individual units to aggregate into

---

[1] *Cf.* Chwala's monograph, *Textilhilfsmittel*, Julius Springer, Vienna, 1939, pp. 60 ff.

micelles. It seems fairly certain that these micelles are so organised that their exteriors are made up of the hydrophilic groups in the individual molecules or ions, the hydrophobic portions being orientated inwards: they are therefore usually non-amphipathic. In general, therefore, micelle formation causes a loss of effective surface-activity, especially if the adsorption of the surface-active agent is a simple amphipathic one. In such a case the technical efficiency of the agent may represent a compromise between two opposing effects. When however we are dealing with surface-active phenomena which are based on the highly specific adsorption of a surface-active agent (*e.g.*, by virtue of its polar group), then it is possible that the micelles could be more effective than the single ions, and the formation of micelles may be actually favourable, even though it may cause a decrease in the amount of adsorption. In either event, the state of solution of the surface-active agent is obviously important.

The plan of the present book will, we hope, be self-explanatory. As in our first edition, we propose first to discuss the physico-chemical basis of our subject, dealing with the states of solution of surface-active agents, their adsorption at interfaces, and the effects of such adsorptions on the fundamental (or basic) interfacial processes into which the more complex technical processes can be analysed. Against this background we propose to consider representative technical processes in which synthetic surface-active agents are used, and in the final section we shall attempt to survey the different chemical types of synthetic surface-active agents, describing their properties by reference to the earlier sections of the book.

CHAPTER 2

THE STATES OF SOLUTION OF SURFACE-ACTIVE AGENTS

We have already pointed out that the possession of hydrophilic and hydrophobic portions by the same molecule tends to make such molecules concentrate at interfaces with the hydrophilic portion in the aqueous phase. In a concentrated solution of an amphipathic substance it is impossible for all the solute molecules to be located in the interface,—what, then, is the state in solution of these substances when the surrounding medium is wholly aqueous? When an amphipathic substance dissolves in water, there is a large "sympathetic" force between the hydrophilic portion and the surrounding water molecules. As Hartley[1] has emphasised, the "antipathy" between the hydrophobic portion (usually a paraffin chain) and the water molecules does not involve an actual repulsive force between the two. There is no conceivable mechanism for this. Neither is there a very strongly attractive force acting between the paraffin chains which are non-polar in character. There is, however, a very strong cohesive force between the water molecules and when a paraffin chain is introduced into this strong field of attraction it tends to be pushed out of solution. At the same time this tendency is opposed by the solubilising influence of the hydrophilic portion, and the result, at any rate in moderately dilute solutions, is a compromise between the two tendencies, so that the paraffin chains form themselves into groups which can remain in solution because of the solubilising power of the hydrophilic portion of the molecule. This effect becomes clearer if we recall that the large cohesive force between the water molecules is due to their dipole character and that this attractive force falls off as a high power (probably between the fourth and seventh) of the distance. The work required to introduce a single paraffin chain into water and accordingly to separate the water molecules by a distance of about 5 Å. is thus not much less than that required to separate them to many times this distance. The introduction of an aggregate of paraffin chains (into which water does not penetrate) is thus accomplished with a much smaller expenditure of energy than would be required if the chains were introduced as separated single chains. The compromise between the cohesive force of the water molecules and the attraction for water of the hydrophilic portion on the amphipathic molecule is thus effected by the aggregation of the hydrophobic portions which are so grouped that the exterior of the aggregate is composed of the hydrophilic portions of the molecules.

---

[1] Hartley, *Paraffin-Chain Salts*, Hermann et Cie., Paris, 1936, p. 45; and *Progress in the Chemistry of Fats and Other Lipids*, Pergamon Press, 1955, p. 21.

As has been pointed out by Hartley (*loc. cit.*) single paraffin chains in the strong cohesive field of the water molecules are subjected to a large compressive force (the internal pressure of water is several thousand atmospheres), which partially relieves the compressive force on the water molecules themselves. If however the same number of separate paraffin chains are in the form of large aggregates, the compressive force per paraffin chain is reduced and the chains expand, while the water molecules on the other hand are subjected to a larger compression than before and undergo contraction. This is borne out by the data of Grindley and Bury[1] on butyric

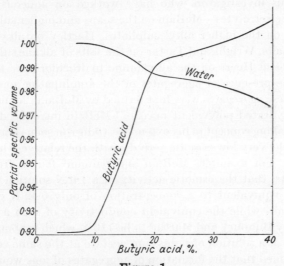

Figure 1
Partial specific volumes of water and butyric acid at 0° C.
(Grindley and Bury, *J. Chem. Soc.*, 1929, 679.)

acid, which are illustrated in Figure 1. The relatively large *increase* in the partial specific volume of the solute in a narrow concentration interval and the corresponding *decrease* in the partial specific volume of the water shown in the figure are evidence that aggregation is taking place. This is also shown by the measurements of Scott and Tartar[2] on decyl and dodecyl trimethylammonium bromide, while for cetyl pyridinium chloride Hartley[3] has shown that its aqueous solutions are lighter than water even though in the solid state its density is greater than that of water.

Relatively few investigations have been carried out on non-ionogenic amphipathic substances, and we will therefore deal first with amphipathic electrolytes, by which we mean comparatively strong electrolytes one of the ions of which is amphipathic. The term "colloidal electrolytes" has

[1] Grindley and Bury, *J. Chem. Soc.*, 1929, 679.
[2] Scott and Tartar, *J. Amer. Chem. Soc.*, 1943, **65**, 692.
[3] Hartley, *Koll. Z.*, 1939, **88**, 22.

been fairly generally used to describe amphipathic electrolytes but it includes, in addition to these, many colloidal substances (*e.g.*, macromolecules and eucolloids) which are not necessarily surface-active. Since we are not concerned here with these non-surface-active colloids we prefer to use the more restricted expression "amphipathic electrolytes" since it conveys a picture of the *dual nature* of the substances with which we shall deal.

A. Paraffin-chain salts

The numerous investigators who have worked on aqueous solutions of amphipathic electrolytes—McBain on the soaps and higher sulphonic acids, Lottermoser on the higher alkyl sulphates, Hartley on alkyl quaternary ammonium salts, Wright and Tartar on the salts of alkane sulphonic acids, and Ralston and Hoerr on the alkylamine hydrochlorides—have all been agreed on the presence of aggregates of the amphipathic ions in aqueous solutions. These aggregates were first termed by McBain[1] "ionic micelles"— "a heavily hydrated polyvalent micelle." McBain introduced this fruitful and epoch-making concept in his extensive studies on soap solutions in order to reconcile the very low osmotic activity with the relatively high electrical conductivity. For example, McBain and Salmon[2] found, from dewpoint measurements, that the osmotic activity of a 1·0 N solution of potassium stearate was equivalent to a concentration of only 0·42 N of simple undissociated salt, while the equivalent conductivity of such a solution had been found by Bunbury and Martin[3] to be 113·4, which is about 67% of the conductivity of a solution of potassium acetate at the same concentration. McBain reasoned that the formation of aggregates of ions would, by reducing the number of particles in solution, bring about a decrease in the osmotic activity, but that these aggregates would be more conducting than the simple ions, since their mobility calculated from Stokes's law would increase on aggregation by a factor of $m^{\frac{1}{3}}$ for a micelle containing m ions. To account for his results quantitatively McBain also postulated the existence in these solutions of aggregates of undissociated molecules (neutral colloid). This latter assumption will be commented upon later.

When practically any physical property of an aqueous solution of an amphipathic electrolyte is considered, the most striking feature is the extremely rapid change in the magnitude of that property which takes place over a limited range of concentration. This is very well illustrated by the data which have been collected by Preston[4] on sodium dodecyl sulphate and which we have reproduced in Figure 2. Jones and Bury[5] in 1927 pointed out that "this sudden departure from the normal is a natural

[1] McBain, *Trans. Faraday Soc.*, 1913, **9**, 99.
[2] McBain and Salmon, *J. Am. Chem. Soc.*, 1920, **42**, 426.
[3] Bunbury and Martin, *J. Chem. Soc.*, 1914, **105**, 424.
[4] Preston, *J. Phys. Coll. Chem.*, 1948, **52**, 84.
[5] Jones and Bury, *Phil. Mag.*, 1927, **4**, 841.

consequence of the law of mass action when applied to the association of simple molecules to form complex molecules containing a *large* number of single molecules." In such a solution there is an equilibrium between the single molecules and the aggregates

$$(A)_m \rightleftharpoons mA$$

and if the concentrations (in equivalent units) of the total solute, single

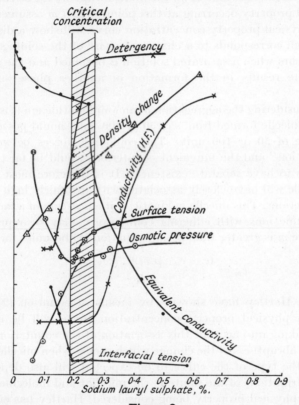

Figure 2

Physical property curves for aqueous sodium dodecyl sulphate

Temperature: 25°–38° c. (Preston, *J. Phys. Coll. Chem.*, 1948, **52**, 85.)

molecules, and aggregates are denoted by c, c_i, and c_m, then the equilibrium constant, K, is given by

$$K = (c_i)^m / c_m$$

if activities are equated to concentrations. Thus

$$c_m = (c_i)^m / K \qquad (1)$$

As Grindley and Bury[1] showed, if c_i has a value appreciably less than $K^{1/m}$ then $(c_i)^m/K$ will, for large values of m, be very small, that is, the

---

[1] Grindley and Bury, *J. Chem. Soc.*, 1929, 679.

fraction of the solute in the aggregated form will be negligible, and only when c_i becomes comparable with $K^{1/m}$ will the concentration of micelles become appreciable. When c_i exceeds $K^{1/m}$ then c_m will increase very rapidly with increase in c. The concentration of total solute at which the concentration of aggregates becomes appreciable was termed by Davies and Bury[1] "the critical concentration for micelles." These authors also pointed out that the larger the value of m, the more abrupt would be the change in any physical property occurring at this point. When m assumes the value infinity a physical property-concentration curve will show a discontinuity of slope which corresponds to a change of phase of the solute such as, for example, occurs when a saturated solution is obtained and the addition of further solute results in the formation of another phase—undissolved solute.

When considering the aggregation of an amphipathic ion it is inconceivable that a micelle formed from say 50 or 100 ions should possess an electrical charge of 50 or 100 units. The coulombic forces between such a polyvalent "ion" and the univalent counterions would be far too great to permit them to have separate existences. It is therefore most likely that such a micelle will have closely associated with it a fairly high proportion of the counterions. This micelle, a kinetic unit consisting of a large number of amphipathic ions with adhering counterions, may be represented as Na_pA_m where m is greater than p, and equation (1) becomes for this case

$$c_m = \frac{(c - c_m \cdot p/m)^p \cdot (c - c_m)^m}{K}. \tag{2}$$

Murray and Hartley have shown,[2] by means of equation (2), that the change in a physical property-concentration curve will be made more abrupt by taking into account this association of the counterions with the micelle. The abruptness of the change which occurs when micelle formation begins and the type of the curve to be expected will also depend on the relative contributions of the solute in the micellar and molecular (or ionic) form to the physical property being considered. Hartley has enumerated[3] the three types of curves to be expected according as the property is a function (1) of the concentration of the solute in the micellar form, (2) of the ratio of the micellar concentration to that of the total solute, or (3) of the ratio of the increment in the concentration of the micelles to the corresponding increment of the total solute. These three types of curves are illustrated in Figure 3. The curves shown in this figure have been calculated from equation (1) for a micelle containing 20 single molecules and taking an arbitrary value of unity for K; c_m being the concentration of the solute in the micellar form and c the total concentration of solute. In Figure 4

[1] Davies and Bury, *J. Chem. Soc.*, 1930, 2263.
[2] Murray and Hartley, *Trans. Faraday Soc.*, 1935, **31**, 183.
[3] Hartley, *Koll. Z.*, 1939, **88**, 22.

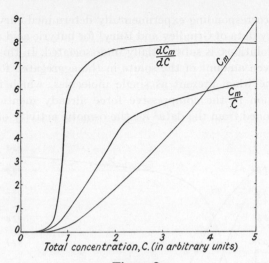

Figure 3

Variation of the concentration of micelles (c_m); the ratio of the micelle concentration to total concentration (c_m/c); and the rate of change of micelle concentration (dc_m/dc) for a micelle consisting of 20 molecules

(m = 20)

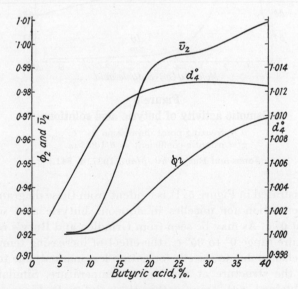

Figure 4

Density of solution and apparent and partial specific volumes of butyric acid in water at 0° C.

(Grindley and Bury, *J. Chem. Soc.*, 1929, 679.)

are shown the corresponding experimentally determined curves calculated from the density data of Grindley and Bury[1] for butyric acid which, except in very dilute solutions, is substantially undissociated. In this example the volume of a given amount of the solute in the aggregated form is greater than its volume when present as single molecules, which is due to the relative reduction in the compressive force already mentioned. Similar curves are obtained from the data[2] for the osmotic activity of butyric acid

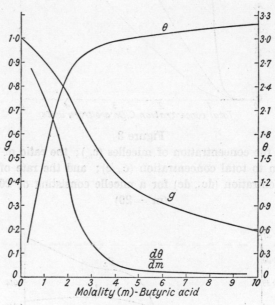

Figure 5

Osmotic activity of butyric acid solutions

θ = freezing point depression in ° c.

g = osmotic coefficient = $\theta/1 \cdot 858$ m.

(Jones and Bury, *Phil. Mag.*, 1927, **4**, 841.)

which are illustrated in Figure 5. It is evident from these diagrams that the critical concentration for micelles in aqueous butyric acid solutions is about 10% at 0° c. As may be seen from Grindley and Bury's results over the temperature range 0° to 35° c., the effect of increasing temperature is to make the change due to micelle formation less marked, due to a general loosening of the structure at the higher temperature. Similar types of curves are obtained with amphipathic electrolytes. In Figure 6 are presented electrical conductivity data[3] for very dilute solutions of a typical

[1] Grindley and Bury, *J. Chem. Soc.*, 1929, 679.

[2] International Critical Tables, 1928, **IV**, p. 262.

[3] Hartley, Collie, and Samis, *Trans. Faraday Soc.*, 1936, **32**, 795.

amphipathic electrolyte, cetyltrimethylammonium bromide, where κ, $\Lambda \left(= \dfrac{\kappa}{c} \right)$, and $\dfrac{d\kappa}{dc}$ are plotted against the concentration. The critical concentration for micelle formation for this substance occurs in much more dilute solutions than that for butyric acid, which is due to the greater length of the hydrophobic paraffin chain.

The physical property of amphipathic electrolytes which has been most frequently measured is undoubtedly the electrical conductivity. This is probably due to the ease with which such measurements may be made with

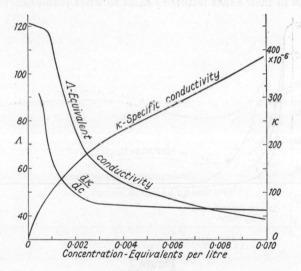

Figure 6
Conductivity of aqueous solutions of cetyltrimethylammonium bromide at 35° C.

(Hartley, Collie, and Samis, *Trans. Faraday Soc.*, 1936, **32**, 795.)

a high degree of precision and to the marked change which occurs in this property when micelles are formed. For a large number of amphipathic electrolytes the critical concentration is shown by an abrupt fall in the equivalent conductivity in relatively dilute solutions, which, as Hartley[1] has emphasised, are mobile, optically clear, one-phase systems. The equilibria between the various solute species in these solutions is rapidly established so that they are thermodynamically stable and reproducible systems. In general, the equivalent conductivity-concentration curves of all amphipathic electrolytes show the same features of a sharp fall over a narrow concentration interval followed by a horizontal or rising portion as the concentration increases. This is well illustrated in Figure 7 which shows

---

[1] Hartley, *Koll. Z.*, 1939, **88**, 22.

the curves for sodium palmitate, sodium tetradecane sulphonate, sodium hexadecyl sulphate, cetyltrimethylammonium bromide, and dodecylamine hydrochloride. The data for sodium palmitate do not extend into sufficiently dilute solutions for the break in the curve to be evident but the conductivity is obviously falling rapidly in the most dilute solution measured. For the other four salts the break occurring at the critical concentration is very sharp.

Although, as has been stated above, there is general agreement on the presence of micelles in solutions of amphipathic electrolytes, there is disagreement as to their exact nature: *i.e.*, as to what is the exact mechanism

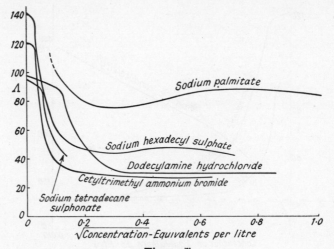

Figure 7
Conductivities of aqueous solutions of amphipathic electrolytes

(1) Cetyltrimethylammonium bromide at 35° c. (Hartley, Collie, and Samis, *Trans. Faraday Soc.*, 1936, **32**, 795.)

(2) Sodium palmitate at 90° c. (McBain and Martin, *J. Chem. Soc.*, 1914, **105**, 957.)

(3) Sodium tetradecane sulphonate at 40° c. (Wright, Abbott, Sivertz, and Tartar, *J. Amer. Chem. Soc.*, 1939, **61**, 549.)

(4) Sodium hexadecyl sulphate at 60° c. (Lottermoser and Püschel, *Koll. Z.*, 1933, **63**, 175.)

(5) Dodecylamine hydrochloride at 25° c. (Ralston, Hoerr, and Hoffmann, *J. Amer. Chem. Soc.*, 1942, **64**, 97; 1948, **70**, 436.)

which produces the abrupt change of slope of the conductivity-concentration curves and the subsequent arrest or even reversal of the fall. Several different configurations have been postulated for the micelle, ranging from the spherical form by G. S. Hartley through oblate and prolate spheroids to large crystalline bimolecular leaflets favoured by the late Professor J. W. McBain and others. Some authors consider that essentially only one type of micelle can exist in a solution at any one time whilst others believe that several species can co-exist in equilibrium. The simplest picture of the state in solution of amphipathic electrolytes is undoubtedly that of Hartley who in 1936[1] published a useful monograph on this subject and in 1955[2] contributed to *Progress in the Chemistry of Fats and Other Lipids* an excellent exposition of his views. Up to the critical concentration he considers that an amphipathic electrolyte is a strong electrolyte, completely dissociated and unaggregated. At the critical concentration, aggregation of the amphipathic ion begins with the formation, at first, of relatively small micelles which grow rapidly over a very limited concentration range to a size which for a given amphipathic electrolyte remains approximately constant with further increase in concentration. He believes that the micelles are liquid and essentially spherical and that their interior approximates to the random distribution state of liquid paraffin (for an amphipathic ion containing a paraffin chain) but with the hydrophilic end of the ion constrained to remain at the surface of the micelle. Harkins[3] agreed with this concept of one type of micelle in simple aqueous solution, but from his X-ray results at first considered it to have some regularity of structure and postulated it as cylindrical or disc shaped. Later consideration of the evidence, especially when attempting to explain solubilisation phenomena,[4] led him to accept the essentially spherical model for the micelle in optically clear solutions. This question of the *shape* of the micelle will be returned to later. Hartley states that the micelle contains, for a straight sixteen carbon atom chain, roughly 70 ions, but that part of this charge is neutralised by adhering counterions which amount to at least one-half the number of the amphipathic ions in the micelle. He considers that the surface of the micelle does not resemble the sharp transition occurring at the interface between two immiscible liquids but rather that it is to be regarded as a gradual transition from paraffin to water with the ion-pairs (formed from the association of a counterion with the hydrophilic head of an amphipathic ion) "dissolved" in this surface transition layer. After the constant micellar size has been attained the addition of further solute leads to an increase in the number of micelles with little, if any, increase in the number of the unaggregated amphipathic ions. Hartley thus postulates only one type of micelle, of approximately constant size (for a given amphipathic electrolyte) in aqueous solutions at all concentrations above the critical concentration except perhaps for a very small concentration range where the micelles first begin to form. The limitation in the size of the spherical micelle is imposed by its structure, a surface of strongly hydrophilic groups and an essentially liquid paraffinic interior. For this to increase in diameter would entail either there being a region in the centre of the micelle to which the paraffin chains could not reach, or the ionic

[1] Hartley, *Paraffin-Chain Salts*, Hermann et Cie., Paris, 1936.
[2] Hartley, *Progress in the Chemistry of Fats and Other Lipids*, Pergamon Press, 1955, Chapter 2.
[3] Mattoon, Stearns, and Harkins, *J. Chem. Phys.*, 1947, **15**, 209.
[4] Harkins and Mittelmann, *J. Coll. Sci.*, 1949, **4**, 367.

groups being drawn into a paraffinic environment—both very unlikely occurrences.

McBain,[1] on the other hand, was of the opinion that it is impossible to explain all the quantitative physico-chemical data on aqueous solutions of amphipathic electrolytes by the simple postulate of only one type of colloidal particle, although he originally tried to do so. His picture of the state of aggregation of these ions in solution has not been so clearly and unequivocally stated as has that of Hartley, but it would appear to the present writers that it can be summarised as follows. McBain visualised "spherical ionic micelles" being formed in dilute solution before the critical concentration is reached. By a spherical ionic micelle McBain meant an aggregation "of not more than ten like ions retaining their charges." It should be noted that this concept of the ionic micelle is an aggregate of ions with an electrical charge equal to the sum of the charges of all the ions in the aggregate and is different from Hartley's micelle. The latter is much larger and an appreciable fraction of the total charge of the ions of which it is composed is neutralised by the adhering counterions. In the region immediately after the critical concentration, McBain[2] considered that appreciable amounts of neutral molecules or ion-pairs are formed "as a precursor to colloid." Presumably, the ionic micelle is still present in this region and its concentration must be increasing with increasing concentration of solute since it appears, at still higher concentrations, as the dominant species. With further increase in concentration, in the region where the conductivity and the osmotic activity are falling rapidly, colloid is formed. At first McBain termed this "neutral colloid" to distinguish it from the ionic micelle, although it was weakly conducting and therefore had a small electrical charge. It was later identified by McBain[3] with the lamellar micelle which has been postulated to account for the X-ray diffraction patterns obtained on solutions of amphipathic electrolytes by a number of workers.[4] The lamellar micelle is described as being composed of alternate layers of water and double amphipathic molecules. These latter layers (see Figure 8) consist of the paraffin chains arranged parallel to each other, in liquid rather than in crystalline packing in the plane perpendicular to that of the figure. The depth of the layer is equal to the length of two fully extended paraffin chains placed end to end. The ionic and lamellar micelles coexist in solution and, in the region in which the conductivity is increasing,

---

[1] McBain, "Solutions of Soaps and Detergents as Colloidal Electrolytes" in Alexander's *Colloid Chemistry*, Reinhold Publishing Corporation, New York, 1944, Vol. V, p. 114.

[2] McBain, *J. Phys. Chem.*, 1939, **43**, 674.

[3] McBain, "Solubilisation and other Factors in Detergent Action" in Kraemer's *Advances in Colloid Science*, Interscience Publishers, New York, 1942, vol. I, p. 124.

[4] Hess and Gundermann, *Ber.*, 1937, **70**, 1800; Krishnamurti, *Indian J. Physics*, 1929, **3**, 307; Stauff, *Naturwiss.*, 1939, **27**, 213; Harkins, Mattoon, and Corrin, *J. Amer. Chem. Soc.*, 1946, **68**, 220.

the amount of the ionic micelle steadily increases with increase in the total solute concentration "until its properties dominate those of the neutral micelle."[1] McBain thus considered that there are present together in aqueous solutions of amphipathic electrolytes, at concentrations greater than the critical concentration, two types of aggregates, which are very dissimilar in structure but presumably in equilibrium with each other.

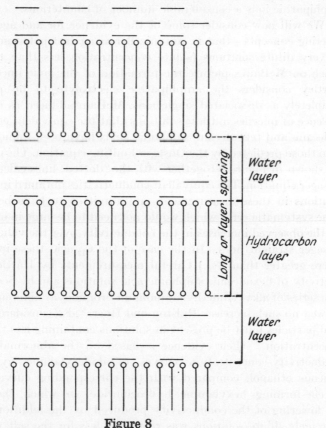

Figure 8
"Lamellar Micelle" in 15% potassium laurate solution—
highly idealised cross section
(Harkins, Mattoon, and Corrin, *J. Amer. Chem. Soc.*, 1946, **68**, 220.)

One (the ionic micelle) is highly charged and spherical, with the hydrophobic chains unoriented, except insofar as the hydrophilic groups are constrained to lie at the micelle-water interface, while the other (the lamellar micelle) has a small charge and, since in it the paraffin chains are arranged parallel to one another, has an orientated structure. (It should

[1] McBain, *J. Phys. Chem.*, 1939, **43**, 674.

be noted, however, that some of McBain's co-workers now incline to the acceptance of a spherical type of micelle.[1])

Hartley, on the other hand, postulated only one type of micelle in all aggregate-containing solutions and, for a given amphipathic electrolyte, considered the size of the micelle to be substantially independent of concentration. His micelle is spherical and essentially "liquid" in structure, is large compared with McBain's ionic micelle, and contains in addition to the amphipathic ions a considerable number of counterions.

We will now consider some of the evidence for and against these two differing concepts—that is, uni-micellar as against poly-micellar solutions. In very dilute solutions (solute concentration less than the critical), in which on McBain's picture the formation of the ionic micelle has begun, Hartley considers the amphipathic electrolyte to be present almost completely as dissociated single ions. McBain adduced as evidence of the presence of micelles in these solutions that the equivalent conductivities of dodecane and tetradecane sulphonic acids have been found[2] to be greater than those predicted by the Onsager limiting equation. The observed values are shown in Figure 9 together with the (dotted) lines calculated from the Onsager equation. The equivalent conductivities obtained in the very dilute solutions in these measurements are admitted to have been affected by some systematic error which would not need to be large in order to account for the observed increases in the conductivity over the values given by the Onsager straight lines. (In the case of the C_{12}-acid these increases are nowhere greater than 1%.) Careful measurements by Hartley[3] of the conductivity of hexadecane sulphonic acid solutions and by Scott and Tartar[4] on a series of alkyl trimethylammonium bromides at different temperatures showed no such increase. Ralston and Hoerr[5] also considered that "associated particles must be present in solutions containing less than the critical concentration." Their evidence is based on the abnormal shapes of the conductivity-concentration curves of dodecylamine hydrochloride in aqueous ethanol, compared with the corresponding curves for the non-micelle-forming hexylamine hydrochloride, in which they found that the lowering of the conductivity produced by the addition of ethanol to extremely dilute solutions was relatively less for the salt with the longer paraffin chain. On the basis of their results, however, their argument leads one to the conclusion that micelles persist into practically infinitely dilute solutions. Moilliet, Collie, Robinson, and Hartley[6] have pointed out that conductivity measurements *alone* may not provide evidence

[1] Laing McBain and Hutchinson, *Solubilisation and Related Phenomena*, Academic Press, 1955.

[2] Laing McBain, Dye, and Johnston, *J. Amer. Chem. Soc.*, 1939, **61**, 3210.

[3] Hartley, *J. Amer. Chem. Soc.*, 1936, **58**, 2347.

[4] Scott and Tartar, *J. Amer. Chem. Soc.*, 1943, **65**, 692.

[5] Ralston and Hoerr, *J. Amer. Chem. Soc.*, 1946, **68**, 2460.

[6] Moilliet, Collie, Robinson, and Hartley, *Trans. Faraday Soc.*, 1935, **31**, 120.

of aggregation. When m ions aggregate to form one micelle of charge m one expects, by the simple application of Stokes's law, an increase in the conductivity since the contribution to the conductivity of such a micelle will be $m^{\frac{2}{3}}$ that of the m separate ions. These authors draw attention, however, to two factors which will operate in a solution containing multivalent ions (the micelles) in the opposite direction. One of these is the braking effect of the ionic atmosphere on the micelle and the

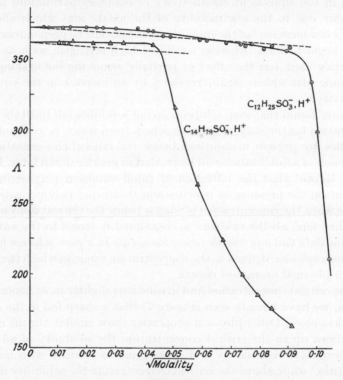

Figure 9

Equivalent conductivity of dodecane and tetradecane sulphonic acids

The dotted lines indicate the limiting Onsager slopes

(Laing McBain, Dye, and Johnston, *J. Amer. Chem. Soc.*, 1939, **61**, 3210.)

other is the "neutralisation" of some of the effective electric charges of the micelle by the inclusion of counterions. For different amphipathic electrolytes the sum of these braking effects may be less or greater than or approximately equal to the increased mobility to be expected by applying Stokes's law and thus aggregation may cause the conductivity, which in dilute solution normally decreases with increasing concentration, to show an increase, a marked (greater-than-normal) decrease, or to be virtually unaffected as the concentration passes through the critical range.

Experimental examples of all three effects were given in their paper, and subsequently evidence for aggregation of a paraffin-chain salt producing an increase in the equivalent conductivity was published by Kraus and co-workers[1] (see Figure 17). It will be noted that the form of the conductivity curve for octadecylpyridinium iodate (Figure 17) shows a striking similarity to that obtained by Malsch and Hartley[2] for the conductivity of aqueous solutions of cetylpyridinium chloride in very strong electric fields. The rise in the equivalent conductivity of octadecylpyridinium iodate is presumably due to the low mobility of the iodate ions which allows the "Stokes's law increase" of the mobility of the micelle to preponderate when micelles begin to form, whereas a field of high strength, such as Malsch and Hartley used, has the effect of partially removing the braking effects of the ionic atmosphere again revealed by an increase in the equivalent conductivity.

Harkins[3] found that soap solutions do not solubilise oils until the critical concentration for the soap has been reached, from which he concluded that no micelles are present in solutions below the critical concentration. The phenomenon of solubilisation will be treated in greater detail later. Harkins has also shown[4] that the initiation of rapid emulsion polymerisation is dependent on the presence of micelles and that rapid polymerisation does not occur when the concentration of soap is below the critical concentration. When, therefore, all the evidence is considered it seems to the authors to be *most unlikely that any micelle formation occurs in a pure solution below the critical concentration*, defined as the concentration range in which the sudden change in physical properties occurs.

At the critical concentration and in solutions slightly more concentrated than this, we have already seen (Figure 7) that a sharp fall in the conductivity takes place. Other physical properties show similar abrupt changes. For solutions up to the critical concentration the solubility of an amphipathic electrolyte rises slowly and approximately linearly with increasing temperature,[5] while above the critical concentration the solubility increases relatively enormously with only a slight increase in temperature. This is shown in Figure 10 in which the solubility-temperature curves of a selection of amphipathic electrolytes are given. Since the solubility curve is so steep at concentrations above the critical, mixtures of a solid amphipathic electrolyte and water will become homogeneous at approximately the same temperature even though they vary greatly in the ratio of water to solute. The temperature of clarification will, of course, be different for different

[1] Brown, Grieger, Evers, and Kraus, *J. Amer. Chem. Soc.*, 1947, **69**, 1835.

[2] Malsch and Hartley, *Z. physik. Chem.*, 1934, **170A,** 321.

[3] Stearns, Oppenheimer, Simon, and Harkins, *J. Chem. Phys.*, 1947, **15**, 496.

[4] Harkins, *J. Amer. Chem. Soc.*, 1947, **69**, 1428.

[5] Adam and Pankhurst, *Trans. Faraday Soc.*, 1946, **42**, 523; Murray and Hartley, *Trans. Faraday Soc.*, 1935, **31**, 183; Ralston and Hoerr, *J. Amer. Chem. Soc.*, 1946, **68,** 851; Tartar and Wright, *J. Amer. Chem. Soc.*, 1939, **61,** 539.

amphipathic electrolytes. This phenomenon in the case of the soaps has been termed the "melting-point of soap curds" and Krafft and Wiglow[1] sought to correlate it with the melting-point of the parent fatty acid. Murray and Hartley,[2] however, disproved any such correlation by measurements of the solubilities of hexadecane sulphonic acid and its salts. The explanation of this effect lies in the formation of aggregates which can present an essentially hydrophilic exterior to the water and which, therefore, are much more soluble than the single molecules which have a large

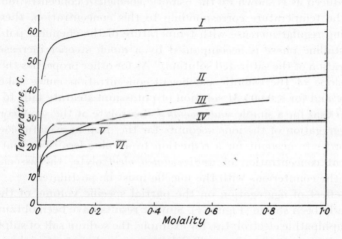

Figure 10
Solubilities of amphipathic electrolytes in water

   I. Sodium 1-palmito-4-anisidine-2-sulphonate (Adam and Pankhurst, *Trans. Faraday Soc.*, 1946, **42**, 523).
  II. Sodium dodecane sulphonate (Tartar and Wright, *J. Amer. Chem. Soc.*, 1930, **61**, 539).
 III. Sodium laurate (Stauff, *Z. physik. Chem.*, 1940, **187A**, 119).
 IV. Dodecylamine hydrochloride (Ralston and Hoerr, *J. Amer. Chem. Soc.*, 1946, **68**, 851).
  V. Cetyltrimethylammonium bromide (Adam and Pankhurst, *loc. cit.*).
 VI. Cetylpyridinium chloride (Adam and Pankhurst, *loc. cit.*).

hydrophobic surface exposed to the water. It has been suggested that "neutral molecules or ion-pairs are forming in this region as a precursor to colloid".[3] The change in slope of the solubility curve in this region is, however, so marked that it is unlikely that a reduction in the degree of dissociation alone could account for a change of such a magnitude in such a short temperature interval.

In this concentration range a rapid fall in osmotic coefficient occurs as

  [1] Krafft and Wiglow, *Ber.*, 1895, **28**, 2566.
  [2] Murray and Hartley, *Trans. Faraday Soc.*, 1935, **31**, 183.
  [3] McBain, *J. Phys. Chem.*, 1939, **43**, 671.

shown by measurements on soaps,[1] alkane sulphonic acids,[2] and dodecyldi-methylbenzylammonium chloride.[3] For a saturated solution the chemical potential of the solute is equal to that of the crystalline solid with which it is in equilibrium. The chemical potentials of the solute and solid will increase regularly with increase in temperature below the critical concentration, but when the critical concentration for micelles has been reached we know, as Winsor[4] has pointed out, that "the rate of increase of the chemical potential of the solute with respect to its concentration becomes much reduced as is shown by the osmotic coefficient/concentration curves. Above the temperature corresponding to this concentration, therefore, a continuing regular increase with temperature of the chemical potential of the crystalline phase is accompanied by a much steeper increase in the concentration of the saturated solution." As for other properties the change in the slope of the osmotic coefficient/concentration curve takes place suddenly and for a 0·005 M solution of potassium stearate falls to a value less than that for a simple *undissociated* electrolyte at the same concentration. Aggregation of the ions accounts for the drop in osmotic coefficient, but in order to account for a reduction to a value less than that for the equivalent concentration of *undissociated* electrolyte, the association of some of the counterions with the micelle must be postulated.

The effect of aggregation on the partial specific volume of the solute has already been shown (Figure 4). Similar results have been obtained with other amphipathic electrolytes, for example, the sodium salt of sulphonated di(2-hexyl)succinate,[5] sodium alkyl benzene sulphonates,[6] and potassium laurate.[7]

The most positive evidence for aggregation in this concentration range is obtained from transport number data. Extensive measurements of this property have been published by Hartley, Collie, and Samis,[8] and by Samis and Hartley,[9] on a number of alkyl quaternary ammonium salts, alkyl sulphates, and hexadecane sulphonic acid, by Hoerr and Ralston on several alkylamine hydrochlorides,[10] and by Laing McBain on dodecane sulphonic acid.[11] The variation of transport number with concentration is illustrated in Figure 11, which shows the results for cetylpyridinium bromide[8] at 35° c.

[1] McBain, numerous references in Alexander's *Colloid Chemistry*, Reinhold Publishing Corporation, New York, 1944, vol. V.

[2] Laing McBain, Dye, and Johnston, *J. Amer. Chem. Soc.*, 1939, **61**, 3210.

[3] Walton, Hiebert, and Sholtes, *J. Coll. Sci.*, 1946, **1**, 385.

[4] Winsor, *Solvent Properties of Amphiphilic Compounds*, Butterworth, 1954, p. 31.

[5] Vetter, *J. Phys. Coll. Chem.*, 1947, **51**, 262.

[6] Paquette, Lingafelter, and Tartar, *J. Amer. Chem. Soc.*, 1943, **65**, 686.

[7] Bury and Parry, *J. Chem. Soc.*, 1935, 626.

[8] Hartley, Collie, and Samis, *Trans. Faraday Soc.*, 1936, **32**, 795.

[9] Samis and Hartley, *Trans. Faraday Soc.*, 1938, **34**, 1288.

[10] Hoerr and Ralston, *J. Amer. Chem. Soc.*, 1943, **65**, 976.

[11] Laing McBain, *J. Phys. Chem.*, 1943, **47**, 196.

and dodecylamine hydrochloride[1] at 60° c. At the critical concentration the transport numbers of the cationic radicals are seen to increase very rapidly with concentration, becoming greater than unity in the case of the pyridinium salt and also for other amphipathic electrolytes.[2] This increase in the transport number of a radical can be due *only* to the aggregation of the ionised portion of that radical and since the increase is so rapid the formation of these aggregates must take place within a small concentration

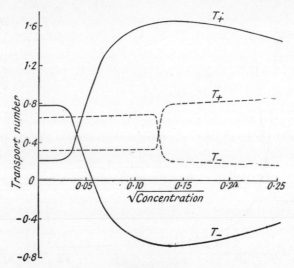

Figure 11
Transport numbers of positive and negative radicals of amphipathic electrolytes

I. Dodecylamine hydrochloride at 60° (Hoerr and Ralston, *J. Amer. Chem. Soc.*, 1943, **65**, 976) (broken lines).
II. Cetylpyridinium bromide at 35° (Hartley, Collie, and Samis, *Trans. Faraday Soc.*, 1936, **32**, 795) (full lines).

interval. The fact that values greater than unity are found for the aggregating radical means that there *must* be included in the aggregate some of the counterions which, under the influence of the electric current, are carried in a direction opposite to that in which they normally travel. This effect predominates over the migration of the *free* counterions, so that the net transfer of the counterion *radical* in its normal direction becomes negative. Neither these negative transport numbers, nor the rapid changes in transport number with concentration, can be adequately explained by postulating a decrease in the degree of dissociation or of the formation of almost neutral micelles. Either postulate would account for a decrease in *total equivalent conductivity*, but both postulates require that the mobilities

[1] Hoerr and Ralston, *J. Amer. Chem. Soc.*, 1943, **65**, 976.
[2] Samis and Hartley, *Trans. Faraday Soc.*, 1938, **34**, 1288.

(radical equivalent conductivities) of the two radicals (or ion constituents) should decrease in about the same proportion, so that the transport numbers should not markedly change. It will be seen by reference to Figure 11, however, that in the region which we are discussing the transport number of the amphipathic radical rises extremely steeply while that of the counterion falls as sharply.

In the more concentrated solutions the equivalent conductivity may

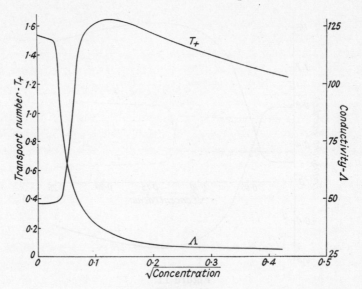

Figure 12
Transport number and conductivity of cetyltrimethylammonium bromide
at 35°

(Hartley, Collie, and Samis, *Trans. Faraday Soc.*, 1936, **32**, 795.)

reach an approximately constant value or it may even increase with increasing concentration (see Figure 7). The transport number of the aggregating radical, after having reached a maximum, is falling in this region, as is shown in Figure 12, although the total conductivity (of cetyltrimethylammonium bromide) is approximately constant. The increasing conductivity in this region (which is obtained with soap solutions) was accepted by McBain as evidence that the effect of the ionic micelle is predominating over that of the lamellar micelle and thus that the relative concentration of the former is increasing as the total concentration increases. If however the effect of increasing the concentration of these highly charged particles is such as to cause an *increase* in the total conductivity, it could not at the same time cause a *decrease* in the transport number of the amphipathic radical—(the McBain ionic micelle does *not* contain any of the counterions) —but the experimental evidence shows that the transport number of this

radical is in fact decreasing in this region. The postulate that the concentration of ionic micelle is increasing relative to that of the lamellar
micelle implies "retrograde dissociation," that is, increasing electrolytic
dissociation of the highly associated lamellar micelle, as the total concentration of the amphipathic electrolyte increases. Hartley in 1936 suggested
that either retrograde dissociation, or an increase in the mobility of the
free counterions, would account for the effects occurring in this concentration range, and at the same time he thought that the former postulate was
the more probable. On his concept of the micelle, which contains counterions, retrograde dissociation accounted for the fall in the transport number
of the amphipathic radical and the simultaneous rise in the total conductivity since it involved a change in the composition of the micelle towards
one containing relatively fewer counterions. The rise in the equivalent conductivity would thus be caused by the increased contribution of the released
counterions as well as by the increased mobility of the micelles, which now
have an increased charge. The transport number of the amphipathic radical
must however fall, since a greater proportion of the counterions than
formerly now travel in their normal direction and thus carry a *larger fraction*
of the total current. Davies[1] has shown that dissociation minima occur in
aqueous solutions of uni-multivalent electrolytes and considers[2] that retrograde dissociation is very probable in solutions of amphipathic electrolytes.

Hartley has pointed out[3] that his unsuccessful attempts to prove his
postulate of retrograde dissociation forced him to examine his alternative
hypothesis, which he later decided offered a more likely explanation. In
order to explain the anomalous increase in the mobility of a *radical* with
increasing concentration, Hartley considered the effect of the ionic atmosphere in solutions of very unsymmetrical electrolytes. In a solution of a
uni-univalent electrolyte, the volume round an ion in which the concentration of the oppositely charged ions is different from that of the bulk concentration is small, and the mobility of an ion is progressively reduced as
the concentration increases, principally on account of the braking effect of
the ionic atmosphere. In a concentrated solution which contains highly
charged "ions" (micelles) and univalent counterions, the volume round the
multivalent micelle, in which the concentration of counterions is appreciably
different from the bulk concentration, is no longer small and must in fact
be an appreciable fraction of the total volume. By the addition to such a
solution of further solute the concentration of counterions in the ionic
atmosphere will be increased relatively less than their concentration in the
region of the solution relatively remote from the multivalent micelle. Since
the counterions in the atmosphere have a lower mobility than those in the
remote region of the solution the mobility of the counterion radical will be

---

[1] Davies, *J. Chem. Soc.*, 1945, 460.
[2] Davies, *Chem. and Ind.*, 1938, 1167.
[3] Hartley, *Koll. Z.*, 1939, **88**, 22.

increased and thus the total equivalent conductivity will tend to be increased. The ordinary effects of increasing concentration considered in the Debye-Hückel theory, which tend to decrease the conductivity, have to be taken into account, in addition to this new effect, which is only of importance for highly unsymmetrical electrolytes and which acts in the opposite direction. Whether the total conductivity increases or remains constant depends on the relative contributions of the "increasing" and "decreasing" factors.

We thus have the two differing explanations of the shape of the physical property—concentration curves of dilute solutions of amphipathic electrolytes (up to moderate concentrations): McBain on the one hand, postulating the simultaneous presence (for any particular amphipathic electrolyte) of *two* types of micelle (spherical ionic micelle and lamellar micelle or neutral colloid), the variations in the relative concentrations of which account for the observed physical properties and Hartley on the other, postulating for any particular amphipathic electrolyte only *one* type of micelle in its aqueous solution. It appears to the authors that the properties (so far considered) of solutions of amphipathic electrolytes can be adequately explained by the postulate of only one type of micelle and that the introduction of more than one type, for a given electrolyte, not only complicates the picture but renders a plausible explanation of the effects observed more difficult.

X-ray diffraction results have been adduced as evidence of the existence of lamellar micelles.[1] Although no X-ray evidence for the presence of the lamellar micelle has been obtained in solutions more dilute than about 0·24 molar (for amphipathic electrolytes containing a hydrocarbon chain of 12 or 14 carbon atoms), which is well above the critical concentration, its existence has nevertheless been assumed in solutions very much less concentrated than this.

The precise and careful work of Harkins and collaborators[2] has in fact shown that the X-ray band, on the presence of which rests the evidence for the existence of the lamellar micelle, *disappears* when the concentration of a solution of potassium laurate or myristate is reduced below 0·24 molar. Moreover these workers, by appreciating the significance of a hitherto neglected X-ray diffraction band, have given an alternative picture of the probable structure of micelle-containing solutions. In the X-ray diffraction patterns obtained with aqueous soap solutions, three bands are obtained, which are designated S. M. and I. The S (short spacing) band has a Bragg spacing, d_S, of about 4·6 Å. d_S appears to be essentially independent of the

[1] McBain, in Alexander's *Colloid Chemistry*, Reinhold Publishing Corporation, New York, 1944, **V**, p. 114.

[2] Mattoon, Stearns, and Harkins, *J. Chem. Phys.*, 1947, **15**, 209; Harkins, *J. Chem. Phys.*, 1948, **16**, 156; Harkins, *The Physical Chemistry of Surface Films*, Reinhold, 1952, Chapter 4.

length of the paraffin chain and of the concentration. This band is now generally recognised as being identical with that obtained from a liquid paraffin and is consistent with the concept of the liquid paraffinic interior of the micelle. The M (micelle thickness) band, which had previously been neglected or overlooked, has a spacing, d_M, of about twice the length of the hydrocarbon chain in the molecule. As can be seen from the results obtained by Mattoon, Stearns, and Harkins,[1] given in Table 1, d_M is somewhat less or somewhat greater than twice the length of the hydrocarbon chain according to whether one uses (a) the equation for many diffracting centres or (b) the equation for two diffracting centres in the calculation of d_M.

Table 1
Correlation of d_M and the chain length

Soap	Length of double hydrocarbon chain	d_M	
		(a)	(b)
	Å	Å	Å
Potassium caprylate . . .	30	29·7	36·5
„ caprate	35	31·7	39·0
„ laurate . : . .	40	35·3	43·4
„ myristate . . .	45	40·3	49·5
„ palmitate . . .	50	47·3	58·1

For a particular soap the value of d_M is independent of the concentration of the soap and it has been detected in solutions as dilute as 0·08 molar potassium myristate[2] and 0·045 molar potassium palmitate.[1] Harkins initially favoured the lamellar micelle but later discarded it in favour of the spherical model since the former configuration could not satisfactorily account for certain solubilisation results.[3] He also postulated a cylindrical micelle, only present when salts were added to the solution, which he considered was the form taken by the micelle when further ions could not be accommodated in the sphere. In the cylindrical form the long-chain ions were arranged radially round the axis of the cylinder, the diameter of the cylinder being then given by d_M. Since it is necessary that the interface hydrocarbon chains-water should be as small as possible the ends of the cylinder would be "somewhat distorted in order to give coverage of the hydrocarbon chains by a few polar-ionic groups of the soap."[4]

The I (intermicellar distance) band makes its appearance at a second

[1] Mattoon, Stearns, and Harkins, *J. Chem. Phys.*, 1947, **15**, 209.
[2] Mattoon, Stearns, and Harkins, *J. Chem. Phys.*, 1948, **16**, 644.
[3] Harkins, *The Physical Chemistry of Surface Films*, Reinhold Publishing Co., 1952, p. 316.
[4] Harkins, *J. Chem. Phys.*, 1948, **16**, 156.

4

"critical concentration" which is about 0·25 molar for potassium laurate and myristate. As is seen in Figure 13 the Bragg spacing, d_I, of this band is about 60 Å. for laurate and 70 Å. for myristate when it first appears and

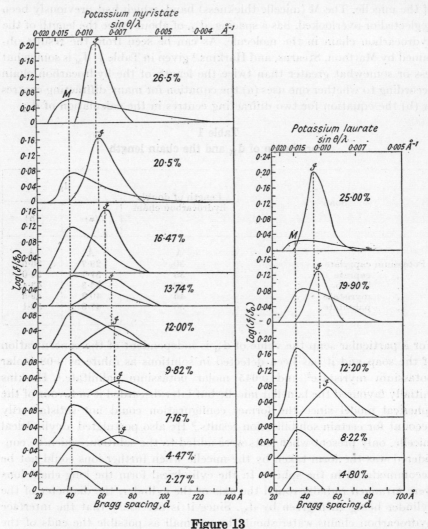

Figure 13

Resolved M-band and I-band from aqueous solutions of potassium laurate and potassium myristate

(Mattoon, Stearns, and Harkins, *J. Chem. Phys.*, 1948, **16**, 649.)

it *decreases* with increasing concentration. Up to the concentration at which the I-band appears the micelles are considered to be free and capable of moving independently as large ions in the solution. As the solution becomes more concentrated, however, the free micelles approach each other so closely that their freedom of movement is restricted and they tend to build up a somewhat regular structure (lamellar micelle) in the solution which gives rise, in the X-ray patterns, to the I-band. The Bragg spacing, d_I, is thus related to the distance between the originally free micelles in this new association.

The argument for the existence of the lamellar micelle was based on the I-band and on the changes in d_I which take place when solubilisation (treated below) occurs. On this interpretation of the X-ray results it appears most unlikely that lamellar micelles can exist below a concentration of 0·25 molar for potassium laurate or myristate which is much higher than the critical concentration (0·024 M for the laurate and 0·006 M for the myristate) at which the formation of neutral colloid (lamellar micelle) was assumed to begin.

The evidence for the existence of a disc-shaped or lamellar micelle largely rests on the interpretation of the X-ray diffraction data. Hartley has for long considered this shape to be improbable[1] and has indicated[2] that the results of the X-ray diffraction patterns are capable of being interpreted on the basis of the spherical micelle. The authors are indebted to Dr. Hartley for a private communication amplifying his interpretation of the X-ray diffraction data. He considers two difficulties which the postulate of the lamellar micelle raises: the first, that the long spacing data, on this model, account for only a small fraction of the water present and that the lamellar micelles "must therefore be separated laterally by a greater depth of water than that held between the ionic faces" in the lamellae, and the second, that the increase in the long spacing due to the solubilisation of an oil is greater than can be accounted for by the volume of oil solubilised. Harkins[3] and his co-workers were aware of this second difficulty and showed that the ratio of τ (the mean thickness of the oil layer calculated from the volume of oil and the area of the double layer of soap in the micelle) to Δd_I (the increase in the long spacing) was approximately independent of the amount of oil dissolved for a single oil in a specific soap solution. The ratio in the case of the solubilisation of n-heptane in 25% potassium laurate was found to be approximately 0·4. At that time they stated "it is difficult at present to see, on the basis of the model assumed, how the expansion of the micelle can be as high as over twice that which corresponds to the volume of oil added." It was this and other difficulties[4] which later led them to discard the lamellar in favour of the spherical micelle, as has been stated above. Hartley considers that with the spherical model these

---

[1] Hartley, *Koll. Z.*, 1939, **88**, 22.

[2] Hartley, *Quart. Rev.*, 1948, **2**, 152 and *Nature*, 1949, **163**, 767, and *Ann. Rep. Prog. Chem.*, 1949, **45**, 47.

[3] Harkins, Mattoon, and Corrin, *J. Coll. Sci.*, 1946, **1**, 105.

[4] Mattoon, Stearns, and Harkins, *J. Chem. Phys.*, 1948, **16**, 644.

difficulties do not arise. Since the micelles mutually repel each other they will array themselves in solution so that the distance between them will be as large as possible. To do this the micelles will take up positions relative to each other corresponding to a hexagonal close-packed space lattice. If d is the distance between the centres of the micelles, r the radius of the micelle, and ϕ the fraction of the total volume occupied by the micelles, it can be shown that

$$d = \left(\frac{4\sqrt{2}\pi}{3\phi}\right)^{\frac{1}{3}} r.$$

If the long spacing obtained from the X-ray data is taken equal to d, then values for r may be calculated. This has been done (Table 2) using the data of Harkins, Mattoon, and Corrin[1] for potassium laurate and myristate.

Table 2
The radius of the micelle from X-ray long spacing data

Potassium laurate			Potassium myristate		
Weight fraction	d(obs.)	r(calc.)	Weight fraction	d(obs.)	r(calc.)
0·091	57·0	14·2	0·130	63·8	17·9
0·121	56·3	15·4	0·167	62·4	19·0
0·139	54·5	15·6	0·200	59·6	19·3
0·167	50·6	15·4	0·231	58·5	19·9
0·199	49·6	16·0	0·259	56·7	20·0
0·250	47·1	16·4			
0·286	45·8	16·7			
0·333	44·1	16·9			
0·411	37·1	15·2			

In the above calculations the weight fraction has been used in place of the more correct volume fraction since the density of the micelle is unknown. This, however, makes only a negligible difference to the values of r.

It will be seen that the calculated values of r are in reasonable agreement with the lengths of fully extended paraffin chains of 12 and 14 carbon atoms (13·7 and 16·2 Å. respectively) when due allowance is made for the size of the ionic heads. The spherical model will thus adequately fit the observed X-ray data without omitting a large fraction of the water. When an oil is solubilised in the micelle Hartley[2] suggested that probably part of the oil will exist at the centre of the micelle as the sole component. Because of this the ends of the paraffin-chain ions need no longer reach to the centre and a larger number of these ions may thus be accommodated in the micelle

[1] Harkins, Mattoon, and Corrin, *J. Amer. Chem. Soc.*, 1946, **68**, 220.
[2] Hartley, "The Solvent Action of Detergent Solutions" in *Wetting and Detergency*, A. Harvey, London, 1937, p. 153.

than was accommodated in the absence of the oil. The solubilisation of an oil in the micelle can thus readily account for the disproportionate increase in d due to an increase in r. In regard to the interpretation of the X-ray data Corrin[1] has shown that by assuming "spherical micelles of uniform radius whose short range order is characterised by a radial distribution function" it is possible to calculate approximately the scattered X-ray intensity curves. His calculated curves are in good agreement with the experimentally determined curves and he concluded that "in the light of our present experimental knowledge, the X-ray measurements alone do not allow a decision between the lamellar and spherical models for micelles" since the long spacing need not necessarily be caused by *co-planar* groups of diffracting atoms.*

Winsor in an excellent treatise[2] dealing mainly with solubilisation considers that after the critical micelle concentration has been reached the solution contains only spherical micelles and that the increasing concentration of these micelles is responsible for the increase in the intensity of the M-band. In the more concentrated solutions, however, Winsor believes that the spherical micelles, which he designates S_1 type, will be in kinetic equilibrium with gel or liquid crystalline regions (G-type micelles) which he pictures as having a lamellar structure. He considers that these regions are not stable but are produced by local thermal variations resulting in the necessary high concentration. Since at the limit of concentration of the S_1 micelles a liquid crystalline phase is precipitated, Winsor considers that this "demonstrates conclusively the possibility of a stable and extensive lamellar arrangement." X-ray diffraction by these G-regions is considered to result in the I-band.

As has been pointed out by James,[3] "the interpretation of the diffraction patterns given by liquids composed of complex molecules is a matter of considerable difficulty . . . and in general the most that it will be possible to say will be that a certain assumed structure and arrangement is not inconsistent with the observed diffraction effects." Fournet[4] also concludes that the influence of the size and shape of the particles is such that the only

---

* Schwartz and Perry (*Surface Active Agents*, Interscience Publishers, New York, 1949, p. 314), consider that "in view of the overwhelming X-ray evidence, there is practically no doubt as to the existence of lamellar micelles." As we have just pointed out, however, Corrin and Hartley have each shown that other pictures of the structure of the micelle agree with the present X-ray data as well as does the lamellar structure. All that can be said is that the lamellar and spherical models for the micelle would both give X-ray diffraction patterns such as have been obtained with solutions of amphipathic electrolytes.

[1] Corrin, *J. Chem. Phys.*, 1948, **16**, 844.

[2] Winsor, *Solvent Properties of Amphiphilic Compounds*, Butterworths, 1954, p. 163 *ff*. See also Winsor, *Manufacturing Chemist*, 1956, **27**, 89, 130.

[3] James, *The Optical Principles of the Diffraction of X-rays*, G. Bell and Sons, London, 1948, **II**, p. 501.

[4] Fournet, *Discussions of the Faraday Society*, 1951, **11**, 121.

way to get precise results from X-ray diffraction data is to build a model and then compare the theoretical with the experimental curves. It would thus appear that the X-ray measurements cannot at present settle whether the micelle is spherical or disc-shaped since the data can be interpreted on the basis of either model.

It would appear that most workers in this field now believe that in an aqueous solution of a particular amphipathic electrolyte only one type of micelle exists but that there are differing views on the exact shape of the micelle. In considering these different views the following facts should be borne in mind. Hartley has explicitly stated[1] that his arguments in favour of a liquid micelle apply only to "the optically clear, homogeneous, and mobile system which is obtained above a fairly well-defined temperature which is only slightly dependent on concentration" and furthermore that "the equilibrium in these clear mobile solutions is established within the ordinary times of observation, since no hysteresis of any accurately measurable property (of the solution and not of its surface) is shown." Hartley has further elaborated[2] this point and stated that his preference for the spherical model was based on "solutions so dilute that there could be no geometrical interference due to difficulty in the packing of spheres." In the more concentrated solutions he considered it possible that the spherical micelles might be deformed and tend towards oblate spheroids. Also, as is well known, the properties of a soap-water system depend to a great extent on its previous history and it is probably on this account that very few precise data on the equilibrium solubilities of soaps in water exist. Much of the X-ray data has been obtained at temperatures of about 25° c. where many of the more concentrated solutions were opaque or clear gels. In the absence of precise solubility data to settle the point it appears possible that some of the evidence for the M-band may have been obtained on solutions which were slightly supersaturated and that the "cylindrical" micelle is a manifestation of incipient crystallisation. Hoeve and Benson[3] have considered micelle formation from the standpoint of statistical mechanics. Although they come to definite conclusions in regard to the micelles in solutions of non-ionogenic surface-active agents, about which more will be said later, the theoretical treatment for solutions of amphipathic electrolytes is very much more difficult because of long range electrical forces and because the surface of the micelle may be rough with the possibility of the ionic heads sticking out into the aqueous medium and the counterions penetrating between them. These authors also consider that at present "no satisfactory experimental proof exists for the constancy of either single ion concentration or micellar size above the critical micelle concentration."

[1] Hartley, *Koll. Z.*, 1939, **88**, 22.
[2] Hartley, *Trans. Faraday Soc.*, 1946, **42B**, 196, "Discussion on Swelling and Shrinking."
[3] Hoeve and Benson, *J. Phys. Chem.*, 1957, **61**, 1149.

Debye and Anacker[1] have applied the light-scattering method to studying the states of solution of tetradecyltrimethylammonium bromide and the hexadecyl (cetyl) analogue. They found that the method was inapplicable to pure solutions of these two compounds, because no dissymmetry was produced in the scattered light, but in the presence of $0\cdot178\,M$ and $0\cdot233\,M$ potassium bromide, the hexadecyl compound gave a measurable dissymmetry. They were able to draw the firm conclusion that, under these conditions, micelles were present which were neither spheres nor discs, but were probably rod-shaped. These results, of course, do not bear on the arguments which we have attempted to summarise above, and are of only limited interest technically, since the solutions in question (which contained over 2% of electrolyte) were visibly turbid.

In the foregoing discussion we have confined our attention to amphipathic electrolytes in which the hydrophobic portion of the surface-active ion consisted of a straight paraffin chain. Surface-active agents in which the paraffin chain is not straight but branched (or double) are becoming increasingly important in many technical processes. As yet, little quantitative data on the aqueous solutions of representatives of this class in the pure state have been published, due principally to the difficulty in preparing single pure substances. There is, however, a growing literature on the properties of solutions of commercial products of this class, but deductions as to the state in solution from such data must be made with great caution since the presence of "impurities" (inorganic salts, homologues of varying chain length, etc.) may profoundly affect the physical properties of their aqueous solutions. The micelle of a straight paraffin-chain salt is essentially hydrophilic and is thus not surface-active. As a consequence, the progressive lowering of the interfacial tension with concentration characteristic of dilute solutions of these salts is arrested at the critical concentration. Hartley pointed out[2] that, if the tendency to micelle formation could be prevented or reduced, then the reduction in the interfacial tension would continue into much more concentrated solutions giving rise to still lower interfacial tension values. One method of achieving this would be by replacing the straight by a branched (or double) paraffin chain and Hartley showed that such effects were in fact achieved by his interfacial tension measurements on solutions of the sulphonates of dialkyl ethers of dihydric alcohols. In these solutions he found, moreover, that the "critical concentration phenomena" such as the abnormal increase in the temperature coefficient of solubility, solubilisation, etc., were absent and, as a consequence of the reduction in the tendency towards micelle formation, the solubility of these compounds at higher temperatures was very much less than that of the straight paraffin-chain salts, although they were much more soluble at lower temperatures.

[1] Debye and Anacker, *J. Phys. Chem.*, 1951, **55**, 644.
[2] Hartley, *Trans. Faraday Soc.*, 1941, **37**, 130.

The conductivities of solutions of various purified "Aerosols" (sodium salts of dialkyl sulphosuccinates) have been measured by Haffner, Piccione, and Rosenblum[1] and of pure double-paraffin-chain quaternary ammonium chlorides by Ralston, Eggenberger, and DuBrow.[2] All these workers found a sharp drop over a limited concentration range similar to that in solutions of the straight chain alcohol sulphates or single-paraffin-chain quaternary ammonium chlorides due to ion aggregation. Vetter[3] has also found evidence for micelle formation in solutions of Aerosol MA (sodium salt of sulphonated di(2-ethylhexyl) succinate, *cf.* however, Haffner *et al.*[1] who designate this compound as the 1-methylisoamyl succinate) from measurements of partial specific volume, viscosity, and diffusion.

Winsor has published an interesting series of papers in one of which[4] he shows the effect of the configuration of the molecule on its amphipathic properties. For a series of tetradecyl sodium sulphates he found that as the sulphate group was moved nearer the middle of the paraffin chain the critical concentration for micelles progressively increased thus indicating a reduction in the hydrophobe/hydrophile ratio as the branches of the chain became more nearly equal. This reduction in the tendency to micelle formation was also shown by his solubility results. The tetradecyl-1- and -2- sodium sulphates had a low solubility in water while the 3-, 4-, and 5-sulphates readily gave 20% solutions at room temperature. A 21% composition of the 6-sulphate at 18° split into a mixture of a clear solution and a gel in which the solution contained relatively less of the amphipathic electrolyte; at higher temperatures this mixture became a homogeneous mobile solution. A 20% solution of the 7-sulphate was a gel at 18° and had to be heated to 90° before it became mobile. Winsor[5] considers that since the critical micelle concentration increases as the sulphate group in this series moves progressively from the 1- to the 7-position then the tendency towards the formation of spherical micelles (S_1-type in his nomenclature) also decreases. This change in molecular configuration at higher concentrations, however, increases the tendency to form lamellar micelles (Winsor's G-type).

Thus although the formation of micelles in aqueous solutions of branched (or double) paraffin-chain salts appears likely and undoubtedly occurs when the branches are of very unequal lengths it is not yet clear what is the state in solution when the chain lengths are more nearly equal and are not of sufficient length to outweigh the strongly hydrophilic character of the ionising group.

[1] Haffner, Piccione, and Rosenblum, *J. Phys. Chem.*, 1942, **46**, 662.
[2] Ralston, Eggenberger, and DuBrow, *J. Amer. Chem. Soc.*, 1948, **70**, 977.
[3] Vetter, *J. Phys. Coll. Chem.*, 1947, **51**, 262.
[4] Winsor, *Trans. Faraday Soc.*, 1948, **44**, 463.
[5] Winsor, *Solvent Properties of Amphiphilic Compounds*, Butterworth, 1954, p. 34.

B. Surface-active electrolytes which do not contain a paraffin chain

The above discussion has been largely taken up with solutions of amphipathic electrolytes which contained long paraffin chains. The inclusion of
a long hydrocarbon chain in the molecule is not, however, a necessary
feature of a surface-active molecule, as reference to Part III will show,
and, indeed, many of the industrially useful surface-active agents do not
have this structure.[1] Among these may be mentioned the important class
of wetting agents which are the salts of the alkylnaphthalene sulphonic
acids[2] in which the alkyl group contains only three or four carbon atoms,
and the condensation products of formaldehyde and aromatic sulphonic
acids,[3] which have been extensively used as "dispersing" agents, although
they were initially developed as synthetic tanning agents. The only
scientific publication dealing with the states of solution of any of this class
of compounds, as far as the authors are aware, is a paper presented by
Ambler[4] at the 11th International Congress of Pure and Applied Chemistry.
In this paper Ambler dealt with aqueous solutions of the condensation
product of formaldehyde and sodium naphthalene-2-sulphonate and
showed from electrophoretic measurements on specially synthesised
material that the condensation product consisted of two naphthalene
sulphonate molecules linked by a methylene bridge, which was most
probably in the $5:5'$ position. In solution the disodium dinaphthyl-
methane-2 : $2'$-disulphonate aggregated into micelles which from diffusion
results were estimated to contain about 20 to 40 amphipathic ions. In the
commercial condensation product some uncondensed naphthalene-2-sul-
phonate and also 1-sulphonate were present and these were shown to form
complex micelles with the condensation product. The naphthalene-2-
sulphonate also existed as a separate but not very highly charged micellar
species. The electrophoretic and diffusion measurements were, of course,
made in the presence of a swamping excess of electrolyte which in this case
had to be large (ionic strength about $1\cdot0$) because the solutes were highly
conducting electrolytes.

A great deal of work has of course been done on the aggregation of
dyestuffs in aqueous solution, the effects of which show certain similarities
to the effects of the aggregation of amphipathic solutes. Valko has admir-
ably discussed[5] the aggregation of dyestuffs in solution and has pointed out
that the forces which are primarily responsible are probably *not* due to
amphipathy in the molecule but are much more specific (of a dipolar
character, or more especially due to the formation of hydrogen bonds). In

---

[1] Stewart and Bunbury, *Trans. Faraday Soc.*, 1935, **31**, 208.

[2] Günther, Badische Anilin-u. Soda-Fabrik. D.R.P. 336,558 (1917).

[3] Badische Anilin-u. Soda-Fabrik. D.R.P. 292,531 (1913).

[4] Ambler, 11th International Congress of Pure and Applied Chemistry, London, 1947.

[5] Valko, *Kolloidchemische Grundlagen der Textilveredlung*, J. Springer, Berlin, 1937,
p. 379.

view of this essential difference, a discussion of the aggregation of dyestuffs in solution is not considered relevant in the present monograph.*

C. Non-ionogenic surface-active agents

Reference has already been made to the relative paucity of published investigations on the physico-chemical properties of solutions of non-ionogenic amphipathic compounds. Several factors have contributed to this neglect of a most interesting class of compounds, which are becoming increasingly important in industry and everyday life. The discovery and development of the non-ionogenic surface-active agents took place at a much later date than those of the ionic type, and they first became prominent in Europe, and particularly in Germany, not long before 1939. The electro-chemical methods (especially conductivity and transport number) which had proved so fruitful in the study of the ionic types are not applicable in the non-ionogenic field. But, perhaps the most serious deterrent to an intensive study of this class lies in their heterogeneity in regard to molecular weight. Like most of the commercial amphipathic electrolytes, the commercial non-ionogenic compounds consist in most cases of a mixture of compounds of differing molecular weights. Whereas it is possible to obtain numerous ionogenic amphipathic substances in a high state of purity, *e.g.*, by synthesis from molecularly homogeneous intermediates, similar syntheses of non-ionogenic compounds lead to mixtures of condensates rather than to molecularly homogeneous products. This fact may be of considerable advantage in the industrial use of these products since it may allow one product to perform adequately several useful functions but the heterogeneity of the starting material must have adversely influenced many workers contemplating the application of precise physical chemical techniques. Furthermore when such measurements have been made the results are far less sharp and clear cut than with amphipathic electrolytes and the interpretation of these results far less satisfying. As far as the authors are aware, no methods of separation have yet been discovered, except perhaps for some of the compounds at the low molecular weight end of a series.

The various chemical types of this class of amphipathic substances will be mentioned in Part III but by far the most important types industrially are the polyglyceryl esters of fatty acids and the polyglycol ether or polyethenoxy compounds, and it is only on the latter that there exist published records of investigations into the constitution of their aqueous solutions. The latter compounds, invented by the I.G. and disclosed[1] in 1932, comprise the condensation products of a compound possessing a hydroxyl,

---

* This topic is dealt with in Vickerstaff's well-known book, *The Physical Chemistry of Dyeing*, Oliver and Boyd, 2nd edition, 1954, p. 59 *ff*.

[1] I.G., B.P. 380,431.

carbonyl, amine, etc., group and a long polyglycol ether radical [—$OC_2H_4]_n$OH. The polyglycol ether chain provides the hydrophilic portion of the molecule and through the formation of hydrogen bonds between the many ether groups and water molecules renders the compound soluble in water. As pointed out in Chapter 14, clear solutions of some polyethenoxy compounds go turbid when the temperature is raised —a consequence of the exothermic nature of the hydrogen bond, the increased temperature leading to decreased solubilising effect. The solubilising effect of an ether group is very much less than that of an ionic group and thus the hydrophilic portion of a water soluble non-ionogenic surface active compound is much larger than that of an amphipathic electrolyte of similar hydrophobic chain length—in many cases the hydrophilic portion is larger than the hydrophobic portion. Schulman has deduced[1] that an increase of one —CH_2— in the hydrocarbon chain is approximately balanced by an increase of one —$CH_2 \cdot CH_2O$— in the polyethenoxy chain.

The polyglyceryl esters are of similar structure to the polyethenoxy compounds *only in the straight-chain cases* where the repeating unit in the hydrophilic chain contains both hydroxyl groups and ether linkages, namely —$O \cdot CH_2 \cdot CH(OH) \cdot CH_2$—. This unit may, however, give rise to branched chains at the hydroxyl group and these branches may also terminate in hydrophobic chains so that a great diversity of types, as well as a diversity of molecular weights may exist in a commercial product.

Because of the amphipathic nature of the polyglycol ether products, the same forces which caused aggregation of the ionic surface-active agents can be assumed to cause aggregation in aqueous solution. Since the hydrophilic portion of the molecule is, in this case, comparable in size with the hydrophobic part, it is to be expected that the transitional layer surrounding the essentially hydrocarbon core of the micelle will be correspondingly thick. McBain and Marsden[2] found evidence for micelle formation in the X-ray diffraction patterns of aqueous solutions of *p*-(2-methyl heptyl)-phenoxy-nonaethoxy ethanol. They observed the short spacing band ($d_S = 4 \cdot 5$A) characteristic of liquid hydrocarbon structure and a further band which was presumably the intermicellar band, since its spacing decreased with increasing concentration. McBain, Wilder, and Merrill[3] have shown that the practically water-insoluble dyestuff, Orange OT, is very soluble in solutions of the above compound and also in solutions of nonaethyleneglycol monolaurate, which is most probably due to micelle formation. These solubility measurements have not been made in sufficiently dilute solutions of the latter to show the increase due to micelle formation nor to indicate the probable critical concentration. The critical concentration

[1] Schulman, Matalon and Cohen, *Discussions of the Faraday Society*, 1951, p. 117.
[2] McBain and Marsden, *J. Chem. Phys.*, 1947, **15**, 211.
[3] McBain, Wilder, and Merrill, *J. Phys. Coll. Chem.*, 1948, **52**, 12.

of the former appears from these measurements to be in the region 1·5 to 5×10^{-4} molar which is very much less than that of an amphipathic electrolyte, the hydrophobic portion of which is of similar size and structure —thus the critical concentration of sodium n-octylbenzene p-sulphonate is $1\cdot2 \times 10^{-2}$ molar.[1] Further evidence for micelle formation in solutions of non-ionogenic surface-active compounds is furnished by the work of Kushner and Hubbard[2] who made viscosity and turbidity measurements on solutions of "Triton" X-100

$$(CH_3)_3\ C \cdot CH_2 \cdot C(CH_3)_2 \left\langle \bigcirc \right\rangle O(CH_2 \cdot CH_2 \cdot O)_n H$$

where $n = 10$.

They calculated that the micelle consisted of about 140 molecules with several thousand molecules of water associated with the hydrophilic chain. Instead of the relatively sharp, well defined critical concentration for micelles which one observes with amphipathic electrolytes, they deduced from their measurements that micelle formation took place over an extended concentration range—a steadily increasing fraction of the added detergent going into the micellar form over this range. Thinking that this might be due to heterogeneity of their starting material, they later[3] carried out further light scattering measurements on a sample of "Triton" X-100 fractionated by molecular distillation. Although they found different values for the mean micellar weight of the two fractions there was no sharpening of the critical micelle concentration. Weston[4] also found for "Lissapol" N (a polycondensate of ethylene oxide and an alkyl cresol) that the critical concentration extends over a concentration range, a fact which he attributed to its molecular heterogeneity.

Although exact measurements on solutions of the non-ionogenic amphipathic substances are relatively much fewer than on their ionic counterparts these compounds are technically of great importance and have a very great advantage over amphipathic electrolytes in that their behaviour is relatively unaffected by the presence of electrolytes in aqueous solution. The most common type found in commerce is that of the polyethenoxy condensates of which more will be said in Chapter 14.

D. Solubilisation in solutions of amphipathic electrolytes

An important property of amphipathic substances is the ability of their aqueous solutions to dissolve, often in considerable amounts, substances

[1] Paquette, Lingafelter, and Tartar, *J. Amer. Chem. Soc.*, 1943, **65**, 686.
[2] Kushner and Hubbard, *J. Phys. Chem.*, 1954, **58**, 1163.
[3] Kushner, Hubbard and Dean, *J. Phys. Chem.*, 1956, **61**, 371.
[4] Weston, *Hexagon Digest*, 1953, **13**, 3.

which have only a slight solubility in water. A number of technically important applications of surface-active agents are based on this phenomenon of solubilisation and these are discussed more fully in a later chapter. It seems worth while however to describe the fundamental basis and theories of solubilisation in the present chapter because this phenomenon furnishes valuable information on the state of solution of surface-active agents. Considerable controversy has arisen in this field, mainly because of the conflicting pictures adopted by various workers for the micelles in solution, but an attempt will be made to present a balanced summary of the various viewpoints. This property of surface-active agents, of solubilising substances only slightly soluble in water, which is illustrated by the classical case of solutions of phenolic substances in soap solutions, must not be confused with the increased solvent power for organic substances conferred by the addition to water of comparatively large amounts of water-miscible organic solvents, such as ethyl alcohol or acetone, or of salts such as sodium benzoate or salicylate. These two effects are entirely different in their mechanism, as is apparent from the behaviour of the solutions on dilution. The latter effect (which is termed hydrotropy*) is due to a change in the nature of the solvent medium and is lost almost completely when the solution is diluted with water. On the other hand, the solutions made in the presence of amphipathic substances may be diluted to a very large extent before separation of the "solubilisate" takes place. Recent work on solubilisation has largely been carried out on pure crystalline organic substances or water-immiscible liquids which have been shown to dissolve in aqueous solutions of amphipathic electrolytes of many varied types; for example, the solubility of the dyestuff Orange OT (1-*o*-tolylazo-2-naphthol) in soap solutions,[1] or of *trans*-azobenzene in aqueous cetylpyridinium chloride,[2] is several thousand times greater than is the solubility in water. For a comprehensive factual review of the results of work on solubilisation up to 1950 the reader is referred to the article by Klevens,[3] and, for a more theoretical and interpretative treatment to the monographs by Winsor[4] and Laing McBain and Hutchinson.[5]

---

* "Hydrotropy" has been very widely used, especially among German writers, to describe the phenomenon of solubilisation. McBain has pointed out (in *Advances in Colloid Science*, 1942, vol. I, p. 119) that the term hydrotropy was introduced to describe "the effect of large additions of various substances to water in increasing the solubility of other substances therein." We prefer to follow McBain and reserve the term hydrotropy for this effect and to use "solubilisation" for the effect by which substantial amounts of an insoluble or sparingly soluble organic substance are dissolved by aqueous solutions of surface-active agents.

[1] Green and McBain, *J. Phys. Coll. Chem.*, 1947, **51**, 286.
[2] Hartley, *J. Chem. Soc.*, 1938, 1968.
[3] Klevens, *Chem. Rev.*, 1950, **47**, 1.
[4] Winsor, *Solvent Properties of Amphiphilic Compounds*, Butterworth, 1954.
[5] Laing McBain and Hutchinson, *Solubilisation and Related Phenomena*, Academic Press, 1955.

Hartley[1] considers that the use of the word "solubilisation" is misleading and unnecessary. "It implies that the solute has suffered some active chemical change, which of course is not the case. There is nothing peculiar about the solute, but only about the solvent, and the peculiarity in the solvent power of the mixed solvent is a peculiarity in degree only, and not in kind." This argument is undoubtedly logical, but we agree with Winsor

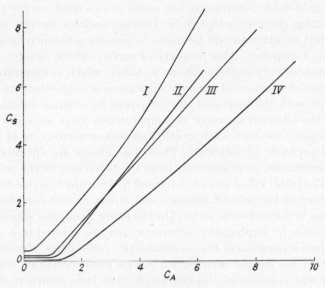

Figure 14

Solubilisation by amphipathic electrolytes

(c_A = concentration of amphipathic electrolyte; c_S = concentration of solubilised material—different scales are used for the different curves.)

I. Benzene in potassium laurate (Stearns *et al.*, *J. Chem. Phys.*, 1947, **15**, 496).
II. Orange OT in potassium laurate (Kolthoff and Stricks, *J. Phys. Coll. Chem.*, 1948, **52**, 915).
III. Azobenzene in cetylpyridinium chloride (Hartley, *J. Chem. Soc.*, 1938, 1968).
IV. Dimethylaminoazobenzene in dodecylamine hydrochloride (Kolthoff and Stricks, *loc. cit.*).

(*loc. cit.*) that the term "solubilisation" has a customary significance which is now well established and understood, and propose to retain it in this discussion.

This solubilising action is possessed by aqueous solutions of amphipathic substances so dilute that it is inconceivable that it could be due to a change in the solvent characteristics of the water brought about by the addition of such small amounts of another solute. It is evident from a study of the results of such solubilisation work, of which a selection is given in Figure 14, that only when the concentration of the amphipathic solute reaches a

---

[1] Hartley, *Progress in the Chemistry of Fats and Other Lipids*. Pergamon Press, 1955, p. 28; *Ann. Rep. Prog. Chem.*, 1948, **45**, 40.

certain value does the concentration of the solubilisate begin to increase appreciably. This sharp increase takes place over the critical concentration range and is due to the fact that micelles are now present. The micelles with their essentially paraffinic interior provide a new solvent medium for the solubilisate—a medium in which it is much more readily soluble than in water—but although the interior of a micelle of potassium laurate, for example, may be considered similar to liquid dodecane, this analogy must not be pushed too far in considering solubilisation. Benzene and other hydrocarbons are miscible with dodecane but nevertheless have a limited solubility in potassium laurate solutions. On the other hand, the solubility of *trans*-azobenzene in the *micelles* of cetylpyridinium chloride is almost exactly the same as its solubility in liquid hexadecane, though Hartley has pointed out[1] that this agreement may be fortuitous. The paraffin chains in a liquid spherical micelle and to a greater extent in a cylindrical micelle will not have complete freedom of movement since one end is, as it were, "anchored" near the surface and this will affect the solvent power of the paraffin chains. Also, the addition of a hydrophobic substance, such as a hydrocarbon, to the micelle cannot be made without limit without destroying the very condition which brought the micelle into being, namely, the production of an essentially hydrophilic surface from particles the greater part of the area of which is hydrophobic.

The layer at the surface of the micelle which covers the transition from a predominantly aqueous to a predominantly paraffinic environment will have a profound effect on solubilisation, particularly of molecules containing both hydrophilic and hydrophobic parts. Such molecules could accommodate themselves very readily in a "heterogeneous" medium such as is presented by the micelles and it would thus be possible for their solubility in such a medium greatly to exceed their solubility in either water or liquid paraffin alone. For example, Stearns, Oppenheimer, Simon, and Harkins[2] found that the solubility of *n*-decane in 10% potassium myristate was 1·05% v/w at 25° while that of *n*-decanol in such a solution was 3·31%. The solubility in the micelles is also not only a function of the amphipathic ion but is affected to some extent, at least for polar solubilisates, by the counterions. Green and McBain[3] found that the solubilities of Yellow AB and Orange OT are greater in solutions of sodium soaps than in solutions of potassium soaps, although this conclusion has been challenged by Kolthoff and Stricks.[4] It is known[5] that the nature of the counterion can affect the size of the micelle and also the fraction of the counterions associated with it; both these factors will affect the solubility in the micelle. The

[1] Hartley, "Solvent Action of Detergents" in *Wetting and Detergency*, A. Harvey, London, 1937, p. 156.

[2] Stearns, Oppenheimer, Simon, and Harkins, *J. Chem. Phys.*, 1947, **15**, 496.

[3] Green and McBain, *J. Phys. Coll. Chem.*, 1947, **51**, 286.

[4] Kolthoff and Stricks, *J. Phys. Coll. Chem.*, 1948, **52**, 915.

[5] Samis and Hartley, *Trans. Faraday Soc.*, 1938, **34**, 1288.

size of the molecules of the solubilisate will also affect the solubility in the micelle since they have to accommodate themselves in a micelle whose size (for a given amphipathic electrolyte) is approximately constant. Stearns, Oppenheimer, Simon, and Harkins[1] showed that the solubilities in potassium laurate of a homologous series of alkylbenzenes and of normal paraffins appear to decrease with increasing molecular weight.

Another factor which will affect the solubility in solutions of amphipathic substances is the effect the solubilisate itself may have on the micellar size, "structure," and adherence of the counterions. If the ratio of the increase in the concentration of the solubilisate to that of the amphipathic solute is plotted against the total concentration of amphipathic solute,[2] a method which emphasises the marked increase in solubility occurring at the critical concentration but unfortunately exaggerates any inaccuracies in the experimental data, it would appear that two types of curves are obtained. These are illustrated in Figure 15 where the results for benzene[1] and Orange OT[3] in potassium laurate, *trans*-azobenzene in cetylpyridinium chloride,[2] and dimethylaminoazobenzene in dodecylamine hydrochloride[4] are shown. It is evident from this Figure that $\Delta C_S/\Delta C_A$ (ΔC_S is the increase in the concentration of the solubilisate caused by an increase of ΔC_A in the concentration of the amphipathic solute) increases very rapidly, for all substances, in a narrow concentration range. For Orange OT and azobenzene, however, $\Delta C_S/\Delta C_A$ becomes nearly constant after this rapid rise while with benzene and dimethylaminoazobenzene the ratios continue steadily to increase, after the rapid rise due to micelle formation, though at much reduced rates and, up to the limits of the experiments, show no signs of having reached constant values. With Orange OT and azobenzene, the system above the critical concentration is analogous to that of a saturated solution where addition of solvent allows a further quantity of solute to dissolve, the ratio of the further quantity of solute to that of the added solvent being the same as their ratio in the saturated solution. In the cases we are considering the solvent is, of course, the amphipathic solute in the micellar form and since we are dealing with concentrations above the critical concentration any additional amphipathic solute will be almost entirely micellar. With benzene (and other hydrocarbons), and dimethylaminoazobenzene, an increase in the solvent (*i.e.*, the micellar amphipathic solute) produces a more than strictly proportional increase in the solubilisate concentration, which suggests that the solubilisate affects either the size or the constitution of the micelles, or both. From the limited amount of precise quantitative data available on solubilisation it would appear that solubilisates which show the continuing increase in

[1] Stearns, Oppenheimer, Simon, and Harkins, *J. Chem. Phys.*, 1947, **15**, 496.
[2] Hartley, *J. Chem. Soc.*, 1938, 1968.
[3] Green and McBain, *J. Phys. Coll. Chem.*, 1947, **51**, 286.
[4] Kolthoff and Stricks, *J. Phys. Coll. Chem.*, 1948, **52**, 915.

the differential curve are much more soluble in the micelles than those whose differential solubility becomes approximately constant after the critical concentration.

It appears that a third type of differential solubility curve has been

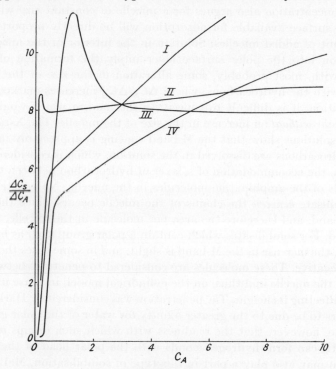

Figure 15

Differential solubilisation by amphipathic electrolytes

(C_A = concentration of amphipathic electrolyte; $\Delta C_S/\Delta C_A$ = molar ratio of increment in solubilisate concentration to increment in concentration of amphipathic electrolyte.)

I. Benzene in potassium laurate (Stearns *et al., J. Chem. Phys.*, 1947, **15**, 496).
II. Azobenzene in cetylpyridinium chloride (Hartley, *J. Chem. Soc.*, 1938, 1968).
III. Orange OT in potassium laurate (Green and McBain, *J. Phys. Coll. Chem.*, 1947, **51**, 286).
IV. Dimethylaminoazobenzene in dodecylamine hydrochloride (Kolthoff and Stricks, *J. Phys. Coll. Chem.*, 1948, **52**, 915).

obtained since Harkins, Mattoon, and Mittelmann[1] reported that $\Delta C_S/\Delta C_A$ for *n*-heptanol in potassium myristate solutions decreases slightly with increasing concentration. These authors divided the mechanism of solubilisation into three types (a) adsorption on the surface of the micelle, (b) solution in the interior of the micelle, and (c) penetration into the polar surface layer of the micelle. Adsorption on the surface of the

[1] Harkins, Mattoon. and Mittelmann, *J. Chem. Phys.*, 1947, **15**, 763.

micelle would mean that the amount solubilised would be relatively small, as is shown by azobenzene and Orange OT, already quoted, where $\Delta C_S / \Delta C_A$ is only 1/1000 to 1/50 (on a molecular basis) of the amount of the polar or non-polar hydrocarbons solubilised. The constancy of $\Delta C_S / \Delta C_A$ above the critical concentration also argues for a micelle of constant size where the increased surface available for adsorption will be directly proportional to the amount of added micelles. Solution in the interior of the micelle and penetration into the polar surface layer imply the formation of mixed micelles with, most probably, some alteration in the size of the micelle. In fact, with the hydrocarbons, where $\Delta C_S / \Delta C_A$ increases markedly with concentration, it is difficult to conceive a mechanism which would allow this to occur *without* an increase in the size of the micelle. The X-ray data[1] on these solutions show that the M-band spacing is appreciably increased when hydrocarbons are dissolved in the solution, which is considered to be caused by the accommodation of a layer of hydrocarbon between the non-polar ends of the amphipathic molecules in the micelle. No penetration of the solubilisate *between* the chains of the micelle occurs, since the short-spacing band, and therefore the area per molecule in the micelle, remains unaffected. For solubilisates which contain a polar group such as hydroxyl or amino, the increase in the M-band is slight, and in some cases the change is even negative. These molecules are considered to penetrate between the chains of the micelle and thus, on the cylindrical model, increase its radius without affecting its height. The penetration was considered by Harkins and co-workers to be due to the greater affinity for water of the polar group. It is possible, however, that the readiness with which such groups as —OH and —NH$_2$ can form hydrogen bonds with the polar head of the amphipathic ion may also play a part in this type of solubilisation. McBain and co-workers[2] also found that $\Delta C_S / \Delta C_A$ was not constant and, for certain solutes could even show a maximum from which they concluded that different kinds of micelles coexisted in the solution.

Additional proof that solubilisation is due to the micelles is furnished by the effects of electrolytes and of ethanol. Stearns, Oppenheimer, Simon, and Harkins[3] have shown that the solubility of 2-nitrodiphenylamine in aqueous potassium laurate and in potassium laurate containing varying amounts of potassium chloride is a function, not of the total concentration of potassium laurate, but of the amount of the laurate in the micellar form (*i.e.*, the total concentration less the critical concentration, the latter of course varying with the amount of the added electrolyte). On the other hand, Smith[4] showed that the partition coefficient of unsaponifiable matter

---

[1] Harkins, Mattoon, and Mittelmann, *J. Chem. Phys.* 1947 **15**, 763.

[2] McBain and Huff, *J. Coll. Sci.*, 1949, **4**, 383; McBain and Lissant, *J. Phys. Chem.*, 1951, **55**, 655.

[3] Stearns, Oppenheimer, Simon, and Harkins, *J. Chem. Phys.*, 1947, **15**, 496.

[4] Smith, *J. Phys. Chem.*, 1932, **36**, 1404.

between water-immiscible organic solvents and soap solutions was increased by the addition of ethanol. Although the ethanol would also be distributed between the organic and aqueous phases, its addition to the organic solvent did not increase its solvent power but rather the reverse. Its presence in the water, where it exerts a disaggregating effect on the micelles, markedly lowered their solvent power for the unsaponifiable matter.

It is important to note that the presence of a solubilisate can lower the concentration at which (mixed) micelles are formed. Ekwall and Danielsson[1] made the interesting observation that sodium tetradecyl sulphate and cetyltrimethylammonium bromide were capable of solubilising decanol at concentrations (0·0003 M and 0·0004 M, respectively) which were well below the critical micelle concentration; they considered that this was evidence that aggregates are present down to these lower concentrations, which they termed the "limiting association concentration." These results do not, of course, prove that micelles are present at these concentrations in the *absence* of the solubilisate, but seem to us to be readily explained on the grounds that, in these particular cases, the "affinity" between amphipathic solute and solubilisate is sufficiently great that mixed micelles are formed below the ordinary critical micelle concentration. In other cases, such as the solubilisation of Orange OT and dimethylaminoazobenzene by sodium and potassium laurates, dodecylamine hydrochloride, *etc.*, which have been studied by Rigg and Liu,[2] this condition is not satisfied, and there is no solubilisation below the critical micelle concentration. (Rigg and Liu draw attention to the possibility, in the cases studied by them, of mistaking deflocculated dyestuff for solubilised material, though this criticism does not appear to apply to Ekwall and Danielsson's experimental work.) There is, in fact, no contradiction between these two sets of results, provided that one bears in mind the possible effect on the critical micelle concentration of an interaction between solubilisate and solubilising agent, and also the fact that the "limiting association concentration" (which is obviously a useful concept) is a characteristic of the combination of the two materials, rather than of the solubilising agent alone.

The foregoing discussion has been to a large extent concerned with solubilisation in fairly dilute solutions of surface-active agents. The behaviour of more concentrated solutions is considered, *inter alia*, in an important series of papers by Ekwall and his collaborators.[3] In the first of these papers the solubility of p-xylene in sodium oleate and sodium tetradecyl sulphate solutions was found to increase linearly with concentration of detergent up to the region 0·19–0·20 M, after which there was a more

---

[1] Ekwall and Danielsson, *Acta Chem. Scand.*, 1951, **5**, 973.

[2] Rigg and Liu, *J. Amer. Oil Chem. Soc.*, 1953, **30**, 14.

[3] Ekwall, Hasan, and Danielsson, *Acta Chem. Scand.*, 1952, **6**, 440; Ekwall and Smeds, *ibid.*, 1952, **6**, 441; Ekwall and Passinen, *ibid.*, 1953, **7**, 1098; Passinen and Ekwall, *ibid.*, 1956, **10**, 1215.

rapid rise. In the second paper, the partial specific volumes of the two agents were determined in aqueous solutions, in the presence and absence of p-xylene, and found to begin to increase more rapidly at approximately the same concentrations, which Ekwall and his collaborators call the "second critical micelle concentration." These results, showing as they do a difference in solubilising power below and above the second critical micelle concentration, support the view that a second type of micelle is formed at this second critical concentration. Similar results are described in the other papers in the series, on the solubility of 1-decanol in sodium oleate, sodium tetradecyl sulphate, sodium laurate, and sodium myristate. Ekwall and his collaborators consider that, at the second critical micelle concentration, the electrical double layers of the micellar aggregates approach so closely that mutual interference begins, and that changes occur in the structure and/or the size of the micelles. The increased solubilising power of the micelles at and above this concentration is believed to be due to the fact that the charge density in the outermost ("palisade") layer of the larger micelles remains large enough, even when decanol is incorporated, to keep the micelle stable.

Another paper by these workers[1] contains some very good pictures of the formation of mesomorphic phases in aqueous solutions containing sodium laurate and fatty alcohols such as 1-decanol, the first signs occurring at the "limiting association concentration." The myelenic growths* which form contain both alcohol and soap, the molar ratio alcohol: soap varying between 1 : 2 and 4·5 : 1. The interaction between the amphipathic solute and the solubilisate is considered to take place in the following steps: (i) formation of soluble micelles when the first addition of the alcohol is made, (ii) formation of a separate alcohol-soap-water mesomorphic phase, (iii) increasing transfer of soap from the aqueous solution into the separated phase, (iv) increasing extraction of alcohol by the mesomorphic phase, (v) appearance of free alcohol in the system as a separate phase. Apart from its intrinsic interest, this picture underlines the strength of the interaction between the two types of molecules—an interaction which plays an important part in detergent action and emulsification as well as in solubilisation.

Kolthoff and Stricks[2] have pointed out that the effect of ordinary electrolytes, to which we have referred earlier, appears to be the result of two tendencies: an increase in the amount of micellar solute present, and a direct effect on the solvent power of the individual micelles. Their conclusion, based on a considerable amount of experimental data on Orange OT and dimethylaminoazobenzene in potassium caprate, sodium and

---

* The possible significance of these myelenic growths in detergent processes is discussed in Chapter 8, p. 289.

[1] Ekwall, Salonen, Krokfors, and Danielsson, *Acta Chem. Scand.*, 1956, **10**, 1146.

[2] Kolthoff and Stricks, *J. Phys. Chem.*, 1949, **53**, 424.

potassium laurates, potassium myristate, potassium oleate, dodecylamine hydrochloride, and sodium diamylsulphosuccinate, is that the former effect is always favourable to solubilisation, but that there is no simple rule for the latter. This picture is amplified by the results of Klevens[1] on the solubilisation of 1-octanol and *n*-heptane by potassium myristate, in which the solubilising power of the detergent at first increased with increasing electrolyte concentration, and then decreased.

The solubilising action of an amphipathic solute on an insoluble substance can sometimes be increased by adding a second sparingly soluble solubilisate, an effect which Kolthoff and Graydon[2] have termed "co-solubilisation." (It is interesting to note that this effect was used empirically in industry before its mechanism was fully elucidated, an example being the use of phenolic materials to solubilise oils in soap solutions, which we discuss in Chapter 6, p. 253.) They found that amyl alcohol continuously increased the solubilising power of potassium laurate for azobenzene and naphthalene, whereas with dimethylaminoazobenzene and the dyestuff Orange OT the co-solubilising effect passed through a minimum with increasing amount of amyl alcohol, and then increased. Octyl alcohol had little effect on polar solutes, but increased the solubility of naphthalene and azobenzene in potassium laurate solutions, while hydrocarbons (*n*-octane, *n*-decane, *n*-dodecane, and *n*-hexadecane) increased the solubilising power of potassium laurate for azobenzene, dimethylaminoazo-benzene, and Orange OT. Kolthoff and Graydon suggested that solubilisation of polar and apolar compounds occurs at different loci in the micelle, that co-solubilisers act by increasing the size of the micelles, and that two polar co-solubilisates will compete for orientated positions in the micelles.

Non-ionic amphipathic molecules also have a marked solubilising action, perhaps the commonest example being the solubilisation of polyethenoxy condensates with short polyether chains by the higher condensates in commercial mixtures (*cf.* Chapter 14, p. 466). A complication which arises with polyethenoxy agents is the possible effect of the solubilisate on the "cloud point" of the agent, *i.e.*, the temperature at which the polyethenoxy agent (which has a negative temperature coefficient of solubility) begins to come out of solution. Weiden and Norton,[3] who studied the solubilisation of benzaldehyde, parathion, phenol, and benzene by two polyethenoxy agents, found that the presence of these solubilisates depressed the cloud point of the agents, which limited the extent of effective solubilisation.

Winsor's theoretical formulation of solubilisation phenomena is summarised in his important monograph,[4] to which reference should be made

[1] Klevens, *J. Amer. Chem. Soc.*, 1952, **74**, 4624.
[2] Kolthoff and Graydon, *J. Phys. Chem.*, 1951, **55**, 699.
[3] Weiden and Norton, *J. Coll. Sci.*, 1953, **8**, 606.
[4] Winsor, *Solvent Properties of Amphiphilic Compounds*, Butterworth, 1954.

for details. He postulates that effective solubilisation requires a suitable balance between the lipophilic and the hydrophilic affinities of the solubilising agent: if $A_{\overline{CO}}$ and $A_{\overline{CW}}$ are the affinities of the solvated agent for the water-saturated "oil" and for the "oil"-saturated water, respectively, then the ratio of these two quantities, $R = A_{\overline{CO}}/A_{\overline{CW}}$, should be approximately unity for good solubilisation. This approach has proved to be useful in explaining the results of Palit and his co-workers on the solubilisation of water in non-aqueous solvents.*

In the first of these papers,[1] the amount of water which could be solubilised by cetyldimethylethylammonium bromide in chloroform-benzene and chloroform-carbon tetrachloride mixtures was found to depend markedly on the ratio of solvents, with pronounced maxima at about 1 : 1 and 2 : 3, respectively, in the two series. Up to 5·5 grams of water for each gram of amphipathic agent, dissolved in 5 c.c. of solvent mixture, could be solubilised, compared with about 0·2 gram of water in pure chloroform. In view of the large amount of water which could be dissolved, Palit decided in favour of a spherical micelle.

In two more papers in this series,[2] the solubilising action was studied of a series of dodecylammonium and octadecylammonium salts of carboxylic acids, from the formate to the palmitate and the oleate, on water in xylene. In each series, there was an optimum size of the carboxylate radical, at the butyrate with the dodecylammonium salts and at the propionate with the octadecyl series. The effect of a range of different solvents with dodecylammonium butyrate was also studied, and considerable differences were observed, the aromatic solvents being generally better than the paraffinic, which were better than the chlorinated hydrocarbons. All these results were readily explainable in terms of the optimum value of Winsor's R function. The theory also offered an explanation of the results when water was solubilised in toluene, carbon tetrachloride, and chloroform, with binary mixtures of dodecylammonium chloride, formate, acetate, laurate, and oleate. When a hydrophilic and a lipophilic salt of this series were mixed in different proportions (*e.g.*, the acetate and the laurate, or the formate and the laurate), it was found that the solubilising power passed through a pronounced maximum as the ratio of hydrophilic to lipophilic agent was varied. An excess of amine was found to increase solubilising power, but the addition of excess acid gave first an increase and then a decrease. This last effect was not really explainable on Winsor's theory, probably because of specific interactions between water and the solubilising agent.

---

* A practical application of this reversed solubilisation, in dry-cleaning solvents, is discussed on p. 299.

[1] Palit, *J. Coll. Sci.*, 1949, **4**, 523.

[2] Palit and Venkateswarlu, *Proc. Roy. Soc.*, 1951, **208A**, 542; *J. Chem. Soc.*, 1954, 2129.

In the last paper of the series,[1] eight amphipathic agents (the dodecyl-and cetyltrimethylammonium, -dimethylethylammonium, -dimethy-propylammonium, and -dimethylbutylammonium bromides) were examined for their solubilising action on water in eight solvents (chloroform, carbon tetrachloride, benzene, toluene, *p*- and *o*-xylenes, tetrachloroethane, and chlorobenzene). The solvents were classified into two types : (I) "water-continuous," in which solubilisation is limited by the separation of oil, and (II) "oil-continuous," in which solubilisation is limited by the separation of water. It was found that solubilisation was considerably enhanced when two solvents were mixed which were of different types, but that there was no increase if they were of the same type. Here again the concept of a value of Winsor's *R* function which is near to unity is useful in interpreting the results.

Although it is clear from what has been said above that solubilisation by amphipathic substances is due to the formation of mixed micelles in solution, it is probable that simple pictures such as "solution" in the interior of the micelle, or the formation of a "sandwich" layer of solubilisate in the interior of the micelle, are insufficient to account for the varied solubilising powers of amphipathic substances, even though greater precision can be given to the "solution" picture by bearing in mind that an amphipathic agent which gives a greater degree of disorder in the micelle is likely to be a better solubilising agent. This point, which is perhaps implicit in the original "Hartley" micelle, has been discussed by Klevens in a more recent paper.[2] Specific effects such as adsorption on the micelle, orientation in the surface layer of the micelle, which for non-ionogenic amphipathic substances may be of considerable depth, penetration into the micellar surface layer, or solution in the middle of the micelle, may all play a part, although in any particular case one of these effects may be the dominant factor in solubilisation.

Further information on the location of solubilised substances in micelles is likely to be provided by a study of the ultra-violet spectra, which are sensitive to changes in the dielectric constant of the environment of a solubilised material : for example, the spectrum of a solubilisate in the hydrocarbon interior of the micelle will be different from that of the same material in water. Thus Riegelman, Allawala, Hrenoff, and Strait,[3] working with aqueous solutions of potassium laurate, dodecylamine hydrochloride, and the polyoxyethylene ether of dodecyl alcohol ("Brij 35"), show that the spectrum of solubilised ethylbenzene is similar to its spectrum in octane and unlike that in water, from which they conclude that it is dissolved in the hydrocarbon interior of the micelle. The spectra for dimethylphthalate show that, when it is solubilised, it is in a highly polar environment, from

---

[1] Palit, Moghe, and Biswas, *Trans. Faraday Soc.*, 1959, **55**, 463.

[2] Klevens, *Koll. Z.*, 1952, **128**, 61.

[3] Riegelman, Allawala, Hrenoff and Strait, *J. Coll. Sci.*, 1958, **13**, 208.

which the authors conclude that it is adsorbed on the surface of the micelle. Solubilised naphthalene (and, to a less extent, anthracene) give rather paradoxical results in that some of the absorption maxima indicate an environment which is somewhat more polar than water, while other maxima indicate that the environment is less polar than octane. The authors suggest that the solubilised naphthalene is situated in the palisade layer of the micelle, but state that their conclusions are "by no means final nor entirely unambiguous," and that further experimental work needs to be done.

An interesting case of solubilisation is that of the "polysoaps," which has been studied by Strauss and his co-workers.[1] Most of their work was done on poly(2-vinylpyridine) in which 34% of the nitrogen was quaternised with dodecyl bromide. This polymer dissolves in water and shows no critical micelle concentration, since the unit molecular species acts as a micelle. The dissolved polymer shows a greater solvent action for iso-octane, benzene, and dodecane than does dodecylpyridinium bromide, and is strictly constant. In general, the addition of hydrocarbon decreases the viscosity of the solution since (it has been suggested) it allows the polysoap molecules to coil up to a greater extent. The addition of benzene, however, causes the viscosity first to increase, then to pass through a maximum, and finally to decrease to a value lower than that of the original solution. This is attributed to the aromatic nature of the benzene molecule, which has some affinity for both the lipophilic and the polar portions of the molecule, because of the pyridine nucleus in the latter.

E. The determination of the critical concentration for the formation of micelles

As we have seen, abrupt changes in the physical property-concentration curves take place over a narrow concentration interval when micelles are formed in solution, and from these curves the critical concentration for the formation of micelles may be obtained. It should be emphasised, however, that the critical concentration is not a unique concentration value, but is a *concentration range* within which the constitution of the amphipathic solute in solution changes from the molecular (or ionic) disperse state to an equilibrium between molecules (or ions) and aggregates.

It seems likely that at first only one type of micelle is present and our knowledge of concentrated solutions is at present insufficient to enable the state of solution to be defined in the concentrated regions. Further solute added after the critical concentration region is considered to go practically entirely into the aggregated form and to produce only relatively slight changes in the constitution of the micelle. No hysteresis effects have been

---

[1] Strauss and Jackson, *J. Polymer Sci.*, 1951, **6**, 649; Jackson and Strauss, *ibid.*, 1951, **7**, 473; Layton, Jackson, and Strauss, *ibid.*, 1952, **9**, 295; Strauss and Layton, *J. Phys. Chem.*, 1953, **57**, 352.

observed in these solutions, which indicates that the equilibrium between the aggregated and unaggregated portions of the solute must be rapid and complete, and there thus appears to be no doubt that the solutions are thermodynamically stable. The values of the critical concentration derived from various physico-chemical properties will not necessarily be identical (see Figure 2) since they will depend on the abruptness of the change of the property. As has been pointed out before, the sharpness of the change is

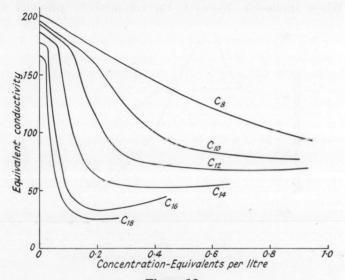

Figure 16
Equivalent conductivities of alkylamine hydrochlorides at 60° C.
(Ralston, Hoerr, and Hoffman, *J. Amer. Chem. Soc.*, 1942, **64**, 97.)
(Ralston and Hoerr, *J. Amer. Chem. Soc.*, 1942, **64**, 772.)

determined by the relative contributions of the aggregated and unaggregated solute to the physical property being measured. The abruptness is also a function of the size of the micelle which is dependent on the length of the hydrophobic portion of the molecule. This is well illustrated by the conductivity results which Ralston and co-workers[1] obtained for the hydrochlorides of a series of alkylamines and which are shown in Figure 16. The curves show no critical concentration for the C_8 compound, the break in the $\Lambda-c$ curve for the C_{10} compound is well-defined, and the break becomes progressively sharper as the chain length is increased. As is seen in the Figure, the range of concentration, within which the rapid fall in the conductivity occurs, decreases very markedly as the chain length increases. The fall in conductivity by itself, however, does not necessarily provide evidence for micelle formation, as has been pointed out earlier,

[1] Ralston, Hoerr, and Hoffman, *J. Amer. Chem. Soc.*, 1942, **64**, 97; Ralston and Hoerr, *ibid.*, 1942, **64**, 772.

and, for some aggregating electrolytes, can be definitely misleading. This is well illustrated by the data of Brown, Grieger, Evers, and Kraus[1] for the conductivities of hexadecyl- and octadecylpyridinium iodates. These results are shown in Figure 17 where it is seen that aggregation produces, at first, not a fall but a rise in the equivalent conductivity. It is obvious from the form of the curves, especially from that of the C_{16} compound, that the critical concentration could not be determined with a high degree of precision. When applicable, however, the conductivity provides a precise

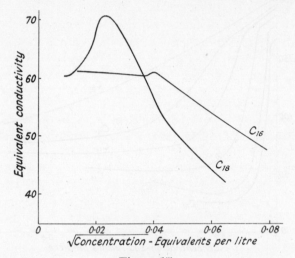

Figure 17
Conductivities of hexadecyl and octadecyl pyridinium iodates

(Brown, Grieger, Evers, and Kraus, *J. Amer. Chem. Soc.*, 1947, **69**, 1835.)

method of determining the critical concentration and has the advantage over some of the other methods of not interfering with micelle formation.

Solubilisation methods have also been used for determining the critical concentration, but when the solubilisate is appreciably soluble in the micelle, although the results may be precise for the particular system on which the measurements are made, the value of the critical concentration obtained is not necessarily its value in water alone, since, as we have seen above, the micellar size and constitution are altered by the presence of the solubilisate.

By far the most rapid, simple, and convenient method for determining the critical concentration is the titration method which was developed by Corrin and Harkins.[2] It has long been known[3] that the colour change of

[1] Brown, Grieger, Evers, and Kraus, *J. Amer. Chem. Soc.*, 1947, **69**, 1835.
[2] Corrin and Harkins, *J. Amer. Chem. Soc.*, 1947, **69**, 679.
[3] See for example, Sörensen, *Biochem. Z.*, 1929, **21**, 215.

many indicators is influenced by the presence of proteins and colloids, and Hartley[1] in 1934 made a systematic study of the changes in the colours of indicators produced by low concentrations of amphipathic electrolytes. The concentrations he used (except for one series of experiments) were greater than the critical concentrations and although he was aware that colour changes took place in passing through the critical concentration range (as shown by his experiments with sodium hexadecane sulphonate) it was essential to the object of his investigation to compare the colours of the indicators in water with the colours in micelle-containing solutions.

Corrin, Klevens, and Harkins[2] showed that a pronounced shift in the absorption spectrum of pinacyanol chloride in aqueous potassium laurate or myristate occurred at the critical concentration for each of these amphipathic electrolytes. Below the critical concentration the dye gave the spectrum characteristic of its aqueous solutions while above the critical concentration the spectrum was that given by a solution of the dye in a non-polar medium. They considered that this dye was soluble in the paraffin-chain micelle in which, since it would be in a non-polar environment, it exhibited its "non-polar" absorption spectrum. Further investigation by Corrin and Harkins,[3] however, showed that such a simple mechanism did not adequately explain all the facts. Although all the factors influencing this phenomenon have not yet been clarified, it would seem that a dyestuff must itself be capable of aggregating and its aggregation must be increased by the addition of small amounts (less than the critical concentration) of amphipathic electrolyte in order to show this pronounced spectrum change. This change could, of course, be brought about by the amphipathic electrolyte altering the form of the dye aggregates, *e.g.*, from a crystalline to a more amorphous aggregate, instead of by its influence on the size of the aggregate, or probably by both effects simultaneously. Corrin and Harkins consider that to obtain the greatest effect the dyestuff and amphipathic ions should be oppositely charged and that it is the interaction between them which produces such marked spectral changes and thus makes a dyestuff a suitable indicator for the critical concentration. When the critical concentration is reached, the marked spectral change which occurs is due to the solubilisation or adsorption of the "induced" dyestuff aggregate by the micelle. With some dyestuffs, *e.g.*, Sky Blue FF in the presence of "cationic" amphipathic electrolytes, the spectrum in micellar solution is almost the same as that in water. The change which occurs with suitable indicators is so pronounced that it is obvious without the use of optical instruments and is, moreover, often accompanied by a change in the fluorescence of the dyestuff solution. The practical means for determining the critical concentration by the indicator method is extremely

[1] Hartley, *Trans. Faraday Soc.*, 1934, **30**, 444.
[2] Corrin, Klevens, and Harkins, *J. Chem. Phys.*, 1946, **14**, 480.
[3] Corrin and Harkins, *J. Amer. Chem. Soc.*, 1947, **69**, 679.

simple since it consists in titrating the aqueous solution of the dyestuff plus
amphipathic electrolyte with an aqueous solution of the same concentration of dyestuff alone until a sharp, characteristic colour change is
observed.

So far this method is applicable only to ionising amphipathic molecules,
since no suitable dyestuffs have as yet been found which show sufficient
alteration in spectrum by non-ionogenic surface-active agents to render
them suitable indicators.

F. Factors which influence the critical concentration

Although the solubility of amphipathic electrolytes changes very rapidly
in a small temperature interval when the critical concentration has been
reached, the critical concentration is not itself markedly influenced by
temperature. Wright, Abbott, Sivertz, and Tartar[1] showed from conductivity data that the critical concentrations of sodium decane, dodecane, and
tetradecane sulphonates increase by about 50% for a temperature increase
of 40° c., while Klevens[2] found a similar increase for potassium laurate and
myristate. It is to be expected that the increased thermal motion at the
higher temperature and the expected increased solubility of the simple
molecules would lead to a slight increase in the critical concentration.

The interplay of the hydrophilic and hydrophobic portions of the amphipathic ion have a much greater effect on the critical concentration. Harkins[3]
collected much of the data on critical concentrations, which have been determined by various methods, and showed that for the paraffin-chain salts
(soaps, alkyl sulphates, alkyl sulphonates, and cationic amphipathic electrolytes) an increase of two carbon atoms in the length of the paraffin chain
leads to a decrease in the critical concentration by a factor of approximately four. This factor appears to decrease slightly with increase in
temperature.

Similar large changes in the critical concentration are obtained when
the polar group is altered, as is shown in the following table for a series of
straight paraffin-chain amphipathic electrolytes.

Although all the factors governing the critical concentration for the
formation of micelles have not been fully elucidated it appears to be true
that an increase in the size of the micelle lowers the critical concentration,
as is seen by the large effect of a slight increase in the length of the hydrocarbon chain. The nature of the ion whose charge is opposite in sign to that
of the amphipathic ion may also affect the size of the micelle and hence
the critical concentration, *e.g.*, the critical concentration for dodecyltrimethylammonium chloride is 0·062 while for the corresponding bromide it

---

[1] Wright, Abbott, Sivertz, and Tartar, *J. Amer. Chem. Soc.*, 1939, **61**, 549.
[2] Klevens, *J. Coll. Sci.*, 1947, **2**, 301.
[3] Harkins, *J. Amer. Chem. Soc.*, 1947, **69**, 1428.

Table 3
Effect of the polar group on the critical concentration

Number of carbon atoms in the chain	Critical Concentration (moles per litre)		
	"Anionic" amphipathic electrolytes (sodium salts)		
	Carboxylate	Sulphonate	Sulphate
16	0·0015	0·00105	0·0004
14	0·006	0·0027	0·0016
12	0·024	0·0098	0·0065
	"Cationic" amphipathic electrolytes		
	$C_{12}H_{25}NH_2HCl$		$C_{12}H_{25}(CH_3)_3N·Cl$
12	0·013		0·062

is 0·016 molar.[1] Samis and Hartley[2] carried out conductivity and transport number measurements on an extensive series of paraffin-chain salts and concluded that the valency of the counterion is not all-important in this respect, but that specific forces are of equal importance. They suggest that the solubility of the ion-pair (counterion + polar head of the amphipathic ion) in the surface region of the micelle is one important factor in determining the size of the micelle and hence the critical concentration.

The effect of strong electrolytes on amphipathic solutes is to increase the tendency to aggregate and probably to increase the size of the micelles. The effect of salts has been studied by numerous workers. Hartley[3] showed that the addition of sodium chloride (0·032N) to solutions of cetylpyridinium chloride reduced the critical concentration from 0·0009N to less than 0·0001N as measured by the solubilisation of *trans*-azobenzene. Higher concentrations of salt reduced the critical concentration still further. Tartar and Cadle[4] showed, from solubility measurements, how sodium chloride decreased the critical concentration of sodium dodecane and tetradecane sulphonates and increased the temperature at which the critical concentration was reached. From a study of the conductivity of sodium dodecane sulphonate at 40° and 80° Wright and co-workers[5] showed that an equimolal concentration of sodium chloride decreased the critical concentration about 20–25%.

Thanks to their development of the very rapid "indicator" method for determining the critical concentration, Corrin and Harkins[6] were able to study the effect of several salts on various amphipathic electrolytes and came to the conclusion that the ion which has an electrical charge of the

[1] Figure quoted by Harkins, *J. Amer. Chem. Soc.*, 1947, **69**, 1428.
[2] Samis and Hartley, *Trans. Faraday Soc.*, 1938, **34**, 1288.
[3] Hartley, *J. Chem. Soc.*, 1938, 1968.
[4] Tartar and Cadle, *J. Phys. Chem.*, 1939, **43**, 1173.
[5] Wright, Abbott, Sivertz, and Tartar, *J. Amer. Chem. Soc.*, 1939, **61**, 549.
[6] Corrin and Harkins, *J. Amer. Chem. Soc.*, 1947, **69**, 683.

same sign as the micelle has a negligible effect, and that only the oppositely charged ion affects the critical concentration. A non-electrolyte such as urea had, even at high concentrations, practically no effect. They also found that amphipathic electrolytes with the greater tendency to aggregate (*i.e.*, those with the lower critical concentration) suffered a relatively larger depression of the critical concentration by the addition of salts. The effect of other amphipathic electrolytes on the critical concentration varies according to the type and concentration of the added electrolyte. In general, a mixture of "anionic" and "cationic" amphipathic electrolytes produces an insoluble precipitate of the two amphipathic ions. When the amphipathic ions have the same charge and the two electrolytes have approximately the same critical concentration it has been found[1] that no mutual effect takes place and that the critical concentration is unaffected by altering the relative proportions of the two solutes. With electrolytes of widely differing critical concentrations, however, the critical concentration of the more readily aggregated solute is usually altered by low concentrations of the other in a way exactly similar to that of a strong non-amphipathic electrolyte. At greater concentrations more complex interactions take place, but the critical concentration of the total (mixed) amphipathic electrolyte is always intermediate between the critical concentrations of the two pure solutes.

Since the hydrophobic portions of an amphipathic molecule are, in general, more soluble in organic liquids than in water the addition of water-miscible organic solvents, such as ethanol or acetone, to aqueous solutions of amphipathic electrolytes will usually have a disaggregating effect on the micelles. This will lead to a shift of the critical concentration towards higher concentrations, as has been shown by Ralston and Hoerr[2] for dodecylamine hydrochloride, which has a critical concentration in pure water of 0·0129 molar, and in 28% ethanol of 0·103 molar, as determined from the break in the conductivity curves. At higher concentrations of ethanol, micelle formation is almost completely inhibited, as has also been reported by Ward,[3] who found that 40% ethanol prevented micelle formation in sodium dodecyl sulphate solutions. Quite the opposite effect on the critical concentration was reported by Corrin and Harkins,[4] who worked with dodecylamine hydrochloride. They found that methanol (in low concentrations), ethanol, propanol, and butanol reduced the critical concentration; the effect being more pronounced the greater the chain-length of the alcohol. In this work the titration "indicator" method was used. Since one of the factors influencing the spectral shift due to the presence of micelles may be that the indicator is adsorbed on or "dissolved" in the

---

[1] Corrin and Harkins, *J. Coll. Sci.*, 1946, **1**, 469.
[2] Ralston and Hoerr, *J. Amer. Chem. Soc.*, 1946, **68**, 851, 2460.
[3] Ward, *Proc. Roy. Soc.*, 1940, **A176**, 412; *Chem. & Ind.*, 1938, 1167.
[4] Corrin and Harkins, *J. Chem. Phys.*, 1946, **14**, 640.

surface layer of the micelle and since this surface layer is likely to be profoundly influenced by a polar organic liquid, it is possible that the titration
method which depends on some interaction between the micelle and the
indicator may not be reliable in a mixed solvent. This method was successfully used by Harkins[1] in styrene-soap solutions, but in these systems the
styrene, being non-polar, is probably not adsorbed on the surface of the
micelle but solubilised in its interior.

---

[1] Harkins, *J. Amer. Chem. Soc.*, 1947, **69**, 1428.

CHAPTER 3

THE ADSORPTION OF SURFACE-ACTIVE AGENTS
AT INTERFACES

REFERENCE has already been made, in Chapter 1, to the fact that the basic phenomenon underlying all the applications of surface-active agents is the adsorption of such agents at the interfaces between their solutions and external gaseous, liquid, or solid phases. The adsorption at a given interface frequently contributes to a particular technical effect by lowering the boundary tension prevailing at that interface, though in other instances it may also act by interposing an interfacial layer or film which mechanically stabilises the interface in question, making it more difficult for the interface to increase or decrease in area, either in isolation or in competition with other interfaces. It is therefore desirable, before we describe in more detail the processes in which surface-active agents find application, to consider the relevant adsorption processes in terms of their effects on the interfacial tensions and of the speed with which they occur.

A. The thermodynamics of the adsorption of surface-active agents

1. THE EQUATION OF GIBBS

The basis of the thermodynamics of the adsorption of dissolved substances at interfaces is Gibbs's equation relating the change in the interfacial tension at the boundary between two incompletely miscible phases to the extent of "adsorption" at the boundary and the compositions of the two phases. At constant temperature and pressure this assumes the form

$$d\gamma = -\Gamma_1 d\mu_1 - \Gamma_2 d\mu_2 - \Gamma_3 d\mu_3 - \ldots \tag{1}$$

where γ is the interfacial tension, Γ's are the "surface excesses" of the components (1, 2, 3, etc.) of the system, and μ's are their chemical potentials in either or both of the phases which meet at the interface.

It is an essential condition for applying Gibbs's equation—at least quantitatively—that the interface in question should be in equilibrium with any bulk phases or other interfaces in the system.

All the quantities in Gibbs's equation require careful definition. The formal definition of γ_i (the interfacial tension of the i'th interface) is

$$\gamma_i = \left(\frac{\partial G}{\partial A_i}\right)_{P,\,T,\,A_j,\,\ldots,\,n_1,\,n_2\,\ldots} \tag{2}$$

where G is the total Gibbs free energy of the *whole system* containing the interface, which we shall define by

$$G = E + PV - TS$$

or $\qquad dG = -SdT + VdP + \Sigma_i \gamma_i dA_i + \mu_1 dn_1 + \mu_2 dn_2 + \ldots$

where E is the total internal energy of the system, P is the pressure, V the volume, T the absolute temperature, and S the entropy.* A_i is the area of the i'th interface in equation (2), A_j . . . refer to all other interfaces, and n's to the total numbers of moles of the components present in the system. It can clearly be seen by reference to Guggenheim's derivation of Gibbs's equation,[1] which we discuss later, that γ can be treated as a *tension* (*e.g.*, in dynes/cm.) acting parallel to the interface, or it can be defined simply as the reversible work required to increase the interface by unit area at constant temperature, pressure, and composition. The latter definition follows from equation (2), whence we see that the increase in the total free energy of the system, when A_i is increased by dA_i (at constant temperature, pressure, composition, and areas of any other interfaces), is given by

$$dG = \gamma_i dA_i \qquad\qquad (2a)$$

which is the fundamental relation behind our consideration of many interfacial processes in Chapter 4.

The definition of the interfacial tension in terms of equations (2) and (2a), for example, is perhaps the reason for the wide-spread use of the expression "interfacial free energy" to denote γ. We propose however to use the latter phrase to denote the *total* free energy of the interface, and to standardise on "interfacial tension" (or "surface tension" when one phase is a gas or a vacuum) for γ.† We have already noted that the existence of

---

* *Cf.* Guggenheim, *Modern Thermodynamics*, Methuen and Co., 1932, p. 165, equation (765). The use of this particular function G is dictated by the facts that (*a*) technical processes involving the use of surface-active agents are generally carried out at constant temperature and pressure, rather than at constant temperature and volume, and (*b*) we are here concerned with defining the interfacial tension in terms of variations in quantities such as total free energy and interfacial area, rather than the converse. When we come to consider variations in the interfacial tension itself, a different function (Guggenheim's $\overline{G}$) is required—see below. If one is dealing with an interfacial process which occurs at constant temperature and *volume*, then it becomes appropriate to define the interfacial tension by

$$\gamma_i = \left(\frac{\partial F}{\partial A_i} \right)_{V, T, n_1, n_2 \ldots A_j \ldots}$$

where F is the Helmholtz free energy. This function G is not the free energy of the interface.

† Alternatively, we might use an expression such as "specific interfacial free energy," which seems to us to be unnecessarily cumbersome. We are indebted to Professor E. A. Guggenheim for pointing out to us that "interfacial free energy" should logically be applied to an *extensive* property such as the total Helmholtz or Gibbs free energy, preferably the former, rather than to an intensive property such as γ.

[1] Guggenheim, *Trans. Faraday Soc.*, 1940, **36**, 397.

the interfacial tension does not necessarily imply that an elastic, contractile skin is present in the interface, and that this tension is due to an inward pull which results from the dissymmetry of the forces acting on the molecules or atoms near the surface of a phase.[1]

The chemical potential is the well-known Gibbs function μ (Lewis and Randall's $\overline{F}$ or partial molal free energy), and is conveniently defined for the solute species (2) in a phase α, for example, by

$$\mu_2^\alpha = \left(\frac{\partial G^\alpha}{\partial n_2^\alpha}\right)_{P, T, n_1, n_3, \ldots, A_i \ldots}$$

The chemical potential and the "activity" a_2^α will be connected by the well-known relation

$$\mu_2^\alpha = \mu_2^{\alpha 0} + RT \ln a_2^\alpha$$

where $\mu_2^{\alpha 0}$ is the standard chemical potential of the species, R is the gas constant, and T is the absolute temperature. Following Lewis and Randall,[2] we can conveniently define the activity so that it becomes equal to the mole fraction N_2 as the latter approaches zero.

The exact significance of the Γ's requires explanation. In Gibbs's general derivation of equation (1), Γ_1 refers to the total number of moles of component (1) per unit area of interface in the actual system, *minus* the total number of moles of (1) in a purely hypothetical system, occupying the same volume, in which the two phases are uniform in composition up to the interface. In order to assign numerical values to the Γ's, it becomes necessary to place the mathematical interface at some arbitrary position at or near the physical interface. The validity of equation (1) is unaffected by the position chosen for this mathematical plane provided that the interface is planar. The actual numerical values (and algebraic signs) of the Γ's are however dependent on the position chosen for the mathematical surface, and confusion has arisen in the past through making assumptions as to the position of this plane which are incompatible with the physical picture which was assumed or implied. This question has been examined with great clarity by Guggenheim and Adam[3] and by Guggenheim,[4] and it seems preferable in the present book to use their forms of Gibbs's equation, which they relate to definite physical pictures, rather than the general form (1).

For the special case that $\Gamma_1 = 0$ (Gibbs's original convention $\Gamma_{(1)}$, which Guggenheim and Adam call "Convention 1") equation (1) reduces to the form which is most often used:

$$\frac{d\gamma}{da_A} = -\frac{RT}{a_A} \Gamma_A^{(1)} \tag{3}$$

---

[1] See Adam, *Physics and Chemistry of Surfaces*, Oxford University Press, 3rd Edition, 1941, p. 3.

[2] Lewis and Randall, *Thermodynamics*, McGraw-Hill Book Co., 1923, p. 258.

[3] Guggenheim and Adam, *Proc. Roy. Soc.*, 1933, **139A**, 218.

[4] Guggenheim, *Trans. Faraday Soc.*, 1940, **36**, 397.

which implies, as they have pointed out, that a portion of the solution containing unit area of interface contains $\Gamma_A^{(1)}$ more moles of a component A, algebraically speaking, than a portion in the interior which contains exactly the same quantity of the solvent (1). One possible physical picture, which is frequently adopted when this convention is used, is to consider that the solution remains sensibly constant in composition up to the interface, and that $\Gamma_A^{(1)}$ consists of a monomolecular layer of A, the interface being at most a few Ångstrom units thick. This picture is of considerable use,[1] especially in considering surface tension data for relatively dilute solutions, but it is not universally applicable.

Guggenheim and Adam[2] also give two other conventions which may be useful on occasion in considering the behaviour of surface-active materials. In the "M" convention, in which $\Gamma_A^{(M)}$ is defined as the number of moles of A in a portion of the solution which contains unit surface area, in excess of that in a portion of the interior which contains exactly the same *total mass*, equation (1) becomes

$$\frac{d\gamma}{da_A} = -\frac{RT}{a_A}\Gamma_A^{(M)}\left(1 + \frac{N_A M_A}{N_W M_W}\right) \tag{4}$$

in which M's are molecular weights and N's are mole fractions.

In convention "V," $\Gamma_A^{(V)}$ is defined as the number of moles of A in a portion of the solution which contains unit interfacial area, in excess of the moles of A in a portion of the interior having exactly the same *volume*, and we have

$$\frac{d\gamma}{da_A} = -\frac{RT}{a_A}\Gamma_A^{(V)}\left(1 + \frac{N_A \overline{V}_A}{N_W \overline{V}_W}\right) \tag{5}$$

where $\overline{V}$'s are partial molal volumes.

It seems to us that the treatment of the Gibbs equation, which gives the clearest physical picture, and is therefore the most useful one in our present connection, is that given by Guggenheim,[3] who treats the system as consisting of two bulk phases α and β, and an interfacial phase σ, each of which has a definite mass, volume, composition, free energy, etc. The boundaries between the σ phase and the phases α and β, respectively, are placed so that the transition from α to β takes place entirely within σ; otherwise there are no restrictions, in the general case, on their positions. The Γ's in this treatment, which we propose to denote by $\Gamma^{(G)}$, are not "surface excesses," but represent the total numbers of moles of the various components which are present per unit area of the interfacial phase. The $\Gamma^{(G)}$'s cannot therefore be negative.

Guggenheim derives general equations connecting variations in γ with

---

[1] *Cf.* for example Alexander, *Trans. Faraday Soc.*, 1942, **38**, 54.

[2] Guggenheim and Adam, *Proc. Roy. Soc.*, 1933, **139A**, 218.

[3] Guggenheim, *Trans. Faraday Soc.*, 1940, **36**, 405.

variations in temperature, pressure, and composition, using as characteristic functions the Gibbs free energies defined, for the bulk phases, by

$$G^\alpha = E^\alpha + PV^\alpha - TS^\alpha$$

or
$$dG^\alpha = - S^\alpha dT + V^\alpha dP + \Sigma_r \mu_r{}^\alpha dn_r{}^\alpha$$

and for the interfacial phase by

$$G^\sigma = E^\sigma + PV^\sigma - TS^\sigma - A\gamma$$

or
$$dG^\sigma = - S^\sigma dT + V^\sigma dP - Ad\gamma + \Sigma_r \mu_r{}^\sigma dn_r{}^\sigma*$$

His most general equation, (4, 17) or (5, 1), for a plane interface, is

$$- d\gamma = s^\sigma dT - \tau dP + \Sigma_r \Gamma_r{}^{(G)} d\mu_r \tag{6}$$

in which τ is the thickness of the σ phase, and s^σ is the entropy of the σ
phase per unit interfacial area. As Guggenheim points out, however, the
temperature, pressure, and chemical potentials are not all independent
variables, since it follows from the phase rule (two bulk phases, r components) that the number of degrees of freedom is equal only to r, the
number of components. It should therefore be possible to eliminate two
differentials on the right-hand side of (6). Guggenheim shows how, by introducing the appropriate Gibbs-Duhem equations for the α and β phases, it
is possible to eliminate P and one of the μ's (for example the chemical
potential of the component which can be treated as the "solvent"
in α).

The special case of equation (6) which is of greatest interest to the
present argument is that in which both temperature and pressure are
constant, so that

$$d\gamma = - \Sigma_r \Gamma_r{}^{(G)} d\mu_r \tag{6a}$$

It must be noted, however, that by fixing the temperature and pressure, we
have left only $(r - 2)$ degrees of freedom for a system of two bulk phases
and a single interface, the area of which is constant. Consequently, unless
we have at least *three* components present, our system is invariant. If for
example we have a solution of a single surface-active agent in a single
solvent, in equilibrium with a phase of pure gaseous solvent, then a small
increase in the concentration of surface-active agent in the solution, at
constant temperature and pressure, will cause the vapour phase to disappear. For the case of three or more components, however, it should be
possible to eliminate two of the chemical potentials from (6a). This we can
do, following Guggenheim, by introducing the Gibbs-Duhem equations for

---

* The G of these two equations is the characteristic function $\bar{G}$ of Guggenheim's
Modern Thermodynamics, applied to a surface phase of finite thickness, so that the
$V^\sigma dP$ term must be included.

the α and β phases (taking for the moment the most general case in which all r components are present in all the phases), *viz.*

$$\Sigma_r N_r{}^\alpha d\mu_r = 0, \text{ and } \Sigma_r N_r{}^\beta d\mu_r = 0$$

Denoting by Σ' the summations from which component (1) is excluded, and by Σ'' those from which components (1) and (2) are both excluded (the particular choice of components is of course immaterial, but we shall for convenience assume that (1) is the solvent in α and that (2) is not a surface-active solute), we can then combine the first of these two relations with (6a) to obtain

$$
d\gamma = \sum_r{}' \left(\Gamma_1{}^{(G)} \frac{N_r{}^\alpha}{N_1{}^\alpha} - \Gamma_r{}^{(G)} \right) d\mu_r
$$

$$
= \left(\Gamma_1{}^{(G)} \frac{N_2{}^\alpha}{N_1{}^\alpha} - \Gamma_2{}^{(G)} \right) d\mu_2 + \sum_r{}'' \left(\Gamma_1{}^{(G)} \frac{N_r{}^\alpha}{N_1{}^\alpha} - \Gamma_r{}^{(G)} \right) d\mu_r \quad (7)
$$

It follows however from the two Gibbs-Duhem equations, and the identity under equilibrium conditions of $\mu_1{}^\alpha$ and $\mu_1{}^\beta$, that

$$
d\mu_1 = -\sum_r{}' \frac{N_r{}^\alpha}{N_1{}^\alpha} d\mu_r = -\sum_r{}' \frac{N_r{}^\beta}{N_1{}^\beta} d\mu_r
$$

or

$$
-\frac{N_2{}^\alpha}{N_1{}^\alpha} d\mu_2 - \sum_r{}'' \frac{N_r{}^\alpha}{N_1{}^\alpha} d\mu_r = -\frac{N_2{}^\beta}{N_1{}^\beta} d\mu_2 - \sum_r{}'' \frac{N_r{}^\beta}{N_1{}^\beta} d\mu_r
$$

Solving for $d\mu_2$, and substituting in (7), we obtain

$$
d\gamma = \sum_r{}'' \left[\left(\frac{N_2{}^\alpha}{N_1{}^\alpha} \Gamma_1{}^{(G)} - \Gamma_2{}^{(G)} \right) \left(\frac{N_r{}^\alpha N_1{}^\beta - N_r{}^\beta N_1{}^\alpha}{N_1{}^\alpha N_2{}^\beta - N_1{}^\beta N_2{}^\alpha} \right) \right.
$$

$$
\left. + \left(\frac{N_r{}^\alpha}{N_1{}^\alpha} \Gamma_1{}^{(G)} - \Gamma_r{}^{(G)} \right) \right] d\mu_r
$$

$$
= -\sum_r{}'' \left[\Gamma_r{}^{(G)} - \frac{\Gamma_1{}^{(G)}(N_r{}^\alpha N_2{}^\beta - N_r{}^\beta N_2{}^\alpha) + \Gamma_2{}^{(G)}(N_r{}^\beta N_1{}^\alpha - N_r{}^\alpha N_1{}^\beta)}{(N_1{}^\alpha N_2{}^\beta - N_1{}^\beta N_2{}^\alpha)} \right] d\mu_r \quad (8)
$$

It can readily be shown that each term in square brackets in equation (8) is (as it should be) invariant with respect to the position chosen for the boundary between the σ phase and either the α or the β phase, provided of course that the transition from the α to the β phase occurs entirely within σ. If for example we move the α–σ boundary further into α, keeping the system completely constant physically, and thus increasing $\Gamma_1{}^{(G)}$ by x moles/cm.^{2}, then we shall also increase $\Gamma_2{}^{(G)}$ by $N_2{}^\alpha x/N_1{}^\alpha$ moles/cm.^{2}, and $\Gamma_r{}^{(G)}$ by $N_r{}^\alpha x/N_1{}^\alpha$ moles/cm.^{2} If we substitute in each term of (8), we find that the net increase inside each square bracket is zero. Similarly, if we increase $\Gamma_1{}^{(G)}$ by y moles/cm.^{2} by moving the β–σ boundary further into the β phase, then $\Gamma_2{}^{(G)}$ and $\Gamma_r{}^{(G)}$ will be increased by $N_2{}^\beta y/N_1{}^\beta$ and $N_r{}^\beta y/N_1{}^\beta$

moles/cm.[2], respectively, and substitution in each term of equation (8) again shows that there is no net increase in the terms in square brackets.

In spite of its thermodynamical rigour, and the clear physical picture on which it is based, equation (8) does not lend itself readily to interpreting changes in the interfacial tension with the composition of a solution containing a surface-active agent, in terms of the amount of adsorption of the agent at the interface in question. It can however be considerably simplified if we fix the β–σ boundary, and make certain assumptions, according to *any one* of the following special cases:

(*i*) "*Inert components.*" Guggenheim[1] has pointed out that his equations can be greatly simplified if there are present in the β phase one or more components (which he calls "inert components"), the concentration of which drops abruptly to zero at a certain plane, remaining at zero throughout the α phase. The β–σ boundary is then fixed at this plane, though no restriction need be placed on the position of the α–σ boundary. If we take equation (8) and assume that component (2), for example, is "inert" in this sense (*e.g.*, that it is a gas, liquid, or solid which is insoluble in the solvent which is the principal component of phase α), then we can place the β–σ boundary at the plane (provided that it is sufficiently abrupt) at which the concentration of (2) falls to zero. It then follows that $N_2{}^\alpha$ and $\Gamma_2{}^{(G)}$ are both zero, and equation (8) reduces to

$$d\gamma = - \sum_r{}'' \left(\Gamma_r{}^{(G)} - \Gamma_1{}^{(G)} \frac{N_r{}^\alpha}{N_1{}^\alpha} \right) d\mu_r. \tag{8a}$$

It can be seen at once that the quantity

$$\left(\Gamma_r{}^{(G)} - \Gamma_1{}^{(G)} \frac{N_r{}^\alpha}{N_1{}^\alpha} \right)$$

gives a measure of the amount of adsorption of component r, relative to the solvent (1), per unit of interface, and that in fact it is identical with $\Gamma_r{}^{(1)}$, so that equations (3) and (8a) are identical. We can therefore use $\Gamma_r{}^{(1)}$ as a convenient "shorthand" expression for the expression in brackets in equation (8a), while still retaining the clear physical picture, including the concept of the interfacial σ phase, used by Guggenheim. This we propose to do for the most part in the present book, especially because we shall then be free of special assumptions about the structure of the interfacial phase. The interfacial phase will then contain all of the transition between the two bulk phases, including ionic atmospheres, hydrated layers, etc., where appropriate. Subject to this *proviso*, the position of the a–σ boundary is immaterial, since the quantity $(\Gamma_r{}^{(G)} - \Gamma_1{}^{(G)} N_r{}^\alpha / N_1{}^\alpha)$ is invariant with respect to that boundary. This is not, however, true of the β–σ boundary, and it is important to bear in mind that the use of equation (8a) implies that the β–σ boundary is fixed at the physical interface.

---

[1] Guggenheim, *Trans. Faraday Soc.*, 1940, **36**, 405.

(*ii*) "*Surface-inactive components.*" Let us suppose that the component (2) is not adsorbed at the interface, *i.e.*, that it is present at a uniform concentration (relative to the solvent) throughout the α phase and up to the physical interface. We can then fix the β–σ boundary at the physical interface, without placing any restrictions on the position of the α–σ boundary. It follows from the postulate of no adsorption relative to solvent that

$$\left(\Gamma_1^{(G)} \frac{N_2^{\alpha}}{N_1^{\alpha}} - \Gamma_2^{(G)} \right) = 0$$

so that equation (7) reduces directly to (8a).

(*iii*) *Single-component phase.* Suppose that phase β consists of a single pure component (2), with which phase α is saturated, and that it may be present in appreciable quantity in α. Let us fix the β–σ boundary at the physical interface. Since μ_2 is constant throughout the system, $d\mu_2 = 0$, and the Gibbs and Gibbs-Duhem equations become, at constant temperature and pressure,

$$d\gamma = - \Gamma_1^{(G)} d\mu_1 - \Sigma_r'' \Gamma_r^{(G)} d\mu_r$$

and

$$0 = N_1^{\alpha} d\mu_1 + \Sigma_r'' N_r^{\alpha} d\mu_r$$

Combining, we obtain equation (8a).

(*iv*) *Special distribution ratios.* Although this case does not seem to be of much practical significance, it is worth noting that such terms on the right-hand side of (8) as satisfy the condition

$$\frac{N_r^{\alpha}}{N_1^{\alpha}} = \frac{N_r^{\beta}}{N_1^{\beta}}$$

will reduce to

$$- \left(\Gamma_r^{(G)} - \frac{N_r^{\alpha}}{N_1^{\alpha}} \Gamma_1^{(G)} \right) d\mu_r.$$

There are cases in which it is neither permissible to fix the β–σ boundary at the physical interface, nor to assume that the special distribution ratio of case (*iv*) is valid. This will be true, for example, in many emulsion systems, containing emulsifying agents which are soluble in both the "oil" and the aqueous phase, and which we must therefore treat as being adsorbed at the interface from both the α and β phases. Here we must consider the amount of such an agent in the interface relative to the solvents in *both* the α and β phases, and consequently we cannot use equation (8a), or any of the conventions behind equations (3), (4), or (5).

Suppose, for example that component (1) is water, component (2) is an "oil," and the different *r* are surface-active agents which are soluble in both α and β, and surface-active from both these phases: *i.e.*, concentration gradients each surface-active component may exist on *both* sides of the physical interface, so that both the α–σ and β–σ boundaries must be placed away from the physical interface. If now the "oil" and the aqueous phase are substantially insoluble in one another, so that we can write $N_1{}^\beta = 0$ and $N_2{}^\beta = 0$, equation (8) reduces to

$$d\gamma = -\sum_r{}'' \left(\Gamma_r^{(G)} - \Gamma_1^{(G)} \frac{N_r^\alpha}{N_1^\alpha} - \Gamma_2^{(G)} \frac{N_r^\beta}{N_2^\beta} \right) d\mu_r. \tag{8b}$$

It will be at once apparent that

$$\left(\Gamma_r^{(G)} - \Gamma_1^{(G)} \frac{N_r^\alpha}{N_1^\alpha} - \Gamma_2^{(G)} \frac{N_r^\beta}{N_1^\beta} \right)$$

has the dimensions of a surface excess, being the amount of r actually in the σ phase, *minus* the amount which the σ phase would contain if its portions on either side of the physical interface had the same concentration of r, relative to (1) and (2), respectively, as the adjoining bulk phases.

If, however, components (1) and (2) are appreciably mutually soluble, and the r are present in both α and β, we are left with the general case to which equation (8) applies. The physical significance of this equation can be made clearer by again considering a hypothetical case in which there is no adsorption, the compositions of the α and β phases remaining uniform up to an abrupt physical interface. If we then include in the σ phase, A total moles of α phase, and B total moles of β phase, we can write

$$\Gamma_r^{(H)} = AN_r^\alpha + BN_r^\beta,$$

where $\Gamma_r^{(H)}$ is the total amount of each r in the hypothetical σ phase. If now we also postulate that this hypothetical σ phase contains the same total amount of (1) and (2) as the actual σ phase, we can also write

$$\Gamma_1^{(G)} = AN_1^\alpha + BN_1^\beta$$
$$\Gamma_2^{(G)} = AN_2^\alpha + BN_2^\beta$$

We can combine these three relations to obtain

$$\Gamma_r^{(H)} = \frac{\Gamma_1^{(G)}(N_r^\alpha N_2^\beta - N_2^\alpha N_r^\beta) + \Gamma_2^{(G)}(N_1^\alpha N_r^\beta - N_1^\beta N_r^\alpha)}{(N_1^\alpha N_2^\beta - N_1^\beta N_2^\alpha)},$$

and substituting in equation (8), we obtain

$$d\gamma = -\sum_r{}'' (\Gamma_r^{(G)} - \Gamma_r^{(H)}) d\mu_r,$$

which can be conveniently abbreviated as

$$d\gamma = -\sum_r{}'' \Gamma_r^{(1,\,2)} d\mu_r \tag{8c}$$

In most of the cases to be considered in the present book, equation (8a) will be applicable, and (8c) comes into the picture only rarely. We have included all these cases, however, in order to re-emphasise Guggenheim's warning, that equations such as (8a) are strictly valid only under carefully specified conditions: at an oil-water interface, for example, it is necessary to remember that adsorption may occur from both liquid phases.*

The important feature of all the above forms of Gibbs's equation, *as applied to solutions containing only one solute*, is that they all require that *the equilibrium interfacial tension must decrease with increasing chemical potential (or increasing activity) of a solute which is positively adsorbed at the interface in question*, the temperature and pressure being constant and external disturbing forces being absent. Since it is necessary, if a solution is to be thermodynamically stable, that the chemical potential of a solute should increase with its concentration, this also means that *the interfacial tension must decrease with increasing concentration* of a single positively-adsorbed solute.

In practice, the various forms of the Gibbs equation are usually written with activities instead of chemical potentials, (8a) becoming, for example, for a single surface-active component:

$$\frac{d\gamma}{da_A} = -\frac{RT}{a_A}\Gamma_A{}^{(1)} = -\frac{RT}{a_A}\left(\Gamma_A{}^{(G)} - \Gamma_1{}^{(G)}\frac{N_A{}^\alpha}{N_1{}^\alpha}\right).$$

It will be noticed that the unit in which a_A is expressed is immaterial, provided that the same unit is used on both sides of the equation. Owing to the paucity of data on activity coefficients, it is usually necessary to use concentrations instead of activities; the limitations which this fact places on the use of the Gibbs equation will become apparent later.

2. THE APPLICATION OF GIBBS'S EQUATION TO CURVED INTERFACES

The preceding discussion was, as stated at the outset, limited to the case of a plane interface. Although this condition will often be satisfied completely, most of the interfaces involved in practice will be curved: *e.g.*, the menisci in wetting processes, or the liquid-liquid or solid-liquid interfaces involved in emulsification or dispersion processes. It is therefore relevant to note that Guggenheim[1] has examined this question and come to the conclusion that "the formulae strictly derived for plane interfaces may be applied to curved interfaces with an accuracy adequate for experimental purposes, provided that the thickness of the inhomogeneous layer is small compared with its radii of curvature." He goes on to show, with some numerical examples, that we should expect this condition to be satisfied down to radii of curvature of the order of 10^{-5} cm. (0·1 μ, or 1,000 Å.). A similar general conclusion can be drawn from a number of subsequent

---

* It is worth recalling here that many oil-in-water emulsifying agents, especially of the polyethenoxy type, are quite soluble in oil media, and are in fact frequently introduced into the emulsion *via* the oil phase.

[1] Guggenheim, *loc. cit.*, pp. 407 ff.

papers, for example those by La Mer and Pound,[1] Koenig,[2] Sherekevsky and Carter,[3] and in particular from the statistical thermodynamical treatment of Hill.[4]

We should therefore anticipate that reasoning based on Gibbs's equation should be quantitatively valid for the interfaces. in wetting processes (provided of course that other conditions such as the maintenance of physico-chemical equilibrium are satisfied), but that departures due to the curvature of the interfaces should become appreciable when we consider very finely divided dispersions. This limitation will apply to all treatments in which a disperse particle or droplet is treated as a small separate phase, and its interfacial tension against the dispersion medium is considered (*cf.* Chapter 4, Sections B, C, D, and E).

3. Gibbs's equation and surface-active electrolytes

The application of the Gibbs equation to ionising surface-active compounds has been discussed in recent years by several authors.[5] The problem can be formulated, in terms of the convention which we use in the present book, as follows, for the case of a single, pure uni-univalent electrolyte, which ionises substantially completely :

$$NaA \rightleftarrows Na^+ + A^-.$$

We will at first assume that the dissociation of the solvent (water) can be neglected, that the surface activity of NaA resides in the amphipathic ion A^-, that no other electrolytes whatever are present, and that there are present one or more surface-inactive additional components (*e.g.*, air), the properties of which allow us to use equation (8a), which becomes

$$d\gamma = - \Gamma_{Na}^{(1)} d\mu_{Na}^{\sigma} - \Gamma_{A}^{(1)} d\mu_{A}^{\sigma}.$$

Since we have placed the boundary between the α and the σ phases at a sufficient distance from the physical interface that any concentration gradients* of the ionic species will be entirely inside the σ phase, it follows that both the α and σ phases will be electrically neutral. The transfer of Na^+ and A^- ions (and of any other ions, for that matter) between the two

---

* According to the generally accepted physical picture, we can suppose that there will in fact be a "concentration gradient" below the interface in that there will be an ionic double layer, consisting of a layer of adsorbed A^- ions, carrying a negative charge, below which there will be an ionic atmosphere carrying a net excess of Na^+ ions. This is discussed more fully in Chapter 4.

[1] La Mer and Pound, *J. Chem. Phys.*, 1949, **17**, 1337.
[2] Koenig, *J. Chem. Phys.*, 1950, **18**, 449.
[3] Sherekevsky and Carter, *J. Amer. Chem. Soc.*, 1950, **72**, 3682.
[4] Hill, *J. Amer. Chem. Soc.*, 1950, **72**, 3923.
[5] Davies, *Trans. Faraday Soc.*, 1952, **48**, 1052; Cockbain, *ibid.*, 1954, **50**, 874; Pethica, *ibid.*, 1954, **50**, 413; Haydon and Phillips, *ibid.*, 1958, **54**, 698; Ohlenbusch, *Z. Elektrochemie*, 1956, **60**, 603, 607.

phases is therefore a "purely chemical process,"[1] and we can use ordinary chemical potentials. The condition of electrical neutrality also means (*in the absence of other electrolytes*) that $\Gamma_{Na}{}^{(1)} = \Gamma_{A}{}^{(1)}$, and the condition of equilibrium between the α and σ phases that $\mu_{Na}{}^{\sigma} + \mu_{A}{}^{\sigma} = \mu_{Na}{}^{\alpha} + \mu_{A}{}^{\alpha}$.

Substituting, we find that

$$d\gamma = - \Gamma_{A}{}^{(1)} \, d(\mu_{Na}{}^{\alpha} + \mu_{A}{}^{\alpha}),$$

or

$$\frac{d\gamma}{d \ln(a_{Na}{}^{\alpha} \cdot a_{A}{}^{\alpha})} = - \Gamma_{A}{}^{(1)} \, RT, \qquad (9)$$

where a's are activities. Individual ion activities cannot be unequivocally determined, but if we use the mean activity, defined by

$$a_{\pm}{}^{\alpha} = \sqrt{a_{Na}{}^{\alpha} \cdot a_{A}{}^{\alpha}},$$

we obtain

$$\frac{d\gamma}{da_{\pm}{}^{\alpha}} = -\frac{2RT}{a_{\pm}{}^{\alpha}} \, \Gamma_{A}{}^{(1)}. \qquad (9a)$$

If we are dealing with sufficiently dilute solutions that the activity co-efficient $f_{\pm}$ remains sensibly constant, then when we substitute $c_{NaA} \cdot f_{\pm}$ for $a_{\pm}{}^{\alpha}$ (which we have perforce to do in most cases), we obtain

$$\frac{d\gamma}{dc_{NaA}} = -\frac{2RT}{c_{NaA}} \, \Gamma_{A}{}^{(1)}. \qquad (9b)$$

For a solution of completely ionised, pure NaA, therefore, a factor 2 appears in the Gibbs equation. When, however, other electrolytes are also present which are not surface-active, equations (9a) and (9b) no longer apply. If, for example, there is present a sufficiently large, constant excess of NaX that $a_{Na}{}^{\alpha}$ remains sensibly constant (when we say that NaA is "swamped" with NaX), then (9) becomes

$$\frac{d\gamma}{da_{A}{}^{\alpha}} = -\frac{RT}{a_{A}{}^{\alpha}} \, \Gamma_{A}{}^{(1)},$$

and if we can again assume a constant activity coefficient, then

$$\frac{d\gamma}{dc_{NaA}} = -\frac{RT}{c_{NaA}} \, \Gamma_{A}{}^{(1)}, \qquad (9c)$$

and the 2 disappears.

It appears, in fact[2], that very little additional electrolyte is necessary to reduce the factor 2 sensibly to 1, though this may be due in many cases, at least partly, to the occurrence of surface hydrolysis (see below). It is worth recalling that in very many technical applications of surface-active agents,

[1] Guggenheim, *Modern Thermodynamics*, Methuen, 1933, p. 134.
[2] Haydon and Phillips, *Trans. Faraday Soc.*, 1958, **54**, 698.

other electrolytes are present, frequently in considerable excess, so that equations (9a) and (9b) are probably mainly of academic interest.

The assumption was made, in deriving equations (9), (9a) and (9b), that the chemical potentials of H^+ and OH^- ions formed by the dissociation of the water were negligible compared with μ_{Na} and μ_A. This will in most cases be true, but it does raise the question of possible *hydrolysis*, especially in the surface, of NaA by a reaction such as

$$A^- + H^+ \rightleftarrows HA.$$

Where such a hydrolysis occurs in a pure solution, equation (8a) becomes

$$d\gamma = -\Gamma_{Na}^{(1)}d\mu_{Na} - (\Gamma_A^{(1)} + \Gamma_{HA}^{(1)})d\mu_A$$
$$- (\Gamma_A^{(1)} + \Gamma_{HA}^{(1)} - \Gamma_{Na}^{(1)})d\mu_H. \quad (10)$$

If the solution is swamped with a non-buffering electrolyte, this equation becomes

$$d\gamma = -(\Gamma_A^{(1)} + \Gamma_{HA}^{(1)})d\mu_A - \Gamma_{HA}^{(1)}d\mu_H, \quad (10a)$$

and when the solution is swamped with buffer, we have

$$d\gamma = -(\Gamma_A^{(1)} + \Gamma_{HA}^{(1)})d\mu_A \quad (10b)$$

If, in the absence of an appreciable amount of buffer and of electrolyte, the total amount of hydrolysis is so small that the pH is sensibly constant (because, for example, the total surface area is small), then (10) becomes

$$d\gamma = -\Gamma_{Na}^{(1)}d\mu_{Na} - (\Gamma_A^{(1)} + \Gamma_{HA}^{(1)})d\mu_A$$

or, since under these conditions $\Gamma_A^{(1)} = \Gamma_{Na}^{(1)}$,

$$\frac{d\gamma}{da_\pm^\alpha} = -\frac{2RT}{a_\pm^\alpha}(\Gamma_A^{(1)} + \Gamma_{HA}^{(1)}). \quad (10c)$$

Finally, if hydrolysis in the surface phase is so nearly complete that $\Gamma_{Na}^{(1)}$ and $\Gamma_A^{(1)}$ can be neglected, while at the same time the pH is constant, we have the interesting case considered by Dixon, Judson, Salley and co-workers:[1]

$$d\gamma = -\Gamma_{HA}^{(1)}d\mu_A \quad (10d)$$

Equations (10), etc., show that surface hydrolysis will alter the effective surface excess if $\Gamma_{HA}^{(1)}$ is different from $\Gamma_A^{(1)}$, and one would in fact expect $\Gamma_{HA}^{(1)}$ to be generally greater than $\Gamma_A^{(1)}$. When surface hydrolysis is appreciable, it can also alter $d\gamma/d\mu_A$ by introducing a term containing $d\mu_H$, and it can affect the question of whether or not the "factor 2" should be present in the Gibbs equation. With soaps and amine salts, it is generally recognised that surface hydrolysis is significant unless the solution is

---

[1] Dixon, Judson, Salley, in *Monomolecular Layers*, ed. Sobotka, American Assoc. for the Advancement of Science, Washington, 1954, p. 63.

buffered at a sufficiently high or low pH value, respectively, and its occurrence in such cases has recently been demonstrated very clearly by Ross and Epstein.[1] The situation is less clear with surface-active electrolytes which are salts of strong acids or bases. Here the work of Dixon, Judson, Salley, *et al.*, by the radio-tracer technique, indicates that in very dilute solutions of sodium dialkyl sulphosuccinates and of a long-chain quaternary ammonium salt, surface hydrolysis is practically complete. The foaming experiments of Wilson, Epstein, and Ross,[2] on the other hand, suggest that no appreciable hydrolysis occurs in the surface of aqueous sodium dodecyl sulphate solutions. This question is discussed more fully below in the section on the direct determination of surface excesses.

4. GIBBS'S EQUATION AND THE FORMATION OF MICELLES

We have seen in Chapter 2 that probably the great majority of amphipathic surface-active compounds form micelles, frequently at concentrations which are of technical importance. Micelle formation can affect the Gibbs equation in two ways:

(a) by affecting the chemical potential of the surface-active component, which will tend towards a constant value, and

(b) by reducing the effective surface excess of the surface-active component, since the micelle is a symmetrical, non-amphipathic species, which is formed at the expense (relatively speaking) of the amphipathic, molecularly disperse solute.

These remarks apply to both ionic and non-ionic surface-active agents, though the detailed treatment of the Gibbs equation in the two cases is not identical. If we assume, for example, that a micelle is formed from a *non-ionic* agent A, by the reversible process

$$mA \rightleftarrows M,$$

and that equation (8a) is applicable, we have

$$d\gamma = -\Gamma_A^{(1)} d\mu_A - \Gamma_M^{(1)} d\mu_M$$

Since, however, it follows from the postulated equilibrium that $d\mu_M = m d\mu_A$,

$$d\gamma = -(\Gamma_A^{(1)} + m\Gamma_M^{(1)}) d\mu_A \qquad (11)$$

If $\Gamma_M^{(1)}$ is less positive than $\Gamma_A^{(1)}$—and it may in fact be *negative*—it is clear that the effective surface excess can be reduced by micelle formation. It has also been pointed out in Chapter 2 that, if the association number m of the micelle is large, then the activity and chemical potential of A will tend to a constant value. It follows from both these effects, therefore, that $d\gamma/da_A$ will tend to a constant value above the critical micelle concentration, and the tendency may be even more marked for $d\gamma/dc_A$ to become

[1] Ross and Epstein, *J. Phys. Chem.*, 1958, **62**, 533.
[2] Wilson, Epstein, and Ross, *J. Coll. Sci.*, 1957, **12**, 345.

constant if **A** is an ion, on account of the more rapid decrease in the activity coefficient when multivalent ionic micelles are being formed.

If we assume that an *ionic* micelle, with included counterions, is formed by the reaction

$$mNa^+ + nR^- \rightleftarrows M^{(n-m)-}$$

n being greater than m, equation (8a), for example, becomes

$$d\gamma = -\left(\Gamma_{Na}{}^{(G)} - \frac{\Gamma_1{}^{(G)}}{N_1{}^\alpha} N_{Na}{}^\alpha\right) d\mu_{Na}{}^\sigma - \left(\Gamma_R{}^{(G)} - \frac{\Gamma_1{}^{(G)}}{N_1{}^\alpha} N_R{}^\alpha\right) d\mu_R{}^\sigma$$
$$- \left(\Gamma_M{}^{(G)} - \frac{\Gamma_1{}^{(G)}}{N_1{}^\alpha} N_M{}^\alpha\right) d\mu_M{}^\sigma,$$

where (1) refers to the solvent (water).

It follows, however, from the conditions of equilibrium that

$$d\mu_M{}^\sigma = md\mu_{Na}{}^\sigma + nd\mu_R{}^\sigma$$

and

$$(\mu_{Na}{}^\sigma + \mu_R{}^\sigma) = (\mu_{Na}{}^\alpha + \mu_R{}^\alpha),$$

and from the conditions of electrical neutrality in both phases that

$$N_{Na}{}^\alpha = N_R{}^\alpha + (n-m)N_M{}^\alpha,$$

and

$$\Gamma_{Na}{}^{(G)} = \Gamma_R{}^{(G)} + (n-m)\Gamma_M{}^{(G)},$$

and substitution gives simply

$$d\gamma = -\left(\Gamma_R{}^{(G)} - \frac{\Gamma_1{}^{(G)}}{N_1{}^\alpha} N_R{}^\alpha + n\Gamma_M{}^{(G)} - n\frac{\Gamma_1{}^{(G)}}{N_1{}^\alpha} N_M{}^\alpha\right)(d\mu_{Na}{}^\alpha + d\mu_R{}^\alpha)$$

or

$$d\gamma = -(\Gamma_R{}^{(1)} + n\Gamma_M{}^{(1)})d(\mu_{Na}{}^\alpha + \mu_R{}^\alpha) \qquad (12)$$

which is the analogue of (11).

Inspection of (12) shows that the quantity $(\Gamma_R{}^{(1)} + n\Gamma_M{}^{(1)})$ is in fact $\Gamma_{NaR}{}^{(1)}$, the surface excess of the *total component* NaR, micellar as well as molecularly disperse, relative to the solvent, so that

$$d\gamma = -\Gamma_{NaR}{}^{(1)}d(\mu_{Na}{}^\alpha + \mu_R{}^\alpha)$$

or

$$\frac{d\gamma}{da_\pm{}^\alpha} = -\frac{2RT}{a_\pm{}^\alpha}\Gamma_{NaR}{}^{(1)}. \qquad (13)$$

Equations (12) and (13) show that the presence of ionic micelles which are in equilibrium with the molecularly disperse material, does *not* introduce a new component into the system, thermodynamically speaking—nor a new phase. Equation (12), like (11), does, however, indicate how micelle formation can affect experimentally significant quantities such as $\Gamma_{NaR}{}^{(1)}$, *the validity of the Gibbs equation being, of course, unaffected.*

The tendency for the surface tension to become constant above the critical micelle concentration can be inferred from some of the earlier work[1] though it was first demonstrated for an unequivocally pure surface-active agent in the now classical work of Miles and Shedlovsky[2] and Miles,[3] which is discussed more fully below. Confirmatory evidence has been obtained by other workers, with a number of different systems. Thus Cockbain[4] has found that the interfacial tension between sodium dodecyl sulphate solutions and *n*-decane became constant at the critical micelle concentration, while Wilson, Epstein, and Ross[5] found, in the foaming experiments referred to above, that the adsorption of sodium dodecyl sulphate at the air-solution interface became constant above the critical micelle concentration. Kling and Lange,[6] in a systematic investigation of the interfacial tension between *n*-heptane and aqueous solutions of a series of sodium alkyl sulphates, both pure and at constant ionic strength, also found that the interfacial tension became constant above the critical micelle concentration, the interfacial tension *vs. ln* (concentration) curves showing breaks at that point. It is also interesting that they found that the "factor 2" came into the Gibbs equation for the pure solutions, except at very low concentrations. Finally, Bell[7] has reported in a preliminary communication that adsorption of the non-ionic agent "Igepal CA" on silica sand reaches a flat maximum near the critical micelle concentration, whereas the more complex "Pluronic L-44," which does not appear to have a critical micelle concentration, does not exhibit this maximum.

5. GIBBS'S EQUATION AND THE OCCURRENCE OF SURFACE TENSION MINIMA

We have just seen that micelle-formation in a solution of a *single* surface-active component can explain the observed attainment of a constant surface or interfacial tension (which, perhaps, occurs fairly suddenly) with increasing concentration. Micelle-formation cannot, however, satisfactorily explain the subsequent *increases* in boundary tensions which have frequently been reported. Such an increase would imply that the chemical potential of a surface-active component was actually *decreasing* with increasing concentration, and/or that adsorption had become negative. The first of these possibilities is thermodynamically impossible for a solution of a single, pure surface-active component (*cf.* p. 102), while the second leads to physical pictures of the interface which are very unlikely, if not unacceptable. This last point was made very clearly by McBain and Mills,[8]

[1] *Cf.* the results of Lottermoser and Stoll, *Koll. Z.*, 1933, **63**, 49, taken with those of Lottermoser and Püschel, *Koll. Z.*, 1933, **63**, 175; also the data of Tartar, Sivertz, and Reitmeyer, *J. Amer. Chem. Soc.*, 1940, **62**, 2375.

[2] Miles and Shedlovsky, *J. Phys. Chem.*, 1944, **48**, 57.

[3] Miles, *ibid.*, 1945, **49**, 71.

[4] Cockbain, *Trans. Faraday Soc.*, 1954, **50**, 874.

[5] Wilson, Epstein, and Ross, *J. Coll. Sci.*, 1957, **12**, 345.

[6] Kling and Lange, *Second Congress*, 1957, **I**, 295.

[7] Bell, *J. Phys. Chem.*, 1959, **63**, 299.

[8] McBain and Mills, *Reports on Progress in Physics*, 1938, **5**, 30.

who pointed out that negative adsorption to the extent required would mean that (a) a solute which was positively adsorbed at low concentrations became desorbed as the activity of the solute increased, and (b) it would be necessary, in order to achieve a large enough negative surface excess, to postulate surface layers of water of excessively great depths: thus in solutions of 0·0056 molar dodecane sulphonic acid, at which McBain and Mills found a minimum in the surface tension, the zero surface excess would correspond to a layer of pure water 8,000 Å. deep, which would increase thereafter with increasing concentration.*

The difficulty of even qualitatively explaining the minima in surface-tension-concentration curves has caused some doubts to be raised as to the validity of the Gibbs equation, even though it is rigorous thermodynamically. Thanks, however, to the very elegant experimental work of Miles and Shedlovsky[1] which has been confirmed and extended by other workers, and to the theoretical work of Reichenberg[2] and Hutchinson,[3] it seems to be well established that, where minima occur, they are evidence for the presence of impurities in the surface-active agents used, the mixtures being such that *regressions occur in the chemical potential of the more surface-active species*, as the total concentration increases.

Miles and Shedlovsky found that the apparently pure sodium dodecyl sulphate which they had been using, which gave a pronounced minimum in the surface tension-concentration curve, contained small amounts of dodecyl alcohol. When the dodecyl alcohol was removed, the minima disappeared. Similar results were obtained by Hutchinson, who found that additions of octyl alcohol to carefully purified sodium dodecyl sulphate caused minima to appear, and by Desalbres,[4] who added cyclohexanol, menthanol, and terpineol to purified sodium dodecyl sulphate, sodium oleate, and sodium laurate, again with similar results. A valuable independent confirmation of these findings is afforded by the foaming experiments of Brady,[5] who found that the surface tension minima were eliminated from solutions of sodium dodecyl sulphate and dodecyl sulphuric acid which had been extensively "foamed" to remove the dodecyl alcohol. Wilson, Epstein, and Ross[6] analysed the foam formed on solutions containing sodium dodecyl sulphate and dodecyl alcohol and found that

---

* The question is sometimes asked whether or not surface-active agents are available which will *increase* the surface tension of water at low concentrations. In so far as the question relates to reversibly adsorbed materials, these calculations by McBain and Mills afford a simple arithmetical demonstration that appreciable increases by small concentrations are not feasible.

[1] Miles and Shedlovsky, *J. Phys. Chem.*, 1944, **48**, 57; Miles, *ibid.*, 1945, **49**, 71.

[2] Reichenberg, *Trans. Faraday Soc.*, 1947, **43**, 467.

[3] Hutchinson, *J. Coll. Sci.*, 1948, **3**, 413. This paper has an acknowledgement of a theoretical contribution by F. O. Koenig.

[4] Desalbres, *Bull. soc. chim. France*, 1949, 591; 1950, 26.

[5] Brady, *J. Phys. Chem.*, 1949, **53**, 56.

[6] Wilson, Epstein, and Ross, *J. Coll. Sci.*, 1957, **12**, 345.

adsorption became constant (but did not decrease) above the critical micelle concentration, supporting the view that surface tension minima are not due to desorption of surface-active material.

All these results refer to the air-water interface. The experiments of Hutchinson suggest that the effect of impurities, such as dodecyl alcohol in sodium dodecyl sulphate, are less marked at the oil-water interface. This is presumably due to the fact that the surface activity of the alcohol is less at the oil-water than at the air-water interface, so that a regression in the chemical potential of the alcohol has a smaller effect on the interfacial tension-concentration curve—the oil may even extract the dodecyl alcohol from the aqueous solution and thus suppress the effect altogether.

The confirmatory evidence from measurements by the radioactive tracer method is discussed below.

It seems fairly certain that the mechanism which can cause a regression in the chemical potential of the more surface-active component is (at least in most cases) the formation of *mixed micelles*. Suppose, for example, that we have a mixture of two surface-active compounds, NaA and B, B being the more surface-active—for example, dodecyl alcohol. We will assume, for the sake of simplicity, that B is unionised, that each component forms a micelle, and that a mixed micelle is also formed:

$$m\text{Na}^+ + n\text{A}^- \rightleftarrows \text{MA}^{(n-m)-},$$

whence

$$d\mu_{\text{MA}} = md\mu_{\text{Na}} + nd\mu_{\text{A}},$$

$$p\text{B} \rightleftarrows \text{MB}, \text{ whence } d\mu_{\text{MB}} = pd\mu_{\text{B}}, \text{ and}$$

$$q\text{MA}^{(n-m)-} + r\text{B} \rightleftarrows \text{MAB}^{(qn-qm)-}, \text{ whence } d\mu_{\text{MAB}} = qd\mu_{\text{MA}} + rd\mu_{\text{B}}.$$

The Gibbs equation for this system can be formally written

$$d\gamma = -\Gamma_{\text{Na}}^{(1)}d\mu_{\text{Na}}^{\sigma} - \Gamma_{\text{A}}^{(1)}d\mu_{\text{A}}^{\sigma} - \Gamma_{\text{MA}}^{(1)}d\mu_{\text{MA}}^{\sigma}$$
$$- \Gamma_{\text{MB}}^{(1)}d\mu_{\text{MB}}^{\sigma} - \Gamma_{\text{MAB}}^{(1)}d\mu_{\text{MAB}}^{\sigma}.$$

When, however, we make the appropriate substitutions from the conditions of the various equilibria, and of the electrical neutrality of the σ phase, this can be written:

$$\frac{d\gamma}{dc} = -(\Gamma_{\text{A}}^{(1)} + n\Gamma_{\text{MA}}^{(1)} + nq\Gamma_{\text{MAB}}^{(1)})d(\mu_{\text{Na}} + \mu_{\text{R}})/dc$$
$$- (\Gamma_{\text{B}}^{(1)} + p\Gamma_{\text{MB}}^{(1)} + r\Gamma_{\text{MAB}}^{(1)})d\mu_{\text{B}}/dc \tag{14}$$

where c is the total concentration of the mixed (impure) agent in the solution.

Owing to the formation of the mixed micelle, from which it follows that

$$\frac{d\mu_{\text{B}}}{dc} = \frac{1}{r}\frac{d\mu_{\text{MAB}}}{dc} - \frac{mq}{r}\frac{d\mu_{\text{Na}}}{dc} - \frac{nq}{r}\frac{d\mu_{\text{A}}}{dc} \tag{15}$$

it is quite possible that $d\mu_B/dc$ can become negative. Consequently, even if both the surface excess expressions in equation (14), *viz.*,

$$(\Gamma_A{}^{(1)} + n\Gamma_{MA}{}^{(1)} + nq\Gamma_{MAB}{}^{(1)}) \text{ and } (\Gamma_B{}^{(1)} + p\Gamma_{MB}{}^{(1)} + r\Gamma_{MAB}{}^{(1)}),$$

are positive—*i.e.* even if both surface-active components are positively adsorbed—it is still possible for $d\gamma/dc$ to become zero, and eventually positive, and this will be more likely to occur if B is more surface-active than A.

It would appear therefore that the anomaly of minima in surface tension-concentration curves can be satisfactorily explained,* and that the lesson to be drawn is the need for extreme purity of surface-active materials when the Gibbs equation is applied. It is worth noting, however, that the presence of impurities which introduce these anomalies does not invalidate the *qualitative* conclusion which we have already drawn, that the presence of a solute which is reversibly adsorbed at an interface, reduces the inter-facial tension. In all the experimental work quoted above, the surface tension-concentration curves for the mixtures which exhibit minima always give steep lowerings of the surface tension, compared with pure water, and in the cases considered they lie below the curves for the pure major components: it may well be that the practical surface activity of sodium dodecyl sulphate, for example, is increased by the presence of the dodecyl alcohol.

The conclusion also appears to be fully justified that the occurrence of a minimum in a surface tension-concentration curve (under equilibrium conditions) constitutes proof of the presence of one or more impurities in a sample of a surface-active agent. Unfortunately, it must be emphasised that the converse is not true—*i.e.*, *the absence of a minimum is not of itself proof of the purity of a sample.* This can be seen at once from equations (14) and (15): the presence of the "impurity" B *can* cause a positive value of $d\gamma/dc$, but will not necessarily do so. All that can be concluded, when minima are absent, is that if any impurities are in fact present, they do not cause a sufficient regression in the chemical potential of one or more components *which are surface-active at the particular interface in question*, to more than offset the effect of the increased chemical potential of the other component.

Reichenberg's paper also makes the point that the chemical potential of a surface-active electrolyte may decrease with increasing "concentration" if it contains sufficient amounts of electrolytes which are not surface-active. This point could be of practical importance under special circumstances: if, for example, a surface-active agent containing a large amount of electrolyte is used at high concentrations. Here the chemical potential of the

---

* Although we have altered the emphasis, and used the Guggenheim convention in conformity with the rest of the present book, we would like to emphasise that the present treatment is based on that of Reichenberg.

surface-active ion A could be so depressed by the increasing total concentration of electrolyte, which would favour micelle-formation as well as directly depressing the activity coefficient through increasing interionic forces, that it is conceivable that $d\mu_A/dc$ might become negative.

The question of whether or not it is possible for reversibly *chemisorbed* surface-active compounds to increase boundary tensions is discussed in more detail in the section on solid-liquid interfaces below. An interesting case, which might at first sight appear to bear on this question, has been described by Netter.[1] He found that the interfacial tension between an aqueous solution, and a paraffin oil containing 0·2% calcium oleate and 0·8% oleic acid, *increased* as calcium ions were added. The data given for this multicomponent system do not permit the Gibbs equation to be applied to it, but the most likely explanation (which is not inconsistent with that advanced by Netter) seems to us to be that the oleic acid is more surface-active at the interface in question than the calcium oleate, and that the two components form a surface-inactive complex (Netter mentions that oleic acid "solubilises" the calcium oleate), the amount of which increases as more calcium ions are added. Apart from its biological significance, Netter's paper is of interest as describing a case in which a surface-active component is removed from an interface by a special, specific addition.

6. Gibbs's equation and the direct determination of surface excesses

The direct determination of surface excesses, as a check on the applicability* of the Gibbs equation, has engaged a number of workers. The very elegant surface microtome method of McBain and his co-workers has been described by McBain and Wood.[2] More recently, attention has been focussed on the radio-tracer techniques which have been developed by Dixon, Weith, Argyle, and Salley,[3] and Aniansson and Lamm,[4] and by Hutchinson.[5] A useful summary of this work up to about 1953 has been published by Dixon, Judson and Salley.[6]

The method of Dixon *et al.*, and of Aniansson and Lamm, consists in "tagging" the surface-active ion (*e.g.*, dodecyl sulphate, oleyl sulphate, or

---

* We use the word "applicability" rather than "validity," because it seems to us that the latter is not in doubt, provided that a genuine condition of equilibrium is attained, and that pure components are used. What is frequently in doubt is how far the Gibbs equation may be used in a given case—whether, for example, bulk concentrations may be used in place of activities—or related to a particular physical picture of the interface.

[1] Netter, *Die Naturwissenschaften*, 1953, **40**, 435, 436.
[2] McBain and Wood, *Proc. Roy. Soc.*, 1940, **174A**, 286.
[3] Dixon, Weith, Argyle, and Salley, *Nature*, 1949, **163**, 845.
[4] Aniansson and Lamm, *Nature*, 1950, **165**, 357.
[5] Hutchinson, *J. Coll. Sci.*, 1949, **4**, 599.
[6] Dixon, Judson, and Salley, in *Monomolecular Layers*, ed. Sobotka, American Association for the Advancement of Science, Washington, 1954, p. 63.

dioctylsulphosuccinate) with radioactive S^{35}, which gives a relatively soft β-radiation. This radiation is strongly absorbed by the solution, so that the ions at or near the interface contribute a preponderant effect when the radioactivity is measured with a Geiger-Müller counter. In order to obtain quantitative data, a reference solution of exactly equivalent pure Na_2SO_4 tagged with S^{35} is also measured; on the assumption that Na_2SO_4 is completely surface-inactive, the surface excess on the solution of the surface-active compound is calculated.* This method can be used both for equilibrium conditions, and for following the kinetics of adsorption.

In Hutchinson's experiments, sodium dodecyl sulphate was tagged with Na^{22}—*i.e.*, the counterion was tagged. A platinum ring was drawn through the surface of the solution, so that a thin film of solution was removed; this was then weighed and analysed radiometrically, the activity being compared with that of the bulk solution. A tagged counterion ($SO_4^{=}$ containing S^{35}) has also been used by Judson, Lerew, Dixon, and Salley,[1] who incidentally also checked Hutchinson's method against their own, with satisfactory agreement.

The results of this large amount of elegant experimental work can be summarised as follows:

(a) At low concentrations, the experimentally determined surface excesses with tagged surface-active ions agree reasonably well with values calculated by the Gibbs equation from surface tension data, using in general bulk concentrations for activities, provided that the factor 2 is omitted from the Gibbs equation.[2]

(b) The disappearance of the factor 2 at very low concentrations is attributed by Salley, Weith, Argyle, and Dixon to substantially complete surface hydrolysis (*cf.* equation 10d in the present chapter).

(c) The results confirm, or are consistent with, the findings of Miles and Shedlovsky that surface tension minima are due to the presence of more highly surface-active impurities.[3] Competition for the surface can also occur between two soluble surface-active compounds, *e.g.*, sodium tetradecyl sulphate (tagged) and sodium dodecyl sulphate,[4] and sodium di-*n*-octylsulphosuccinate (tagged) and sodium di-(2-ethylhexyl)-sulphosuccinate.[5]

(d) Perhaps the most striking finding reported by Dixon, Weith, Argyle, and Salley, confirmed by Nilsson and Lamm, by Ruyssen, and by

---

* The assumption is, of course, also made that decomposition of the surface-active material by the radiation is negligible.

[1] Judson, Lerew, Dixon, and Salley, *J. Phys. Chem.*, 1953, **57**, 916.

[2] Dixon, Weith, Argyle and Salley, *Nature*, 1949, **163**, 845; Aniansson and Lamm, *ibid.*, 1950, **165**, 357; Salley, Weith, Argyle, and Dixon, *Proc. Roy. Soc.*, 1950, **203A**, 42; Ruyssen, *Bull. soc. chim. Belge*, 1953, **62**, 97.

[3] Hutchinson, *loc. cit.*; Ruyssen, *loc. cit.*

[4] Nilsson and Lamm, *Acta Chem. Scand.*, 1952, **6**, 1175.

[5] Judson, Argyle, Salley, and Dixon, *J. Chem. Phys.*, 1950, **18**, 1302.

Judson, Lerew, Dixon, and Salley with tagged counterions, is that the surface excesses determined from radioactivity counts continue to rise with increasing concentration to very high values, corresponding in quantity to as much as 30 monomolecular layers, whereas the surface excesses calculated from the Gibbs equation reached constant values, corresponding to monomolecular layers.

One possible explanation for these very high surface excesses, which is advanced by Dixon, Judson, and Salley,[1] is that *micelles* are the adsorbed species. This interesting suggestion is consistent with the reported experimental facts, though it seems to us that the precise meaning to be attached to a "micelle" in such a case is important, and that the fact that high surface excesses occur only above the critical micelle concentration, is not conclusive evidence for the adsorption of the micelle (which, it will be remembered, is not amphipathic) *as such* at the air-water interface. Dixon, Judson, and Salley's explanation could be alternatively expressed as follows : Above the critical micelle concentration, the chemical potential of a pure surface active component becomes substantially constant, although the total concentration continues to increase. Under the same conditions, the total concentration in the surface phase also increases (well beyond the usually pictured monomolecular layer), even though its chemical potential in the surface phase must also have become substantially constant. This is best explained on the assumption that association *of some sort* is also occurring in the surface phase—*or that a new surface phase is forming*. If associates are in fact formed, they are not necessarily of the same type as those in the bulk phase, and it might be preferable to describe them by McBain's expression, "surface pellicles."

It is also interesting to note that Judson, Lerew, Dixon, and Salley found that large and increasing quantities of tagged $SO_4^=$ ions were also adsorbed by surface layers of the soluble *non-ionic* agent, N-2-hydroxyethyllauramide condensed with 10 molecular proportions of ethylene oxide.

These high surface excesses have not been observed by other workers. Thus Roe and Brass[2] determined surface excesses on solutions of potassium palmitate which had been tagged with C^{14}, similarly tagged sodium acetate being used as the indicator. The solutions were buffered at pH 12·3, and the concentration of K^+ ions was kept constant. They also determined surface tensions and applied the Gibbs equation to potassium palmitate, potassium laurate, dodecylamine hydrochloride, and sodium dodecyl sulphate. In each case, they found a constant adsorption over a considerable range of concentrations up to the critical micelle concentration. The results for sodium palmitate agreed well with the tracer results and with the values calculated for a monomolecular layer.

Roe and Brass's paper provides a good illustration of the well-known

[1] Dixon, Judson, and Salley, in *Monomolecular Layers*, p. 91.
[2] Roe and Brass, *J. Amer. Chem. Soc.*, 1954, **76**, 4703.

advantage of plotting the surface tension against the *logarithm* of the
concentration when the Gibbs equation is used. This gives a more nearly
straight line, the slope of which can be more accurately determined than is
usually the case for a surface tension-concentration curve. The Gibbs
equation is then written in the form (for a swamped, buffered solution)*

$$\frac{d\gamma}{d \ln c} = - RT\Gamma_R^{(1)},$$

or

$$\frac{d\gamma}{d \log c} = - 2 \cdot 303 \, RT\Gamma_R^{(1)}.$$

More recently, Nilsson[1] has done measurements on sodium dodecyl
sulphate, tagged with a much softer β-emitter, tritium, the reference
solution being tritiated dodecyl alcohol dissolved in ordinary dodecyl
alcohol. The results, which were in reasonably good agreement with excesses
calculated from surface tension data, indicated that the surface excess
became constant at a value corresponding to monomolecular layer adsorption. (Nilsson also gives some interesting further verification of Miles
and Shedlovsky's work on the effect of dodecyl alcohol in causing surface
tension minima in solutions of sodium dodecyl sulphate.) Finally, Wilson,
Epstein, and Ross[2] have analytically determined the adsorption of sodium
dodecyl sulphate on small bubbles of known size, and obtained a limiting
value over the concentration range 0·01 to 0·025 molar, which agrees with
monolayer adsorption.

There is therefore at present a contradiction of results, from different
workers, on direct measurements of surface excesses, the results with
sodium dodecyl sulphate being in direct conflict. The radiotracer results
with S^{35} point to surface excesses which are considerably greater than
correspond to monolayer adsorption at the air-water interface, while
tritiated sodium dodecyl sulphate, and the bubble analysis results, point
to monolayer adsorption, in reasonable agreement with the calculated
"Gibbsian" excesses. It does not seem possible to decide at present between
these two sets of results. It can be argued that the sensitivity of the tritium
method is greater, but on the other hand it is such a soft emitter that, if
multilayers are in fact present, it might miss them altogether. The bubble-
adsorption technique has the attraction of unequivocal simplicity, but it
could be argued that it did not ensure complete attainment of equilibrium.

---

* The values of $\Gamma_R^{(1)}$ calculated by Roe and Brass appear to need correction for the
factor 2·303 for converting natural to base-10 logarithms, and should, in fact, be about
half the values given. This gives about 2×10^{-10} moles/cm.^{2} for the calculated results,
compared with radiotracer results which rise from $2 \cdot 5 \times 10^{-10}$ at $1 \cdot 17 \times 10^{-5}$ molar, to
$4 \cdot 3 \times 10^{-10}$ at $9 \cdot 4 \times 10^{-5}$ molar. This discrepancy might well be due to a decrease in
the activity coefficient of the soap as its concentration increases, which would be corrected for by making the negative slope of the γ-log c curve greater.

[1] Nilsson, *J. Phys. Chem.*, 1957, **61**, 1135.
[2] Wilson, Epstein, and Ross, *J. Coll. Sci.*, 1957, **12**, 345.

A possible explanation, which cannot be completely eliminated at present, is of course that *radiolysis* of the surface-active material occurred. This explanation does not seem to be very convincing, however, since one would have expected more variable and discordant results among the radiotracer data than seems actually to be the case. A further possibility, which we mention with considerable diffidence, is that there may have been very slight differences in the purity of materials used by different workers, and that the evidence for multilayer adsorption has been obtained with samples containing traces of insoluble matter which has caused surface "pellicles" or "micelles," or otherwise altered the nature of the interface. This very speculative idea occurred to us from comparing the results of Roe and Brass referred to above, with those of Flengas and Rideal[1] on sodium stearate tagged with C^{14}, and containing some untagged heptadecane. The latter authors found that the surface excesses by the tracer technique were higher than those from surface tension measurements, and that the absolute $\Gamma^{(1)}$ values by the former method (up to $17 \cdot 5 \times 10^{-10}$ moles/cm.^{2}, equivalent to a surface area per molecule of about 10 Å.^{2}) were greater than those corresponding to a monomolecular layer. It seems just possible that the high values were due to the presence of the heptadecane, forming some sort of surface complex or mixed layer with the soap.

7. GIBBS'S EQUATION AND THE OCCURRENCE OF INTERFACIAL COMPLEXES

As a result of their studies of the effect of the presence of oil-soluble amphipathic compounds (*e.g.*, cetyl alcohol) during the emulsification of medicinal paraffin in aqueous solutions of surface-active compounds such as sodium cetyl sulphate, Schulman and Cockbain[2] have advanced the important theory that the increased ease of emulsification in such cases is due to the formation of interfacial complexes at the oil-water interface. The implications of this theory as it affects the preparation of emulsions are referred to more fully in Chapter 6. In view of the great utility of the Schulman-Cockbain concept, and of the fact that it may not be restricted to liquid-liquid interfaces, the effect of the formation of interfacial complexes on predictions from the Gibbs equation is worth examining.

For the present purpose an interfacial complex will be defined as an associate of two or more types of surface-active molecules which can exist only in the σ phase (Guggenheim convention), each of the bulk phases α and β containing at least one of the compounds which combine to form the complex. (It is of course possible for one or more of these compounds to be present in both the α and β phases.) An interfacial complex is therefore in a sense the opposite case to the ionic micelle, which is either absent altogether from the σ phase or at any rate "negatively adsorbed" in it. It therefore

---

[1] Flengas and Rideal, *Trans. Faraday Soc.*, 1959, **55**, 339.
[2] Schulman and Cockbain, *Trans. Faraday Soc.*, 1940, **36**, 651, 661.

follows from the principle of Le Chatelier, for example, that the existence of this interfacial complex will increase the $\Gamma^{(G)}$'s for the individual solutes which enter into it, and that consequently the interfacial tension would be expected to decrease more rapidly with increasing concentration of either solute than if no interfacial complex were formed.

The formation of an interfacial complex is, of course, distinct from simple "coexistence" of an oil-soluble and a water-soluble surface-active agent in an interfacial layer. In the latter case, each agent will, subject to competition for space in the interface and to general interactions among all the adsorbed molecules, contribute its quota to the total lowering of the interfacial tension (*cf.* equations 8b and 8c). This appears to be the situation at the benzene-water and *n*-decane-water interfaces studied by Cockbain and McMullen,[1] where cholesterol and β-sitosterol were the oil-soluble agents, and potassium laurate or sodium dodecyl sulphate was added to the aqueous phase. Here the results showed no evidence of specific interactions at the interfaces in question.

8. "TRAUBE'S RULE"

One of the first attempts to relate surface-activity to chemical constitution is represented by Traube's rule,[2] which states that in an homologous series of surface-active molecules, each additional —CH_2— group increases the negative value of the slope of the initial, linear portion of the surface-tension-concentration curve by a constant multiple, to which he assigned the value 3. The "rule" has not been found to hold exactly with simple molecules of relatively low surface-activity, and we doubt whether it will ever prove to be of much use with modern synthetic surface-active agents of relatively complex structure.

An interesting treatment of the theoretical significance of Traube's rule has been published by Ward,[3] who dealt with a case in which the "rule" has been found to hold fairly well, *viz.*, the effect of a series of fatty acids on the interfacial tension air-water. Ward finds that the conformity of the most reliable of these experimental results to Traube's rule does not in fact prove the frequently stated assumption, which is also regarded as the theoretical basis of the rule, that each —CH_2— group added to the paraffin chain occupies a similar position to that occupied by the —CH_2— groups already present, which would mean that the paraffin chains lie flat along the surface. He concludes instead that the paraffin chains, both in the bulk of the solution and in the interface, are present in the form of "most probable spheroids," and that the applicability of Traube's rule to the data examined by him is entirely fortuitous, and due to the fact that the molecular volumes of the series of fatty acids are such that the surface areas of

[1] Cockbain and McMullen, *Trans. Faraday Soc.*, 1951, **47**, 322.
[2] Traube, *Lieb. Ann.*, 1891, **265**, 27.
[3] Ward, *Trans. Faraday Soc.*, 1946, **42**, 399.

the molecules (as spheres) happen to vary almost linearly with the number of carbon atoms.

Aranow and Witten[1] also attack the idea that Traube's rule proves that the hydrocarbon chains of adsorbed amphipathic molecules lie flat at an air-water interface. They suggest instead that the chains stick up into the gas phase, where they undergo random, hindered rotations. Since each —CH$_2$— group added to the chain adds three new possible configurations of the tail, then, if each configuration is equally probable, the entropy increases by R ln 3 for each —CH$_2$—, which is the origin of "Traube's constant." At high surface pressures, this constant diminishes. Aranow and Witten also give some preliminary results which suggest that in "per-fluoro" radicals (in which every H of the original hydrocarbon chain is replaced by a fluorine atom) there is a similar "Traube constant."

The applicability of Traube's rule to non-ionic surface-active agents has recently been studied by Lange,[2] who determined the surface tension-concentration curves of aqueous solutions of a series of compounds of the general formula $C_nH_{2n+1}[OCH_2CH_2]_m \cdot OH$, where n varied from 8 to 18, and m from 4 to 11. Up to and including $n = 12$, the surface activity increased with increasing value of n, and Traube's rule was qualitatively true, but when there were 14 or more carbon atoms in the molecule, surface activity actually decreased with increasing n. Lange attributes this to the formation of associates which affect the thermodynamics of adsorption. Lange also makes the interesting observation that, with increasing value of n, the shape of the surface tension-concentration curves is independent of whether m or the ratio $m : n$ is kept constant, which leads him to the conclusion that the size of the hydrophobic chain determines surface activity rather than the size of the hydrophilic group. Lange's work was of necessity done with mixtures of m values; consequently his data do not lend themselves to interpretation by the Gibbs equation.

9. THE APPLICATION OF THE GIBBS EQUATION TO SOLID-LIQUID INTERFACES

The general validity of the Gibbs equation means that it can be applied to reversible adsorption processes occurring at the interfaces between solids and solutions of surface-active agents, and that the general arguments so far adduced will be applicable to these interfaces. The fact that it has not so far been possible to measure solid-liquid interfacial tensions directly means, of course, that its applications are more limited: thus it can be used to estimate changes in solid-liquid interfacial tensions from adsorption data, but not for the converse purpose of studying adsorption by measuring interfacial tensions as a function of concentration. There are in addition several fundamental points of difference, which it is necessary to examine carefully.

---

[1] Aranow and Witten, *J. Chem. Phys.*, 1958, **28**, 405.

[2] Lange, *Koll. Z.*, 1959, **163**, 9.

In the first place, it is necessary to re-examine what is meant by the concept of the "interfacial tension" when it is applied to the interface between a liquid phase and a crystalline solid. The definition given in Section A—1 of the present chapter, *viz.*,

$$\gamma_i = \left(\frac{\partial G}{\partial A_i}\right)_{P,\, T,\, n_1,\, n_2,\, \ldots A_j \ldots}$$

states that the areas of all interfaces other than the i'th remain constant as we vary the area of that interface. Liquid-liquid or liquid-vapour interfaces may be either planar or curved, but solid-liquid interfaces include in addition interfacial edges and corners, with each of which a free energy is associated. The length and/or number of these must therefore also remain constant in the above definition of the interfacial tension.

In the second place, it is impossible, in any physically realisable system, to vary the area of only one interface on a solid crystal at a time, without simultaneously altering the area of at least one other interface, and/or altering or introducing edge and corner free energies.[1] Suppose for example that we are considering a "wetting" process (*cf.* Chapter 4, Section A), in which one fluid phase is being displaced from the surface of a solid by another fluid phase: it is obvious that we cannot alter the area of one of the solid-fluid interfaces without altering the area of the other solid-fluid interface—and perhaps of the fluid-fluid interface as well. A more subtle case which illustrates this point even better is that in which a completely immersed crystal is partly or completely sheared in two. It might at first sight appear, if the two freshly formed interfaces happened to be identical in nature, that we had changed the area of only one type of interface, but a brief reflection will show that we shall also have created or increased corners and edges. It is therefore necessary to note that our definition of the interfacial tension of a particular solid-liquid interface (the rate of increase of total Gibbs free energy with the area of that interface) is a formal one, which must never be considered as representing a physical process which can occur alone. This in no way diminishes the value of the concept of the interfacial tension in analysing interfacial processes. Thus if we consider a process in which the areas of three interfaces are simultaneously altered, at constant temperature, pressure, and composition of the total system, the important criterion, in terms of the thermodynamics of surfaces, is the variation in the total Gibbs free energy of the system, given by

$$dG = \left(\frac{\partial G}{\partial A_1}\right) dA_1 + \left(\frac{\partial G}{\partial A_2}\right) dA_2 + \left(\frac{\partial G}{\partial A_3}\right) dA_3$$
$$= \gamma_1 dA_1 + \gamma_2 dA_2 + \gamma_3 dA_3.$$

[1] We are indebted to Mr. A. J. Hailwood for drawing our attention in a private communication to this very important point.

Now although none of the three interfacial tensions γ_1, γ_2, or γ_3 is directly measurable, and although none of the three interfacial areas A_1, A_2, or A_3 can be altered without also changing the other two, the values to be assigned to these formal quantities are decisive in determining the sign and magnitude of dG, and it is the values of these quantities γ_1, γ_2, and γ_3 which will be altered by the adsorption of surface-active agent(s) at one or more of the three interfaces in question.

The argument which we have just presented is of course a rigorous one, and in interfacial processes which involve simultaneous changes in the areas of different interfaces, it cannot be ignored even in making an approximation. When however we are dealing with a process in which the area of only one interface is changed, along with changes in corner and edge energies, then it is frequently permissible, in our opinion, to ignore the change in total edge and corner energies by comparison with the change in the total interfacial free energy. Thus Lennard-Jones and Taylor[1] have calculated that the values of edge energies and surface energies, per atom involved, are of the same order of magnitude. If therefore we are considering the cross-wise shearing of a single crystal, it will frequently happen that the number of atoms in the freshly created surface will be enormously greater than the number of atoms in the freshly created edges, so that the effect of the latter can be ignored. (Suppose we are dealing with the cross-wise shearing of a cube which is one micron on each side, the spacing of the atoms being such that there are $\frac{1}{3} \times 10^8$ atoms per cm. of edge and $\frac{1}{9} \times 10^{16}$ atoms per cm.[2] of surface. If the cube is sheared completely in two, the change in interfacial free energy will be about 3×10^7 times as great as the change in edge free energy, and the two free energy changes will be of the same order of magnitude only if the distance of shear is only a matter of atomic diameters.) The same argument applies with even greater force to the changes in corner free energies.

The third important distinction between solid-liquid and liquid-fluid interfaces arises from the fact that, in the case of the former, the interfacial tension is defined as the work required to create unit area of fresh i'th interface reversibly, without stretching the interface, by bringing the appropriate number of fresh atoms into the interface, so that the new interface created is exactly like the old; it is not the same as the work required to *stretch* the interface over unit additional area without bringing fresh atoms or molecules into it. The latter quantity was called the "superficial tension" by Gibbs.[2] We propose to refer to it as the *stretching interfacial* (or *surface*) *tension*, and to refer to the quantity

$$\gamma_i = \left(\frac{\partial G}{\partial A_i}\right)_{P,\,T,\,n_1\,n_2\,\ldots\,Aj\,\ldots} = \left(\frac{\partial F}{\partial A_i}\right)_{V,\,T,\,n_1,\,n_2\,\ldots\,Aj\,\ldots}$$

[1] See Adam, *The Physics and Chemistry of Surfaces*, Oxford University Press, 3rd Edition, 1941, pp. 297–299.

[2] Gibbs, *Collected Works*, Yale University Press, 1928, **I**, p. 315.

as the *thermodynamical interfacial tension** or, when the distinction is obvious, simply the interfacial (or surface) tension.

In the case of a liquid-liquid interface, provided that the surface atoms or molecules are sufficiently mobile, it is permissible to equate the stretching interfacial with the thermodynamical interfacial tension, since it can then be assumed that rearrangement of the molecules in the interface occurs much more rapidly than the relaxation of the shear stress in the interior of the liquid.[1] This is probably generally true for most solutions of surface-active agents in the processes at air-liquid and liquid-liquid interfaces in which we are interested. For solid-liquid interfaces, on the other hand, the distinction must be continually borne in mind even if, for convenience, the thermodynamical interfacial tension is treated mathematically as a virtual tension acting parallel to the interface in a single plane, because

(*i*) it is the thermodynamical, rather than the stretching interfacial tension, which appears in Gibbs's equation, and in integrated forms of it, from which we deduce the probable effects of surface-active materials, and

(*ii*) it is the thermodynamical interfacial tensions which determine the change in the total free energy of a system when an interfacial process takes place (provided that this is done reversibly)—or the equilibrium state towards which the system will tend to strive in such a process.

The distinction between the two interfacial tensions has been examined in the paper by Shuttleworth (*loc. cit.*), which is particularly useful for our present purposes. He points out that the definition of the stretching tension (our nomenclature) of a crystal face implies that the process of stretching is done reversibly and is the same in all directions. For a non-isotropic solid surface, the two stretching tensions, $\bar{\gamma}_1$ and $\bar{\gamma}_2$, in the two directions will be related to the thermodynamical tension, γ, by

$$\bar{\gamma}_1 dA_1 + \bar{\gamma}_2 dA_2 = d(A\gamma) = A d\gamma + \gamma dA \qquad (16)$$

where A is the area, and dA_1 and dA_2 are the increases in area in the two directions.

For an isotropic substance, or for a crystal face with a three (or greater)-fold axis of symmetry, there will be a single stretching tension, $\bar{\gamma}$, and (16) reduces to

---

* We are here departing from the purely arbitrary terminology of our first edition, when we used the expressions "superficial tension" and "interfacial tension," respectively. The quantity γ_i, which we are now calling the thermodynamical interfacial tension, is often referred to as the "interfacial free energy." As pointed out in the footnote on p. 75, however, this expression should apply to an extensive property, such as the total interfacial free energy of the system, $\Sigma A_i \gamma_i$. One could refer to γ_i as the "specific interfacial free energy," for example; it is simpler to call it the (thermodynamical) interfacial tension.

[1] Shuttleworth, *Proc. Phys. Soc.*, 1950, **63A,** 444.

$$\bar{\gamma} = \gamma + \frac{d\gamma}{dA}, \tag{17}$$

Shuttleworth also considers the relevance of the stretching and of the thermodynamical interfacial tensions to typical interfacial processes, and concludes that the thermodynamical tension, γ, relates to the equations for equilibrium contact angles (and, we would add, for spreading coefficients) in wetting processes, and to the Gibbs-Thomson equation for the chemical potential (or solubility) of very small crystals: these are expressions of which we make considerable use in Chapter 4 and subsequent chapters. Shuttleworth concludes that the stretching tension, on the other hand, applies to expressions for differences in pressure across curved (solid) interfaces; this is a case with which we shall not be concerned.

Although, as mentioned above, it is γ rather than $\bar{\gamma}$ which appears in the Gibbs equation, it is instructive to consider the effect of an adsorbed surface-active agent, which lowers γ, on the value of $\bar{\gamma}$, in (for example) a process in which a solid is subdivided, where the amount of reversible work required will depend on $\bar{\gamma}$. Examination of equation (17), for example, shows that a lowering of γ will also lower $\bar{\gamma}$ (*i.e.*, less work will be required to *stretch* the interface reversibly by a given amount) unless the adsorbed material increases $d\gamma/dA$ by a sufficient amount. An increase in $d\gamma/dA$ would mean that, as a result of the adsorption of the surface-active agent, the free energy residing in each element of surface was being increased more rapidly by reversible stretching (at constant temperature, pressure, and composition), *i.e.*, that the presence of the absorbed layer caused a more rapid increase in the heat content of the surface, or a more rapid decrease in its entropy, as the surface was stretched. Such an increase in $d\gamma/dA$, if it were large enough, could mean that the adsorption of a surface-active material could actually increase the work needed for a given degree of disruption. Since this is at least theoretically possible, its likelihood must be considered in every case, with special reference to the most probable physical picture of the adsorbed layer.

When we are dealing with a sufficiently mobile liquid-liquid or gas-liquid interface, it is obvious that only equation (17) applies, and that, owing to the mobility of the surface atoms or molecules, $d\gamma/dA = 0$, and $\bar{\gamma} = \gamma$. It is also clear that, even with solid-liquid interfaces, $d\gamma/dA$ will decrease as the surface atoms or molecules become more mobile, and that $\bar{\gamma}$ will approach nearer to γ. An appreciable degree of mobility in the surfaces of many solids is well established (examples will be found, for example, in Adam's book), and Gurney[1] has shown that the existence of thin liquid layers on the surfaces of solids is thermodynamically probable except at very low temperatures. He points out that, if these surface atoms or molecules are so mobile that there is no delay in attaining thermal equilibrium

---

[1] Gurney, *Proc. Phys. Soc.*, 1949, **62A**, 639.

after a surface is formed, then $\bar{\gamma}$ and γ (our nomenclature) are equal. If this condition is not satisfied, then the surface possesses excess Helmholtz free energy, the significance of which is further considered in Chapter 4, Section D.

In applying the Gibbs equation to solid-liquid interfaces, the case which is most frequently encountered is that in which the α-phase is the liquid medium containing the surface-active agent, saturated with a solid S, and the β-phase consists of pure S. We can then fix the β–σ boundary at the physical interface, and the α–σ boundary at a sufficient distance inside the solution to include all the potential and concentration gradients, and use equation (8a). If the surface-active agent is an electrolyte, or if micelles are present, or if it must be assumed that the solid contains some of the solvent and/or the surface-active agent, then we use the appropriate variation of equation (8). If, however, we use equation (12), for example, it is important to bear in mind one possible difference in interpretation. We have already noted that, at air-liquid or liquid-liquid interfaces, one would expect micelles to be surface-inactive or even negatively adsorbed, owing to their non-amphipathic nature. If, however, the external phase is a *solid*, it may present faces to the solution which are rich in highly polar groups, and these groups may be capable of causing adsorption of the micelle as such, by specific attractive forces such as salt linkages, hydrogen bonds, or dipole interactions. Micelle-formation might then actually *increase* the surface excess at a solid-liquid interface: this point is referred to again below.

A property of solid-liquid interfaces which is worth special examination is the possible occurrence of "chemisorption" processes, *i.e.*, specific chemical reactions between solids and surface-active agents which occur in the interface, at least one product of the reaction remaining substantially completely in the interface. Examples of this phenomenon are furnished by the adsorption of soaps at the interfaces between aqueous solutions and solids such as chalk or lead pigments, the adsorption of cationic surface-active agents by glass or by certain pigments, and the adsorption of flotation agents by ores. These adsorption processes very frequently cause the surface of the solid to become water-repellent, and frequently oil-wetted. A classical example is furnished by the adsorption of sodium palmitate from aqueous solution by finely divided lead chromates; since the pigment is much more readily transferred from aqueous to oily media as a result of this adsorption, it seems reasonable to assume that the "lead palmitate" molecules are present as a unilayer in the interface, with their paraffin chains orientated on the whole outwards towards the aqueous medium. (An excess of surface-active agent over the amount required for a unilayer may cause the surface to become water-wetted again, presumably on account of the amphipathic adsorption of a second unilayer of sodium palmitate, with the polar groups orientated outwards and the paraffin chains inwards.)

It will be seen in a later chapter that it does not necessarily follow, from the fact that the surface of a solid may become water-repellent as the result of the sorption of a water-soluble surface-active agent, that the solid-liquid interfacial tension has actually been *increased* by the sorption, since the occurrence of this water-repellency is best interpreted as a decrease in the work of adhesion solid-water, in which three different interfacial tensions are involved. It is therefore of interest to enquire at the present stage, in terms of the Gibbs equation, whether or not it is possible or likely that the solid-liquid interfacial tension could be increased by a chemisorption process such as those to which reference has just been made. Let us consider a case of chemisorption by double-decomposition (ion exchange), in which the following reaction is assumed to occur in the σ phase:

$$BY + R^- \rightleftarrows BR + Y^-$$

it being assumed that the whole system is saturated with BY, so that μ_{BY} remains constant. (We may also assume if we wish that the BR molecules are so orientated that the surface of the solid becomes "hydrophobic," though this is immaterial to the present argument.) Equation (8a) becomes

$$d\gamma = -\Gamma_{BR}^{(1)}d\mu_{BR}^{\sigma} - \Gamma_{Na}^{(1)}d\mu_{Na}^{\sigma} - \Gamma_{R}^{(1)}d\mu_{R}^{\sigma} - \Gamma_{Y}^{(1)}d\mu_{Y}^{\sigma}$$

It follows from the postulated equilibria, and from the condition of electrical neutrality of each phase that

$$d\mu_{R}^{\sigma} = d\mu_{BR}^{\sigma} + d\mu_{Y}^{\sigma}$$

$$\mu_{BR}^{\sigma} = \mu_{BR}^{\alpha}$$

$$(\mu_{Na}^{\sigma} + \mu_{R}^{\sigma}) = (\mu_{Na}^{\alpha} + \mu_{R}^{\alpha})$$

$$(\mu_{Na}^{\sigma} + \mu_{Y}^{\sigma}) = (\mu_{Na}^{\alpha} + \mu_{Y}^{\alpha})$$

and

$$\Gamma_{Na}^{(1)} = \Gamma_{R}^{(1)} + \Gamma_{Y}^{(1)}$$

and, substituting, we obtain

$$\frac{d\gamma}{d\bar{n}^{\alpha}} = -(\Gamma_{BR}^{(1)} + \Gamma_{R}^{(1)})\frac{d\mu_{BR}}{d\bar{n}^{\alpha}} - (\Gamma_{R}^{(1)} + \Gamma_{Y}^{(1)})\frac{d(\mu_{Na} + \mu_{Y})}{d\bar{n}^{\alpha}} \quad (18)$$

where $\bar{n}^{\alpha}$ is the total amount of the radical R which is present in the α phase.

In general, one would expect that *both* $d\mu_{BR}/d\bar{n}^{\alpha}$ and $d(\mu_{Na} + \mu_{Y})/d\bar{n}^{\alpha}$ would be positive. In that case, $d\gamma/d\bar{n}^{\alpha}$ could be positive only if $\Gamma_{Y}^{(1)}$ were negative, and if moreover $|\Gamma_{Y}^{(1)}| > |\Gamma_{R}^{(1)}|$ and the last term in equation (18) preponderated. This is thermodynamically possible, but a sufficiently large negative excess of Y^- ions raises the difficulty about the physical picture of the interface to which McBain and Mills[1] have drawn attention, and which we have discussed on p. 80, *viz.*, that it becomes necessary to

---

[1] McBain and Mills, *Reports on Progress in Physics*, 1938, **5**, 30.

postulate surface layers of improbably great depth. If, for example, $d\mu_{BR}/d\bar{n}^{\alpha}$ and $d(\mu_{Na} + \mu_Y)/d\bar{n}^{\alpha}$ are of comparable magnitude, and we make the most favourable possible assumptions for a positive value of $d\gamma/d\bar{n}^{\alpha}$, viz., that $\Gamma_R^{(1)}$ is negligible, and that Y^- is completely absent from the σ phase, and we also assume that the amount of BR in the α phase is very small, we have, as an approximation, $\left|\Gamma_Y^{(1)}\right| > \left|\Gamma_{BR}^{(1)}\right|$, whence

$$\Gamma_W^{(G)} n_Y^{\alpha}/n_W^{\alpha} > \Gamma_{BR}^{(G)}, \text{ or } n_W^{\sigma} n_Y^{\alpha}/n_W^{\alpha} > n_{BR}^{\sigma}.$$

Since, however, $n_Y^{\alpha} = n_{BR}^{\sigma}$, we have $n_W^{\sigma} > n_W^{\alpha}$, which leads to the physically very improbable picture that n_W^{σ} is of the same order of magnitude as n_W^{α}, *i.e.*, that one must postulate a layer of pure solvent in the interfacial phase which contains something like half of the total amount of solvent in the system. If, for example, we consider the case of a suspension of one gram of solid of density 2 and specific area 3×10^4 cm.²/gm. (which corresponds to cubes one micron on each edge), in contact with 10 c.c. of a dilute aqueous solution of NaR, the layer of pure water in the σ phase would be of the order of 16,000 Å. thick.

This difficulty can only be avoided by assuming that $d\mu_{BR}/d\bar{n}^{\alpha}$ is much smaller than $d(\mu_{Na} + \mu_Y)/d\bar{n}^{\alpha}$. If in the case which we have just considered we assume that the layer of water is 5 Å. thick,* we find that the value of $d\mu_{BR}/d(\mu_{Na} + \mu_Y)$ must not exceed $1\cdot5 \times 10^{-4}$, which would imply that the interfacial layer was in a very special state.

It is, however, necessary at this point to re-examine the statement that in general one would expect *both* $d\mu_{BR}/d\bar{n}^{\alpha}$ and $d(\mu_{Na} + \mu_Y)/d\bar{n}^{\alpha}$ to be positive. This statement is based on the fact that, as NaR is added to the system, and the interfacial reaction proceeds, Y^- ions and BR are formed, but it is not rigorously true for all values of $\bar{n}^{\alpha}$. (The situation for a single solute, in the absence of an interfacial reaction, is quite different, and is considered on p. 102.) This can be seen by examining the Gibbs-Duhem equation for the α phase in the present case:

$$n_W^{\alpha} d\mu_W^{\alpha} + n_{Na}^{\alpha} d\mu_{Na}^{\alpha} + n_R^{\alpha} d\mu_R^{\alpha} + n_Y^{\alpha} d\mu_Y^{\alpha} + n_{BR}^{\alpha} d\mu_{BR}^{\alpha} = 0.$$

When we introduce the conditions of the various equilibria and of electrical neutrality, we have

$$- n_W^{\alpha} \frac{d\mu_W}{d\bar{n}^{\alpha}} = n_R^{\alpha} \frac{d\mu_{BR}}{d\bar{n}^{\alpha}} + (n_R^{\alpha} + n_Y^{\alpha}) \frac{d(\mu_{Na} + \mu_Y)}{d\bar{n}^{\alpha}}. \tag{19}$$

Now thermodynamical stability of the α phase demands (*cf.* p. 102) that $d\mu_W/d\bar{n}^{\alpha}$ must be negative, which means that $d\mu_{BR}/d\bar{n}^{\alpha}$ and $d(\mu_{Na} + \mu_Y)/d\bar{n}^{\alpha}$ cannot both be negative, though both can be positive. The implications of

---

* This figure is calculated for the surface of concentrated salt solutions from surface tension data; *cf.* Adam, *Physics and Chemistry of Surfaces*, Oxford University Press, 1941, 3rd edition, p. 125.

this statement are worth examining with reference to equations (18) and (19).

Let us first assume that $d(\mu_{Na} + \mu_Y)/d\bar{n}^\alpha$ is negative, which implies, as we have just pointed out, that $d\mu_{BR}/d\bar{n}^\alpha$ must be positive. Since we can assume, on the grounds of the physical picture involved, that $\Gamma_{BR}^{(1)} > \Gamma_Y^{(1)}$, it follows that $d\gamma/d\bar{n}^\alpha$ can be positive, provided that

$$\left|d(\mu_{Na} + \mu_Y)/d\bar{n}^\alpha\right| > d\mu_{BR}/d\bar{n}^\alpha.$$

If, however, this condition is combined with equation (19), it leads to the conclusion, since $d\mu_W/d\bar{n}^\alpha$ must be negative, that $n_R^\alpha > n_R^\alpha + n_Y^\alpha$, which is absurd.

Suppose, however, that $d\mu_{BR}/d\bar{n}^\alpha$ is negative and $d(\mu_{Na} + \mu_Y)d\bar{n}^\alpha$ is positive. Since $(n_R^\alpha + n_Y^\alpha) > n_R^\alpha$, equation (19) demands in this case that

$$\left|d\mu_{BR}/d\bar{n}^\alpha\right| > d(\mu_{Na} + \mu_Y)/d\bar{n}^\alpha.$$

Since, however,

$$(\Gamma_{BR}^{(1)} + \Gamma_R^{(1)}) > (\Gamma_R^{(1)} + \Gamma_Y^{(1)}),$$

a positive value of $d\gamma/d\bar{n}^\alpha$ in equation (18) does not demand that

$$\left|d\mu_{BR}/d\bar{n}^\alpha\right| < d(\mu_{Na} + \mu_Y)/d\bar{n}^\alpha,$$

so that a positive value of $d\gamma/d\bar{n}^\alpha$ becomes thermodynamically possible under these conditions, viz., that $d\mu_{BR}/d\bar{n}^\alpha$ is negative and $d(\mu_{Na} + \mu_Y)/d\bar{n}^\alpha$ is positive, and that μ_{BR} is decreasing with increasing $\bar{n}^\alpha$ more rapidly than $(\mu_{Na} + \mu_Y)$ is increasing.

This possibility must obviously be borne in mind in considering the adsorption of surface-active materials by ion-exchange mechanisms at solid-liquid interfaces, but it seems unlikely that it will occur very frequently. If we examine the condition that $d\mu_{BR}/d\bar{n}^\alpha$ is negative, it implies that either $d\mu_{BR}/d\bar{n}^\sigma$ or $d\bar{n}^\sigma/d\bar{n}^\alpha$ is negative, where $\bar{n}^\sigma$ is the total amount of the R radical in the σ phase. Either condition means that some special mechanism is operating to reverse the trend which prevailed when NaR was first added to the system. The special mechanism is either causing a phase transition in which BR disappears from the interface as the total adsorption increases, or else is causing *desorption* to occur. As we shall see later, desorption is a distinct possibility, although it is still possible that experimental cases of adsorption going through a maximum are due to surface-active impurities. It seems reasonable to conclude, therefore, that even in the case of chemisorption by ion-exchange, an actual increase in a solid-liquid interfacial tension can be ruled out at low concentrations of surface-active materials, is unlikely in general, but may occur at higher concentrations (for example above the critical micelle concentration) under special conditions. It will be clear, however, that the formation of fresh components such as inorganic electrolytes or other solutes, must be taken

8

into account if attempts are made to estimate lowerings in solid-liquid interfacial tensions from adsorption data.

Finally, it must be noted that a solid-liquid interfacial tension cannot be increased, under equilibrium conditions, by an apparent "adsorption" phenomenon in which a fresh bulk phase (however thin) is deposited at a solid-liquid interface. Suppose, for example, that a bulk layer of BR is formed, and that the interfacial tension between this new bulk phase and the α phase (γ_1) is greater than that between the solid BY and the α phase (γ_2). In order for the new phase to remain spread over the physical interface, under equilibrium conditions, it would be necessary that $\gamma_2 > \gamma_1 + \gamma_3$, where γ_3 is the interfacial tension between the two bulk phases BR and BY. Since all these γ's are positive, this is clearly incompatible with the condition $\gamma_1 > \gamma_2$. It would obviously be misleading to attempt to apply the Gibbs equation to such a case.

10. Adsorption maxima at solid-liquid interfaces

The adsorption of surface-active agents from aqueous media at solid-liquid interfaces is the subject of an extensive literature, from which only a few examples can be given here. It has been shown, for example, that detergents and other amphipathic materials are adsorbed by textiles,[1] and by other solids.[2] Adsorption is in some cases amphipathic (*i.e.*, with the polar groups orientated towards the water, and the hydrophobic groups towards the solid phase), in others it occurs with reversed orientation, and in other cases multilayer adsorption occurs, with an amphipathically adsorbed layer superimposed on a layer which is adsorbed with reversed orientation. It seems to be generally agreed that adsorption with reversed orientation is usually a case of "chemisorption," while amphipathic adsorption is clearly "physical," and that the type of adsorption is determined by the particular system involved.

One of the most striking observations in recent work on the adsorption of amphipathic agents at solid-liquid interfaces is the occurrence of *maxima in the adsorption isotherms*, which have been reported by several workers. Corrin, Lind, Roginsky, and Harkins[2] determined the adsorption isotherms of sodium dodecyl sulphate (at 30° c.) and potassium myristate (at 35° c.) on graphite, analyses being done interferometrically. They found that, at the critical micelle concentration, the curve for adsorption as a function of concentration went through a pronounced *upward* inflection, and then

---

[1] See, for example, Aickin, *J. Soc. Dyers Colourists*, 1944, **60**, 60; Gardiner and Smith, *J. Amer. Oil Chem. Soc.*, 1949, **26**, 194; McLaren, *J. Soc. Dyers Colourists*, 1950, **66**, 521; Meader and Fries, *Ind. Eng. Chem.*, 1952, **44**, 1636; Flett, Hoyt, and Walter, *Amer. Dyes. Reporter*, 1952, **41**, 139.

[2] Wolstenholme and Schulman, *Trans. Faraday Soc.*, 1950, **46**, 488; Rose, Weatherburn, and Bayley, *Text. Research J.*, 1951, **21**, 427; Schulman, Waterhouse, and Spink, *Koll. Z.*, 1956, **146**, 77; Welton, *Second Congress*, 1957, **III**, 161.

[2] Corrin, Lind, Roginsky, and Harkins, *J. Coll. Sci.*, 1949, **4**, 485.

reached a maximum, after which adsorption actually *decreased* with increasing concentration. Vold and Phansalkar[1] found curves of similar shape for the adsorption of sodium dodecyl sulphate on cotton and on carbon; they took the precaution of purifying their sample of sodium dodecyl sulphate until it showed no minimum in the surface tension-concentration curve. (It is interesting to note that they obtained clear evidence that the initial adsorption of sodium dodecyl sulphate on carbon takes place with reversed orientation, the carbon particles becoming slightly hydrophobic and going into the foam.) Fava and Eyring,[2] in an important paper on both the thermodynamics and kinetics of adsorption (the latter aspect is discussed on p. 131), found similarly shaped curves for the adsorption of sodium dodecylbenzene sulphonate on cotton, nickel, and lead, using the radio-tracer technique in which the surface-active compound was labelled with S^{35}. They found that the maximum became more pronounced when NaCl (N/100) was present, and even more so when the solutions were made acid (N/100) with HCl; additions of NaOH (to N/100) diminished, but did not eliminate the maximum. These workers also ensured that their surface-active agent did not show a minimum in the curve for surface tension against concentration. Maxima in adsorption isotherms have also been found by Vold and Sivaramakrishnan[3] for sodium dodecyl sulphate on carbon black; they also calculated the component adsorptions on the polar and non-polar portions of the carbon black, and found that the upward inflections (at the critical micelle concentration) and the maxima occurred at the same concentration of surface-active agent.

A rather different picture is given by the recent results of Tamamushi and Tamaki[4] for the adsorption of dodecyl ammonium chloride, dodecyl pyridinium bromide, and sodium dodecyl sulphate on alumina, titanium dioxide, barium sulphate, calcium fluoride, and carbon black. They report flat saturation curves, with no subsequent decrease in adsorption (though in most cases their concentrations do not go to as high values as those used by the other workers quoted above). These flat saturation values are reached at about the critical micelle concentration, with the upward inflections at lower concentrations.* The presence of NaCl increases the adsorption of dodecyl ammonium chloride on alumina, but not the saturation value; a higher pH increased the adsorption of dodecyl ammonium chloride on alumina, while a lower pH increased the adsorption of sodium dodecyl

---

* It is interesting to note in this connection that Fuerstenau (*J. Phys. Chem.*, 1956, **60**, 981) reports that the electrokinetic potential of quartz particles in solutions of dodecyl ammonium chloride falls sharply at a concentration of agent just below 10^{-3} N, which they explain by the formation of "hemi-micelles" among the amphipathic ions, which have become concentrated in the ionic double layer.

[1] Vold and Phansalkar, *Rec. trav. chim.*, 1955, **74**, 41.
[2] Fava and Eyring, *J. Phys. Chem.*, 1956, **60**, 890.
[3] Vold and Sivaramakrishnan, *J. Phys. Chem.*, 1958, **62**, 984.
[4] Tamamushi and Tamaki, *Trans. Faraday Soc.*, 1959, **55**, 1007.

sulphate. These workers postulate a two-stage adsorption (first with reversed orientation, followed by a superimposed amphipathic adsorption) in order to explain the values which they obtained for areas occupied per molecule adsorbed.

Several explanations have been advanced for the occurrence of these maxima in adsorption isotherms. Corrin, Lind, Roginsky and Harkins suggest that it is due to the fact that the activity of the single amphipathic ions begins to fall. Vold and Phansalkar postulate the formation of a mono-molecular layer at the maximum, followed by desorption; this is elaborated by Vold and Sivaramakrishnan, who work out "Langmuir"-type equations for the adsorption of single ions in competition with micelles, and suggest that the decrease after the maximum is due to a sudden aggregation of the adsorbed ions into surface micelles, this aggregation occurring at a concentration at which the potential of the double layer is such that there is no longer an excess of electrical repulsion over van der Waals attraction among the adsorbed ions. Fava and Eyring, on the other hand, suggest that the upward inflection in the isotherm is not due to any sort of phase transition in the surface, but to the formation of aggregates; the solution contains two types of aggregates: small ones which are strongly adsorbed, and less strongly adsorbed larger aggregates. The maximum is due, on this picture, to an increase in the larger aggregates at the expense of the smaller ones, though once the aggregates are adsorbed, they are present as only one kind of adsorbate.

There can be no doubt of the practical importance of these maxima in the adsorption isotherms of surface-active agents, since it means that for many applications (*e.g.*, in the deflocculation of solid particles, and perhaps in detergent processes) an optimum concentration can exist under certain conditions. It seems to us that the theoretical significance of these observations is not so straightforward, and that none of the explanations which has been advanced is entirely satisfactory for a *single pure solute*. This can, perhaps, be made clearer by considering the thermodynamics of the case.

Let us suppose that we have present, at constant temperature and pressure, a pure component (B) which constitutes the β phase, and which is insoluble in the α phase, which consists of water (W) and a single surface-active electrolyte (NaR). Since there are present, at constant temperature and pressure, three components and two phases, there is one degree of freedom, represented by the addition of NaR to the system. (If the σ phase is treated as separate for purposes of the phase rule, then an extra degree of freedom must be added for the interfacial tension, which cancels the addition of one more phase, and we are still left with one degree of freedom.) We will suppose that aggregates (micelles and/or "hemi-micelles") can be present in both the solution and the interface, and that they are formed by the *completely reversible* equilibria:

α phase: $\qquad m\text{Na}^+ + n\text{R}^- \rightleftarrows \text{M}^{(n-m)-} \qquad (n > m)$

σ phase: $\qquad p\text{Na}^+ + q\text{R}^- \rightleftarrows \text{X}^{(q-p)-} \qquad (q > p)$

We can write for the Gibbs-Duhem equation of the α phase

$$n_W{}^\alpha d\mu_W{}^\alpha + n_{Na}{}^\alpha d\mu_{Na}{}^\alpha + n_R{}^\alpha d\mu_R{}^\alpha + n_M{}^\alpha d\mu_M{}^\alpha = 0$$

It follows, however, from the conditions of equilibrium and of electrical neutrality within the α phase (*cf.* p. 75), and from the definition of $\bar{n}^\alpha$, the total number of gram-moles of NaR present as all species, that

$$d\mu_M{}^\alpha = m\,d\mu_{Na}{}^\alpha + n\,d\mu_R{}^\alpha;$$
$$n_{Na}{}^\alpha = n_R{}^\alpha + (n-m)n_M{}^\alpha;$$
$$\bar{n}^\alpha = n_{Na}{}^\alpha + mn_M{}^\alpha = n_R{}^\alpha + nn_M{}^\alpha;$$

and substitution gives us simply

$$n_W{}^\alpha d\mu_W{}^\alpha + \bar{n}^\alpha d(\mu_{Na}{}^\alpha + \mu_R{}^\alpha) = 0 \qquad (20)$$

Similarly, we can write for the Gibbs equation of the σ phase

$$n_W{}^\sigma d\mu_W{}^\sigma + n_{Na}{}^\sigma d\mu_{Na}{}^\sigma + n_R{}^\sigma d\mu_R{}^\sigma + n_X{}^\sigma d\mu_X{}^\sigma = -A\,d\gamma$$

and introducing the conditions of equilibrium, electrical neutrality, and definition of the total number of gram-moles of NaR in the σ phase, this reduces in the same way to

$$n_W{}^\sigma d\mu_W{}^\sigma + \bar{n}^\sigma d(\mu_{Na}{}^\sigma + \mu_R{}^\sigma) = -A\,d\gamma \qquad (21)$$

(It is worth noting that equations (20) and (21) are obtained irrespectively of the number of different types of associates in the two phases, provided that they are all in equilibrium with one another and with the simple ions. Both equations could have been written down by inspection, but the present algebraic exercise, like that on p. 78, serves to show that the presence of micelles, provided that they are in equilibrium with their constituent ions or molecules, does not affect the fundamental thermodynamics of the system, and in particular, does not introduce a new component into the system.)

It follows from the equilibrium between the α and σ phases that $\mu_W{}^\alpha = \mu_W{}^\sigma = \mu_W$, and $(\mu_{Na}{}^\alpha + \mu_R{}^\alpha) = (\mu_{Na}{}^\sigma + \mu_R{}^\sigma) = (\mu_{Na} + \mu_R)$. We can accordingly combine (20) and (21) to obtain equation (12) in the form

$$\left(\bar{n}^\sigma - \frac{\bar{n}^\alpha}{n_W{}^\alpha}n_W{}^\sigma\right)\frac{d(\mu_{Na} + \mu_R)}{d\bar{n}^\alpha} = -A\frac{d\gamma}{d\bar{n}^\alpha}$$

or $\qquad \Gamma_{NaR}{}^{(1)}\dfrac{d(\mu_{Na} + \mu_R)}{d\bar{n}^\alpha} = -\dfrac{d\gamma}{d\bar{n}^\alpha}$

Now it can readily be shown that, *for a stable phase*, $d(\mu_{\mathrm{Na}} + \mu_{\mathrm{R}})/d\bar{n}^{\alpha}$ must be positive;* consequently, since $\Gamma_{\mathrm{NaR}}^{(1)}$ is positive, $d\gamma/d\bar{n}^{\alpha}$ must be negative, and $d\bar{n}^{\sigma}/d\bar{n}^{\alpha}$ can be negative only if $d(\mu_{\mathrm{Na}} + \mu_{\mathrm{R}})/d\bar{n}^{\sigma}$ is negative, *i.e.*, if $d\gamma/d\bar{n}^{\sigma}$ is positive. Either of these equivalent statements implies that the σ phase is metastable, a slight local fluctuation in the composition of the σ phase leading to its spontaneous disappearance: *i.e.*, to a sharp break in the adsorption curve rather than to a steady decline.

This argument can also be illustrated by means of a hypothetical "osmotic machine." Suppose that we have solutions of NaR of concentrations c' and $(c' + \Delta c)$, where c' is the concentration corresponding to the maximum in the adsorption isotherm, separated by a permeable membrane of an adsorbent on which this maximum occurs (*e.g.* cellophane, or a plug of carbon black). We will suppose the membrane to have been brought into equilibrium with the two solutions, which means that on the side next to the concentration c', the amount of solute adsorbed per unit weight (or specific area) is x, while on the other side it is *less*, *i.e.*, $x - \Delta x$. A *complete state of equilibrium* would mean that the concentration became equalised throughout the membrane, but this would lead to adsorption from the more dilute solution (c'), and desorption into the more concentrated solution, with a spontaneous *increase* in the difference in vapour pressure, osmotic pressure, *etc.*, between the two solutions which is, of course, absurd.†

This metastability difficulty cannot be solved by postulating the formation of a separate surface phase. (Vold and co-workers and Fava and Eyring have in any case pointed out that the occurrence of maxima in the adsorption isotherms appears to be a function of the solution rather than of the substrate.) If a fresh surface phase formed, $\dfrac{d(\mu_{\mathrm{Na}} + \mu_{\mathrm{R}})}{d\bar{n}^{\sigma}}$ could approach zero, but it could not become *negative* without implying that there were present two contiguous surface phases having different values for $(\mu_{\mathrm{Na}} + \mu_{\mathrm{R}})$ and for the surface tension. This state of affairs is, of course, not impossible, but it implies an incomplete state of equilibrium.

The formation of metastable surface phases is accordingly a possible explanation of the adsorption maxima, though against it must be noted the apparent independence of the effect from the nature of the substrate, to say nothing of the great experimental care which was taken to ensure

---

* See Guggenheim, *Modern Thermodynamics*, p. 24. We are indebted to Mr. S. Horrobin for the following expression of the argument for the present case. We know that $d\mu_{\mathrm{W}}^{\alpha}/d\bar{n}^{\alpha}$ is initially negative. It cannot become positive, because this would lead to *two* values of $\bar{n}^{\alpha}$ which gave the same value of $\mu_{\mathrm{W}}^{\alpha}$, which would cause two bulk phases to form at the concentration range in question, which we know does not occur. Consequently, so long as $d\mu_{\mathrm{W}}^{\alpha}/d\bar{n}^{\alpha}$ is negative, $d(\mu_{\mathrm{Na}} + \mu_{\mathrm{R}})/d\bar{n}^{\alpha}$ must be positive—although it may become extremely small, it cannot become negative.

† We have been anticipated in the construction of this "osmotic machine" by Mysels—see the communication by Vold in *J. Phys. Chem.*, 1959, **63**, 1645, in which the possibility is clearly noted that adsorption maxima may prove to be due to the presence of impurities. This point is discussed later.

equilibrium, Fava and Eyring having studied both adsorption and desorption rates without finding any discrepancies. The same arguments apply even more strongly against the suggestion that the effective adsorptive surfaces might have decreased because shrinkage of the adsorbent, clogging of pores, etc., may occur.

An alternative approach is to examine the mass-law expression for the formation of micelles in the α phase,

$$K = \frac{a_M}{a_{Na}{}^m \cdot a_R{}^n},$$

where K is the association constant, and a's are activities, to see whether or not the *concentration* of individual R^- ions can pass through a maximum. Unfortunately, it becomes necessary to make simplifying assumptions, for example, that the activities of the ions are directly proportional to their concentrations, which is equivalent to assuming that their activity coefficients are constant. Such an assumption means abandoning the thermodynamical rigour of the treatment, and even as an approximation it seems to us to be doubtful, since the activity coefficients of the various ionic and micellar species would be considerably affected by increasing concentrations of ionic micelles.

A more promising explanation for the adsorption maxima would seem to us to be the presence of further component(s) in the systems studied, different in nature from the impurities which cause minima in the curves for surface tension against concentration. This hypothesis can be expressed as follows. It seems to be well established that the presence of very small quantities of dodecyl alcohol in sodium dodecyl sulphate causes a minimum in the surface tension just above the critical micelle concentration, because of a combination of circumstances:

(a) the alcohol is much more strongly adsorbed at the air-water interface than is the sodium dodecyl sulphate (and homologous sulphates, if any), and contributes largely to the initial fall in the equilibrium surface tension with increasing concentration of agent;

(b) above the critical micelle concentration, the dodecyl alcohol is effectively "sequestered," so that its chemical potential falls, resulting in a *net* increase in the air-water interfacial tension with increasing total concentration.

Suppose, however, that the solute contains an "impurity" NaZ (perhaps a lower homologue of sodium dodecyl sulphate?), which has a comparable or little lower surface activity at the air-water interface, is present in larger amounts than was the dodecyl alcohol, forms mixed micelles with the sodium dodecyl sulphate (NaR), and is considerably *less* strongly adsorbed at the solid-water interfaces. It can be seen from equation (14) in the present chapter (p. 81) that the chemical potential ($\mu_{Na} + \mu_Z$) of such an agent could increase with increasing total concentration, while the chemical potential ($\mu_{Na} + \mu_R$) of sodium dodecyl sulphate decreased, leading to a decreased total adsorption at the solid-water interface. The boundary tension at the air-water interface could, however, continue to decrease if $\Gamma_{NaR}^{(1)}$ and $\Gamma_{NaZ}^{(1)}$, the surface excesses at that interface, had appropriate (positive) values.

Another possible explanation for the occurrence of adsorption maxima is suggested by the recent papers of Sexsmith and White[1] and Gotshal, Rebenfeld, and White,[2] *viz.*, that the adsorption process is an ion-exchange phenomenon, in which the adsorbed R^- ions displace an equivalent amount of one or more other anions. This is, of course, a special case of the introduction of a further component into the system, and can be formulated as follows:

We will suppose that, in the case which we have just been discussing, there is a further equilibrium due to the reaction in the σ phase:

$$BY + R^- \rightleftharpoons BR + Y^-,$$

it being assumed that all the phases are saturated with BY, and that there is a mechanism which maintains this saturation equilibrium. The analogous equations to (18) and (19) now become

$$\frac{d\gamma}{d\bar{n}^\alpha} = -\Gamma_{NaR}^{(1)} \frac{d\mu_{BR}}{d\bar{n}^\alpha} - (\Gamma_{RF}^{(1)} + \Gamma_Y^{(1)}) \frac{d(\mu_{Na} + \mu_Y)}{d\bar{n}^\alpha} \tag{18a}$$

and

$$-n_W^\alpha \frac{d\mu_W}{d\bar{n}^\alpha} = \bar{n}^\alpha \frac{d\mu_{BR}}{d\bar{n}^\alpha} + (\bar{n}^\alpha + n_Y^\alpha) \frac{d(\mu_{Na} + \mu_Y)}{d\bar{n}^\alpha} \tag{19a}$$

where $\Gamma_{NaR}^{(1)}$ is the surface excess of the radical R *in all forms*, $\Gamma_{RF}^{(1)}$ is the surface excess of that part of the radical R which is present as R^- ions and $M^{(n-m)-}$ and $X^{(q-p)-}$ micelles (*i.e.*, it excludes that part which is combined as BR), and $\bar{n}^\alpha$ is the total amount of the radical R (in all forms) which is present in the α phase. As in the case of the ion exchange adsorption which was discussed on p. 95, we can say that, since $d\mu_W/d\bar{n}^\alpha$ must be negative, one or both of $d\mu_{BR}/d\bar{n}^\alpha$ and $d(\mu_{Na} + \mu_Y)/d\bar{n}^\alpha$ must be positive, but not necessarily both. $\Gamma_{NaR}^{(1)}$ is positive, and it can again be shown, on the grounds of the physical picture involved, that $(\Gamma_{RF}^{(1)} + \Gamma_Y^{(1)})$ is very unlikely to be negative. It can also be shown that $d(\mu_{Na} + \mu_Y)/d\bar{n}^\alpha$ cannot be negative and satisfy both (18a) and (19a). Since, however, $d\mu_{BR}/d\bar{n}^\alpha$ can be negative, it can no longer be argued rigorously that $d\gamma/d\bar{n}^\alpha$ must be negative, and it now becomes possible for $d\bar{n}^\sigma/d\bar{n}^\alpha$ to be negative, *i.e.*, for desorption to occur with increasing total concentration of NaR.

Both of the explanations advanced here for the occurrence of adsorption maxima are conjectural at present, but it seems to us that they are not

[1] Sexsmith and White, *J. Coll. Sci.*, 1959, **14**, 598.
[2] Gotshal, Rebenfeld, and White, *ibid.*, 619.

mutually exclusive, and that they are both more probable than a still further possibility, *viz.*, that there is present a strongly adsorbed impurity which *competes* with the sodium dodecyl sulphate, for example, for available sites in the solid-liquid interface, the impurity being of a lower molecular weight, or of such a molecular configuration that it occupies less surface area per unit weight. This explanation would seem to imply a rather high degree of specificity in the adsorption properties of the impurity.

11. INTERFACIAL EQUATIONS OF STATE

We have seen that the Gibbs equation predicts that the (thermo-dynamical) interfacial tension must be decreasing as the chemical potential of a component which is positively adsorbed increases. Unless the equation can be integrated, however, it does not tell us the *total* decrease of interfacial tension which corresponds to a given chemical potential or surface excess of a surface-active compound. Some information can, of course, be obtained by graphical integration of adsorption data. It follows from equation (9a), for example, that if we plot $\Gamma_A^{(1)}/a_A$ against a_A, the area under the curve between two activities will give us the total lowering in interfacial tensions between those two values. (In practice, of course, it is usually necessary to use concentrations instead of activities.) This procedure is of considerable use for estimating lowerings in solid-liquid interfacial tensions from adsorption data.

An alternative approach is to attempt a mathematical integration of Gibbs's equation, which for the present purpose we can consider in one of the following two forms, for a single surface-active solute:

$$d\gamma = -\Gamma_R^{(1)} d\mu_R \qquad (8a)$$

or

$$\frac{d\gamma}{da_\pm^\alpha} = -\frac{2RT}{a_\pm^\alpha} \Gamma_A^{(1)} \qquad (9a)$$

the first relating to an unionised surface-active compound or an ionised compound which is swamped with another electrolyte, and the second to an unswamped, completely ionised surface-active uni-univalent electrolyte.

The simplest solution of the problem is, of course, to assume that the surface excess is present as an ideal, two-dimensional solution or gas, so that we can write either

$$\mu_R = \mu_R^0 + RT \ln \Gamma_R^{(1)}$$

or

$$a_\pm^\alpha = k \Gamma_A^{(1)}$$

when we find that (8a) and (9a) can be integrated to give

$$\gamma_0 - \gamma = RT\Gamma_R^{(1)} = \pi \qquad (22)$$

or

$$\gamma_0 - \gamma = 2RT\Gamma_A^{(1)} = \pi \qquad (23)$$

where γ_0 is the interfacial tension of the solution in complete absence of R or NaA, and π is the interfacial tension lowering, usually referred to as the "surface pressure."

Equations (22) and (23) are, of course, forms of the familiar equation for the surface pressure exerted by an ideal, mobile surface film, usually written

$$\pi A = kT, \text{ or } \pi A = 2kT, \text{ respectively,}$$

where A is the area occupied by each adsorbed molecule (or ion), and k is the Boltzmann constant. Unfortunately, these equations are of very limited use for our present purposes, since they represent only the limiting case of extremely low adsorption.

A considerable number of corrected forms of (22) and (23) have been proposed. One can, for example, correct for A_0, the area occupied by each adsorbed molecule or ion at the closest possible packing:

$$\pi(A - A_0) = kT, \text{ or } \pi(A - A_0) = 2kT$$

and also for "van der Waals" forces between the adsorbed ions, as in the well-known equation proposed by Langmuir:[1]

$$(\pi - \pi_0)(A - A_0) = C$$

where C is a constant.

A more empirical equation is the Amagat type:

$$\pi = \Gamma_R^{(1)}(k_1\pi + k_2 RT)$$

where k_1 and k_2 are empirical constants.

Allowance for interionic forces in adsorbed layers of surface-active electrolytes, which presents formidable problems, has been considered by several workers.[2] The most recent of these papers, that of Haydon and Taylor, contains a useful summary of the previous literature. For our present purposes we should note especially Davies's and Phillips and Rideal's equations for the swamped and unswamped cases, respectively, in the forms given by Haydon (*loc. cit.*):

$$\pi = \frac{kT}{A - A_0} + 6 \cdot 1 \sqrt{c}\left[\sqrt{1 + \left(\frac{134}{A\sqrt{c}}\right)^2} - 1\right] \tag{24}$$

and

$$\pi = \frac{2kT}{A - A_0} + 6 \cdot 1 \sqrt{c}\left[\sqrt{1 + \left(\frac{134}{A\sqrt{c}}\right)^2} - 1\right] \tag{25}$$

where c is the concentration of the surface-active compound in the bulk phase in moles/litre.

---

[1] Langmuir, *J. Chem. Phys.*, 1933, **1**, 756.

[2] See, for example: Davies, *Proc. Roy. Soc.*, 1951, **208A**, 224; Phillips and Rideal, *Proc. Roy. Soc.*, 1955, **232A**, 159; Davies, *J. Coll. Sci.*, 1956, **11**, 377; *Proc. Roy. Soc.*, 1958, **245A**, 417, 429; Haydon, *J. Coll. Sci.*, 1958, **13**, 159; Haydon and Taylor, *Phil. Trans.*, 1960, **252**, 225.

Where the forces of interaction between the hydrocarbon chains of the adsorbed ions are small, as for example at oil-water interfaces,[1] equation (24) becomes

$$\pi = \frac{3kT}{A - A_0} - \frac{2kTA_0}{A(A - A_0)} - 6 \cdot 1 \sqrt{c}$$

which Cockbain[1] found to agree reasonably well with the experimental data for sodium dodecyl sulphate at the *n*-decane-water interface in the presence of an excess of sodium chloride.

Recently, Haydon and Taylor[2] have re-examined the derivation of equations of state which take account of interionic forces in the interfacial layer, and concluded that the earlier equations for the unswamped case fail to allow for the fact that the concentration of surface-active solute is a variable. For the case that the surface potential is not too small, and that the activity of the (unswamped) solute in the bulk phase can be set equal to the concentration, they prefer the equation

$$\pi = \frac{kT}{A - A_0} + \frac{2kT}{A}.$$

Where, on the other hand, activities and concentrations cannot be equated, it becomes necessary to do a graphical integration.

Haydon and Taylor also give experimental results for interfacial films of several solutes, including sodium dodecyl sulphate and dodecyltrimethyl-ammonium bromide, at the interface between water and petroleum ether. They interpret their results, and those of other workers, in terms of the equation just given, and of the more complicated, more general forms which involve graphical integration, the latter giving a better agreement with the experimental curves for surface pressure against area occupied per molecule.

The equations which we have been discussing apply to mobile interfacial layers. Where the adsorbed ions are at fixed sites, equation (24) becomes

$$\pi = \frac{kT}{A_0} \ln \frac{A}{A - A_0} + 6 \cdot 1 \sqrt{c} \left[\sqrt{1 + \left(\frac{134}{A \sqrt{c}} \right)^2} - 1 \right].$$

A simple equation of state which is useful for considering interfacial tension lowerings at solid-liquid interfaces, is the classical equation of Volmer and Frumkin. If we assume that our surface-active species *R* is non-ionic, or swamped with excess electrolyte, and that it is adsorbed at specific, fixed sites in the surface ("Langmuir adsorption"), then we can write for its chemical potential Fowler's expression:

$$\mu_R = \mu_R{}^0 + RT \ln \frac{\theta}{1 - \theta}.$$

[1] Cockbain, *Trans. Faraday Soc.*, 1954, **50**, 874.
[2] Haydon and Taylor, *Phil. Trans.*, 1960, **252**, 225.

where θ is the fraction of available sites occupied, so that $\theta = \Gamma_R^{(1)}/\Gamma_{RS}^{(1)}$, where $\Gamma_{RS}^{(1)}$ is the "saturation value" of the surface excess. When this equation is differentiated, combined with (8a) to eliminate $d\mu_R$, and integrated, one obtains

$$\pi = RT\,\Gamma_{RS}^{(1)} \ln \frac{\Gamma_{RS}^{(1)}}{\Gamma_{RS}^{(1)} - \Gamma_R^{(1)}}$$

$$= RT\,\Gamma_{RS}^{(1)} \ln \frac{1}{1-\theta}$$

$$= \frac{kT}{A_0} \ln \frac{A}{A - A_0} \qquad (26)$$

where A_0 is the area occupied by each molecule on a saturated surface.

Further illustrations are given by Davies of the derivation of equations of state by combining Gibbs's equation with various adsorption isotherms, which give us working relationships between the activity (or concentration) and the surface excess in equations such as (9a), (9b) or (9c). This general approach will, we believe, prove to be very useful, especially with unionised surface-active agents, or surface-active electrolytes which have been swamped with other electrolytes.

12. THE ADSORPTION OF SURFACE-ACTIVE MACROMOLECULES

So far in the present chapter we have been considering the amphipathic or specific adsorption of relatively small molecules, typified by the frequently investigated case of the adsorption of sodium dodecyl sulphate from aqueous solutions at various types of interfaces. When, however, we consider the adsorption of *macromolecules*, which is the basis of most cases of protective colloid action (*cf.* Chapters 4, 6 and 7), we find that the situation is much more complicated and the picture quite different. A full discussion of interfacial films of macromolecules, which would take us well into the fields of polymers and proteins, is beyond the scope of this book, but a summary* of the main differences between such films and those of conventional amphipathic agents must be included. At the same time, it must be pointed out that there is no sharp distinction between the two types: for example the higher condensates of ethylene oxide with alkyl

---

* A good summary of surface films of polymers has been published by Crisp in *Surface Phenomena in Chemistry and Biology*, edited by Danielli, Pankhurst, and Riddiford, Pergamon Press, 1958, p. 23. This includes a large number of references. Among shorter papers which are also useful in the present connection are those of Ullman, Koral, and Eirich, *Second Congress*, **III**, p. 485 (1957), Rideal, *J. Polymer Sci.*, 1955, **16**, 531, and Davies, *J. Coll. Sci.*, 1954, **Suppl. 1**, 9. Although these papers, with the exception of that of Ullman, Koral, and Eirich, deal primarily with interfacial films of *insoluble* polymers, they throw considerable light on the probable behaviour of soluble macromolecules when they are adsorbed at phase boundaries.

alcohols and amines, or the condensation products of aromatic sulphonic acids with formaldehyde, are on the borderline between "macromolecular" and conventional surface-active agents.

Certain similarities between macromolecular and conventional surface-active agents must nevertheless be noted. In the first place, macromolecules may possess *amphipathy* in the sense that a single kinetic unit may contain both hydrophobic and hydrophilic groups, as for example in the cetyl and other higher alkyl acrylate polymers, the vinyl cyclohexyl ethyl ether polymers, the sulphonated polystyrenes, and the quaternised (pyridinium) co-polymers of styrene and 4-vinylpyridine. One can also, as pointed out in Chapter 1, regard soluble polymers such as polyvinyl alcohol, and condensation products of aromatic sulphonic acids with formaldehyde, as having hydrophobic and hydrophilic "sides." It seems reasonable to assume that this amphipathy, though of a special type, can be the cause of the adsorption of such macromolecules at many interfaces. It also seems reasonable to assume that many macromolecules (especially when they function as protective colloids or flocculating agents, *cf.* Chapter 4) are adsorbed as the result of interactions between *specific* groups in the macromolecules and in the surfaces of the solids.

The three features which distinguish macromolecular surface-active materials from the conventional types, apart from their greater average molecular weight, are that (*i*) they consist of a number of structural units or segments, which are linked together in such a way that they usually possess appreciable degrees of internal freedom; (*ii*) each macromolecule usually contains a number of possible points which can become attached to external (especially solid) phases, and (*iii*) macromolecules are capable of forming more highly condensed interfacial structures by virtue of multiple lateral adhesions or "entanglements" between adsorbed molecules. All these factors obviously make for slower adsorption, and in general for considerably smaller lowerings of boundary tensions than those caused by conventional surface-active agents, but they tend to give stronger, thicker, and more stable (more "robust") interfacial films.

The "segmentation" of surface-active macromolecules means that, in general, they do not behave consistently either as single "molecules" of very large molecular weight, nor as fully independent small units, but in an intermediate fashion. They may under certain conditions of surface pressure or surface concentration, approximate to one or other of these two pictures, but the amount of internal freedom can vary widely, depending *inter alia* on how far the polymer in question is linear or cross-linked, on the nature of the bonds between segments, on the presence of bulky groups in the segments which may hinder free rotation, on the nature of the polar groups (in particular on whether or not they are ionised), and on the nature of the two phases which meet at the interface in question. All these factors, taken with the considerable chemical heterogeneity of nearly all polymers, make it very doubtful in many cases whether the adsorption of a soluble macromolecule at an interface can be safely interpreted in terms of the Gibbs equation: it is usually very difficult, for example, even to decide on how to define the molecular weight, or the surface excess.

The presence of multiple attachment points in most polymers which are adsorbed at solid-liquid interfaces means that they are capable of being very strongly held, and that the attainment of equilibrium (especially when equilibrium is approached *via* desorption) may be exceedingly slow. As we shall see in Chapter 4, this is conducive to good protective colloid action. This multiplicity of points of attachment also frequently favours protective colloid action by leading to the formation of very thick interfacial films. If, for example, some of the polar groups in a macromolecule are attached to the surface of a solid by specific linkages of some sort, the others may extend for some distance into the medium, frequently causing the polymer to uncoil, and giving a high degree of "steric protection" to dispersed particles. (At very low concentrations, this type of adsorption may lead to "bridging" between these particles, causing flocculation; this is also discussed in Chapter 4.)

The stability of films of adsorbed macromolecules may also be increased by the considerable possibility of lateral adhesions and interactions among them. This effect, an extreme example of which is the "surface denaturation" of proteins, is important in determining the suitability of soluble macromolecules for stabilising liquid-liquid and liquid-gas interfaces in emulsions and foams, respectively.

Although, as we have pointed out above, the Gibbs equation is of very limited applicability with soluble polymers, other thermodynamical analyses of adsorption data may be very useful. Such an analysis is given by Ullman, Koral, and Eirich, to explain the fact that the adsorption isotherms for a vinyl acetate polymer from carbon tetrachloride on to iron powder, although regular in shape, lie at *higher* values at higher temperatures, which means that the adsorption process must be *endothermic*. They explain this in terms of the change in the total Gibbs free energy of the system when adsorption occurs, as follows. The change in free energy ΔG, given by

$$\Delta G = \Delta H - T \Delta S$$

where ΔH is the heat of adsorption, and S is the total entropy of the system, must of course be negative. When each polymer molecule is adsorbed, its entropy (translational, rotational, and vibrational) will decrease. If, however, it is adsorbed on to several adsorption sites, a number of solvent molecules will be displaced, and each of these will gain translational entropy. Since the solvent molecules are independent once they are desorbed, this gain in entropy will far outweigh that lost by the polymer, so that ΔS is positive, and ΔG can be negative, even though ΔH is positive.

This argument seems to us to be of considerable importance to the theory of how soluble surface-active macromolecules are adsorbed at solid-liquid interfaces. This postulated large increase in total entropy, when several solvent molecules are displaced from the interface by one macro-molecule, may well help to explain why soluble macromolecules exhibit such a *general* deflocculating and protective colloid action at such a wide variety of solid-liquid interfaces—*i.e.*, why they appear to be so generally adsorbed—since its effect would be to magnify the effect of relatively weak individual attachments to the surface.

Although, as we have pointed out above, it is doubtful that the Gibbs equation can be used quite generally for interpreting the adsorption of macromolecules, especially at solid-liquid interfaces, it has been used with considerable success by Katchalsky and Miller[1] in considering the adsorption of polymethacrylic acids, of degrees of polymerisation between 500 and 8,000, at the air-water interface. They found that the surface activity decreased with increasing molecular weight of the polymer, the lowering of surface tension $\Delta\gamma$ for each case being given by $\Delta\gamma = \text{const.}/\sqrt{P}$ where P is the degree of polymerisation. For a given value of P, the surface tension fell linearly with the logarithm of the concentration (as happens over certain concentration ranges with smaller surface-active molecules), lowerings of up to 3·9 dynes/cm. being measured. On the assumptions that the surface excess $\Gamma^{(1)}$ resides substantially completely in a monolayer of polymer, that the chemical potential of the polymer is given by $d\mu_b = kTd\ln v_b$ (where v_b is the volume fraction of the polymer in the solution), and that the standard free energy of adsorption is not too small, Katchalsky and Miller obtained the relation

$$\Delta\gamma = \frac{\delta kT}{Pw}(0\cdot5772 + \phi/kT + \ln v_b) = A + B\ln v_b \qquad (27)$$

where δ is the thickness of the adsorbed layer, w is the volume of each monomer unit, P is the degree of polymerisation, and ϕ is the change of standard free energy when the polymer is adsorbed.

Katchalsky and Miller used this equation to estimate values of δ for different degrees of polymerisation, and found that they were close to the independently calculated values of the mean diameters of the randomly coiled polymeric molecules. From equation (27) they derived the expression

$$A/B = 0\cdot5772 + \phi/kT$$

which enabled them to calculate values of ϕ from the experimental data: the value of ϕ/kT proved to be 9·18, independent of the molecular

[1] Katchalsky and Miller, *J. Phys. Chem.*, 1951, **55**, 1182.

weight of the polymer. This indicated, since the energy of adsorption of a

$$(. \ . \ . \ CH_2 \cdot C(CH_3) \ . \ . \ .)$$
$$|$$
$$COOH$$

group is about $2 \cdot 5 \, kT$, that about three or four monomeric units are adsorbed in the surface.

Katchalsky and Miller found that the surface activity of polymethacrylic acid at air-water interfaces fell steeply as the degree of ionisation was increased by raising the pH of the solution. The decrease was linear at low degrees of ionisation, and the surface activity became negligible at about 40% ionisation. They interpreted this on the assumption that the standard free energy of adsorption of the polymer molecule is made up of two additive parts, ϕ_0 and ϕ_i, for the unionised and ionised groups, respectively, connected by the relation

$$\phi = (1 - \alpha)\phi_0 + \alpha\phi_i$$

where α is the degree of ionisation. Depressing the degree of ionisation by adding sodium chloride had the expected effect of increasing the surface activity.

Katchalsky and Miller also made some interesting observations of the behaviour of adsorbed layers of polymethacrylic acid. Material which was adsorbed from solution showed no tendency to form surface layers which could be detected on a Langmuir trough, while material which had been spread on the trough from alcoholic solution showed no tendency to pass into solution at low surface pressures. This is attributable to the existence of an energy barrier between the "spread" material (present as unfolded molecules lying flat on the water) and the "adsorbed" material (which is still coiled). For the case of a 15% ionised molecule, this barrier was estimated to be of the order of magnitude of $1,000 \, kT$.

It will be appreciated that Katchalsky and Miller's picture of the adsorption of polymethacrylic acid at the air-water interface, at which specific interactions between the macromolecules and the external phase are excluded, could not be expected to apply *in toto* to the behaviour of water-soluble polymers at *solid-liquid* interfaces, as for example in cases of protective colloid action. This work, nevertheless, yields valuable information on what might be termed the *non-specific* aspect of the adsorption of soluble macromolecules.

Several equations of state have been proposed as a result of the considerable amount of work which has been done on insoluble polymer interfacial layers, spread at both air-water and oil-water interfaces, which is summarised in the papers cited above. The most interesting of these equations for our purposes is that of Singer:

$$\frac{\pi A_0}{kT} = \frac{(x-1)}{x} \frac{z}{2} \ln \left[1 - \frac{2A_0}{zA} \right] - \ln \left[1 - \frac{A_0}{A} \right]$$

where π is the surface pressure, A_0 is the area occupied by each polymer segment in the closely packed film, k is Boltzmann's constant, x is the number of segments per polymer molecule, and z is the "co-ordination number" of each segment in the postulated two-dimensional lattice which makes up the interface. When $z = 2$, each segment has exactly two positions in which its two neighbours must fit, so that the chain is inflexible; the flexibility can be defined, according to Davies, by $\omega = z - 2$.

By the use of Singer's equation, estimates have been made of the flexibility of a number of insoluble polymers in adsorbed layers, in terms of ω. These numbers vary considerably, from 1·3–2·0 for typical methacrylate polymers, to 0·5 for polyvinyl alcohol, 0·2 for cellulose triacetate, and 0·15 for ovalbumin, all at air-water interfaces. It seems reasonable to deduce from results such as these that, qualitatively speaking, the polymer "skeletons" in question will give similar orders of flexibility in interfacial layers containing soluble polymers—provided that there have not been changes such as the introduction of very bulky groups. This flexibility would be expected to be one of the factors which determine the properties of soluble macromolecules, in particular, protective colloid action and other properties which depend on the mechanical stabilisation of interfaces.

B. The kinetics of the adsorption of surface-active agents at interfaces

In the preceding sections it has been pointed out that surface-active agents may alter interfacial tensions considerably, and that the extent, and under very special conditions the direction, of these changes may not always agree with the results anticipated from a cursory examination of Gibbs's equation. Before considering the practical results of changes in interfacial free energies, however, it should be recalled that the preceding arguments were all of necessity based on the assumption that equilibrium had been reached, *i.e.*, that either an interface was formed infinitely slowly during a particular process, or else that sufficient time had elapsed to allow the interfacial tensions to reach their final values. In many technical processes it is fairly certain that not all the interfaces involved will in fact have reached equilibrium—thus in many wetting processes the air-liquid interface, for example, will be continually formed afresh during the process. It is accordingly to be expected that, although there may often be a general parallelism between high technical effectiveness and high equilibrium surface-activity, the correlation may be by no means perfect, and that due allowance must be made for the velocity of adsorption at the interfaces involved in the particular process. It is therefore unfortunate that, for the great majority

of surface-active processes, there is no exact information as to the rate at
which the relevant interfacial tensions change with time, though a number
of qualitative observations or predictions can be made.

It has been known for some time that the surface tensions of aqueous
solutions against air change with time: thus Lord Rayleigh showed in 1890
that the surface tensions of soap solutions fall considerably as they age.
Subsequent work can be conveniently considered with reference to two
distinct phenomena: (a) a rapid ageing of many freshly-formed surfaces,
which usually appears to be complete in a few seconds at most, and (b) a
slower ageing effect which may last for several days or weeks.

1. Rapid surface-ageing phenomena

The first comprehensive and systematic experimental work in this field
is Addison's[1] study of the dynamic surface tensions of aqueous solutions of
a series of aliphatic alcohols by means of the method of the vibrating jet.
Although most of the alcohols which he studied are not to be considered as
very effective surface-active agents, his work is of considerable interest to
the present monograph in that it reveals the general nature of the time-
dependence of the surface tension of solutions during rapid surface-ageing
phenomena.

Addison studied aqueous solutions of methyl, ethyl, *n*-propyl, *n*-butyl,
n-amyl, isoamyl, *n*-hexyl, *tert.*-hexyl, *n*-heptyl, *n*-octyl, and iso-octyl
alcohols, and found that equilibrium was established so rapidly with the
alcohols up to and including the butyl, that no ageing could be detected
by the experimental method used. A measurable time-lag was found with
the other members of the series, the surface tensions falling continuously
from that of pure water to the final equilibrium values. For full details,
reference should be made to Addison's papers; the table on top of
p. 115 gives some typical figures for the time required for the surface
tension to reach the final equilibrium values (within the experimental
error).

The rate at which equilibrium was attained with a given alcohol was
also found by Addison to be greater the greater the concentration.

A theoretical treatment of even the relatively simple cases studied by
Addison is not easy. The most important question is whether the rate-
determining process is a simple diffusion of surface-active solute from the
interior of the solution to the interface, or whether the velocity of attainment of equilibrium is determined by processes involving activation at
energy barriers in the system, orientation in the surface layer, or other
effects which are likely to be highly specific to the nature of the surface-
active molecule. In considering this question, Addison introduced the concept of the "migrational velocity" of the solute molecules, *i.e.*, the mean

---

[1] Addison, *J. Chem. Soc.*, 1943, 535; 1944, 252, 477; 1945, 98, 354; *Nature*, 1945,
156, 600; *Phil. Mag.*, 1945, **36**, 73.

Table 4

Rapid ageing of the surfaces of aqueous solutions of aliphatic alcohols— Times required for the establishment of the equilibrium surface tension

(from Addison's data, *J. Chem. Soc.*, 1945, 103)

Alcohol	Concentration (%)	Time for establishment of equilibrium (secs.)
n-Amyl	0·10	0·023
do.	0·20	0·016
do.	0·40	0·012
n-Hexyl	0·03	0·055
do.	0·18	0·023
tert.-Hexyl	0·14	0·019
n-Heptyl	0·08	0·029
n-Octyl	0·03	0·052

velocity at which they travel to the surface. By applying the Gibbs equation (convention 1) to the *equilibrium* surface tension-concentration curves (perforce identifying activities and concentrations, which seems to be quite justified at the low concentrations of non-electrolytes involved), Addison calculated the total surface excesses, $\Gamma_2^{(1)}$'s, at various concentrations. He then supposed that these excesses were drawn from a disc of unit cross-sectional area placed with one face in the surface. On this assumption he then calculated the thickness d of this disc from the values of $\Gamma_2^{(1)}$ and the bulk concentrations, using the equation $d = \Gamma_2^{(1)}/c_2$, where c_2 is the bulk concentration in moles/c.c. Addison then assumed that surface equilibrium was established when the last of the molecules initially in the disc had reached the surface, and obtained the "migrational velocity" by dividing d by the time just required for the attainment of equilibrium. The value of the (mean) "migrational velocity" thus calculated was found to be characteristic of each aliphatic alcohol studied, and to be independent, within the experimental error, of the concentration. Addison considers that this is evidence that "migration is at least the major (if not the only) factor determining surface tension changes over the experimental range of surface ages."

A further interesting characteristic of Addison's "migrational velocity" is that, in a homologous series of straight-chain alcohols, it increases with increasing chain length and is lower (for a given number of carbon atoms) if the aliphatic chain is branched. This leads to the suggestion that the driving force behind the transport of solute to the interface is what Addison calls the "free energy of the surface," $(\gamma_t - \gamma_E)$, where γ_t is the surface tension at time t, and γ_E is the equilibrium value.

The convention evolved by Addison for expressing his experimental results is as follows. It is assumed, as indicated above, that the rate-determining process is one of simple diffusion, the solute which is adsorbed being treated as if drawn from the flat cylinder of thickness d and unit cross section. At any instant during the diffusion process, all the molecules in this cylinder are assumed to be moving towards the surface with a uniform velocity v, though v will of course vary with the time; the "migrational velocity" will therefore be the time-average value of v. It is further assumed that, for any given alcohol, a given value of the surface tension corresponds to a definite value of $\Gamma_2^{(1)}$ (the surface excess of the solute), even though equilibrium has not been reached. This assumption enables values to be calculated for $\dfrac{d\Gamma_2^{(1)}}{dt}$ from the surface tension-time curves, and from the concentration and the assumptions previously made, v is obtained and plotted as a function of time for different concentrations of the surface-active agents. Addison finds that the resulting v–t curves obey an equation of the form

$$v = a^n t e^{-akt}$$

in which k and n are constants which are characteristic of the alcohol (and of its chain length), and a is a function of concentration. Since certain relationships are found between these constants and the chain length of the straight-chain alcohols, Addison suggests that this equation can be used for extrapolating to alcohols of greater chain length, or even to compounds of similar chain length such as decanoic acid.

The great value of Addison's experimental work is not, in the present authors' opinion, diminished by the fact that his first theoretical treatment does not present an acceptable physical picture.* A more satisfactory theoretical treatment is Ward and Tordai's[1] examination of the question whether or not simple diffusion can be the rate-determining process in the rapid ageing of surfaces. Their picture of a simple diffusion to the surface is that, when a surface is formed, equilibrium is established instantaneously between the physical surface and the "sub-surface," which is that portion of the bulk solution, a few molecules thick, which lies immediately below the surface. As a result, the concentration in the sub-surface falls practically to zero immediately, on account of the fact that initially all the solute molecules reaching the surface are accommodated in it. Thereafter, as the surface accommodates a continually decreasing fraction of the molecules reaching it, the concentration of the sub-surface increases until, at equilibrium, it is equal to that of the bulk of the solution (which is considered to be an inexhaustible reservoir of solute molecules). During this stage there will be a complicated set of diffusion and back-diffusion processes between the surface, the sub-surface, and the bulk of

---

* The authors are indebted to Dr. Addison for the explanation that his method of interpreting the results is intended as a convenient mathematical description, rather than as a definite physical picture of the mechanism of diffusion. For example, he does not intend his treatment to imply that all the solute molecules inside the cylinder of thickness d are in fact moving towards the surface with identical velocities at a given instant. (See also Addison and Hutchinson, *J. Chem. Soc.*, 1949, 3391.)

[1] Ward and Tordai, *J. Chem. Phys.*, 1946, **14**, 453.

the solution, which Ward and Tordai consider in some detail. For the early stages, when back-diffusion from the sub-surface to the bulk is negligible, they obtain Langmuir and Schaefer's[1] equation for diffusion into unilayers, viz.,

$$M = \int_0^t \left(\frac{\partial M}{\partial t}\right)_{x=0} dt = 2n_0 \left(\frac{Dt}{\pi}\right)^{\frac{1}{2}} \tag{28}$$

where x is the distance from the surface, t is the time, n_0 is the bulk concentration of solute (which is constant), M is its surface concentration, and D is the diffusion coefficient.

For the more general case in which back-diffusion is not negligible, Ward and Tordai obtain an extended form of equation (28), viz.,

$$M = 2n_0 \left(\frac{Dt}{\pi}\right)^{\frac{1}{2}} - 2 \left(\frac{Dt}{\pi}\right)^{\frac{1}{2}} \int_0^{(t_E)^{\frac{1}{2}}} \phi(t) d(t_E - t)^{\frac{1}{2}} \tag{29}$$

in which $\phi(t)$ is the concentration of the sub-surface at time t, and t_E is the time required for the surface to come to equilibrium.

The second term on the right-hand side of equation (29) allows for back-diffusion; since it is not capable of explicit integration, Ward and Tordai evaluate it graphically by employing a special physical picture, in order to test the assumption that diffusion is the rate-determining process. If it is assumed that there is no activation barrier between the sub-surface and the surface, then it follows that the time required for diffusion of solute from the sub-surface to the surface is much smaller than that for diffusion from the bulk of the solution to the sub-surface: *i.e.*, at any instant the surface and sub-surface can be considered to be in equilibrium with respect to the solute. Ward and Tordai next assume that the observed surface tension is determined by the concentration of solute in the surface, and that this is in turn determined by $\phi(t)$; consequently they consider that, for a given value of γ *during* the diffusion, $\phi(t)$ will be equal to the concentration of a bulk solution which exhibits the same surface tension at equilibrium—*i.e.*, a relationship is established between $\phi(t)$ and γ by using the equilibrium surface tension-concentration curve. This relationship enables $\phi(t)$ to be plotted against time, and the integral in (29) is obtained graphically between $t = 0$ and $t = t_E$. Substitution in (29) gives M in terms of the diffusion constant D, but since M is simply $\Gamma_2^{(1)}$ of the solute, which can be obtained from the surface tension-concentration curve by applying Gibbs's equation, it is possible to calculate D.*

Ward and Tordai have calculated the diffusion coefficient D for the series of fatty alcohols from Addison's data and find that the value for

* In the absence of exact activity values, it is necessary to use concentrations in Gibbs's equation. As Ward and Tordai point out, however, these are sufficiently accurate for the purpose at low concentrations.

[1] Langmuir and Schaefer, *J. Amer. Chem. Soc.*, 1937, **59**, 2400.

isoamyl alcohol (0.141×10^{-6} cm.^{2}/sec.) is lower than the diffusion co-efficient in bulk solution determined by Thovert,[1] which is 7.9×10^{-6} cm.^{2}/sec., corrected for the difference in temperature. Moreover, the diffusion constants for the other alcohols, as determined from Addison's data, increase with increasing chain length, whereas they should decrease if a simple diffusion process were determining the rate of attainment of equilibrium. Ward and Tordai therefore conclude, especially on the grounds of this latter fact, that diffusion is not the rate-determining process, and that an activation barrier must exist.

The magnitude of the energy barrier which must be surmounted during the diffusion of surface-active molecules to the surfaces of aqueous solutions has been considered by Blair.[2] In the first place he assumes that the energy barrier is constant, and that the surface film obeys a two-dimensional Amagat equation

$$F = N(FJ + LkT)$$

in which F is the surface pressure (defined by $F = \gamma_0 - \gamma$, where γ is the surface tension of the solution and γ_0 is the surface tension of pure water at the same temperature and pressure), N is the number of molecules of solute per square centimetre of surface, J and L are constants, k is the Boltzmann constant, and T is the absolute temperature. Under conditions at which back-diffusion is negligible, Blair obtains the equation

$$e^{\lambda/kT} = \frac{2n_0(FJ + LkT)}{F} \left(\frac{Dt}{\pi}\right)^{\frac{1}{2}} \tag{30}$$

where λ is the energy barrier, n_0 is the bulk concentration of the solute, and D is the diffusion constant. Applying Addison's data for surfaces at which adsorption is half complete, he obtains values for the magnitude of the energy barrier such as the following:

isoamyl alcohol (0.122%): 1930 cal./mole
     ,,   ,,   (0.406%): 2010 cal./mole
n-hexyl alcohol (0.05 %): 1360 cal./mole
     ,,   ,,   (0.20 %): 1350 cal./mole
n-heptyl alcohol (0.02 %): 690 cal./mole
     ,,   ,,   (0.06 %): 710 cal./mole

Blair also considers the more complicated case of an energy barrier which is not constant, but which varies with the surface pressure, viz.

$$\lambda = (A + BF)kT$$

where A and B are constants, and the surface pressure F is again determined by an Amagat relation. He finds that for isoamyl alcohol the value of the barrier is given by

$$\lambda = 1860 + 23F \text{ (at } 20° \text{ c.),}$$

[1] Thovert, *Ann. d. Physik*, (9), 1914, **2**, 369.
[2] Blair, *J. Chem. Phys.*, 1948, **16**, 113.

so that the values calculated on these assumptions are:

isoamyl alcohol (0·122%): 1959 cal./mole
„   „   (0·406%): 2095 cal./mole

A further important series of experimental papers has been published by Addison and his co-workers,[1] who describe the use of several additional techniques for following the properties of ageing surfaces: Wilhelmy's vertical plate method, the dynamic drop weight method, a contracting (as distinct from a vibrating) jet technique, a dynamic pendant drop method, a method based on the measurement of stationary waves when a jet impinges on a plane, and methods for studying expanding and contracting surfaces. The most interesting papers of this series as regards our present subject are those on the surface tension of expanding drops of solutions of sodium dodecyl sulphate, and on determinations of the energy barriers in solutions of a series of aliphatic alcohols.

In the first of these two papers, Addison and Hutchinson[2] determined the surface tensions of solutions of sodium dodecyl sulphate at different concentrations, in drops which were expanding at different rates. They found that the surface tension increased with the rate of expansion of the surface, rapidly at first, but eventually approaching a constant value at higher rates of expansion. The difference between these limiting "expanding" values and the static values depended on the concentration, increasing to a maximum difference of about 9 dynes/cm. just below the critical concentration range for micelle formation, and thereafter decreasing rapidly to about 2 dynes/cm. A similar effect was observed with the interfacial tension between aqueous solutions of sodium dodecyl sulphate and toluene, except that the effect of rate of expansion was less pronounced. Addison and Hutchinson attributed this time effect to re-orientation of the adsorbed molecules in the interface.

Blair's equation (30) for the size of the energy barrier was used by Addison and Hutchinson[3] in interpreting their experimental data for decyl and other aliphatic alcohols. Their measurements by the dynamic vertical plate method give the following values:

n-octyl alcohol (0·02 %): 378 cal./mole
n-decyl alcohol (0·002%): 176 cal./mole

Curves are also given for the size of the energy barrier as a function of chain length in a series of aliphatic alcohols (C_5–C_{10}): the barrier decreases with

---

[1] Addison, *J. Chem. Soc.*, 1946, 579; Addison and Hutchinson, *ibid.*, 1948, 930; Addison, Bagot, and McCauley, *ibid.*, 1948, 936; Addison and Elliott, *ibid.*, 1949, 2789; Addison and Hutchinson, *ibid.*, 1948, 943; 1949, 3387, 3395, 3404, 3406; Addison and Elliott, *ibid.*, 1950, 3090, 3096, 3103.

[2] Addison and Hutchinson, *J. Chem. Soc.*, 1948, 943.

[3] Addison and Hutchinson, *J. Chem. Soc.*, 1949, 3387.

increasing chain length, the curves being concave upwards rather than linear.

The vibrating jet method of Addison and co-workers has been further investigated by Rideal and Sutherland,[1] who made a careful re-examination of the theory of the method, as well as a number of measurements on aqueous solutions of n-heptanol and 3-methyl-1-butanol. Their work shows quite clearly that *convection* plays a considerable part in the transport of surface-active material to the interface, the rate at which the surface tension falls with time being dependent on the actual orifice used and on the jet velocity. Their analysis of the data also shows that liquid motions due to oscillation and to differences in surface pressure along the jet are significant, though the latter effect is not predominant. They find that 3-methyl-1-butanol molecules accumulate at the interface more slowly than would be expected from simple diffusion, whereas heptanol and octanol accumulate more rapidly; they deduce from this that molecules of *all* alcohols are hindered on entering the interface, but that with heptanol and octanol, for example, the effect of movements of liquid predominate.

The problem is further considered in a review by Sutherland.[2] He concludes that convection in the jet methods (and all other experimental techniques which produce a flow of liquid) renders them unreliable for elucidating the kinetics of adsorption of surface-active materials, and prefers the method of Addison and Hutchinson,[3] in which the surface of the solution is swept with a barrier and the fall of surface tension with time is followed with a Wilhelmy balance. (The surface ages are inevitably greater than with the vibrating jet technique.) Even with this method, however, Sutherland concludes that convection occurs, probably as the result of evaporation at the surface, which sets up convection "Bénard cells." Sutherland examines a number of possible physical pictures of the system, those in which stirring occurs being (i) a quiescent layer above a stirred interior, (ii) the same, with an energy barrier at the surface which hinders the entry of surface-active molecules, and (iii) a completely stirred system, with an energy barrier. For aqueous solutions of n-decanol, the data of Addison and Hutchinson give reasonable agreement with the rates calculated theoretically for all three pictures. When, however, the data of Guastalla and Saraga[4] and of Saraga[5] are examined, for the desorption of lauric acid from a monolayer at constant pressure, Sutherland finds that only picture (ii) is applicable, an activation energy of about 16 RT being required to fit the results. Sutherland suggests that it is important in

---

[1] Rideal and Sutherland, *Trans. Faraday Soc.*, 1952, **48**, 1109.

[2] Sutherland, *Australian Journal of Scientific Research*, 1952, **5A**, 683.

[3] Addison and Hutchinson, *J. Chem. Soc.*, 1949, 3387.

[4] Guastalla and Saraga, *Surface Chemistry* (Supplement to *Research*), Butterworth, 1949, p. 103.

[5] Saraga, *Comptes rend.*, 1950, **231**, 46.

such measurements to work with as shallow layers of solution as possible in order to minimise cell convection.

The Wilhelmy balance method has also been used by Dervichian[1] to follow the change of surface tension with time of dilute aqueous solutions of a series of C_6–C_{11} fatty acids. He found an induction time, the value of which was smaller the greater the concentration, after which the surface tension fell rapidly, and then approached the constant equilibrium value for that concentration. (The equilibrium values showed an initial rapid fall with concentration, and then became sensibly constant.) Dervichian interprets these results (which are on a still longer time scale than those of Addison and Hutchinson or Guastalla and Saraga), expressed as surface excesses calculated from the Gibbs equation, in terms of activation energies of adsorption and desorption. Thus he uses an "adsorption coefficient" A, and a "desorption coefficient" D, in the equations

$$\frac{d\Gamma_a^{(1)}}{dt} = Ac$$

and

$$\frac{d\Gamma_d^{(1)}}{dt} = D\Gamma^{(1)}$$

where $\dfrac{d\Gamma_a^{(1)}}{dt}$ and $\dfrac{d\Gamma_d^{(1)}}{dt}$ are the rates of adsorption and desorption, respectively, and c is the bulk concentration. When the calculated values of A are plotted against $\Gamma^{(1)}$, the curve is at first horizontal, after which there is a sharp rise, followed by a flat maximum and a steep fall. The plot of calculated D values against $\Gamma^{(1)}$ is similar, except that there is a fairly sharp maximum. Dervichian concludes that the molecules being adsorbed must overcome an energy barrier which is due to their competing for place in the interface, while molecules which are being desorbed must overcome an energy barrier which is due to cohesional forces among the adsorbed molecules.

Some of the most comprehensive data on the dynamic surface tensions of *technically important* surface-active agents have been obtained by Burcik,[2] by Burcik and Vaughn,[3] and by Burcik and Newman,[4] using the vibrating jet technique of Addison and co-workers. Their results can be summarised as follows. On a time scale from 0 to about 0·03 seconds, the surface tension of pure sodium laurate, sodium dodecyl sulphate, and sodium oleate fell from the value for pure water by amounts varying from about 20 dynes/cm. to about 40 dynes/cm. As would be expected, the surface tension falls more rapidly at first, and then levels off, the equilibrium value never being

[1] Dervichian, *Koll. Z.*, 1956, **146**, 96.
[2] Burcik, *J. Coll. Sci.*, 1950, **5**, 421; 1953, **8**, 520.
[3] Burcik and Vaughn, *J. Coll. Sci.*, 1951, **6**, 522.
[4] Burcik and Newman, *ibid.*, 1954, **9**, 498.

reached in the times in question. The surface tension falls more rapidly at higher concentrations, and the fall is accelerated by the presence of ordinary electrolytes. These show a marked "valency effect": the rate of fall of surface tension of solutions of sodium dodecyl sulphate is increased by the presence of multivalent *cations* (Mg^{++}), but that of sodium laurate solutions is uninfluenced by multivalent anions ($SO_4^=$). With a cationic agent (dodecyl pyridinium chloride), on the other hand, sodium sulphate has a greater accelerating effect than sodium chloride, but magnesium chloride and lanthanum chloride are no more effective than sodium chloride. In harmony with these findings, the non-ionic agent "Tween 20" (*cf.* p. 473) is relatively unaffected by the presence of sodium chloride. With sodium laurate, the surface tension falls more rapidly as the temperature is raised, from $9 \cdot 2°$ to $29 \cdot 4°$ c.

Burcik and Vaughn found that the rate of decrease of surface tension of solutions of hydrolysable surface-active agents is greater if the pH is adjusted in the direction which suppresses hydrolysis, even though such a change in pH gives higher equilibrium values: thus increasing the pH of $0 \cdot 005$ N sodium myristate solutions accelerates markedly the fall in surface tension, but increases the equilibrium value from $23 \cdot 8$ to $30 \cdot 8$ dynes/cm., while the opposite holds true for $0 \cdot 01$ N dodecylamine hydrochloride. In conformity with this picture, the pH has no significant effect on the rate of fall of surface tension of $0 \cdot 005$ N sodium dodecyl sulphate solutions.

Burcik and Newman found that substances such as dodecyl alcohol and lauric acid, which form complex micelles with sodium dodecyl sulphate, decrease the rate of fall of surface tension, whereas decane, which does not form a complex and gives a cloudy solution, has no significant effect.

These results of Burcik and his co-workers lead to a clear qualitative picture of diffusion against an energy barrier which is due to electrostatic repulsion between adsorbed surface-active ions and the surface-active ions which are approaching the interface, this barrier being reduced (with a valency effect) by the presence of ordinary electrolytes. Diffusion is also slowed down by the formation of micelles of the surface-active electrolyte, this aggregation being increased by partial hydrolysis of the surface-active electrolyte, or by the addition of substances with which it forms mixed micelles. The practical importance of the results is scarcely affected by the fact that, in the technique used, stirring (as distinct from diffusion) will have contributed to the transport of surface-active material to the immediate vicinity of the interface, though not, one would imagine, to its entry through any energy barrier into the interface.* Stirring, it will be recalled,

---

* These remarks seem to us to apply also to the results of Addison and his co-workers and others who have used the vibrating jet. Even though stirring may have rendered their data unsuitable for elucidating the fundamental adsorption kinetics, the practical significance of their results is obvious, especially in the qualitative sense. This significance, moreover, is not affected by doubts as to the actual interfacial ages in their results, which are discussed below.

is present in the processes (spraying, foaming, wetting-out, and detergency) which the work of Burcik and others was designed to elucidate, and unless the degree of stirring in such processes is very different, their results are relevant; in any case, their value as comparisons among different surface-active agents is considerable.

Hansen, Wallace, and co-workers[1] have recently suggested that the earlier results by the vibrating jet method are significantly in error as regards the calculated surface ages near the orifices, the true ages being appreciably greater. The experimental refinements which they have introduced into the technique are (*i*) avoidance of turbulence at the orifice exit, (*ii*) elimination of stagnant regions (by "hydrophobing" the exterior of the jet with a silicone resin), and (*iii*) choosing a suitable shape of orifice, preferably a right circular cylinder. Using these precautions, they determined dynamic surface tensions of aqueous solutions of pentanoic acid, heptanoic acid, octanoic acid, and heptanol-1, and found that their data fitted the empirical relation

$$\frac{\pi}{\pi_\infty - \pi}\, e^{\frac{-b\pi}{\pi_\infty}} = k\pi_\infty^2 t$$

where π is the spreading pressure at time t, π_∞ is the spreading pressure at equilibrium, and b and k are constants for a given solute.

Hansen and Wallace did not find any mechanism of adsorption which led to the above empirical equation: thus their analysis of the results in terms of the general diffusion equation of Ward and Tordai (29) led to the conclusion that the adsorption kinetics are not diffusion-controlled, the rates of decrease of surface tension being too low. They found, however, that the results could be interpreted in terms of a second-order kinetic mechanism implying a dimeric transition state located substantially in the surface, the rate equation being given by

$$\frac{d\Gamma^{(1)}}{dt} = \frac{\beta \gamma_S C_B}{\gamma^\pm f_0}\,(\pi_\infty \gamma_S - \pi)$$

where β is the second-order rate constant, γ_S and $\gamma^\pm$ are the surface and transition state activity coefficients, respectively, C_B is the molar bulk concentration of solute, and f_0 is the reference fugacity of the solute in the surface, defined by $f_0 = \lim\limits_{C \to 0}\left(\dfrac{\pi}{C_B}\right)$. The entire treatment is based on the explicit assumption that the surface tension depends only on the surface excess $\Gamma^{(1)}$, regardless of whether or not the system is in equilibrium.

The work discussed above indicates, as we have seen, that rapid surface-ageing phenomena, which generally occur during periods of a few seconds,

---

[1] Hansen, Purchase, Wallace, and Woody, *J. Phys. Chem.*, 1958, **62**, 210; Hansen and Wallace, *ibid.*, 1959, **63**, 1085.

cannot be explained in terms of simple diffusion processes, but that these are overshadowed by special effects such as activated diffusion through energy barriers, orientation in the interface, and/or changes in the degree of association in the interface. Apart from concluding in general terms, however, that surface tensions fall more slowly than would be expected from simple diffusion, it does not appear possible at present to decide what is responsible for this slowness in every case. It must also be noted that, even before this general conclusion is accepted without qualification, one point still requires elucidation. Fordham[1] has pointed out the lack of complete rigour when the Gibbs equation is used for calculating instantaneous surface excesses from dynamic (*i.e.*, non-equilibrium) surface tension values, these surface excesses then being used in examining various mathematical formulations of the problem. This lack of rigour arises from the fact that the Gibbs equation (as we have seen earlier in the present chapter) takes no account of temporary concentration deficiencies in the region immediately below the physical interface (what we might call the "fine structure" of the surface phase), but relates only to overall differences between the amount of surface-active solute in the actual system and in a hypothetical system in which compositions are uniform up to an abrupt transition at the physical interface. Fordham draws attention to the extreme case of moving the boundary between the α and σ phases (Guggenheim convention) to infinite distance from the physical interface, which is permissible in using the Gibbs equation, but leads, when the kinetics of adsorption are considered, to the absurd conclusion that the surface tension could never decrease. Under the assumption that free energy barriers are completely absent, Fordham derives some approximate expressions for the corrections to be applied when surface excesses are calculated from non-equilibrium surface tension values by means of the Gibbs equation: the values obtained for Addison and Hutchinson's data for $0 \cdot 001\%$ decyl alcohol are of the right order to explain the rates of adsorption without invoking special energy barriers.

It remains to be seen how important is Fordham's *caveat*. If it is shown that the surface tension can be considered to be due to the amount of adsorbed material actually in a monomolecular layer, the concentration of the sub-surface being of little or no importance in the non-equilibrium case, and identical with the bulk concentration in the equilibrium case, the orientation of the adsorbed molecules being relatively unimportant, then of course the Gibbsian excesses can be used in the kinetic equations with confidence. (Some support is afforded to this view by the results of Alexander and Posner[2] on surface potentials, which suggest that, although the adsorbed molecules undergo a reorientation, this has little effect on the surface tension.) This problem is, of course, avoided if the changes of surface

---

[1] Fordham, *Trans. Faraday Soc.*, 1954, **50**, 593.

[2] Alexander and Posner, *Trans. Faraday Soc.*, 1949, **45**, 651.

excesses with time can be followed by a more direct measuremental technique, such as the radio-tracer measurements which are discussed below.

The conclusion that energy barriers to the attainment of adsorption equilibrium are present quite generally in solutions of surface-active materials, though justified by the data available to the earlier workers, may also need revision in the light of the recent series of papers by Defay and Hommelen.[1] These workers carried out measurements by the vibrating jet method on a series of aliphatic alcohols, both normal and branched-chain, and dicarboxylic acids. They found that solutions of the branched-chain heptyl and hexyl alcohols reached surface tension equilibrium inside 0·01 second, while n-heptyl and branched-chain octyl alcohols were adsorbed more slowly. They also determined dynamic surface tensions by the method of the falling meniscus. This method depends on the fact that the air-liquid meniscus in a small capillary hole is capable of supporting a column of liquid of height h_0 by virtue of the surface tension γ, these two quantities being related by the equation

$$\gamma = \frac{\rho g r}{2}\left(h_0 - \frac{2r}{3}\right)$$

where ρ is the density of the liquid, r is the radius of the capillary hole, and g is the gravitational constant. By increasing the height of the column at different rates until the meniscus broke, they were able to find γ for different surface ages. Hommelen also found that, with the solutes in question, an appreciable error could be introduced into the values for the *equilibrium* surface tension by solute evaporation at the surface, which gave values for the surface tension which were too high. (It seems unlikely that this effect will be significant with at least the great majority of technical surface-active agents, the volatility of which will be much lower than that of the compounds studied by Defay and Hommelen.) Hommelen therefore worked with enclosed vessels, and he and Defay used these values for the equilibrium surface tension, along with their dynamic surface tensions by the falling meniscus method, for calculating diffusion coefficients from Ward and Tordai's general equation (equation 29 in the present chapter). The calculated diffusion coefficients for the smaller, branched-chain alcohols and acids were in good agreement with a mechanism of pure diffusion, without any energy barrier. With decyl alcohol, the results were inconclusive, while with azelaïc acid the calculated values were too low, suggesting that in that case an energy barrier was present.

One point which emerges very clearly from the present discussion is that one cannot expect a complete correlation between technical effects and the final equilibrium values of interfacial tensions, surface excesses, etc. It also suggests (admittedly *post hoc*) why it is that the "designer" of

---

[1] Defay and Hommelen, *J. Coll. Sci.*, 1958, **13**, 553; Hommelen, *ibid.*, 1959, **14**, 385; Defay and Hommelen, *ibid.*, 1959, **14**, 401, 411.

surface-active agents is not necessarily faced with the simple problem of striking a compromise between a high equilibrium surface activity and a high rate of diffusion, but rather with a much more complicated problem, which is imperfectly understood at present, but offers far greater possibilities for chemical ingenuity.

2. SLOW SURFACE-AGEING PHENOMENA

The conclusions just reached apply with far greater force to the much slower surface-ageing effects which are observed with paraffin-chain salts of high surface-activity. Here there has never been any doubt of the inadequacy of any theory based on simple diffusion, the rate of attainment of equilibrium frequently being 10^{-7} of that to be expected on such a theory. This phenomenon appears to have been first studied by Adam and Shute,[1] though it was observed independently by Reed and Tartar,[2] at air-water interfaces. Confirmatory evidence, extensions of the data, and theoretical discussions will be found in the papers by Doss,[3] Nutting, Long, and Harkins,[4] Tartar, Sivertz, and Reitmeier,[5] Nutting and Long,[6] Alexander,[7] Alexander and Rideal,[8] Ward and Tordai,[9] Ward,[10] Salley, Weith, Argyle, and Dixon,[11] Davies, Smith, and Humphreys,[12] Fava and Eyring,[13] Flengas and Rideal,[14] and Sutherland.[15]

Further references will be found in these papers.

Adam and Shute determined the surface tensions, by the sessile bubble method, of aqueous solutions of three anionic surface-active compounds (sodium cetyl sulphate, sodium dodecyl sulphate, and potassium hexadecane sulphonate) and of four compounds with surface-active cations (cetylpyridinium bromide, dodecylpyridinium bromide, cetyltrimethylammonium bromide, and dodecyltrimethylammonium bromide). The general result was always the same: the surface tension in dilute solutions (below a concentration corresponding approximately to the critical concentration for micelle formation) fell extremely slowly for a week or longer, eventually reaching a value which was practically independent of the concentration. At higher concentrations of the surface-active salt, the final

[1] Adam and Shute, *Trans. Faraday Soc.*, 1935, **31**, 204; 1938, **34**, 758.

[2] Reed and Tartar, *J. Amer. Chem. Soc.*, 1936, **58**, 322.

[3] Doss, *Koll. Z.*, 1938, **84**, 138; 1939, **86**, 205.

[4] Nutting, Long, and Harkins, *J. Amer. Chem. Soc.*, 1940, **62**, 1496.

[5] Tartar, Sivertz, and Reitmeier, *ibid.*, 1940, **62**, 2375.

[6] Nutting and Long, *ibid.*, 1941, **63**, 84.

[7] Alexander, *Trans. Faraday Soc.*, 1941, **37**, 15.

[8] Alexander and Rideal, *Nature*, 1945, **155**, 18.

[9] Ward and Tordai, *J. Chem. Phys.*, 1946, **14**, 453.

[10] Ward, *Surface Chemistry* (Supplement to *Research*), Butterworth, 1949, p. 55.

[11] Salley, Weith, Argyle, and Dixon, *Proc. Roy. Soc.*, 1950, **A203**, 42.

[12] Davies, Smith, and Humphreys, *Second Congress*, 1957, **I**, 281.

[13] Fava and Eyring, *J. Phys. Chem.*, 1956, **60**, 890.

[14] Flengas and Rideal, *Trans. Faraday Soc.*, 1959, **55**, 339.

[15] Sutherland, *Australian Journal of Chemistry*, 1959, **12**, 1.

value of the surface tension was reached almost at once, and the addition of other electrolytes also accelerated the attainment of equilibrium. Adam and Shute showed that the ageing phenomenon pertained to the surface and not to the solution itself, since they found that, when a fresh surface was formed in an old solution, the initial surface tension and its subsequent fall with time were practically identical with the values obtained with the freshly prepared solution. It is interesting to note that Adam and Shute's equilibrium values, though not numerous enough to give complete surface tension-concentration curves, show unmistakable evidence of the existence of minima.

Adam and Shute's most interesting observation was undoubtedly that equilibrium was reached almost at once if the solutions contained appreciable numbers of ionic micelles.* They reject the possibility of this being due to the micelles themselves having a high surface-activity, and suggest instead that the micelles, which carry considerable electrical charges, may drive the surface-active ions more rapidly into the surface by virtue of the greater electrostatic repulsion which they will exert on these ions. Alternatively, they suggest that the adsorbed surface layer might itself be considered as a kind of two-dimensional micelle, the formation of which is favoured by the same conditions as favour the formation of micelles in the bulk of the solution.

Doss, who also observed surface-ageing effects with aqueous solutions of substantive dyestuffs, has suggested that the phenomenon is one of activated adsorption at the air-water interface. He considers that a diffuse electrical double layer is formed, consisting of a unilayer of surface-active ions in the surface and a "Gouy-region" below it which is poorer in solute. The resulting potential, which is set up as soon as the first surface-active ions are adsorbed, acts as an activation barrier which succeeding surface-active ions must surmount before they are adsorbed. He therefore points out that it would be expected that equilibrium would be reached very much more slowly than in a simple diffusion process, and that the barrier would be reduced if the ionic strength of the solution were increased by the addition of more electrolyte and/or the formation of micelles, which are effectively of very high valency. A similar general picture of the formation of an electrical double layer, which acts as a barrier to the free diffusion of surface-active ions to the surface, was put forward by Nutting, Long, and Harkins. They also pointed out that, alternatively, the results could be explained on the basis of McBain's theory that "neutral colloid" (*i.e.*, a micelle of very low charge density) is formed at the "critical concentration"

---

* It will, of course, be appreciated that the sessile bubble method is not capable of detecting rapid surface-ageing effects such as those studied by Addison with the technique of the vibrating jet. It can be taken for granted, in our opinion, that the latter technique would reveal the existence of a rapid surface-ageing in these solutions above the critical concentration for the formation of micelles.

—the diffusion of such a particle to the surface would of course be much less affected by the electrical double layer.

On the basis of experiments with the Langmuir trough, J. W. McBain and Perry[1] have put forward the view that surface-ageing phenomena may be due in some cases (*e.g.*, aqueous solutions of hydrocinnamic acid) to the slow formation (or dissolution) of "surface pellicles" of the surface-active agent, *i.e.*, leaflets consisting of two or more superimposed monomolecular layers. McBain and Perry also find that hydrocinnamic acid gives incompletely reversible pellicles, which will not redissolve unless a definite surface pressure is applied. This observation may be of considerable importance in studying practical processes, since it suggests that apparent "equilibrium" boundary tensions may in some cases depend on the history of the surface. Thus for example it might be found that, in a wetting process which proceeded so slowly as to suggest that equilibrium surface tension values could be used, the actual surface tension values might depend on whether the "equilibrium" position were approached with contraction or with expansion of the air-water interface.

A critical review of the theories of the surface-ageing of solutions which had been published up to the end of 1940 is given in the paper by Alexander,[2] who also reports several interesting experimental observations:

(a) Slow ageing phenomena are absent at the interface between benzene or *n*-heptane and aqueous 0·00193 *N* solutions of sodium dodecyl sulphate —at this concentration a distinct slow ageing occurs in the surface tension against air.

(b) Slow ageing phenomena at the interface between air and an aqueous solution of sodium dodecyl sulphate or hydrocinnamic acid are eliminated if a unilayer of an insoluble long-chain compound (*e.g.*, ethyl laurate) is present.

(c) The slow ageing effect with hydrocinnamic acid at air-water interfaces was almost unaffected by the addition of hydrochloric acid, but disappeared if sodium hydrocinnamate was substituted for free hydrocinnamic acid.

(d) Surface potential measurements were carried out during the slow ageing effects at interfaces between air and aqueous solutions of sodium dodecyl sulphate, hexadecane sulphonic acid, cetylpyridinium bromide, and hydrocinnamic acid, and indicated that in each case the number of molecules in the surface film was increasing, and that the film was homogeneous to the movable electrode in the air.

On the basis of these and other facts, Alexander rejects the theory that an activated diffusion across an electrical potential barrier is the rate-determining process. Thus he points out that such a theory is incompatible with (a), (b), and (c), and with the observation by M. E. L. McBain and

[1] McBain and Perry, *Ind. Eng. Chem.*, 1939, **31**, 35.
[2] Alexander, *Trans. Faraday Soc.*, 1941, **37**, 15.

Perry[1] that slow ageing occurs with solutions of dodecane sulphonic acid in
tetra*iso*butylene (which can be considered to be a substantially non-ionising
solvent). Alexander also considers that surface pellicle formation is inadequate to explain all the slow ageing observations, on the grounds *inter alia*
that the steady increase in the surface potential during surface ageing is of
the type obtained when there is a slow increase in the number of similarly
orientated molecules in the surface. Alexander concludes that, although the
presence of a repulsive electrostatic barrier may play a minor part in slow
surface-ageing phenomena in aqueous solutions, the main factor determining the rate of adsorption in *non-micellar* solutions is a steric one, *viz.*, the
rate of penetration and re-orientation of the solute molecules in the surface
layer.

The first measurements by the radio-tracer technique of the kinetics of
adsorption of a surface-active agent (sodium dodecyl sulphate) were made
by Salley, Weith, Argyle, and Dixon,[2] who showed that the method offered
a promising experimental approach. More recently, Flengas and Rideal[3]
have used the method to follow the adsorption of sodium stearate at the
air-water interface, from pure water and from 10^{-6} and $10^{-3} M$ NaOH
solutions. Their results were in reasonably good agreement with equation
(28) for the early stages of the process, in that plots of log M against log t
(where M is the surface concentration calculated from the radioactivity
counts, and t is the time) gave slopes between 0·41 and 0·59, compared with
the value of 0·5 required by the theory. The values obtained for the diffusion
coefficient of the surface-active agents increased from $1·9 \times 10^{-5}$ in pure
water to $7·0 \times 10^{-4}$ in the presence of $10^{-6} M$ NaOH; these values appear
to be consistent with the picture of a process which is essentially one of
ordinary diffusion, the effect of the alkali being explicable on the grounds
that it prevents the formation of aggregates containing acid soap. The
equilibrium data of Flengas and Rideal have already been discussed earlier
in the present chapter.

Sutherland[4] has recently published an important paper which throws
doubts on much of the early work on slow-ageing phenomena. He finds
that the rate of fall of the surface tension at 40° c. of solutions of sodium
hexadecyl sulphate (measured with a vertical film balance) is greatly
influenced by very small traces of electrolyte impurities.* The effect was
so marked that reliable results could only be obtained by "swamping" the
solutions with sodium chloride. Above the critical micelle concentration,
the effect of these impurities becomes negligible. The presence of hexadecyl

---

* This observation appears to have been first made by Powney and Addison, *Trans.
Faraday Soc.*, 1937, **33**, 1243.
 [1] Laing McBain and Perry, *J. Amer. Chem. Soc.*, 1940, **62**, 989.
 [2] Salley, Waith, Argyle, and Dixon, *Proc. Roy. Soc.*, 1950, **A203**, 42.
 [3] Flengas and Rideal, *Trans. Faraday Soc.*, 1959, **55**, 339.
 [4] Sutherland, *Australian Journal of Chemistry*, 1959, **12**, 1.

alcohol, in quantities below about 1% on the sulphate, has no effect, nor does contamination with octadecyl sulphate.

From a careful analysis of his results, Sutherland concludes that simple diffusion from an *unstirred* solution (equation 28) is not a satisfactory physical model for the system; instead, he finds a reasonable agreement with a model which postulates diffusion through an unstirred layer, the remainder of the liquid being convectively stirred. Sutherland concludes that "there is very little evidence that slow falls in surface tension (or interfacial tension) are due to other than the transport of very small amounts of electrolyte impurities to a surface," there being no evidence that electrical energy barriers play any appreciable part in determining the rate of fall of surface tension.

The view that slow surface-ageing effects are due to the diffusion of trace impurities is also supported by the work of Davies, Smith, and Humphreys[1] on the adsorption of cetyltrimethylammonium bromide at the carbon tetrachloride-water interface, using a dynamic drop-weight method. They find that the bulk of the fall in interfacial tension occurs during the first second.* An approximate interpretation of their results in terms of Ward and Tordai's treatment does not suggest the presence of any electrical energy barrier.

The kinetics of adsorption of lauric and palmitic acids at the hexane-water interface, *from the hexane side*, has been studied by Ward and Tordai.[2] Here we are dealing with a substantially unionised diffusing molecule, but Ward concludes that the fraction of collisions of different molecules with the surface which are effective in causing adsorption is only of the order of 0·01. He suggests that this can be explained by assuming that, before a molecule can be adsorbed, it must be in an activated state where it has lost some of its degrees of freedom: *i.e.*, the slowness of adsorption is due to an *entropy barrier*.

An alternative explanation for the time lag in the adsorption of surface-active agents from oil media has been proposed by Alexander and Rideal,[3] *viz.*, that the surface-active molecules are associated in the oil, and that there is a time lag in the breakdown of these associates at the interface. This suggestion is based on experiments with palmitic acid and "Aerosol OT" (sodium dioctylsulphosuccinate) at the interfaces between air and medicinal paraffin, benzene, and nitrobenzene, the speed with which equilibrium was approached being in the reverse order to that of the degree of association. It will be appreciated that the question of an electrical energy barrier does not arise—in any event, such an explanation

---

* This paper accordingly has a considerable bearing on the rapid-ageing phenomena discussed earlier in the present chapter.

[1] Davies, Smith, and Humphreys, *Second Congress*, 1957, **I**, 281.

[2] Ward and Tordai, *Nature*, 1944, **154**, 146; Ward, *Surface Chemistry* (Supplement to *Research*), Butterworth, 1949, p. 55.

[3] Alexander and Rideal, *Nature*, 1945, **155**, 18.

cannot apply to these results, since it was found that equilibrium was reached more rapidly the more strongly ionising the medium.

An important study of the kinetics of adsorption of a surface-active agent at a *solid-liquid interface* (sodium dodecylbenzene sulphonate on to cotton from aqueous solution) is given in the paper by Fava and Eyring[1] to which we have referred earlier in the chapter, in the discussion on maxima in equilibrium adsorption isotherms. These authors found *inter alia* that the kinetics of both adsorption and desorption could be fitted to the same reduced equation:

$$-\frac{d\phi}{dt} = 2k'\phi \sinh b\phi$$

where ϕ is the distance from equilibrium at time t, divided by the initial distance from equilibrium, *i.e.*

$$\phi = \frac{a - a_f}{a_i - a_f}$$

where a_i, a and a_f are the amounts adsorbed at times 0, t and ∞, respectively. A further remarkable observation was that, although k' was different for adsorption and desorption and also temperature-dependent, the constant b (which had a value of 1·26) was the same for adsorption and desorption, and independent of temperature.

Fava and Eyring go on to consider the adsorption and desorption processes in terms of reaction rate theory, the constant k' for adsorption and desorption being the true rate constants for these two processes; from their values at different temperatures, the heat of activation for adsorption was found to be 2,075 cal., and for desorption 2,720 cal., the difference of 645 cal. agreeing satisfactorily with the value (778 cal.) from equilibrium adsorption data at 2° and 38° c. The entropies of activation for adsorption and desorption (− 62·3 and − 62·9 entropy units, respectively) were also calculated. The significance of this paper to the theory of detergency is obvious.

---

[1] Fava and Eyring, *J. Phys. Chem.*, 1956, **60**, 890.

CHAPTER 4

FUNDAMENTAL INTERFACIAL PROCESSES

SURFACE-ACTIVE agents are usually applied technically in processes which are in reality complexes of several physico-chemical phenomena. A good example is furnished by the process of detergency in the scouring of textiles, which may involve *inter alia* (a) the displacement of air from a porous mass by the aqueous solution, (b) the displacement of a liquid "grease" by the aqueous solution, (c) the emulsification of the grease in the solution, (d) the deflocculation of adherent solid particles, which become suspended in the aqueous solution, and (e) a protective colloid action by the dissolved detergent on the suspended particles and emulsified droplets, which reduces their tendency to flocculate or to be redeposited on the cloth. Before we attempt to describe the application of surface-active agents in complex technical processes such as detergency, therefore, it seems desirable to examine their effects in the component physico-chemical phenomena, which can be conveniently designated as "fundamental" interfacial processes. It will be appreciated that a full discussion of these fundamental processes is beyond the scope of the present work, and that we will attempt to consider them only in sufficient detail to clarify the function of surface-active agents in technical processes. It should also be made clear that the criteria by which we judge an interfacial process to be "fundamental" are to some extent pragmatic and based on current usage, rather than on an appeal to first principles. Thus "protective colloid action" is itself a complex phenomenon, but it has a well-defined and generally accepted meaning, and in the present state of knowledge appears to be sufficiently "fundamental" for our purposes.

A. Wetting phenomena

1. GENERAL: THERMODYNAMICAL CONSIDERATIONS

"Wetting"[1] can be defined as the process in which one fluid phase is displaced, completely or in part, by another fluid phase from the surface of a solid or liquid, all three phases being of course co-existent, though a certain amount of mutual solution of the components is not only possible but usual. Examples of typical wetting processes are the displacement of air from a clean glass surface by water, of water from the surface of paraffin wax by air, or of water from the surface of a pigment by an oil medium. Each wetting phenomenon involves of course a converse process of

---

[1] A valuable collection of papers is given in the discussion on "Interaction of Water and Porous Materials," *Discussions of the Faraday Society*, 1948, No. 3.

"recession": thus the three processes just mentioned can also be considered as recessions by air, water, and water, respectively. In general, but not always, it is more convenient to speak of "wetting" and to think in terms of the advancing fluid phase.

A very convenient fundamental classification of wetting processes, in terms of the changes of the total interfacial free energy, has been proposed by Osterhof and Bartell.[1] Thus spreading wetting, in which a layer of a fluid (1) (*e.g.*, a liquid) spreads over the surface of a solid (3), and displaces another fluid (2) (*e.g.*, a gas), is characterised by the fact that a certain area of (3)–(2) interface (*e.g.*, solid-gas) disappears and is replaced by equal areas of interfaces (1)–(3) and (1)–(2) (liquid-solid and liquid-gas, respectively). Under certain conditions, spreading can be spontaneous, *i.e.*, one fluid may completely displace another as the result of interfacial forces only. Frequently, however, gravitational or mechanical forces, or chemical changes, will also play a part in the spreading process, though the interfacial tensions (more properly, the interfacial free energy changes) may still play a decisive rôle. The thermodynamical condition for the occurrence of a spontaneous spreading, due to interfacial forces only, is that there shall be a net decrease in the total interfacial free energy of the system. This net decrease is given by $dG = SdA$, where dA is the area over which spontaneous spreading occurs, and S is Harkins' "spreading coefficient," defined by

$$S = \gamma_{23} - \gamma_{12} - \gamma_{13} \tag{1}$$

where S is the spreading coefficient of the fluid (1) against the fluid (2), on the surface of a third phase (3), which we shall consider to be a solid, and γ_{23}, etc., are the interfacial tensions at the interfaces between (2) and (3), etc. The condition for spontaneous spreading to be possible is that $S > 0$, and S can therefore usually be considered as the driving force behind a simple spreading process. If other influences such as gravity or mechanical work are also appreciable, then S will represent the contribution of the interfacial tensions (through which surface-active agents will exert their influence) to the total process.

If the fluid (1) does not spread spontaneously and displace the fluid (2) completely, then (in the absence of other forces) a state of equilibrium may be reached in which both (1) and (2) remain in contact with the solid (3) and meet at a three-phase boundary marked P in Figure 18, which represents a cross-section at the junction of the three phases. In such a case the relative wetting or spreading tendency of (1) against (2) is conveniently measured by means of the contact angle θ, which is the angle (measured inside fluid (1)) between the surface of the solid and the tangent to the boundary between (1) and (2) at P. If the mathematical convention is adopted of treating the interfacial tensions as forces acting parallel to the

[1] Osterhof and Bartell, *J. Phys. Chem.*, 1930, **34**, 1399. See also Bartell, in Alexander's *Colloid Chemistry*, Reinhold Publishing Co., New York, 1931, **III**, p. 41.

surfaces, then Figure 18 can be treated as a vector diagram, and we obtain the well-known Young equation:

$$\gamma_{23} = \gamma_{13} + \gamma_{12} \cos \theta \tag{2}$$

It should be emphasised that equation (2) is no longer valid when the contact angle *disappears*, *i.e.*, when $S > 0$, since under such conditions it is impossible for a genuine state of equilibrium to exist. If the contact angle is *exactly zero*, *i.e.*, if $S = 0$, equation (2) is still theoretically valid. This state of affairs is, of course, unlikely to occur very often, and it is so difficult to distinguish experimentally between zero contact angle on the one hand, and the case where the contact angle has disappeared on the other, that the experimental usefulness of (2) is in fact limited to the case $180° > \theta > 0$. It is also for this reason completely fallacious to assume that the

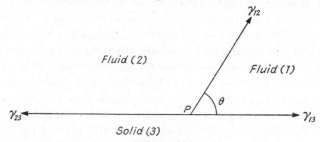

Figure 18
Equilibrium state corresponding to finite contact angle (θ)

spreading coefficient is the same in a number of spreading processes in each of which three is no measurable contact angle. This assumption, which is sometimes explicitly or implicitly made, is due to a failure to distinguish between these two cases of (exactly) zero contact angle, and a contact angle which has disappeared.

Equation (2) can also be derived thermodynamically, by applying the criterion of the minimum total free energy.[1] Suppose, for example, that a droplet of the fluid (1) is resting on the solid (3), in the presence of the second fluid (2), as shown in Fig. 19. If the radius of the droplet and/or the difference in density between (1) and (2) are small enough, the effect of gravity can be neglected, and the droplet will be a segment of a sphere, of height h and radius r. The total interfacial free energy* of the system will be given by

---

* It will be noted that, since we define our interfacial tensions by a series of expressions of the form

$$\gamma_i = \left(\frac{\partial G}{\partial A_i} \right)_{P,T,n \ldots Aj \ldots}$$

where G is the *total* Gibbs free energy of the system, we are in fact using as our criterion of equilibrium that the *total* free energy of the system is at a minimum, at constant temperature, pressure and composition.

[1] See, for example, Shuttleworth and Bailey, *Discussions of the Faraday Soc.*, 1948. **3**, 16.

$$G_s = \pi\gamma_{13}(2hr - h^2) + 2\pi hr\gamma_{12} + A\gamma_{23} - \pi\gamma_{23}(2hr - h^2)$$

where A is the total available area of the solid surface (a constant). If we differentiate G_s with respect to r, set $dG_s/dr = 0$, and make the substitutions which are possible from the fact that the volume of the droplet

$$V = \tfrac{1}{3}\pi h^2(3r - h)$$

is a constant, so that $dV/dr = 0$, we find that

$$(\gamma_{13} - \gamma_{23})hr + \gamma_{12}(hr - h^2) = 0 \tag{3}$$

It can be seen from Fig. 19, however, that r, h, and the contact angle θ (measured inside phase 1) are related by $\cos\theta = (r - h)/r$, and substitution in (3) gives Young's equation (2).

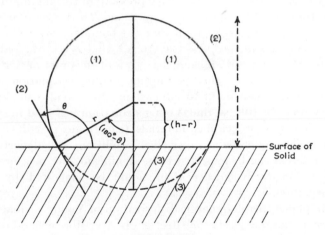

Figure 19
Thermodynamical derivation of Young's equation

Doubts have been raised about the validity of Young's equation on the grounds that, when Fig. 18 is treated vectorially, only the horizontal component of γ_{12}, viz., $\gamma_{12}\cos\theta$, is considered, the vertical component $\gamma_{12}\sin\theta$ being neglected.[1] We are indebted to Dr. G. R. Lester for the following communication* on this question. He points out that, in both the vectorial and thermodynamical derivations of Young's equation, the implicit assumption is made that the surface of the solid is completely rigid and undeformable.† In so far as this condition is satisfied, the thermodynamical derivation given above is applicable, and in the vectorial

---

* To be published in *J. Coll. Sci.*

† See the remarks by Bailey, *Second Congress*, 1957, **III**, 189, and the recent paper by Johnson, *J. Phys. Chem.*, 1959, **63**, 1655.

[1] Bikerman, *Second Congress*, 1957, **III**, 125; see also the discussion on p. 187 *ff*.

derivation the $\gamma_{12} \sin \theta$ component is balanced without appreciable deformation of the surface. If, however, the solid is appreciably deformable, then Young's equation is no longer strictly applicable: in the vectorial derivation (Fig. 18) there will be an upward displacement at P. Similarly, in the thermodynamical picture, the pressure difference inside and outside the drop will deform the surface in Fig. 19.

Lester also considers the difficult problem of calculating the effect of deformability on Young's equation, and obtains the expression

$$\gamma_{12} \cos \theta = (\gamma_{23} - \gamma_{13}) \cos \left[\tan^{-1} \frac{4\gamma_{12}(1 - \nu^2)}{\pi \zeta ER} \right]$$

where E is the Young's modulus of the solid substrate, ν is Poisson's ratio, ζ is the ratio of the downward capillary pressure to the maximum negative (upward) stress near the edge of the droplet, and R is the radius of curvature of the droplet. On the assumption that the boundary layer is only a few molecular diameters in thickness (say 10 Å.), that R and the radius of the drop are of similar magnitude, and that γ_{12} is of the order of that of water, Lester concludes that on this assumption, Young's equation will apply for values of E less than about 10^{10} dynes/cm.^{2} Most solids will have a value of E of the order of 10^{12}, so that Young's equation will hold in such cases, but for "rubbery" or gel-like materials (e.g., many textiles, especially relatively polar materials in a swollen condition) the departures from Young's equation can be expected to be significant, the measured contact angles being generally *greater* than would be suggested by applying Young's equation.

The simplified thermodynamical derivation of Young's equation which we have reproduced neglects the effect of gravity. More general derivations have recently been published by Collins and Cooke[1] and by Johnson[2] for the shape of a sessile bubble, and the angle at the line of contact, under the influence of interfacial tensions (in the sense used by us) and gravity, at equilibrium. Both papers conclude that Young's equation obtains under these conditions.

Equation (2) can be combined with (1), provided that an equilibrium contact angle exists, to give

$$S = \gamma_{12}(\cos \theta - 1) \tag{1a}$$

This has the practical advantage over equation (1) that both γ_{12} and θ are experimentally determinable. Padday[3] has pointed out that, for the same

[1] Collins and Cooke, *Trans. Faraday Soc.*, 1959, **55**, 1602.
[2] Johnson, *J. Phys. Chem.*, 1959, **63**, 1655.
[3] Padday, *Second Congress*, 1957, **III**, 136.

condition of a finite contact angle, the spreading coefficient can also be conveniently determined from the relation

$$S = - \tfrac{1}{2}\rho g h^2 \tag{4}$$

where ρ is the difference in density between the fluid phases (1) and (2), and h is the maximum height of a sessile drop of (1) on the solid (3), in competition with (1). Padday gives some experimental results for water on paraffin wax surfaces which agree with those obtained by contact angle methods.

An alternative method of characterising the wetting behaviour of one fluid phase (1) against another (2) is by means of the work of adhesion: *i.e.*, the work required to separate reversibly the fluid phase (1) from the solid phase (3), over unit area of contact, in the presence of fluid phase (2). This work can be seen at once to be given by

$$W_{13} = \gamma_{12} + \gamma_{23} - \gamma_{13} \tag{5}$$

If $180° > \theta > 0$,* this can be combined with equation (2) to give

$$W_{13} = \gamma_{12}(1 + \cos \theta) \tag{6}$$

The work of adhesion W_{13} can be seen to be a measure of the resistance which (1) offers to being displaced by (2) from the surface of (3); as Osterhof and Bartell[1] have pointed out, its value characterises the process of adhesional wetting, in which solid-liquid interface is formed at the expense of the solid-air and the liquid-air interfaces. It is a particularly useful quantity for describing the wetting properties of a solid surface when a finite contact angle is involved, or when external forces are applied, as usually happens in technical processes. Thus if a particle of a solid (3) is being agitated in the presence of two liquids (1) and (2), then increasing W_{13} in equation (5) or equation (6), by adding a surface-active agent, will favour the wetting of the solid by liquid (1) at the expense of liquid (2). To take an opposite case, if drops of water (1) are falling randomly on the surface of a solid (3), then a treatment of the surface of the solid which decreases W_{13} will decrease the proportion of the drops which will adhere by adhesional wetting.

The third fundamental type of wetting according to Osterhof and Bartell's classification is the immersional, in which the liquid-air interface is unchanged, while solid-liquid interface is formed at the expense of the

---

* Harkins and Loeser (*J. Chem. Phys.*, 1950, **18**, 556) rightly drew attention to the absurdity of using equation (6) when the contact angle disappears. Nevertheless, it seems to us that it would be a mistake to abandon the work of adhesion as a wetting criterion —as they suggest—merely because it has been misapplied. Provided that the condition is satisfied that θ must be greater than 0 and less than 180°, then the work of adhesion is a very useful wetting criterion, especially in considering many industrial problems.

[1] Osterhof and Bartell, *J. Phys. Chem.*, 1930, **34**, 1399.

solid-air. This corresponds physically to the process of immersion of a particle of a solid (3), which was initially in air (2), in a relatively large volume of a liquid (1). The thermodynamical condition, in terms of interfacial tensions, for immersion to occur spontaneously is evidently that the work of immersion, given by

$$W_{i,31} = \gamma_{23} - \gamma_{13} \tag{7}$$

should be positive.

When there is a finite contact angle, equation (7) can be combined with Young's equation to give

$$W_{i,31} = \gamma_{12} \cos \theta \tag{8}$$

which can be used, for example, to characterise the tendency of individual water-repellent particles to float on the surface of water.

Osterhof and Bartell have pointed out that the above classification applies principally to initial and final states, but that several types may be involved during an actual wetting process. Thus if a solid cube is immersed in a liquid, the total process is one of immersional wetting, but it may be analysable into successive stages of adhesion, immersion, and spreading.

Where Young's equation is applicable, and hence equations such as (6) and (8) can be used, numerical values can be obtained to characterise the extent of wetting of a surface, since all the quantities in (6) and (8) are experimentally determinable. Equations such as (1), (5) and (7), on the other hand, contain the two solid-fluid interfacial tensions γ_{13} and γ_{23}, which are not generally determinable. There is a considerable literature on possible methods of determining the boundary tensions of solids, or for estimating them theoretically, which is beyond our present scope. These include experiments in which the cleavage of solid particles is quantitatively studied (which one would expect frequently to give "stretching" rather than thermodynamical interfacial tensions—*cf.* Chapter 3, p. 91), as well as attempts to determine the effect of particles size on solubility (*cf.* p. 190). Another "classical" method, which has recently been refined by Mitchell and Elton,[1] is based on the application of the so-called "Antonoff rule." This "rule" states that, where the three phases are completely mutually saturated with each other,

$$\gamma_{13} = |\gamma_{23} - \gamma_{12}|$$

where (1) is a liquid, (2) is air, and (3) is the solid. If the "rule" is valid, then for a finite contact angle,

$$\gamma_{23} = \gamma_{12}(1 + \cos \theta)/2$$

permitting the calculation of γ_{23}. Mitchell and Elton have adduced evidence to suggest that, for water in contact with acetophenone, diphenyl ether, *n*-hexadecane, and *n*-octadecane, "Antonoff's rule" is in fact valid, the

---

[1] Mitchell and Elton, *J. Chem. Soc.*, 1953, 839.

values calculated for γ_{23} lying between 24 and 36·5 dynes/cm. It would nevertheless be unwise to generalise to all cases in the present state of knowledge. Even without numerical values for the solid-fluid interfacial tensions, however, it should be noted that equations such as (1), (5) and (7) are of considerable value for our purposes, since they enable one to see at once (in qualitative terms) the probable thermodynamical role of a surface-active agent which is known to be adsorbed at one or more solid-fluid interfaces.

Most of the "classical" work on contact angles, as well as on their practical significance, was done on surfaces such as paraffin wax, iron or aluminium salts of fatty acids, or minerals such as galena. A more recent development is the discovery of surfaces of very low intrinsic surface free energies, such as those of highly fluorinated hydrocarbons. Fox and Zisman[1] have published an interesting paper on the spreading of a range of organic liquids on polymerised tetrafluoroethylene. Unlike the behaviour of these liquids on paraffin wax, finite contact angles were observed, which is explicable on the grounds that γ_{23} in equation (1) was lower in the case of the fluorinated surface, and that γ_{13} was not so much lower, or even greater. The value of $\cos \theta$ in equation (2) was found to be a linear function of the air-liquid interfacial tension γ_{12}, indicating that the quantity $(\gamma_{23} - \gamma_{12})$ was remaining constant for the range of liquids. (The possibility that *both* γ_{23} and γ_{13} remained constant cannot be checked.) Where the air-liquid interfacial tension was less than 17·5 to 20·5 dynes/cm., the contact angle disappeared; *i.e.*, spontaneous spreading occurred. A similar "critical surface tension" (air-liquid) for wetting has also been reported by Bernett and Zisman[2] for the wetting of polythene and polytetrafluoroethylene by aqueous solutions of several "perfluoro" carboxylic acids.

2. The effect of surface roughness on wetting equilibria

The preceding discussion dealt, strictly speaking, only with surfaces which are perfectly smooth, a condition which will practically never be completely satisfied by actual surfaces of solids. It is therefore necessary to consider the effect of surface roughness, and particularly to distinguish between a simple roughness, which has the effect only of increasing the effective areas of the two solid-fluid interfaces (the "valleys" being completely filled by the respective fluids), and a roughness which is accompanied by the formation of composite surfaces (in which the "valleys" are incompletely filled by one of the fluids).

The effect of a simple roughness on the contact angle has been considered by Wenzel,[3] who obtained the equation

$$\cos \theta_r = f_{13} \cos \theta \qquad (9)$$

[1] Fox and Zisman, *J. Coll. Sci.*, 1950, **5**, 514.
[2] Bernett and Zisman, *J. Phys. Chem.*, 1959, **63**, 1911.
[3] Wenzel, *Ind. Eng. Chem.*, 1936, **28**, 988.

where θ_r is the contact angle on the rough surface, θ is the "true" contact angle (*i.e.*, that which would be obtained if the same surface were perfectly smooth), and f_{13} is the "roughness factor," *i.e.*, the actual area of solid-liquid interface per unit area of rough surface, which will always be greater than 1. Substitution in equation (6) gives, for the work of adhesion to a rough surface,

$$W_{13}' = \gamma_{12}(1 + f_{13} \cos \theta) \qquad (10)$$

It will be seen from (9) and (10) that the effect of surface roughness in this case is to accentuate any differences in wetting behaviour already present. Thus if the true contact angle θ is greater than 90°, θ_r will be greater still and may in fact reach 180° when $\theta < 180°$; if θ is less than 90°, on the other hand, θ_r will be less than θ, and may be as low as 0 when θ is still finite. Similarly, if $\theta > 90°$, the roughness factor f_{13} will decrease the work of adhesion for the liquid to the solid, but f_{13} will increase the work of adhesion if θ is less than 90°.

If the true contact angle is vanishingly small or disappears, the effect of simple roughness is only to increase the spreading coefficient in equation (1) to

$$S = f_{13}(\gamma_{23} - \gamma_{13}) - \gamma_{12}$$

i.e., to increase the thermodynamical driving force behind a spontaneous spreading. In such a case it should be noted, however, that the actual mechanical resistance to spreading may also be increased.

The second type of surface roughness, in which a composite surface or interface is formed as the result of porosity, has been discussed by Cassie and Baxter,[1] who consider the case in which pores in the solid-liquid interface remain filled with air, so that the apparent solid-liquid interface is in reality a composite interface containing an area f_{13} of true solid-liquid interface, and an area f_{123} of air-liquid interface, per unit area of apparent solid-liquid interface. They obtain, and experimentally verify, the relation

$$\cos \theta_r' = f_{13} \cos \theta - f_{123} \qquad (11)$$

where θ_r' is the contact angle on the rough surface, and θ is the true contact angle on a smooth surface. (It will be noted that, when the pores are completely filled with liquid and f_{123} therefore becomes zero, this equation becomes identical with Wenzel's equation.) Combining equations (11) and (6), we obtain for the work of adhesion on a composite surface

$$W_{13}'' = \gamma_{12}(1 + f_{13} \cos \theta - f_{123}) \qquad (12)$$

The derivation of Cassie and Baxter's equation has been criticised by Good,[2] who gives a thermodynamical derivation of Wenzel's equation (9) for a rough surface, though not of (11) for a composite surface. It seems to

---

[1] Cassie and Baxter, *Trans. Faraday Soc.*, 1944, **40**, 546. See also *Nature*, 1945, **155**, 21, and *J. Textile Inst.*, 1945, **36**, T67.

[2] Good, *J. Amer. Chem. Soc.*, 1952, **74**, 5041.

us that Cassie and Baxter's equation is, given their assumptions, quite valid, which can perhaps be made clearer by modifying the thermo-dynamical derivation given above for equation (3), to fit the case of a composite surface. We will suppose that in Fig. 19 the (1)–(3) surface of the solid (3) is rough and composite: *i.e.*, fluid (2) is trapped in the pores, so that each square centimetre of *apparent* (1)–(3) interface consists in reality of f_{13} cm.^{2} of genuine (1)–(3) interface, f_{123} cm.^{2} of genuine (1)–(2) interface, and f_{23} cm.^{2} of genuine (2)–(3) interface. (It is convenient to think of fluid (1) as being an aqueous solution and (2) as being a gas or an "oil," but the treatment is, of course, quite general.) By the same token, each cm.^{2} of *apparent* (2)–(3) interface will consist of $(f_{13} + f_{23})$ cm.^{2} of genuine (2)–(3) interface, the area corresponding to f_{123} under the droplet being replaced by an unreal "(2)–(2) interface," *i.e.*, by open capillaries. The total inter-facial free energy is now given by

$$G_s = \pi(2hr - h^2)(f_{13}\gamma_{13} + f_{123}\gamma_{12} - f_{13}\gamma_{23})$$
$$+ 2\pi hr\gamma_{12} + k(f_{13}\gamma_{23} + f_{23}\gamma_{23})$$

If we again differentiate with respect to r, note that the volume of the droplet is constant, and make the appropriate substitutions, we obtain by analogy with equation (3)

$$(f_{13}\gamma_{13} + f_{123}\gamma_{12} - f_{13}\gamma_{23})hr + \gamma_{12}(hr - h^2) = 0 \tag{13}$$

The contact angle on the composite surface, θ_r', is given by $cos\, \theta_r' = (r - h)/r$, and substitution in (12) gives

$$f_{13}(\gamma_{13} - \gamma_{23}) + f_{123}\gamma_{12} + \gamma_{12}cos\, \theta_r' = 0$$

It follows, however, from Young's equation that the contact angle θ on a smooth, homogeneous surface of the same solid would be given by $cos\, \theta = (\gamma_{23} - \gamma_{13})/\gamma_{12}$, and substitution gives Cassie and Baxter's equation

$$cos\, \theta_r' = f_{13} cos\, \theta - f_{123} \tag{11}$$

There are two implicit assumptions behind equations (9) and (11) which should be borne in mind. In the first place, we assume, in considering small virtual displacements on the surfaces, that the process can be treated as a fully *continuous* one, *i.e.*, either that the elements of roughness are extremely small compared to the size of the droplets, or that the direction of spreading is exactly parallel to grooves in the surface, these grooves constituting the surface roughness. (The latter was the case in Cassie and Baxter's experi-mental work, which used a physical model for the spreading of a liquid on the surface of a gabardine fabric, for example.) Where neither of these con-ditions is satisfied, it becomes necessary to consider the wetting process more "microscopically," in terms of what happens as the meniscus climbs over ridges and into valleys. It has been known for some time that extra energy is needed to carry a meniscus over an edge or a convex surface,[1] and Bikerman[2] has pointed out that this "contortional energy" increases the apparent contact angle. This effect has been made very clear by the work of Good[3] and of Bartell and Shepard,[4] which also shows how the apparent contact angle can be locally distorted.

The other implicit assumption, which is especially important when f_{13} or f_{123} is greater than unity, is that the *surplus* interface is of the same type (*i.e.*, has the same boundary tensions) as the normal interface. One would expect this to be strictly true for an isotropic solid, but in the case of anisotropic solids at least part of the surplus surface must be different in type, so that equations such as (9) and (11) become approximations.

The most important conclusion to be drawn from (11) and (12) is that they both predict that, when the true contact angle θ is finite, then the effect of a surface roughness which leads to the formation of a composite surface will always be to increase the contact angle. This of course means that the work of adhesion will always be decreased, *i.e.*, that the liquid (1) will be more readily detached from the surface than if either (a) the surface were substantially smooth, or (b) the air were completely displaced from the pores in the rough surface (Wenzel's case).

The question of whether or not a rough surface will also be a composite one is important and may be rather complex, depending on the true contact angle θ, the geometrical structure of the surface, and the manner in which the three phases (*e.g.*, solid, liquid, and air) have been brought together. It should be noted that it is quite feasible that there be no true contact angle θ, but that the geometrical factor prevents the complete escape of entrapped air, so that the solid-liquid interface becomes "mixed" with liquid-air interface. In such a case (*e.g.*, woven structures such as textile fibres and yarns), Cassie and Baxter have calculated that the apparent contact angle could be finite and could even exceed a value of 90° under quite feasible geometrical conditions. This can be readily seen by dividing Cassie and Baxter's equation (11) by their equation numbered (5), when we obtain

$$\cos \theta_r' = f_{13}\left(\frac{\gamma_{23} - \gamma_{13}}{\gamma_{12}}\right) - f_{123} \tag{14}$$

Let us suppose that $\gamma_{23} > \gamma_{13} + \gamma_{12}$, and hence that a true contact angle θ does not exist. This means that $\frac{\gamma_{23} - \gamma_{13}}{\gamma_{12}} > 1$, but it is still quite possible that $\cos \theta_r'$, as calculated from equation (14), is less than unity, and hence that θ_r' exists, provided that f_{123} is sufficiently larger than f_{13}.

[1] Coghill and Anderson, *J. Phys. Chem.*, 1918, **22**, 245.
[2] Bikerman, *Surface Chemistry*, Second Edition, Reinhold, 1958, p. 352.
[3] Good, *J. Amer. Chem. Soc.*, 1952, **74**, 5041.
[4] Bartell and Shepard, *J. Phys. Chem.*, 1953, **57**, 211, 455, 458.

3. "Hysteresis effects" in wetting

Before considering the possible effects of the adsorption of surface-active agents at the interfaces involved in wetting processes, it is necessary to note the existence of the so-called "hysteresis effect," *i.e.*, the fact that the contact angle measured in a liquid (1) on the surface of a solid (3), in the presence of a fluid phase (2), is invariably greater if the position of "equilibrium" has been reached by (1) advancing across (3), rather than by the reverse process.

There are several possible explanations for the hysteresis effect. The "classical" one is that the orientation of the surface atoms, ions, or molecules in a solid is affected by its previous history. If, for example, fluid (1) in Fig. 18 is water, and fluid (2) is air or oil, then it is postulated that, if the surface has been in contact with water, so that water is the *receding* phase, then the surface contains more hydrophilic groups than it does if water is *advancing* over a surface which has been in contact with air or oil. An alternative explanation is that hysteresis is due to surface roughness, so that an advancing water meniscus represents the wetting of a surface which is (at least momentarily) a composite one, while the receding meniscus is leaving behind it an apparent solid-air interface which, in fact, contains a considerable amount of trapped water. It has also been shown that simple roughness (as distinct from compositeness) can explain hysteresis, on the grounds of distortion of the menisci by the "contortional energy" referred to above. For details, the reader is referred to papers by Baxter,[1] Good,[2] Bartell and Shepard,[3] and Ray and Bartell.[4]

It seems to us that all these explanations may apply on occasion, and that they may even apply *simultaneously* at a single meniscus. The explanations based on surface roughness and compositeness are particularly attractive because of their simplicity, and are well established. Where surface-active agents are involved, the "molecular re-orientation" theory may also be important, especially when one considers the possibility of re-orientation of adsorbed surface-active molecules as they are left behind, for example, by a retreating aqueous phase.* Our purpose in mentioning wetting hysteresis here is to draw attention to the necessity for employing the appropriate type of contact angle in equations such as (2), (6), etc., when a particular case of wetting is considered. Thus Cassie and Baxter derive forms of equation (11) for both advancing and receding contact angles, it being of course understood that, if for example θ is the "true"

---

* Anyone who has encountered the difficulty of wetting out some of the paraffin chain salts as a preliminary to dissolving them will appreciate this point. See also the discussion on re-wetting on p. 235.

[1] Baxter, *Nature*, 1950, **165**, 198.
[2] Good, *J. Amer. Chem. Soc.*, 1952, **74**, 5041.
[3] Bartell and Shepard, *J. Phys. Chem.*, 1953, **57**, 211, 455.
[4] Ray and Bartell, *J. Coll.. Sci.*, 1953, **8**, 214.

advancing angle, then θ_r' will be the advancing angle on a rough surface. It will be appreciated that the strict application of equations (2), etc., implies that thermal, dynamic, and physico-chemical equilibrium has been reached at the point of contact of the three phases: thus the phrases "advancing" and "receding" contact angles are in strict logic misleading and ought perhaps to be replaced by more cumbersome expressions such as "the contact angle after advancing (or recession)."

Although the existence of the hysteresis effect has raised doubts about the genuine thermodynamical significance of the contact angle, it seems that in general the concept represents a useful method of characterising the "wettability" of surfaces, especially if the effects of porosity (composite surfaces) and of roughness are allowed for as far as possible. The advantages of an equation such as (6), when it can be validly applied, are obvious: thus both the experimental quantities θ and γ_{12} in (6) can be measured, whereas equation (5) is of purely theoretical interest, since the solid-fluid interfacial tensions γ_{23} and γ_{13} are not capable of measurement.

The use of contact angles is most open to doubt when information is desired about the intrinsic wettability of a surface: *e.g.*, in deciding which of several chemical substances is intrinsically more water-repellent. In such a case it is obviously essential to eliminate surface roughness and compositeness, as well as re-orientation effects. The most effective precautions are clearly to demonstrate experimentally that a particular contact angle is reproducible and independent of time, to take steps to eliminate surface roughness, and to show that the contact angle is independent of measures which will alter the degree of compositeness, such as working under reduced pressures.

4. THE EFFECT OF THE ADSORPTION OF SURFACE-ACTIVE AGENTS ON WETTING PROPERTIES

We have seen in Chapter 3 that the adsorption of a surface-active compound at any interface can be generally assumed to be accompanied by a *decrease* in that interfacial tension. The effects of such adsorptions in the wetting cases already considered are therefore fairly obvious from inspection of equations (1) to (14), and can be briefly summarised as follows:

In a case of spreading wetting, the likelihood of the spreading coefficient being positive (equation 1), and hence of spontaneous spreading occurring, is increased if an added surface-active solute is adsorbed at the interface (1)–(3) and/or (1)–(2) (*e.g.*, solid-liquid and/or liquid-air). By the same token, a positive spreading coefficient will become more positive if adsorption occurs at either of these two interfaces. It is therefore not surprising that most surface-active compounds which cause water to spread on solids, or which favour the maintenance of stable films of water on solids, also lower the surface tension of water (against air), though the converse does not necessarily hold true. It also seems probable that such compounds are adsorbed at the solid-liquid interface. Any tendency for the spreading coefficient to become more positive (or less negative) as the result of adsorption of surface-active material at the solid-liquid interface means of course that the contact angle will (if it is finite) tend to decrease. Adsorption at the (1)–(2) (*e.g.*, liquid-air) interface will also decrease the contact angle if it is already less than 90°, but will increase any contact angle which is greater than 90° (equation 2).

Where a process of adhesional wetting of a solid by a liquid is concerned, adsorption of a surface-active agent at the solid-liquid interface again favours wetting, *i.e.*, increases the reversible work necessary to separate the liquid from the solid. Adsorption at the liquid-air interface, on the other hand, is always unfavourable to adhesional wetting (equations 5 and 6). In the third type of wetting, the immersional, the thermodynamical criterion is not affected by adsorption at the liquid-air interface, but the driving force of the process (free energy decrease) becomes greater if a surface-active agent is adsorbed at the solid-liquid interface (equation 7). It will therefore be seen that all three types of wetting are favoured by adsorption at the solid-liquid interface, but that contrary to the frequently made assumption, *adsorption at the liquid-air interface (and hence lowering of the liquid-air interfacial tension) is not always favourable, but depends on the type of wetting involved.* Exactly the same qualitative arguments apply to the effect of the adsorption of surface-active agents on the wetting characteristics of rough surfaces; special attention should however be given to the possibility that an added surface-active agent alters a composite surface to a simple rough one, *i.e.*, leads to the complete displacement of the phase (2) from the pores.

Although it is usually instructive, when considering the effect of a surface-active agent in a wetting process, to consider each interface separately, it will be unusual in practice for a surface-active agent to be adsorbed at one interface only. This is true of the paraffin-chain salts, for example, which show a general, non-specific surface activity in aqueous media, owing to the tendency for the water molecules to expel the paraffin chains from the interior of the solution; it seems likely that such amphipathic molecules will be adsorbed to some extent at most interfaces. It is particularly worth noting that the great majority of surface-active compounds will, if they are soluble in water, measurably lower the surface tension of water against air (or against a vacuum saturated with water vapour). Consequently, when the function of a surface-active agent in a wetting phenomenon is considered in terms of its possible effect on a solid-liquid interfacial tension, it will usually be necessary to reckon with a lowering of the liquid-air interfacial tension as well, regardless of whether or not the latter effect is desirable.

The question of whether or not a surface-active solute in a liquid (1), in contact with a solid (3) and another fluid phase (2), will also lower the interfacial tension γ_{23} between the solid and phase (2), is unfortunately not capable of being answered at present. It would however be very unsafe to assume that γ_{23} was necessarily unaffected. Where an aqueous solution of a surface-active agent has been receding across the surface, for example, it seems highly probable that the properties of the solid-air interface will have been altered. Even when a solution has apparently *advanced* continuously against air, it would be unwise to assume that none of the surface-active agent has spread on to the solid-air interface by molecular diffusion. The occurrence of such an interfacial diffusion, which would need to take place over only a very short distance, would be enough to alter the contact angle and hence the work of adhesion, and the mere fact that it occurred would be evidence for a lowering of the solid-air interfacial tension.

The fact that the wettability of solids by water may be reduced when certain surface-active agents are dissolved in the water (*e.g.*, many cationic paraffin-chain salts can increase the contact angle of water against glass from no value to over 90°) was alluded to in Chapter 3, when it was pointed out that this occurrence was not conclusive evidence that the particular surface-active agent had actually increased the glass-water interfacial tension. It seems worth while to examine this phenomenon more fully in the light of equations (1) and (2). There being no finite contact angle for pure water on glass, we can write for the initial state of affairs, from equation (1),

$$\gamma_{23} - \gamma_{13} - \gamma_{12} \geq 0$$

If now the addition of a surface-active agent causes the contact angle to become greater than 90°, we have (denoting interfacial tensions in the presence of the surface-active agent by γ_{23}', etc.)

$$\gamma_{23}' - \gamma_{13}' - \gamma_{12}' \cos \theta = 0$$

or, since $\cos \theta$ is negative,

$$\gamma_{23}' - \gamma_{13}' + |\gamma_{12}' \cos \theta| = 0$$

whence $\qquad\qquad \gamma_{23} - \gamma_{13} > \gamma_{23}' - \gamma_{13}'$

or $\qquad\qquad \gamma_{13}' - \gamma_{13} > \gamma_{23}' - \gamma_{23}.$ $\qquad\qquad\qquad$ (15)

If now it could be independently shown that γ_{23} (the solid-air interfacial tension) was unaffected by the addition of the surface-active agent to the water, we would have $\gamma_{13}' - \gamma_{13} > 0$, *i.e.*, we could not escape the conclusion that the interfacial tension of the glass-water interface had been spontaneously increased by adsorption. The fact that positive adsorption has actually occurred is readily demonstrated by the fact that the surface of the glass remains water-repellent even after prolonged washing with clean water. Since, however, we cannot exclude the possibility that γ_{23}' is less than γ_{23}, the increase in the contact angle does not in fact constitute proof of an increase in the solid-liquid interfacial tension.

5. WETTING IN CAPILLARY SYSTEMS

The three types of wetting just described are characterised by the fact that they deal with the behaviour of two fluid phases in contact with a single, isolated, approximately plane surface. The conditions become more complicated if we consider the wetting of porous masses or other capillary systems, when the interfacial tensions may act by setting up pressure differences across curved menisci. Two general cases of this type are of considerable interest and will serve as illustrations. In both of them we shall for convenience assume that the fluid phase which is being displaced is *air*, but the treatment will be valid, in general terms, for any two immiscible fluids which are in contact in a capillary system.

The first case, in which a liquid is allowed to penetrate into a porous mass, or a porous mass is allowed to sink in a liquid, is essentially the well-known phenomenon of the capillary rise. In the simplest form of this process, the advancing liquid phase (1) is driven upwards in a cylindrical capillary of uniform bore, by the pressure difference across the meniscus between (1) and a second fluid phase (2) (*e.g.*, air). This pressure difference Δp will be a function of the interfacial tension γ_{12} and of the radii of curvature of the meniscus between (1) and (2):

$$\Delta p = \gamma_{12} \left(\frac{1}{R_i} + \frac{1}{R_{ii}} \right) \tag{16}$$

where R_i and R_{ii} are the radii of curvature.[1] If the capillary is small enough and circular in cross-section, then the meniscus represents a portion of the surface of a sphere, $R_i = R_{ii} = R$, and

$$\Delta p = 2 \frac{\gamma_{12}}{R}.$$

If now the spreading coefficient of the advancing liquid is zero or positive, so that there is no finite contact angle measured in (1), the meniscus becomes a hemisphere, and R becomes equal to r, the radius of the capillary, or

$$\Delta p = 2 \frac{\gamma_{12}}{r} \tag{17}$$

If there is a finite contact angle θ,* then it can be shown by simple geometry that, provided that the meniscus represents a portion of the surface of a sphere, $R = r/\cos \theta$, and

$$\Delta p = 2\gamma_{12} \frac{\cos \theta}{r} \tag{18}$$

---

* If $\theta > 90°$, the liquid (1) will of course cease to be the advancing liquid; *i.e.*, the interfacial tensions will act to drive the meniscus *downwards* in the capillary.

[1] Adam, *Physics and Chemistry of Surfaces*, Oxford University Press, 3rd Edition, 1941, p. 9.

If the contact angle can be taken to conform to a condition of equilibrium, then we can combine equations (18) and (2) to obtain

$$\Delta p = \frac{2}{r} \left(\gamma_{23} - \gamma_{13} \right) \tag{18a}$$

Depending on whether it is positive or negative, the pressure difference Δp in equations (17), (18), and (18a) will assist or work against the gravitational and mechanical forces which are tending to force the liquid into the pores of the capillary system.

The preceding arguments are based on the assumption that the "capillaries" in a porous mass are of uniform bore. As Adam[1] has pointed out in a review of capillary penetration, however, this condition is rarely satisfied. He then considers some of the methods by means of which the effect of irregularities can be allowed for. Firstly, the walls of the pores in a textile fabric, for example, may be treated as composite surfaces, and Cassie and Baxter's expression (equation (11), this chapter) substituted for $\cos \theta$ in equation (18), when we have

$$\Delta p = \frac{2\gamma_{12}}{r} \left(f_{13} \cos \theta - f_{123} \right) \tag{19}$$

where f_{13} is the area of true solid-liquid interface, and f_{123} the area of true air-liquid interface, per unit area of apparent solid-liquid interface. The use of this equation involves the assumption that the air is not completely displaced from the porous mass—it is therefore probably more widely applicable to water-repellent systems, for example, than to processes in which complete wetting is achieved. Adam refers, secondly, to the approach in which porous masses are treated formally as capillaries, equation (18) being applied, and the radius r of the "equivalent capillary" being independently obtained, for example by measuring the viscous resistance to flow of a liquid of known viscosity. Adam concludes: "Such methods have their uses, but they may conceal our present ignorance of how the liquid actually finds its way into the nooks and crannies of a solid, where the pores suffer frequent changes of size and shape."

Perhaps the most interesting part of Adam's paper is his theoretical treatment of the behaviour of menisci in tapering capillaries. Thus if a meniscus is rising in a capillary, the walls of which taper inwards at an angle of ϕ_1 to the horizontal (Figure 20a), then equation (18) assumes the form

$$\Delta p_1 = \frac{2\gamma_{12}}{r_1} \sin \left(\theta_A + \phi_1 \right) \tag{20}$$

where θ_A is the advancing contact angle, and r_1 is the radius of the capillary at the line of meeting of the meniscus and the capillary wall. If however

---

[1] Adam, *Discussions of the Faraday Society*, 1948, No. 3 ("Interaction of Water and Porous Materials"), p. 5.

the meniscus is advancing in a capillary, the walls of which taper outwards at an angle of ϕ_2 to the horizontal (Figure 20b), then the wetting pressure is given by

$$\Delta p_2 = -\frac{2\gamma_{12}}{r_2}\sin(\theta_A - \phi_2). \tag{21}$$

The mechanism of action of a wetting agent in the simpler cases of the capillary rise process, in terms of its effect on the interfacial tensions, can be seen from equations (17), (18), and (18a) to be simply that it should lower the advancing contact angle as much as possible, but that it should

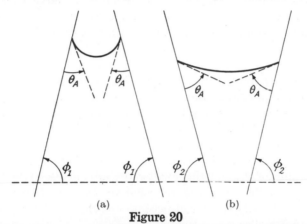

(a)   (b)

Figure 20
Capillary rise in inwardly and outwardly tapering capillaries
(Adam, *Discussions of the Faraday Society*, 1948, No. 3 ("Interaction of Water and Porous Materials"), p. 5.)

lower the interfacial tension between the two fluid phases as little as possible. In other words, the ideal wetting agent should lower the solid-liquid interfacial tension as much as possible, but the liquid-air interfacial tension only enough—if at all—to ensure that we have a vanishingly small contact angle. In practice, however, a wetting agent will usually lower both interfacial tensions simultaneously, since it will generally be adsorbed at both interfaces amphipathically (*i.e.*, non-specifically).* This, coupled with the fact that in general a wetting agent will be used only with a solid which is difficult to wet, means that by far the most important function of the wetting agent will usually be to lower the advancing contact angle, and especially to lower it from a value near or above 90°, thus ensuring that the

* This will probably be true, for example, if we are dealing with the wetting of a raw textile fibre, the surface of which is heavily contaminated with substances such as lanoline or cotton wax. Amphipathic wetting agents will probably be adsorbed indiscriminately at both the air-liquid and the solid-liquid (*e.g.*, wax-liquid) interfaces in such a system. There is also evidence that amphipathic agents are adsorbed at the cellulose-water interface, as discussed in Chapter 3, p. 99, though the lowering of the cellulose-water interfacial tension may be too small to be significant.

wetting pressure Δp has a positive value. This argument also holds for wetting processes in irregular capillaries insofar as we can still apply equation (18), together with the concept of the "equivalent capillary," or insofar as we can treat the capillary as having a composite wall and thus apply equation (19).

The effect of a wetting agent in a capillary rise process in irregular capillaries becomes much more difficult if we try to examine the process "microscopically": *i.e.*, if we try to follow each meniscus in detail. Thus equation (20) predicts (assuming that both θ_A and ϕ_1 lie between $0°$ and $90°$) that, as a meniscus approaches a constriction, its advance is favoured by a high air-liquid interfacial tension, but not necessarily by a low contact angle. The most favourable contact angle is in fact defined by

$$\phi_1 + \theta_A = 90°$$

and it can be seen from equation (20) that, if the inward taper is very marked (ϕ_1 being small), and the advancing contact angle is low, then very small values may result for Δp_1, though they will not actually be negative unless $(\theta_A + \phi_1) > 180°$. Equation (21), on the other hand, leads to two predictions, again assuming that both θ_A and ϕ_2 lie between $0°$ and $90°$. Thus if $\phi_2 > \theta_A$, Δp_2 will be positive, and its value will be greater the greater the value of γ_{12} and the smaller the advancing contact angle. If however $\phi_2 < \theta_A$, then Δp_2 will be negative and will work against the wetting process, but its effect will become less the smaller the interfacial tension and the smaller the contact angle.

The complex situation described in the preceding paragraph is probably frequently simplified in practice, especially when we are dealing with the sinking of a porous mass rather than the rise of the water line in a fixed mass, by the facts that (*i*) the various capillaries in the mass are usually inter-connected, (*ii*) the simpler situation represented by the cylindrical capillary will also obtain at many of the menisci, and (*iii*) it will be more important to avoid negative values of Δp_1 and Δp_2, than to have the largest possible positive values. These arguments suggest that, on the whole, very low values of the advancing contact angle, with the smallest possible lowering of the liquid-air interfacial tension, will be desirable, as in the simpler case previously discussed. At the same time, however, it should be noted that the present arguments may lose much of their force if we consider specially shaped porous bodies. Suppose for example that the capillaries in a porous system contain a large number of very sharp constrictions, so shaped that ϕ_1 approaches zero, while ϕ_2 is larger (say $45°$), and there are virtually no cylindrical capillaries. (Such a structure might occur in a specially "organised" system such as a living or dead organism, for example.) If now a wetting agent be used which causes the contact angle to disappear, the wetting pressure at each meniscus in an inwardly tapering capillary will be zero, while the pressure at each meniscus in an outwardly tapering capillary will be negative. Although the wetting pressure would be positive at each meniscus situated exactly at a constriction, the proportion of such menisci will be negligibly small, since we assumed that the constrictions were sharp. Complete wetting in such a case will therefore be impossible. If however the radii at the constrictions are not too small, then the walls of the capillaries may behave as composite surfaces, apparent wetting occurring if $(f_{13} \cos \theta - f_{123})$ in equation (19) is not too negative. In such an event the capillary walls will of course retain a quantity of entrapped air.

An interesting case of a porous mass containing capillaries of irregular shape, which is applicable to textile yarns, has been treated by Baxter and Cassie.[1] They consider a set of cylinders of radius r, arranged equidistantly and parallel to each other in a series of parallel layers, the distance between layers being equal, and the cylinders in each layer being in echelon to those in the adjacent layers. If now we bring this structure into contact with a liquid, so that each layer lies parallel to the macroscopical air-liquid interface, Baxter and Cassie find that the pressure P required to force water between the cylinders into the structure (which is equal to $- \Delta p$ in our previous treatments) is given by

$$P = \frac{\gamma_{12}}{r \cos \theta_A + \sqrt{(r + \mathrm{d})^2 - r^2 \sin^2 \theta_A}} \tag{22}$$

where d is half the distance between adjacent cylinders (fibres) in each layer, the term $(r \cos \theta_A + \sqrt{(r + \mathrm{d})^2 - r^2 \sin^2 \theta_A})$ being equal to R, the radius of curvature of the cylindrical menisci. This equation fails when R is very large (θ_A very small), when water will enter at values of P lower than those given by (22). When it is valid, equation (22) predicts that the opposition to wetting will diminish with decreasing values of either the interfacial tension liquid-air or the advancing contact angle.

Another wetting phenomenon which is of practical importance, and which involves the pressure differences across curved menisci, is that in which a porous mass, containing air (for example) is totally immersed in a liquid, the wetting process consisting of the displacement of air by the liquid. Two types of moving menisci will be involved: advancing menisci at which the capillary forces may assist the wetting process, and receding menisci at which by the same token the capillary forces may oppose the displacement. The simplest case is that in which a bubble of air is advancing along a smooth, narrow cylindrical capillary, which is completely immersed in a liquid (1). The advancing and receding contact angles (which we shall always measure inside the displacing liquid (1)), θ_A and θ_R, will be assumed to lie between 0° and 90°, and the radius of the capillary will be denoted by r. At any instant during the movement of the air bubble, there will be a

[1] Baxter and Cassie, *J. Textile Inst.*, 1945, **36**, T80 *ff*.

pressure difference at the lower meniscus which will tend to drive the air bubble up the capillary and will be given by $\Delta p_A = \dfrac{2\gamma_{12}}{r} \cos\theta_A$. At the upper meniscus the pressure acting in the opposite direction will be given by $\Delta p_R = \dfrac{2\gamma_{12}}{r} \cos\theta_R$, the net upward pressure (favouring the displacement of the air bubble) being given by

$$(\Delta p_A - \Delta p_R) = \frac{2\gamma_{12}}{r}(\cos\theta_A - \cos\theta_R). \tag{23}$$

If now $\theta_A = \theta_R$, the net capillary effect will be zero, and the addition of a surface-active agent will have no effect on the pressure difference, unless the agent causes the values of θ_A and θ_R to diverge. If however $\theta_A > \theta_R$, as is usually the case, then $(\Delta p_A - \Delta p_R)$ will be negative, and a surface-active agent will assist the buoyancy in displacing the bubble upwards if it decreases the interfacial tension and/or decreases the difference between θ_A and θ_R.

When the air bubble which we have been considering reaches the upper end of the capillary, the value of θ_R probably becomes relatively unimportant. At this stage we have a stream of bubbles of air escaping into the solution, and the situation becomes analogous to that obtaining in the measurement of surface or interfacial tensions by the maximum bubble pressure method. We can then assume, with sufficient accuracy for our purposes, that air bubbles will escape into the solution only if the pressure due to the combined effects of buoyancy and the advancing meniscus exceeds the "maximum bubble pressure" at the top of the capillary, given by $2\gamma_{12}/r$.[1] In other words, since the upward pressure due to buoyancy will be given by $\dfrac{V(\rho_1 - \rho_2)}{\pi r^2}$ (where ρ_1 and ρ_2 are the specific gravities of the solution and of air, respectively, and V is the total volume of air in the capillary), and the upward pressure due to the advancing meniscus is $2\gamma_{12}\dfrac{\cos\theta_A}{r}$, the condition for wetting to occur is that

$$\frac{V(\rho_1 - \rho_2)}{\pi r^2} + \frac{2\gamma_{12}}{r}\cos\theta_A > \frac{2\gamma_{12}}{r} \tag{24}$$

Provided that $\theta_A \not> 90°$ (which condition will almost always be satisfied if a wetting agent is present), we can re-write this expression in the form

$$\frac{V(\rho_1 - \rho_2)}{\pi r^2} > \frac{2\gamma_{12}}{r}(1 - \cos\theta_A) \tag{24a}$$

It follows from (24a) that wetting will be favoured by a surface-active agent which reduces the advancing contact angle as far as possible. As the

<hr>

[1] Adam, *Physics and Chemistry of Surfaces*, Oxford University Press, 3rd Edition, 1941, p. 372 *ff*.

contact angle becomes smaller, the value of the interfacial tension γ_{12} becomes less important, but as long as $\theta_A > 0$, then wetting is also favoured by a low value of the interfacial tension.

The escape of air from a porous mass which has been immersed in a liquid becomes a very complicated case if the capillaries are tapered rather than cylindrical. If for example a bubble of air is being displaced upwards in an inwardly tapering capillary, the net pressure P_1 assisting the wetting at any instant is the resultant of a positive pressure given by

$$\frac{2\gamma_{12}}{r_A} \sin (\theta_A + \phi_1) \text{ (equation 20)},$$

and the opposing negative pressure given by

$$\frac{-2\gamma_{12}}{r_R} \sin (\theta_R - \phi_1) \text{ (equation 21)},$$

where r_A and r_R are the radii of the capillary at the advancing and receding menisci, respectively, and ϕ_1 is the angle of taper (to the horizontal). Combining these two terms we have

$$P_1 = 2\gamma_{12} \left[\frac{\sin (\theta_A + \phi_1)}{r_A} + \frac{\sin (\theta_R - \phi_1)}{r_R} \right]. \tag{25}$$

If the air bubble is being displaced up an outwardly tapering capillary, we find, similarly, that

$$P_2 = - 2\gamma_{12} \left[\frac{\sin (\theta_A - \phi_2)}{r_A} + \frac{\sin (\theta_R + \phi_2)}{r_R} \right]. \tag{26}$$

where ϕ_2 is the angle of taper to the horizontal.

If the advancing meniscus is in an inwardly tapering capillary, but the receding meniscus is in a capillary which tapers outwards (*e.g.*, if the air bubble is being displaced *past a constriction*), then we have

$$P_3 = 2\gamma_{12} \left[\frac{\sin (\theta_A + \phi_1)}{r_A} - \frac{\sin (\theta_R - \phi_2)}{r_R} \right]. \tag{27}$$

Finally, if we consider the reverse of the last case (*e.g.*, if the bubble is being displaced past a bulge in the capillary), then

$$P_4 = 2\gamma_{12} \left[\frac{\sin (\theta_R - \phi_1)}{r_R} - \frac{\sin (\theta_A - \phi_2)}{r_A} \right]. \tag{28}$$

It is at once apparent that a very large number of possibilities arise from equations (25)–(28), which we cannot hope to consider in detail here, and that no simple generalisations can be made from them. We have recorded these four equations because it seems possible that each of them might on occasion be the critical stage of a wetting process. In practice, however, it seems likely that the most important stage in the wetting of an immersed porous mass, containing virtual capillaries of irregular bore, will be that during which air bubbles are escaping from openings at the top of the porous mass ("maximum bubble pressure" analogy), the driving pressure which causes displacement of the air being the resultant of the effect of buoyancy and the pressure differences set up across the advancing menisci. If we consider that there are capillaries of different sizes, and that all the capillaries are inter-connected, then at any instant air bubbles will be escaping provided that

$$\frac{V(\rho_1 - \rho_2)}{\pi \Sigma_i n_i r_i^2} + P_{AM} > \frac{2\gamma_{12}}{r_{max}} \tag{29}$$

where r_{max} is the radius of the openings of largest size along the top of the porous mass, and $\pi \Sigma_i n_i r_i^2$ is the total area of openings of all sizes, and P_{AM} is the smallest upward pressure difference obtaining at any of the advancing menisci at the instant involved. There will be three possibilities for P_{AM}, corresponding to menisci which are situated in capillaries which are cylindrical, taper inwards, or taper outwards, respectively, the values for P_{AM} being:

Cylindrical capillary: $P_{AM}' = \dfrac{2\gamma_{12}}{r'} \cos \theta_A$

Inwardly tapering capillary: $P_{AM}'' = \dfrac{2\gamma_{12}}{r''} \sin (\theta_A + \phi)$

Outwardly tapering capillary: $P_{AM}''' = -\dfrac{2\gamma_{12}}{r'''} \sin (\theta_A - \phi)$

ϕ is the angle of taper in each case, *i.e.*, the angle between the capillary wall and a plane drawn at right angles to the axis of the capillary. This angle of taper is not necessarily constant along the capillary, nor equal in different cases.

Since we can safely assume that each advancing meniscus must traverse in turn lengths of capillary which are of all three types, the criterion of whether or not substantially complete wetting can occur is that (29) should still be satisfied for the smallest possible value of P_{AM}, algebraically speaking. Since V is decreasing throughout the process, the value of P_{AM} will become increasingly important towards the end. For the extreme case that $\phi \to 0$ (maximum inward or outward taper of the capillaries), we have, provided that θ_A is finite but small,

$$P_{AM}'' = \frac{2\gamma_{12}}{r''} \sin \theta_A$$

and

$$P_{AM}''' = -\frac{2\gamma_{12}}{r'''} \sin \theta_A$$

in which case P_{AM}'' will be positive, but P_{AM}''' must be negative. For intermediate values of ϕ and small values of θ_A (say $\theta_A + \phi < 90°$), P_{AM}''

will be positive, but P_{AM}''' will become negative if $\phi < \theta_A$. When therefore we are considering the wetting of a porous mass, in which the advancing menisci must traverse regions in which in effect the capillaries taper very markedly outwards (ϕ being small), and if the advancing contact angle is small, then the critical stages of the process will occur when the menisci are in such regions, and the pressure at the advancing menisci is given by P_{AM}''', and we have the condition for wetting to continue that

$$\frac{V(\rho_1 - \rho_2)}{\pi \Sigma n_i r_i^2} + \frac{2\gamma_{12}}{r'''} \sin(\phi - \theta_A) > \frac{2\gamma_{12}}{r_{max}} \tag{30}$$

Since the second term will be negative, the final stages of the wetting process will be favoured by a surface-active agent which gives low values of both γ_{12} and θ_A, though in theory such a wetting process cannot go spontaneously to absolute completion, when $V \to 0$.

It will be apparent from the foregoing discussion that the effect of a surface-active agent in a capillary wetting phenomenon is not always obvious, and that *the widely-held view that the chief function of a wetting agent is to lower the surface tension of water can be quite misleading*. It will have been noted that the *desiderata* of a good wetting agent depend on the geometry of the capillary system concerned, especially if it is desired to follow a wetting process microscopically: in fact it is not even invariably true in such a case that the wetting agent should lower the contact angle(s), measured inside the wetting medium. We have however pointed out that, for the great majority of practical cases, it is probably possible to simplify the picture greatly. Thus if (*i*) we agree that the function of a wetting agent is in practice to make a wetting process possible, or more nearly complete, rather than to improve on an already favourable state of affairs, (*ii*) we consider the wetting process "macroscopically," and (*iii*) we make certain apparently reasonable assumptions about the structure of the capillary system, then we can conclude that the chief function of a wetting agent is usually to lower the contact angle, especially the advancing contact angle. We can also conclude that, when we are displacing air from an immersed porous mass, it is advantageous for the interfacial tension air-solution to be lowered at the same time by the wetting agent. For a "sinking" wetting, on the other hand, or for the simple "capillary rise" of a liquid into a porous mass, it is desirable for the decrease in contact angle to be accompanied by as small a decrease in the interfacial tension as possible. We have seen, however, that this last point loses much of its force when we recall that lowerings of the interfacial tension air-water, and of the contact angle, usually occur together when we are considering amphipathic surface-active agents, and that practically speaking we are usually more concerned with achieving wetting than with accelerating an already effective wetting process. It is therefore probably generally true to take the *lowering of the advancing contact angle as the most important measure of the effectiveness of a wetting agent,* which is to be used in capillary systems.

6. THE KINETICS OF WETTING PROCESSES

The arguments in the preceding sections have dealt with wetting phenomena, and with some of the effects which are likely to be achieved by the addition of surface-active agents, in terms of the thermodynamical driving force behind such processes, *i.e.*, the decrease in the total interfacial free energy of the system if a small portion of the process is assumed to be carried out reversibly at constant temperature and pressure. The implicit assumption was made that any increase (algebraically speaking) in this thermodynamical driving force by the addition of surface-active agents would favour the process, *i.e.*, would increase its speed or degree of completion under practical conditions. Although it must be admitted that this assumption cannot be claimed to be rigorously true, especially in the quantitative sense, it does seem to offer a rough qualitative guide in the majority of cases, presumably because at least two of the phases involved are mobile. It should however be noticed that, if the dynamics of a wetting process are to be treated in terms of interfacial tensions, then it is clearly necessary to use dynamic values for the interfacial tensions, at surface ages which are relevant to the particular process. We have already seen that the dynamic interfacial tensions of solutions of surface-active agents may differ very greatly from the "static" values which are usually measured. It is therefore most unfortunate that there exists no comprehensive body of data at present on the interfacial tensions (and contact angles) at freshly formed interfaces in the presence of powerfully surface-active agents. It seems quite clear that, until such information is available, it will be impossible fully to explain the relative efficiency in wetting processes of different surface-active compounds. Thus the general surface-activity of C_{16} paraffin-chain salts, under equilibrium conditions, is considerably greater than that of the C_{12} homologues, but the latter are well known to be better technical wetting agents (in the displacement of air by aqueous solutions from textile fibres). It seems almost certain that the answer lies, at least in part, in the more rapid adsorption of the short-chain (or branched-chain) agents at the relevant interfaces.

The time-lag in the adsorption of surface-active agents in capillary wetting processes can have two effects, *viz.*, increasing the disparity between advancing and receding contact angles, and causing a time-lag in the reduction of the liquid-fluid (*e.g.*, air-water) interfacial tensions at the relevant menisci. It will be apparent from the arguments developed in the preceding pages that the increase in contact angle hysteresis will in general hinder wetting, and that conversely it is desirable to have as rapid adsorption as possible. The effect of the time-lag in the decrease of the interfacial tension at the menisci will, of course, depend on whether or not a low tension is desirable *per se*. An interesting study of the kinetics of adsorption at such menisci has been published by Lange,[1] who measured the rate of fall of columns of solutions of surface-active agents in inclined glass capillaries, the contact angle against air being always zero. At the upper (retreating) meniscus the interface was expanding, while at the lower (advancing) meniscus the interface was contracting. The result was that the surface tension at the upper meniscus was greater than that at the lower one, so that (given equal contact angles) there was a net upward "braking" effect. The extent of this braking effect, expressed in the rate of travel of the column of solution, relative to that of a similar column of pure water, was a measure of the "inertia" of each wetting agent; there was a good inverse correlation between this "inertia" and the wetting power in practical tests. Lange also found that, over a certain region, the distance travelled by the column was proportional to the square root of the time, which he considers to be evidence that the reduction of surface tension is a diffusion-controlled process.

When pure liquids are involved in wetting processes, the deviations between static and dynamic interfacial tensions are much less likely to be appreciable. An interesting treatment of two capillary wetting processes involving pure liquids has been published by Eley and Pepper,[2] who studied the rate of displacement of air by various liquids, and of organic liquids (benzene, nitrobenzene, medicinal paraffin) by water, from capillary tubes and glass powder. The cases studied can be described as "pure" wetting processes, in that gravity and other extraneous forces had a negligible effect in comparison with the capillary forces.

For the displacement of a fluid (2) by a fluid (1) from a horizontal capillary, Eley and Pepper obtained the equation

$$\frac{\gamma_{12} \cos \theta_A rt}{4} = \frac{(\eta_1 - \eta_2)x^2}{2} + \eta_2 lx \tag{31}$$

where x is the distance through which the meniscus had advanced in time t, r is the radius of the capillary and l is its length, η's are the viscosities of the two fluids and θ and γ_{12} have their previous meanings. Equation (31) predicts that x will not be a linear function of time unless $\eta_1 = \eta_2$, but that the experimentally determinable quantity, $\left[\frac{(\eta_1 - \eta_2)}{2} x^2 + \eta_2 lx\right] = f(x)$, should be a linear function of time, and that the slope of the $f(x) - t$ curve should give $\gamma_{12} \cos \theta_A$ from the equation

$$\gamma_{12} \cos \theta_A = \frac{4}{r} \frac{df(x)}{dt}. \tag{32}$$

---

[1] Lange, *Koll. Z.*, 1954, **136**, 136, 141.

[2] Eley and Pepper, *Trans. Faraday Soc.*, 1946, **42**, 697, *q.v.* for references to earlier work. See also the papers by Barrer, *Discussions of the Faraday Society*, 1948, No. 3, p. 61, and by Peek and McLean, *Ind. Eng. Chem. (Anal.)*, 1934, **6**, 85.

If the viscosity of the fluid (2) is much less than that of (1) (*e.g.*, if (1) is a liquid and (2) is a gas), equation (31) reduces to the earlier relation obtained by Washburn[1] and by Rideal,[2] *viz.*,

$$x = \sqrt{\frac{\gamma_{12} \cos \theta_A r t}{2\eta_1}}.$$ (33)

For the displacement of a fluid from a powder, Eley and Pepper introduce the well-known "tortuosity factor" k (a constant to allow for the tortuous path of the capillaries) and obtain equations which are analogous to (31) and (32), *viz.*,

$$\gamma_{12} \cos \theta_A \frac{r't}{4k^2} = \frac{(\eta_1 - \eta_2)x^2}{2} - \eta_2 l x = f(x)$$ (34)

and

$$\gamma_{12} \cos \theta_A = \frac{4k^2}{r'} \frac{df(x)}{dt}$$ (35)

where r' is the "average radius" of the capillaries. Both k and r' are obtained from measurements of bulk density and gas permeability.

Eley and Pepper found that equations (31) and (32) were in good agreement with their experimental data for the displacement of medicinal paraffin or benzene by water, or of medicinal paraffin by nitrobenzene, from a single glass capillary, provided that the tube was always wetted beforehand with the advancing liquid. If this precaution was taken, the contact angle was zero and the values obtained for $\gamma_{12} \cos \theta_A$ agreed reasonably well with the values of the static surface tension determined by direct measurement. If the surface was not well wetted beforehand, the meniscus was found to advance more slowly and less reproducibly, being occasionally halted at areas which were presumably contaminated. In their experiments with glass powders of different grists, Eley and Pepper obtained reproducible results with liquids (water, benzene, and medicinal paraffin) advancing against air, and a good agreement with equation (35) was indicated by the fact that values calculated for r'/k^2 (using directly measured values for $\gamma_{12} \cos \theta_A$) were constant for a given powder with different liquids. When however they attempted to measure the rate of displacement of benzene or medicinal paraffin by water, the reproducibility was much poorer. Although smooth displacements were frequently observed, in which the linear relation between t and $f(x)$ demanded by (34) and (35) was obtained, considerable time-lags were frequently observed before the displacement started, and the advance was often uneven, leaving "pockets" of liquid (2) behind.[3] Values for $\gamma_{12} \cos \theta_A$ were also calculated by using the r'/k^2 values from corresponding experiments with single

---

[1] Washburn, *Phys. Rev.*, 1921, **17**, 374.

[2] Rideal, *Phil. Mag.*, 1922, **44**, 1152.

[3] *Cf.* the results reported by Atkinson in *Discussions of the Faraday Society*, 1948, No. 3, p. 121, and the subsequent discussion.

liquids; although the values obtained were of the correct order of magnitude, they fluctuated considerably.

It will be observed that the conclusions to be drawn from equations (31)–(35) are the same as the qualitative deductions already drawn for the case of "sinking" wetting (*cf.* equation 18), *viz.*, that the velocity of wetting will be greater the greater the surface (or interfacial) tension, and the lower the contact angle. This is of course to be expected from the equivalence of the two processes, and from the fact that Eley and Pepper's treatment is based on the same assumption that the pressure difference across the curved meniscus, which is due to the curvature and to the existence of the interfacial free energy, can be used in dynamic equations for capillary flow. The value of Eley and Pepper's work to the present subject seems to us to lie in the demonstration of the admissibility of that assumption, though it illustrates the experimental difficulties involved in obtaining reproducible surfaces and the appropriate contact angles. Thus their best results were obtained when steps were taken to ensure that there was no finite contact angle (and hence no possible hysteresis factor); as soon as a hysteresis factor became possible, it also appears to have become variable.* Eley and Pepper's work was done with pure liquids: it remains to be seen whether or not a similar treatment can be applied to solutions of highly surface-active materials, relevant dynamic values being of course used for the boundary tensions and contact angles. The possible methods of measuring dynamic boundary tensions have been discussed in Chapter 3, while progress has recently been reported by Elliott and Leese[1] on the measurement of dynamic contact angles on paraffin wax, though not so far with technical wetting-out agents.

It is interesting to compare Eley and Pepper's work with the more recent results of Kling and Lange[2] on the displacement of fluids in smooth capillary tubes, to which additional hydrostatic pressures (both positive and negative) were applied. The particular interest of this work is that the behaviour of water was compared with that of aqueous solutions of sodium dodecyl sulphate, the displaced fluids being air, paraffin oil, and olive oil, respectively. For pure water against air, an equation analogous to (33) was found to apply, but it no longer held for solutions of the surface-active agent ($M/100$ to $M/1,000$ in concentration). At relatively low rates of

---

* The magnitude of the hysteresis factor in many practical wetting processes involving two liquids is probably difficult to exaggerate. Thus many pigments will remain completely wetted by an oil medium, in competition with water, if the pigment particles were first wetted by the oil, while the situation is reversed if the pigment was initially wetted with water, and the oil is the advancing phase (1). The same holds true for many textile fibres, as is well known. Surface-active agents which cause the particular solid to become decisively wetted by one of the two liquid phases appear greatly to reduce this hysteresis effect, if not to eliminate it almost completely.

[1] Elliott and Leese, *J. Chem. Soc.*, 1957, 22; 1959, 1466.
[2] Kling and Lange, *Koll. Z.*, 1958, **158**, 150.

displacement of the meniscus, a wetting "inertia" was set up which slowed down the displacement, the effect being explicable in terms of the contraction or expansion of the meniscus previously discussed by Lange. At higher rates, a constant capillary pressure was reached, but rather surprisingly this did not approach the value for pure water. When the competing fluid was oil, the wetting inertia was less pronounced, in agreement with the general experience that the adsorption of surface-active materials approaches equilibrium more rapidly at oil-water interfaces. The results did not obey the theoretical equations so well as with air-water menisci, and appreciable wetting hysteresis was encountered, though the presence of sodium dodecyl sulphate reduced the extent of this hysteresis.

B. Deflocculation and flocculation

1. DEFINITIONS

It is well known that many surface-active agents are capable of profoundly affecting the state of dispersion of the particles of a disperse phase (solid, liquid, or gaseous) in a liquid medium. If the tendency for spontaneous mutual adhesion to occur among the disperse particles in a system is diminished by the addition of a surface-active agent, we can say that it has a "deflocculating"* action; if on the other hand the tendency towards mutual adhesion is increased, then the surface-active agent can be conveniently referred to as a "flocculating agent."

Although disperse systems are frequently described as "flocculated" if all the particles are adhering together, and "deflocculated" if they are not, with no provision for intermediate states, it seems to us to be necessary to adopt a rather broader definition, especially when dealing with industrial dispersions. We propose in fact to describe a disperse system as completely flocculated if substantially every approach between particles leads to a mutual adhesion, and as completely deflocculated if a negligible proportion of such approaches results in adhesions, and to distinguish (qualitatively speaking) between different degrees of flocculation and deflocculation. In dealing with the relatively dilute hydrophobic sols of classical colloid science, there is frequently nothing to be gained in trying to distinguish between degrees of deflocculation between the two extremes: such a sol

---

* The use of the expression "dispersing agent" is not, in our opinion, to be recommended in the present context, since it often implies in practice that the agent is also a "protective colloid." Another possible expression, "peptising agent," suffers from the disadvantage that it is often used to describe a substance which assists the spontaneous dissolution of a so-called "eucolloid," *i.e.*, a soluble substance, such as a protein, which yields a colloidal solution by virtue of the composition, temperature, etc., of the solution, and not just on account of the history of the system. We therefore propose to standardise on the expressions "deflocculation" and "deflocculating agent" when dealing with disperse systems, and to restrict the meaning of "peptisation" to the process of spontaneous solution of a eucolloid.

will usually become either completely aggregated or completely "defloccu-lated" in a relatively short time, and it may be impossible to reverse the process of aggregation on account of the high ratio of surface to mass of the individual particles. If on the other hand we consider the coarser and more concentrated disperse systems which are used technically, then degrees of deflocculation have a real significance. In such systems the looser aggregates may be continually broken down by mechanical agitation, and then reform spontaneously when the agitation ceases—in other words, the state of affairs prevailing at the solid-liquid interfaces is only one of a number of factors which determine the state of aggregation of the system. In such a case it seems worth while to reserve the expressions "floccula-tion" and "deflocculation" for describing the conditions prevailing at the interfaces, as judged by the tendency for adhesion to occur as particles approach each other.

2. FACTORS DETERMINING THE STATE OF FLOCCULATION OF DISPERSE SYSTEMS

In order to examine the mechanism of the action of surface-active agents in deflocculation or flocculation phenomena, it is necessary to review briefly the factors which determine the stability of disperse systems. It should be noted in the first place that every disperse system, in which there is a measurable interfacial tension between the two (or more) phases present, is thermodynamically unstable compared with the same system in which the disperse particles have coalesced. Thus if we consider a disperse phase S in a liquid medium L, the interfacial tension will be given (at constant temperature and pressure) by

$$\gamma_{SL} = \left(\frac{\partial G}{\partial A_{SL}}\right)_{P,\,T,\,n_S,\,n_L,\,A_L}$$

where G is the total Gibbs free energy of the system, A_{SL} is the interfacial area, and n_S, n_L, etc., are the total numbers of moles of the different com-ponents present (*i.e.*, the composition of the total system is constant), and A_L is the area of the interface between L and its surroundings. Since γ_{SL} must always be finite and positive—otherwise the phases S and L would be completely miscible and we should no longer have a disperse system— any decrease in A_{SL} at constant temperature, pressure, etc., will decrease the total free energy of the system, and will therefore represent a thermo-dynamically favoured state. Under the conditions postulated, A_{SL} can decrease only by coalescence of the particles of the disperse phase; con-sequently the effect of the existence of the interfacial free energy is always to diminish the degree of dispersion. It is therefore clear that, although the degree of thermodynamical instability of a disperse system will be consider-ably lowered by a surface-active agent which lowers the interfacial tension, and therefore lowers the total interfacial free energy, we must look for mechanisms other than a simple lowering of the interfacial tension in order to account for the fact that dispersions can exist at all: *i.e.*, we must look for stabilising energy barriers.

Since many of the dispersions of technical importance are hydrophobic, and the surface-active agents and protective colloids which are used to stabilise these dispersions are hydrophilic, it is necessary to examine both hydrophobic and hydrophilic stability in order to understand the stabilising energy barriers which are involved. It is well known that hydrophobic sols or suspensions in water are very sensitive to small concentrations of added simple electrolytes, and that valency plays a very important part in the critical concentration required to flocculate the sol or suspension completely (Schultze-Hardy rule). Hydrophilic colloids, on the other hand, are much less sensitive to the addition of simple electrolytes, and here the solubility seems to be the determining factor (salting-out effect). In many cases the addition of a deflocculating agent to a hydrophobic sol or suspension alters the behaviour of the suspension towards flocculating electrolytes from a hydrophobic to a hydrophilic type.

The concept of the electrical double layer as the stabilising barrier which prevents aggregation has been developed by Derjaguin and Landau, and by Verwey and Overbeek, into a quantitative theory to explain the stability of lyophobic sols.[1]

In their book Verwey and Overbeek consider that the total potential energy set up by the interaction of two colloid particles is the barrier which decides whether or not the sol will be flocculated, and that the total potential energy is made up of terms which are due to attraction and to repulsion. The repulsive force arises from the interaction of the electrical double layers which exist around the particles. This double layer, as the name implies, consists of two parts, the inner part arising from the preferential adsorption of one species of ion at the surface of the particle. The outer part of the double layer is more diffuse, since the thermal motion acting on the counterions (of opposite charge to those adsorbed at the surface) tends to counteract to a certain extent the electrostatic attraction which tends to keep them in the neighbourhood of the preferentially adsorbed ions. Each particle is thus surrounded by a "cloud" of counterions, which screen off the particle charge. In order to calculate how the potential behaves with respect to the distance from the surface, it is necessary to choose some model of the double layer, and Verwey and Overbeek select the Gouy-Chapman model on account of its simplicity, but point out that an extension to Stern's model is comparatively easy.

In their consideration of the potential energy due to the interaction of the double layers, Verwey and Overbeek examined first the possibility of

[1] Derjaguin and Landau, *Acta Physicochim. U.R.S.S.*, 1941, **14**, 633; *Zh. Eks. Teor. Fiz.*, 1941, **11**, 802; 1945, **15**, 662; Verwey and Overbeek, *Theory of the Stability of Lyophobic Colloids*, Elsevier, Amsterdam, 1948.

deriving an expression for the force acting between the particles as a function of their distance apart, and then integrating with respect to distance to obtain the potential energy. This approach leads to mathematical difficulties, and the integrations involved must be carried out by numerical or graphical methods. The second method is to consider the free energy of the system of the two double layers as a function of their distance of separation: *i.e.*, the difference in free energies of the system with and without the double layers. This gives the potential curve for the double layer interaction directly, since the free energy is identical with the work associated with some hypothetical isothermally reversible process for building up the double layers. The variation of the free energy with particle separation is equal to the variation of the potential energy of the two particles with respect to each other.

The second part of the total potential energy curve of interaction arises from the attraction due to the London-van der Waals forces. A knowledge of the behaviour of these forces with respect to the distance between the particles is required in order for the potential energy to be calculated. The theoretical basis of these attractive forces has been reviewed by Margenau,[1] and recorded in more recent papers by several authors.[2] The attractive potential between two atoms is inversely proportional to the *sixth* power of the distance of separation when that distance is small, and inversely proportional to the *seventh* power when the distance is large. The attractive potential between two particles can be approximately calculated as a summation or integration of the attractive potential over all pairs of atoms. The change in the power law dependence is due to a relativistic correction introduced because of the finite propagation of electromagnetic radiation. The distance at which the change in the power begins to occur depends on a function of the imaginary part of the dielectric constant of the material.

When the potential energies due to the attractive forces and the repulsive forces are combined, a total potential energy curve is obtained which may be of one of three types, as shown in Figure 21. Curve 1, in which the maximum is very much greater than kT, represents a "stable" sol; curve 2 corresponds to the flocculation state (rapid), and curve 3 to a completely flocculated system. The theory is made more quantitative by Verwey and Overbeek by the incorporation of Smoluchowski's[3] well-known theory of rapid coagulation, as extended by Fuchs[4] for the probability of aggregation of colloidal particles. The problem is treated as one of diffusion, and the number of collisions against one particle in one second can be calculated.

---

[1] Margenau, *Reviews of Modern Physics*, 1939, **11**, 1.
[2] Casimir and Polder, *Phys. Rev.*, 1948, **73**, 360; Lifshitz, *Zh. Eks. Teor. Fiz.* 1955, **29**, 94; Dzialoshinskii, *Zh. Eks. Teor. Fiz.*, 1956, **30**, 1152.
[3] Smoluchowski, *Z. phys. Chem.*, 1917, **19**, 129.
[4] Fuchs, *Z. Physik*, 1934, **89**, 736.

In the absence of any interaction between the particles, this is a direct measure of the flocculation velocity, but if any interaction is present, so that the potential energy is positive, then the velocity of flocculation is diminished by a factor which can be calculated if the function of potential energy against distance of separation of the particles is known. The factor depends upon the radius of the particles, their concentration, the concentration and valency of the electrolyte present, the surface potential ψ_0, and the value of the London-van der Waals constant A. Verwey and Overbeek have calculated the factor by graphical integration for a number

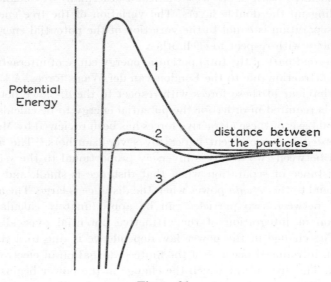

Figure 21

Total potential energy curves of interaction between two spherical particles

of cases and conclude that the maximum in the total potential energy curve has to be about $25\ kT$ units if the sol is to be stable for all practical purposes. Figure 22, which has been taken from Verwey and Overbeek's book, gives some idea of the magnitude of the various terms involved and the effect of a variation of the surface potential ψ_0. The curve in which $\psi_0 = 32$ mV would represent a stable sol under the stipulated conditions, $\psi_0 = 25\cdot6$ mV would represent a sol exhibiting slow flocculation, and for $\psi_0 < 19\cdot2$ mV, the barrier to flocculation would be so small that any sol with these characteristics would flocculate very rapidly. Similar curves can be drawn for variations in the particle radius (a), van der Waals constant (A), and for changes in concentration of electrolyte which are reflected in the value of the Debye-Hückel function (κ). Further calculations show that the effect of the valency of the flocculating electrolyte on the critical concentration which is needed to flocculate the sol, with a surface potential of 100 millivolts (a reasonable value) and a radius of 10^{-6} cm., is in good agreement with the Schultze-Hardy rule.

It is well known that many flocculated colloid systems, *e.g.*, the metal sulphides, can be deflocculated by simply washing out the electrolytes which are present. This deflocculation can be explained in the theory of lyophobic stability by the introduction of the "Born repulsion," which is due to the

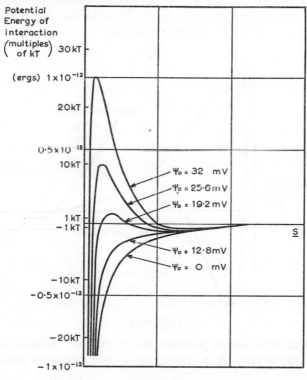

Figure 22

The effect of the surface potential (ψ_0) on total potential energy of interaction

repulsive forces set up when the electronic shells of two atoms inter-penetrate. This alters the infinitely large negative potential well which would otherwise arise from the London-van der Waals forces, and consequently any minimum in the potential energy curve has a finite value (see Figure 23). In some cases, the difference between this minimum and the maximum in the total potential energy curve is only a few kT units, and consequently if the electrolyte concentration is substantially reduced by washing, deflocculation can occur. Figure 23 also shows a curve with a minimum at a large distance of separation of the particles, and it has been suggested that for rod-shaped particles this minimum, which will be found at low electrolyte concentrations, is responsible for a secondary, more reversible type of flocculation, of the type shown by tobacco mosaic virus and certain inorganic sols which give thixotropic gels. The difference in the flocculating effects of ions of the same valency can be explained satisfactorily by the introduction of the Stern correction.

Many attempts have been made in the past to correlate the electrokinetic (ζ) potential with lyophobic colloid stability, but as Verwey and Overbeek point out, the ζ-potential has quite a different character from the surface potential ψ_0, which is the basic factor in their theory. The ζ-potential is derived from electrokinetic experiments such as electrophoresis,

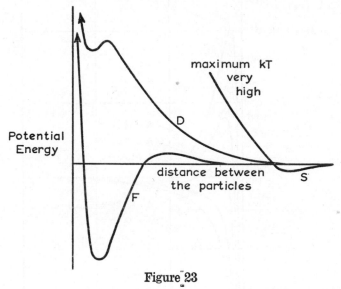

Figure 23

Effect of Born repulsion on potential energy curves; flocculation (F) and deflocculation (D). Also shown, curve with secondary minimum

electroendosmosis, and sedimentation potentials, all of which involve the measurement of a flow of liquid along the particle boundary (or *vice versa*). The flow of liquid does not occur exactly at the particle-liquid interface but at a plane in the liquid some distance from the true interface. This plane is called the "plane of slip," and the ζ-potential is the potential (relative to the bulk of the liquid) at this plane. The ζ-potential is therefore generally much smaller than the surface potential ψ_0, and is considerably affected by changes in the concentration of any non-potential-determining ions. (The potential-determining ions are defined by Verwey and Overbeek as those which set up a distribution equilibrium between the surface of the particle and the liquid, and thus give rise to the electrical double layer.)

Most of the preceding remarks applied to the stability of dispersions of solid particles, but as Verwey and Overbeek point out, these arguments can also be applied to emulsions of oil in water, after due consideration of some important differences. In the case of emulsions, the double layer consists of *two* diffuse charge layers, one in each liquid phase. The electrical potential function in each of these layers is given by exactly analogous equations to that used for the solid-liquid phase boundary. As a result, the total potential drop is divided between the two phases, the greater part of this drop being found in the oil phase. The preparation of an emulsion requires an emulsifying agent, but the stability of an emulsion, once formed, closely resembles that of the normal lyophobic colloids.

Van den Tempel[1] has considered the stability of oil-in-water emulsions, in terms of the rate of flocculation and the rate of coalescence in the presence of added electrolytes. Flocculation is regarded by van den Tempel as the formation of more or less reversible aggregates, while coalescence is the irreversible process of aggregation which leads to a decrease in the number of oil droplets and finally to the "breaking" of the emulsion. The emulsions were made by stirring a mixture of monochlorobenzene and paraffin oil (density $1 \cdot 006$ gm./cm.^{3}) into aqueous soap solutions. Diluted portions of this stock emulsion were mixed with salt solutions of varying concentrations. After a predetermined time, the emulsions were mixed with a solution of a non-ionic emulsifying agent. This reduced the salt concentration and prevented further coagulation, even in the presence of considerable amounts of electrolyte. Microscopical examination revealed that the aggregates which were formed during the coagulation were completely redispersed after addition of the non-ionic surface-active agent. The rate of coagulation was followed by counting the particles microscopically. The Schultze-Hardy rule was applicable to the systems studied by van den Tempel, but only when the flocculating electrolyte had no appreciable effect on the rate of coalescence; this was the case when no insoluble soap was formed at the interface.

An examination of the rate of flocculation is complicated, as van den Tempel points out, by (a) the particle size distribution, which is not uniform and consequently increases the rate of flocculation, (b) flocculation occurring during the mixing of the salt solution and the emulsion, (c) increased flocculation caused by creaming and sedimentation, and (d) the possibility that the van der Waals attractive forces cause an increased rate of diffusion towards a central particle as another particle approaches to within a distance of about one particle radius.

Since it is important to distinguish between coalescence and adhesion, we propose to define a completely flocculated system as one in which all geometrically possible adhesions take place, but without the occurrence of any coalescence: *i.e.*, the particles are still separated by a film or barrier of some sort. This condition can often be reversed (the word not being used

---

[1] Van den Tempel, *Rec. trav. chim.*, 1953, **72**, 419, 433, 442.

here in the strict thermodynamical sense): momentarily by mechanical means, or permanently by adding a deflocculating agent or otherwise changing the composition of the system. It is important to note in this connection that the behaviour of dispersed solid particles may be very different from that of disperse liquid or gaseous phases, in emulsions or foams, respectively. Thus coalescence is much less likely to occur if the particles are solid, partly as a direct consequence of their rigidity, and partly on account of the fact that a deflocculating agent is more likely to be irreversibly adsorbed at a solid-liquid than at a fluid-liquid interface. A further difference between dispersions (of solids in liquids) and emulsions or foams is that the coalescence between two fluid particles, if it occurs, is usually complete. Dispersed solid particles, on the other hand, normally undergo only partial coalescence, actual union of the crystal lattices occurring only over relatively restricted areas. It is therefore convenient generally to speak of "coalescence" in emulsions or foams, but to introduce another name for the corresponding effect in dispersions containing solid particles, *e.g.*, "agglomeration."

The theory of the stability of lyophobic sols can be applied successfully to many systems of finely divided inorganic and organic sols, but in many cases it is not sufficient to explain their stability to flocculation. If we consider a dispersion in a medium of low ionising power, instead of in water, it would be expected that the stabilising effect of the electrical double layer would be largely eliminated. Although in many cases some other stabilising mechanism has to be postulated, van der Minne and Hermanie[1] have shown that in the flocculation of carbon black suspensions in dry benzene, stabilised by the calcium salt of di*iso*propyl salicylate and by tetraisoammonium picrate, there is a good correlation with their electrophoretic mobility and adsorption behaviour. Mackor and van der Waals,[2] on the other hand, have examined theoretically the effect of the adsorption of rod-shaped molecules on the stability of colloidal suspensions. The adsorption of the rod-shaped molecules from solution on to an adsorbent is examined by statistical methods, and they show that the free energy of the system consisting of two planes covered by an adsorbed layer increases as they approach one another, on account of *steric interactions* of the adsorbed layers. From an examination of some experimental data, they conclude that this steric effect must be responsible for the stabilisation of certain colloidal dispersions in non-aqueous media. Previously, van der Waarden[3] had suggested that, since the flocculation of carbon black dispersions stabilised by hydrocarbons in organic media decreased with increasing chain length, the factor causing this enhanced stability was a steric one.

---

[1] Van der Minne and Hermanie, *J. Coll. Sci.*, 1953, **8**, 38.
[2] Mackor and van der Waals, *J. Coll. Sci.*, 1952, **7**, 535.
[3] Van der Waarden, *J. Coll. Sci.*, 1950, **5**, 317.

Further experimental evidence that a steric effect helps to stabilise hydrophobic suspensions has been given by Heller and Pugh.[1] These authors consider that flexible molecules of moderately high molecular weight are adsorbed in such a way that they are anchored to the surface by only a few segments of the molecule. This structure gives rise to "steric protection," which is due to the negligible interpenetration of the adsorbed polymeric peripheries of two colliding colloidal particles. This makes the nearest possible distance of approach so large that the attractive interaction energy of the particles is as small as or smaller than their thermal energy or Brownian movement. Tests of this theory were carried out by studying the effect of polyethylene glycols of different molecular weight on the stability of gold sols. Protection against coagulation by potassium chloride increased with increasing polymer concentration to a maximum value. When the molecular weight of the polymer was varied, at a constant concentration of polymer, an enormous increase in the stability occurred at a molecular weight of 6,000. Heller and Pugh consider that the only possible explanation for this sudden rise in protective efficiency is that the critical minimum distance between the colloidal particles is reached at this molecular weight. A combination of "steric protection" and electrostatic stabilisation was also studied. In this case the system considered was polysulphonated polystyrene, with a molecular weight of 110,000, on a ferric hydroxide sol. The sol was initially positively charged, and sensitisation occurred at a low concentration (10^{-6} moles per litre), but at concentrations greater than this the resistance to flocculation by added electrolytes was greatly increased.

According to the generally accepted picture, the stability of an aqueous dispersion (*i.e.*, the fact that mutual adhesion between the particles does not invariably occur) is due to an energy barrier which is set up by one or more of three complementary mechanisms, *viz.*, an electrical double layer, a steric protective layer, and a solvation energy effect. In many cases it is impossible to separate the various stabilising mechanisms, since the electrical double layer contributes to the solvation effect in water, and to the possible hydration sheath, as pointed out by Derjaguin and Titijevskaya.[2] The hydrated sheath acts by virtue of the fact that the free energy of the system is smaller when the hydrated layers are separated. The "steric protection" mentioned above might be considered to be exactly the same as what we have termed a hydrated sheath, and here again it is not possible to separate the various factors involved—electrical, solvational, and steric —but the importance of the steric effect can be discerned in the preparation of dispersible powders, which will re-disperse easily into water to give highly disperse, stable sols (*cf.* Chapter 7).

Since the above mechanisms are independently operative, at least to a

[1] Heller and Pugh, *J. Chem. Phys.*, 1954, **22**, 1778; 1956, **24**, 1107.
[2] Derjaguin and Titijevskaya, *Second Congress*, **I**, 211 (1957).

certain extent, it follows that there are several possible types of disperse systems, which are stabilised by (*i*) an electrical double layer only, (*ii*) a steric mechanism, (*iii*) a solvated (if water is the continuous medium, hydrated) sheath, and (*iv*) a combination of two or more of these effects. In general, systems which are stabilised by combined effects are the most stable. In some cases the combinations of some of these mechanisms can be reduced to a single type of system: for example, a combination of (*i*) and (*iii*) can be reduced to (*iii*) by the addition of electrolyte, especially of one with multivalent ions of opposite charge, which reduces the effective range of the double layer, or to type (*i*) by a treatment which "dehydrates" the surface of the dispersed particles: *e.g.*, freezing the dispersion, or heating it, or adding a dehydrating solvent such as alcohol. This means that very often a disperse system of type (*iv*) can only be flocculated by reducing both the effectiveness of the electrical double layer and the degree of hydration at the surface of the particles.

The above picture of flocculation and deflocculation is most useful when we consider very fine dispersions, the particles in which are characterised by high surface to mass ratios and by a powerful Brownian motion which effectively eliminates any tendency towards sedimentation. The great majority of technically useful dispersions and emulsions are, however, considerably coarser, and this fact has two main results, *viz.*: (a) the adhesion between flocculated particles is more easily broken mechanically, and (b) the dispersed particles will settle (upwards or downwards, depending on the specific gravity relationships), even if they are completely deflocculated. The first of these two effects means that a condition of flocculation may alternate, under suitable mechanical influences, with a state in which the flocculated particles are momentarily separated. Consequently the thermodynamical criterion of dispersion stability may assume a direct, practical significance: *i.e.*, a low value of the interfacial tension may mean that less reversible work is needed to separate the flocculated particles, and this may be reflected in an easier mechanical separation of the particles under practical conditions. The whole concept of degree of flocculation, which includes both the thermodynamical criterion of stability and the relative effectiveness of the energy barriers, becomes very useful in considering these temporary separations, as has already been pointed out.

The fact that even completely deflocculated particles will settle out of a dispersion, if they are large enough and the Brownian motion is therefore sufficiently feeble, leads to an effect which at first appears to be paradoxical. If such particles are deflocculated or only very slightly flocculated, either in aqueous or non-aqueous media, their mutual approaches during sedimentation will only very occasionally result in adhesions, and the particles will therefore glide freely past one another as they settle. As a result, the volume occupied by a given mass of sediment will be small, and if the disperse phase is a solid, an extremely stiff, clay-like* mass may be formed. If the supernatant liquid is removed, this clay will usually prove to be "dilatant": *i.e.*, an applied stress will disturb the close packing, giving an increase in volume and a resistance to deformation or stirring which increases with the applied stress. If however the suspended particles can be brought into a more flocculated condition, so that an appreciable proportion of mutual approaches during sedimentation result in adhesions, the particles will tend to form a loose structure as they settle. The sediment will accordingly be more voluminous and more easily broken up by stirring, its volume increasing with increasing degree of flocculation. Such flocculated sediments will tend to exhibit an anomalous apparent viscosity, which decreases with the applied stress, and they may even be thixotropic; *i.e.*, they may form gel structures which break down when they are stirred and re-form when they are left undisturbed.

This sedimentation paradox, the practical applications of which are discussed in a later chapter, is all the more striking when it is recalled that the apparent viscosity of a deflocculated dispersion, which has not been allowed to settle to a clay, will be lower than that of the same system in a flocculated condition. With relatively coarse suspensions (containing particles 1 μ and greater in diameter), the relative degree of deflocculation is more easily and more reliably characterised by the final sedimentation volume, or by the apparent viscosity, than for example by measurements of the speed of sedimentation in diluted suspension. An excellent account of the sedimentation paradox, with illustrations, is given by Chwala.[1]

More recently, Dintenfass[2] has published an interesting advance note on the effect of *temperature* on the sedimentation volumes of some pigment suspensions. He reports that the sedimentation volumes of deflocculated suspensions are not affected by temperature, while those of flocculated suspensions increase with increasing temperature.

3. Deflocculation by surface-active agents

It will be at once apparent from the preceding section that surface-active agents can increase the degree of deflocculation of disperse systems in several ways.

(a) A surface-active agent may be positively adsorbed at the interface (solid-liquid, liquid-liquid, or gas-liquid), reducing the interfacial free energy, and thus reducing (but never entirely eliminating) the intrinsic thermodynamical instability of the dispersion. The effect of this is more

---

* In view of the obvious analogy with clay, which is characterised by being in a highly deflocculated condition, the term "claying," which is often applied to this phenomenon, appears to be particularly appropriate.

[1] Chwala, "Zerkleinerungschemie," in *Koll. Beih.*, 1930, **31**, 222.

[2] Dintenfass, *Koll. Z.*, 1959, **162**, 47.

likely to be appreciable if the disperse phase is a liquid or a gas than if it is a solid, and the thermodynamical criterion is also more likely to be important when the degree of flocculation is concerned, rather than the question of whether a system is flocculated or deflocculated.

(b) The deflocculating agent may, in water or other ionising media, increase the potential of the electrical double layer, thus increasing the electrostatic repulsive forces between the disperse particles. This increase will usually operate with ionogenic surface-active agents, provided that the adsorption process does not destroy the ionisation. Thus compounds of the types

$$Alkyl \cdot OSO_3{}^-Na^+$$

and $$Alkyl \cdot CON(CH_3) \cdot CH_2CH_2 \cdot SO_3{}^-Na^+$$

will tend to make the stabilising potential more negative, provided that the ionisation is not destroyed by the medium or by the adsorption mechanism (*cf.* Chapter 3, p. 95) Cationic surface-active agents, on the other hand, such as the type

$$Alkyl(CH_3)_3N^+Br^-$$

will tend to make the stabilising potential more positive under the same conditions. In view of the high flocculating power of multivalent ions, or of ions of small radius such as H^+ or OH^-, on dispersions of opposite ionic sign, it is not surprising to find that anionic agents are usually more effective deflocculators in alkaline solutions, or in solutions containing multivalent anions, while the opposite is true of the cationic surface-active agents.

It is possible for ionogenic surface-active agents to be adsorbed at certain solid-water interfaces with a "reverse orientation," *i.e.*, with the paraffin chain turned toward the water. This usually causes flocculation. It is partly for this reason that agents with more than one hydrophilic group in the molecule are so widely used for deflocculating dispersions of solids in aqueous media. These agents, and the polymeric deflocculating agents, are less likely to be completely adsorbed at the interface in such a way as to present a water-repellent surface to the aqueous medium, because of their molecular configuration. It is, however, possible for polymeric surface-active agents to cause flocculation: thus several authors[1] have reported cases which are similar to the well-known "sensitisation" of colloidal suspensions by very small amounts of protective colloids, such as the proteins. Reverse orientation adsorption is suggested by Sheppard, O'Brien, and Beyer as the cause of the flocculation of silver bromide particles by polyvinyl alcohol. It is worth noting, however, that another mechanism may also contribute to the flocculation of hydrophobic particles

---

[1] Sheppard, O'Brien, and Beyer, *J. Coll. Sci.*, 1946, **1**, 213; Heller and Pugh, *J. Chem. Phys.*, 1956, **24**, 1107.

by small concentrations of soluble polymers, *viz.*, "bridging" of the particles by long polymer chains which have been adsorbed on more than one particle.[1]

(c) A deflocculating agent will always to some extent form an adherent sheath of solvent molecules around the dispersed particle on which it is adsorbed, provided of course that it is not adsorbed in the reverse sense. Ionogenic surface-active agents will contribute to this hydration in aqueous media by virtue of the ionising groups themselves, but other polar groups present may also contribute, for example the —$CON(CH_3)$— grouping in oleyl-N-methyltaurine (Igepon T). If the surface-active agent contains no ionising groups, or if the dispersion medium is non-ionising, then it seems reasonable to conclude that solvation and/or a "steric" mechanism are the essential factors causing deflocculation. Recently our knowledge of solvated layers has been considerably increased by the measurements carried out by Derjaguin and his co-workers[2] on the stability of free films and froths and by studying the viscosity of liquid boundary layers by a novel "blow-off" method. From these measurements they conclude that there must be orientation of solvent layers adjacent to adsorbed monolayers at air-water and solid-nonaqueous liquid interfaces. In spite of these very useful advances we have no precise picture of such solvent layers, but certain tentative conclusions appear to be justifiable. If, for example, we are dealing with an aqueous dispersion, the particles of which are deflocculated by a polyglycol ether of the type

$$\text{Alkyl} \cdot [OCH_2CH_2]_n OH$$

it seems reasonable to assume that at least a portion of each $[OCH_2CH_2]_n OH$ chain will be oriented towards the water. We can assume that these chains will be heavily hydrated, the water molecules being attached to at least some of the ether oxygen atoms by hydrogen bonds:

$$\ldots \ CH_2CH_2 - O - CH_2CH_2 \ \ldots$$
$$\downarrow$$
$$HOH$$

and/or dipole interactions. The actual sheath of bound water will be thicker than one molecule on account of dipole interactions and hydrogen bonds among the water molecules themselves. This picture does not exclude the possible existence of a ζ-potential as well, which could be due to the presence of an adsorbed ionising surface-active agent or other electrolyte. Mention should also be made of the possible development of a ζ-potential arising from the feebly basic character of the polyglycol chain. Thus

[1] See, for example, Michaels, *Ind. Eng. Chem.*, 1954, **46**, 1485; Drexler and Franke, *Second Congress*, **IV**, 203 (1957).

[2] Derjaguin and Titijevskaya, *Second Congress*, **I**, 211 (1957); Derjaguin and Karassev, *Second Congress*, **III**, 531 (1957).

in a sufficiently strongly acid medium, "oxonium" salt linkages may be formed, *e.g.*,

$$\ldots \text{CH}_2\text{CH}_2\text{—O—CH}_2\text{CH}_2 \ldots$$
$$\downarrow$$
$$\text{H}^+$$
$$\text{Cl}^-$$

at some of the ether oxygen atoms, and these could cause the surface-active agent to acquire cationic properties.

It seems likely that solvated layers in non-polar dispersion media, of low dielectric constant, will be much thinner than those in aqueous media. This can be illustrated by reference to the well-known deflocculating action of fatty acids on particles of white lead in oil media, which was referred to in Chapter 3. It seems reasonable to assume that the fatty acid molecules are chemisorbed as the result of a surface reaction involving their polar groups, the hydrocarbon chains being oriented towards the "oily" medium. Molecules of the medium will be held to these hydrocarbon chains by van der Waals forces, but these forces will be less powerful than the dipole interactions and hydrogen bonds which are possible in aqueous media. The effective orientation will also extend less far into the liquid, which will be less strongly associated than is water.

4. Flocculation by surface-active agents

We have already noted that amphipathic surface-active agents can cause flocculation if they are adsorbed in the reverse sense by dispersed particles in aqueous media. This is due to the fact that, although the interfacial free energy has almost certainly been lowered by the adsorption, the surface has become more water-repellent, the hydrated sheath having been destroyed, and there is nothing to prevent mutual adhesion of the particles. The effect is therefore ascribable to a destruction of the energy barrier, even though the thermodynamical instability of the disperse system has actually been diminished. This water-repellency may in fact reach the stage at which the solid particles are preferentially wetted by air rather than by water (*i.e.*, the contact angle measured in the water is greater than 90°), and the particles tend to be expelled from the water phase. This represents an extreme case of flocculation.

It is important to note again in this connection that surface-active agents which cause flocculation in aqueous media in small concentrations will frequently act as deflocculators if they are present in larger amounts. This phenomenon is a fairly common one, and it seems to be generally agreed that it is due to the fact that an initial reverse adsorption occurs, causing flocculation, but that this is followed, if enough surface-active agent is present, by the formation of a second adsorbed layer. The polar groups in this second layer are oriented towards the aqueous phase, thus finally giving a deflocculated system. This effect is well illustrated by the results of R. W. Tomlinson,[1] who investigated the mechanism of the action of cetyltrimethylammonium bromide (CTMAB) in causing Prussian Blue particles in aqueous suspension to become preferentially wettable by oil.[2] He found (Figure 24) that increasing the percentage of CTMAB on the pigment present, increased the sedimentation volume of a Prussian Blue dispersion in water (showing an increasing degree of flocculation) up to a maximum value, after which the sedimentation volume fell again. Eventually a highly deflocculated suspension was reached in which complete sedimentation did not occur. It was shown by independent adsorption

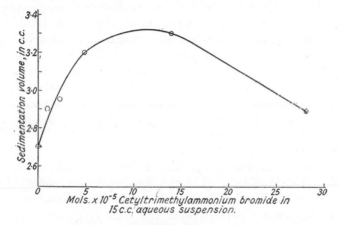

Figure 24
Equilibrium sedimentation volume of 1 gm. Prussian Blue as function of amount of cetyltrimethylammonium bromide

measurements that the CTMAB was quantitatively completely adsorbed until the maximum sedimentation volume was reached, after which the adsorption was much less avid. The initial adsorption was irreversible, while the secondary adsorbed material could be washed off. The maximum sedimentation volume in water coincided fairly closely with the minimum sedimentation volume in benzene, and to the maximum ease of transfer from aqueous to non-aqueous media. Tomlinson therefore concluded that, up to this point, CTMAB was chemisorbed by the Prussian Blue particles as a monomolecular layer, with the paraffin chains oriented towards the water, thus increasing the degree of flocculation in water and of defloccu-lation in benzene. Once the surface was saturated, however, a second unilayer was formed on top of the first, as the result of amphipathic adsorp-tion, the polar, ionising groups in this second layer being oriented towards the water and reversing the effect of the first adsorbed unilayer. The final state of the dispersion would, on this picture, be highly deflocculated.

[1] R. W. Tomlinson, private communication.
[2] Du Pont, B.P. 499,334 = U.S.P. 2, 192, 954.

Surface-active agents, especially if they are present in aqueous solution as ionic micelles, can also cause flocculation by a similar mechanism to that of ordinary electrolytes. Thus if a compound with surface-active cations is added to a dispersion the particles of which carry a negative electrokinetic potential, then the surface-active agent can increase the degree of flocculation by several mechanisms, which may be complementary.

(a) The surface-active cations may be adsorbed at the interface and thus diminish the original negative electrokinetic potential.

(b) The surface-active cations may form an insoluble compound or complex at the interface by reaction with an anionic deflocculating agent.

(c) The surface-active cations may simply reduce the stabilising electrokinetic potential, without being actually adsorbed, by crowding into the diffuse portion of the electrical double layer. One would expect cationic micelles to be particularly effective in this respect, on account of their very high effective valency, it being well known that the flocculating action of an ionic species increases rapidly with its valency (the so-called Schultze-Hardy principle).

5. REVERSIBLE FLOCCULATION

The technical importance of the fact that flocculation in aqueous dispersions can sometimes be reversed, apparently completely, has been referred to by Stewart and Bunbury,[1] who give two illustrations. The first presumably depends on the fact that agents of the type represented by condensation products of naphthalene-2-sulphonic acid with formaldehyde, are fairly strongly adsorbed on the solid and interact strongly at high concentrations in the presence of flocculating electrolytes such as sodium chloride, which compresses the double layer. This means that conditions can be so arranged, by using a mixture of a deflocculating agent and a flocculating electrolyte, that relatively concentrated dispersions will be flocculated, but not agglomerated, so that they are free from claying and can be stored almost indefinitely. When the dispersion is diluted with water, the interaction is reduced by lowering the concentration of the flocculating electrolyte and thus increasing the electrical repulsive effect. The fact that the concentration of the deflocculating agent is also reduced may also enhance the electrical repulsive effect, so long as the adsorption of surface-active agent is not materially affected.

The second type of reversible flocculation described by Stewart and Bunbury illustrates the principle of the reversible insolubilisation of an adsorbed surface-active agent, in this case a mixture. If we acidify a dispersion stabilised with a mixture of gelatine and sodium dinaphthyl-methane disulphonate, an insoluble complex is formed between the protein and the surface-active agent, and the dispersion flocculates and can be

---

[1] Stewart and Bunbury, *Trans. Faraday Soc.*, 1935, **31**, 208.

filtered. If conditions are suitably chosen (*e.g.*, concentration of surface-active materials, pH, attainment of a considerable degree of adsorption before precipitation), the addition of alkali, which re-dissolves the complex between surface-active agent and protein, will also substantially regenerate the original state of dispersion.

6. Deflocculation and wetting

Before the present discussion on deflocculation is concluded, it seems desirable to recapitulate the essential distinction between this phenomenon and the related processes of wetting, since the two terms are often used indiscriminately.* We have seen that in a wetting process one fluid phase is displaced from an interface by another fluid, the case most frequently encountered in practice being the displacement of air by a liquid. The degree of wetting may vary, but even the fact that a solid may be completely wetted by a liquid is no guarantee that dispersed particles of the solid will be even partly deflocculated in that liquid. Unless however a disperse phase is completely wetted by the dispersion medium, it cannot be completely deflocculated: *i.e.*, complete wetting is a necessary, but not a sufficient condition for a high degree of deflocculation.

This distinction becomes clearer when it is recalled that the thermo-dynamical criterion of the decrease in interfacial free energy appears to be important, if not decisive, in determining the course (and even the speed) of wetting processes. The degree of deflocculation of disperse systems, on the other hand, appears to be more independent of the interfacial free energy criterion, depending on the effectiveness of the energy barriers which prevent the full attainment of the thermodynamically stable, coalesced state.

C. Protective colloid action

In contrast to the two processes just described, the phenomenon of protective colloid action is difficult to define precisely, probably because it overlaps considerably with the concept of deflocculation. As we have already seen, many surface-active agents, especially of the polymeric types, owe their deflocculating power to "steric protection" in addition to solvation and/or electrostatic repulsion, and it is probable that protective colloid action can be ascribed to this type of behaviour. We propose to ascribe "protective colloid" properties to a surface-active agent when it stabilises a particular disperse system against aggregation (flocculation, agglomeration, or even coalescence) by such special agencies as added electrolytes or dehydrating agents, violent agitation, heat, or freezing. It

---

* We are of course referring to wetting and deflocculation as here defined. "Wetting" is often used, quite consistently, to describe what we have called deflocculation: the objection to such a usage is of course that it leaves us without a convenient term with which to describe the process in which one fluid phase is displaced by a second fluid phase.

should be noted that a surface-active agent can be described as an effective protective colloid with reference only to a particular system or systems; *i.e.*, protective colloid power is not necessarily a general property of a substance, but will depend on the nature of the disperse phase, the composition of the dispersion medium, and the particular aggregating agency in question.* Thus in neutral aqueous media, a protein such as gelatine may "protect" a suspended pigment against additions of electrolytes, but it may fail in acid media, in which a cationic agent such as cetyltrimethylammonium bromide may be effective.

The chief difficulty about the definition of a protective colloid given above is that any surface-active agent which has a marked deflocculating action in a disperse system is also to some extent a protective colloid, and the converse may also hold true. It is probably logically impossible to separate these two functions entirely, but certain differences in degree are of very real practical importance. The primary function of a good protective colloid can be described as that of maintaining the *status quo* in a deflocculated system: it will therefore usually form interfacial films of great stability, of a high degree of hydration, and frequently of very great mechanical strength. The velocity of adsorption will be much less important, and the adsorption will generally be less "reversible" (or alternatively the adsorption equilibrium will be less labile), than in the case of a surface-active material which is acting as a deflocculating agent.

Frisch and his co-workers[1] have published several theoretical papers on the statistical mechanics of polymer adsorption, which suggest that desorption of whole chains is unlikely to occur, because of the flexibility of the chains.† Some of the properties which usually characterise an efficient deflocculating agent may be less evident: these include a high velocity of adsorption, the formation of an electrical double layer, or a marked lowering of the interfacial tension. Broadly speaking, one associates protective colloid power with surface-active materials which exist in solution in a highly "colloidal" state: *e.g.*, proteins, synthetic macromolecules such as polyvinyl alcohol and water-soluble synthetic resins, and paraffin chain salts at concentrations well above the critical concentration for micelle formation.

In the practical sense deflocculating action and protective colloid power are frequently additive: *i.e.*, it may be possible to use a mixture of surface-active agents in order to obtain both effects simultaneously. A good

---

* In the authors' experience such tests as Zsigmondy's classical "gold number"— in which protective colloid power is measured in terms of the stabilising effect on a red gold sol, against the flocculating effect of additions of sodium chloride—show no significant correlation with the protective colloid power of surface-active agents in industrial processes.

† See also Chapter 3, p. 109.

[1] Frisch, Simha, and Eirich, *J. Chem. Phys.*, 1953, **21**, 365; Frisch and Simha, *J. Phys. Chem.*, 1954, **58**, 507; Frisch, *J. Phys. Chem.*, 1955, **59**, 633.

example among the many possible ones is afforded by B.P. 258,551 of the I.G., in which a protective colloid such as glue or gelatine is mixed with a deflocculating (or emulsifying) agent of the alkylated aromatic sulphonic acid type.

D. Mechanical phase-subdivision processes

A technical dispersion process such as the grinding of a solid in a liquid medium, or the formation of an emulsion, foam, or spray, is nearly always the resultant of two opposing mechanisms, *viz.*, a process of mechanical disruption of the disperse phase into smaller particles, and a process of re-aggregation by flocculation, agglomeration, or coalescence. Under very favourable conditions, re-aggregation may be substantially absent, but in general it will be significant, and the addition of a deflocculating agent, especially of one which is rapidly adsorbed at freshly formed interfaces, will therefore usually favour the dispersion process by reducing the tendency to re-aggregation, and may in fact be essential. Thus if a dispersion of a solid, or an emulsion, is in a highly flocculated condition, it will usually be found that mechanical treatments such as grinding or so-called "colloid-milling" have an adverse effect on the state of dispersion, since they simply accelerate the process of re-aggregation. By the same token it is essential, for the carrying out of a mechanical dispersion process, that the disperse phase be completely wetted by the dispersion medium and *vice versa*.* The inter-action between the initial process of phase-subdivision, and the secondary effects which may lead to re-aggregation, is discussed more fully in Part II of the present book, and the present discussion will be limited to a brief discussion of the possible effects of surface-active agents on the initial process of disruption of a disperse phase.

It seems fairly obvious that the disruption of a fluid phase in a second fluid phase, under fixed mechanical conditions, will usually be favoured by a low interfacial tension. Thus if a jet of a liquid is forced into a gas, or into another liquid with which it is immiscible, then the first liquid will break up into smaller drops if the interfacial tension is lowered by the addition of a surface-active agent, other factors such as viscosity being equal. Similarly, a jet of gas will break up into smaller bubbles in a liquid medium if the interfacial tension is lowered. It will of course be appreciated that the relevant interfacial tension will be the dynamic one, *i.e.*, the value, not necessarily constant throughout the system, of the interfacial tension at the appropriate surface age. This, and the occurrence of re-aggregation

---

* This statement implies, under most circumstances, that the dispersion medium completely displaces air from the surfaces of the dispersed particles or droplets. Other phases may, however, be relevant: thus it is common knowledge that an emulsion may be destroyed if the disperse phase, rather than the dispersion medium, preferentially wets the material of which the emulsifying machine is made.

after the phase-disruption stage, probably account for the fact that the general correlation between the lowering of a static boundary tension by a surface-active agent, and its effect on ease of emulsification, etc., is only qualitative, and far from perfect.

A noteworthy characteristic of the formation of emulsion systems by mechanical means is the possible achievement of extremely low values for liquid-liquid interfacial tensions, especially by the use of surface-active agents. Whereas static air-water interfacial tensions are not obtained much below 20–30 dynes/cm., and the dynamic values are substantially higher, it is not uncommon for "oil"-water interfacial tensions to be only a small fraction of a dyne. Thus Robinson[1] reports that sodium cetyl sulphate at 0·0012 N lowers the interfacial tension between lanoline and water at 60° c. to about 0·07 dyne/cm., the value being too low for accurate measurement. Clayton and Sumner[2] list a number of examples of interfacial tensions which, even though surface-active agents have not been added, are so low that emulsification appears to occur spontaneously under experimental conditions. Further examples of this effect are furnished by the self-emulsifiable oils of industry (sometimes referred to, though strictly speaking incorrectly, as "miscible oils") which are solutions of proprietary oil-soluble emulsifying agents in light lubricating oils, for example. The common feature of all these phenomena is that extremely fine emulsions are obtained if the oil and the aqueous solution are mixed with very gentle agitation; if an attempt is made to measure the interfacial tension, for example with a drop-volume apparatus fitted with a very fine capillary tip such as that used by Robinson, the meniscus is too unstable and appears to break up "spontaneously": *i.e.*, as the result of the mechanical work which is done when the two liquid phases are brought in contact.

The particular interest of "spontaneous" emulsification phenomena to the present discussion lies in the fact that they probably represent processes of phase-subdivision in which the lowering of the interfacial tension by a surface-active agent is the predominant mechanism by which the agent functions. It even appears to be possible, if we accept March's[3] treatment of the stability of disperse systems, that the (microscopic) interfacial tension is so low and the particles so small that the dispersions are rendered thermodynamically stable, against subsequent flocculation, by the Brownian motion alone. This does not of course exclude the possibility that a stabilising hydrated sheath and ζ-potential are also present. Thus March's theory predicts than an emulsion containing particles with a radius of 0·1 μ would be thermodynamically stable at a concentration of 1% by volume of

[1] Robinson, *Wetting and Detergency*, a symposium organised by the International Society of Leather Trades Chemists, A. Harvey, London, 1937, p. 146.

[2] Clayton, *The Theory of Emulsions and Their Technical Treatment*, J. and A. Churchill, London, 5th Edition by C. G. Sumner, 1954.

[3] March, *Koll. Z.*, 1928, **45**, 97.

disperse phase if the interfacial tension were reduced to about 0·0017 dyne/cm., a value which does not appear to be impossible.

A further special characteristic of emulsion systems, which affects the rôle played by surface-active agents in their formation, is that it is frequently possible for either liquid to be the disperse, discontinuous phase. However, in a large number of cases, probably representing the majority, a particular surface-active agent will favour the emulsification of one liquid (A) in another (B), but not the reverse. The agent may in fact reduce the stability or even destroy an emulsion of B in A, although the interfacial tension is presumably about the same in both possible types of emulsion. This tendency for many surface-active agents to favour one particular type of emulsion, to the exclusion of the opposite type, is obviously a function of the structure of the interfacial film. At one time it was thought that the curvature of the interface might make it possible for adsorption of an emulsifying agent to occur only if one phase were the discontinuous one— the so-called "oriented wedge theory"—but it now seems to be generally agreed that the usual curvatures are too slight for this idea to furnish a quantitative explanation. The effect has been discussed in considerable detail in the literature, notably in Clayton and Sumner's book, and is referred to again in Chapter 6. It will suffice for the present to note that

(a) a surface-active agent which assists in the phase subdivision stage of an emulsification process by lowering the interfacial tension must also give an interfacial film which permits the appropriate liquid to act as the disperse phase, and

(b) an interfacial film will tend to favour the establishment of a particular phase as the continuous one if the particles adsorbed at the interface (ions, molecules, interfacial complexes, or even microscopic particles) are relatively more soluble in or wetted by that phase. This principle, with which in its general form the name of Bancroft is usually associated, is of considerable utility: thus it explains the well-known fact that sodium stearate favours the formation of "oil"-in-water emulsions, and calcium stearate the formation of emulsions of the reverse type.

The mechanical disruption of solid particles in liquid media will also be favoured, roughly speaking, by the adsorption of surface-active agents, which will lower the solid-liquid interfacial tension and thus decrease the work necessary to disrupt each solid particle. Although this effect has been used for many years in technical dispersion processes, the mechanism involved has become much clearer as the result of the experimental work of Rehbinder and his collaborators,[1-5] who have studied the breaking

[1] Rehbinder, *Nature*, 1947, **159**, 866.
[2] Rehbinder and Wenström, *Bull. Acad. Sci. U.R.S.S. ser. phys.*, 1931, 531.
[3] Rehbinder, Lichtman, and Maslennikov, *C.R. Acad. Sci. U.R.S.S.*, 1941, **32**, 125.
[4] Lichtman and Rehbinder, *ibid.*, 1941, **32**, 130.
[5] Rehbinder and Logginov, *ibid.*, 1941, **30**, 491.

strains and rates of deformation of solids such as metal wires, sheets of
mica, and single crystals of metals, in liquids to which surface-active agents
were added. The effect of adding the surface-active agent was always to
decrease the breaking stress, or alternatively to increase the rate of plastic
flow under standardised conditions. The results of a typical series of
experiments by Rehbinder, Lichtman, and Maslennikov on the effect of
additions of oleic acid on the yield value of single crystals of tin in a non-
polar hydrocarbon oil are shown in Fig. 25. Two of the most interesting
observations of these workers were that the electrical resistance of a metallic
crystal, after elongation by a certain percentage, was always greater in the

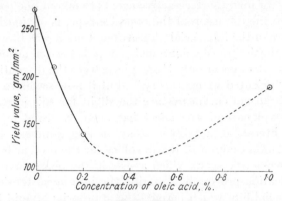

Figure 25
Effect of oleic acid on yield value of tin crystal in pure hydrocarbon oil
(From data of Rehbinder, Lichtman, and Maslennikov, *C.R. Acad. Sci.
U.R.S.S.*, 1941, **32**, (No. 2), 125.)

presence of the surface-active compound, and that the deformation was
reversible, the mechanical properties and the electrical resistance reverting
to their original values when the stresses were removed.

Rehbinder and his colleagues explain their results on the basis of very
fine "microcracks," which may extend for considerable distances into a
crystal when a stress is applied, the electrical conductivity therefore
decreasing with increasing strain, but which heal reversibly when the
applied stress is removed. A surface-active agent which is adsorbed at the
solid-liquid interface increases the number and depth of these cracks, since
the solid-liquid interfacial tension is reduced, and therefore lowers the yield
value of the crystal and increases its ease of deformation. The adsorption
of the surface-active agent is highly reversible, the agent being expelled
from the strain cracks when the crystal recovers. It is interesting to note
that the curve for yield value against concentration of surface-active agent
in Fig. 25 passes through a minimum, suggesting that the solid-liquid
interfacial tension also passes through a minimum. In the absence of
directly determined adsorption data, it is not possible to conclude whether

this is due to an anomaly of the type discussed in Chapter 3 (*cf.* pp. 79–83) or whether it indicates that the adsorption of oleic acid becomes negative, though we have seen that the latter type of explanation is improbable for physical reasons.

Doubts have been raised as to the genuineness of the "Rehbinder effect," and in particular the suggestion has been made that the effect of the surface-active materials on metal crystals may have been due to the removal of surface films of metallic oxides, which are known to strengthen the metal crystals.[1] These criticisms have been considered by Rehbinder and Lichtman,[2] in an important summary of the work of their school.* Although the strengthening effect of metal oxides films is well known, Rehbinder and Lichtman point out that it cannot explain the effects of surface-active materials in reducing the breaking stresses, because these effects are still found when oxide films cannot exist, or when steps have been taken to ensure their elimination. The effects are, however, much more pronounced at higher extension rates, and Rehbinder and Lichtman in fact suggest that the failure of British workers to confirm the results of their school may have been due to working at different extension rates.

The importance of the *kinetic* aspect of the Rehbinder effect is emphasised in the paper by Rehbinder and Lichtman.† This follows from the fact that the occurrence of the Rehbinder effect requires the simultaneous fulfilment of two conditions which are (to quote Rehbinder and Lichtman):

"(1) The state of stress should aid the development of weak spots (ultramicrocracks) in the surface layers of the solid, *i.e.*, sufficiently high tensions (superstresses) should be present.

"(2) During the time of development of the defects the surface energy over a sufficiently large portion of the newly formed solid surface should be lowered by penetration of surface-active components from the medium in the form of adsorption layers, *e.g.*, by two-dimensional migration."

Rehbinder and Lichtman also present evidence against the effect being due to local corrosion. They point out that adsorbed surface-active materials can increase the "creep" of individual crystals and can cause phenomena of inelasticity to appear. For our present purposes the most interesting results reported in their paper are perhaps those of Aslanova, who found that the breaking stress of glass fibres (from two to sixty microns in diameter) was markedly reduced by aqueous solutions of sodium dioctylsulphosuccinate,

---

* A useful summary of Russian work on this and related topics has also been published in a monograph by Kuznetsov, available in an English translation entitled *Surface Energy of Solids*, H.M. Stationery Office, 1957.

† See also the remarks by Rehbinder, with which we fully agree, in the discussion of a paper by one of us, *Second Congress*, 1957, **IV**, 238.

[1] *Cf.* Kemsley, *Nature*, 1949, **163**, 404; Andrade and Randall, *Nature*, 1949, **164**, 1127; Andrade, Randall, and Makin, *Proc. Phys. Soc.*, 1950, **63B**, 990; Harper and Cottrell, *Proc. Phys. Soc.*, 1950, **63B**, 331.

[2] Rehbinder and Lichtman, *Second Congress*, 1957, **III**, 563.

stearamidomethylpyridinium chloride ("Velan PF"), soaps, etc., which were adsorbed "with hydrophobisation": *i.e.*, with reversed orientation (*cf.* Chapter 3). Inelastic after-effects, hysteresis, and irreversible creep also appeared.

The effect of reductions in the "specific interfacial free energy" (what we have called the thermodynamical interfacial tension in Chapter 3) in promoting the disruption of solids is also considered in a review by von Engelhardt.[1] Although the experimental arrangements were rather different from those used by Rehbinder and his co-workers, the general picture which emerges is similar. A further relevant contribution is that of Ramsauer,[2] who ground glass balls with various abrasive powders and found that the effect of surface-active media or agents was different with different abrasives: *i.e.*, the effect of lowerings of interfacial tensions must be interpreted in terms of the relative effects on *both* the abrasive and the material being ground.

The work described above shows, therefore, that surface-active agents can assist the primary processes of disruption of solid particles in liquid media, as well as hindering their re-aggregation. The disruption, at least in its initial stages, can be reversible, even in the presence of adsorbed material, but this is not necessarily always true: thus it seems quite possible that in some systems a surface-active agent might act by reducing the degree of reversibility, *i.e.*, by interfering with the healing of the cracks in the strained crystal when the applied stress is removed. But perhaps the most striking observation is that *surface-active agents can alter the effective physical properties of the solid particles*, *i.e.*, render them more brittle and liable to show irreversible "creep." The relevance of this in the milling processes which are described in Chapter 7 will be obvious.

An analogue of the Rehbinder effect is that of adsorbed vapours[3] or added liquids[4] in the dry grinding of solids.

In considering the rôle of surface-active agents in phase-subdivision processes, it is necessary to note that in practice we are almost never concerned with the disruption of a single size of particle or droplet, but rather with a statistical process involving a very large number of particles of different sizes, and perhaps shapes. Thus in the grinding of a dispersion of a solid in a liquid medium in a ball mill, the solid particles are subjected in a purely random fashion to intermittent mechanical stresses, which will vary rapidly and widely in intensity. During any short interval of time, therefore, the mechanical stresses will act on only some of the particles, a proportion of which will be disrupted and a proportion only deformed, perhaps only temporarily. A suitable surface-active agent may function in

[1] von Engelhardt, *Naturwissenschaften*, 1946, **33,** 195.

[2] Ramsauer, *Koll. Z.*, 1951, **121,** 71.

[3] Röttig, *Z. phys. Chem.*, 1956, **205,** 366.

[4] Berry and Kamack, *Second Congress*, 1957, **IV,** 196.

several ways in such a process, *viz.*, by reducing the tendency towards re-aggregation throughout the system, by reducing the breaking stress or yield value for each species of particles and hence increasing the frequency of disruption, and by increasing the extent of subdivision resulting from each disruption. The second of these mechanisms is worth special examination, in considering why the presence of a surface-active agent may be necessary in a milling process in order to obtain substantially complete elimination of oversize particles in an economically feasible time.

If we take the simplest case and assume that at all times the rate of disruption of a particular species of particle is directly proportional to the number of these particles present in the system, then we can write

$$\frac{dZ}{dt} = -kZ \tag{36}$$

where Z is the number of particles present at time t, and k is a constant which characterises the efficiency of milling. Integration of this equation gives

$$lnZ = lnZ_0 - kt \tag{37}$$

where Z_0 is the number of particles of the species which were present at zero time. It is obvious from equation (37) that Z will be an asymptotic function of t, and "infinite" time would be required to reduce Z to zero with absolute certainty. In practice, however, it will not be necessary to reduce Z to zero, but to what we may term the maximum permissible value Z' (the size of which will be determined by the strictness of the user's criteria!), which will be attained in time t', the two being connected by the relation

$$t' = \frac{lnZ_0 - lnZ'}{k} \tag{38}$$

If now we add a surface-active agent which increases the frequency of disruption and hence increases k, it follows that the time required to reach the quality of dispersion characterised by Z' will be decreased in exact proportion. If the original value of k was small enough and the proportional increase large enough, the effect on the economics of a process can be quite striking. Thus the practical asymptotic value for Z, at which Z becomes sensibly constant, may be decreased from greater than Z' to less than Z', so that a completely unsuccessful process may be transformed into a technically feasible one.

The above treatment, which is purely illustrative,* implies at least two simplifying assumptions: that k is unaffected by the increase in the number of very fine particles during the process, and that the species under consideration is not being formed by disruption of still larger particles. It

---

* A much fuller treatment of the kinetics of grinding is that of Theimer, *Koll. Z.*, 1953, **132**, 134.

therefore applies strictly only to the final stages of the elimination of oversize particles, but it will serve to illustrate the complexity of technical phase-subdivision processes and the mode of action of surface-active agents.

The present discussion will perhaps have made clearer the fact that, although any process of mechanical phase-subdivision is necessarily accompanied by an increase in the total interfacial free energy of the system on account of the increase in total interfacial area, the efficacy of a surface-active agent is not due directly to any saving in this energy increase, but rather to an improvement in the very low efficiency with which mechanical energy is utilised in the process. The unimportance of the direct reduction of the interfacial free energy of the system can be illustrated by considering an emulsion containing 20% (by volume) of a disperse phase in the form of spheres 1 μ in diameter, the total interfacial area in 1000 litres (*ca.* one ton) of the system being 12×10^9 cm.[2] If an added surface-active agent reduces the interfacial tension by 30 dynes/cm., then the resulting diminution in the total interfacial free energy of the system will be only $3 \cdot 6 \times 10^{11}$ ergs, equivalent to 8570 gm. cal. or about $0 \cdot 01$ kilowatt-hours. Expressed as a direct economy in the energy which must be put into making the emulsion, this figure is of course of no practical significance whatever.

E. Precipitation processes

Surface-active materials are extensively used in processes of precipitation (phase-formation) in liquid media in order to control or modify such properties of the new phase as the size of the solid particles or fluid droplets formed, their state of aggregation, or (if they are solid) their shape. Since our first edition was written, there has been a marked increase in interest in the fundamental kinetics and thermodynamics of phase-formation processes. This has been due to a large extent to interest in the crystallisation of semi-conductors and metals from pure melts, and there is now a considerable literature on the subject. We shall not concern ourselves here with this particular aspect of phase-formation processes, but many of the more important theoretical papers on crystallisation and precipitation can be found under such headings.

The theory of the kinetics and thermodynamics of phase-formation can be roughly divided into two main parts, which arose historically in a quite logical manner. The earlier period up to about 1948 was mainly concerned with the kinetics and thermodynamics of ideally perfect crystals. In this field the work of Volmer and collaborators is especially important, and the knowledge of the subject up to about the late thirties is conveniently summarised in his admirable monograph.[1] In the early 1950's, an

[1] Volmer, *Kinetik der Phasenbildung*, Steinkopff, 1939. Reprinted by Edwards in 1945, under licence from the U.S. Alien Property Custodian.

increasing interest was taken in the kinetic behaviour of imperfect crystals, some of the earlier workers in this field being Burton, Cabrera, and Frank.

The growth of perfect crystals was considered from a thermodynamical point of view by Gibbs,[1] who observed that a perfect crystal substance could only grow by repeated two-dimensional nucleation of new layers. The edges of each nucleus provided a growth step at which molecules could be deposited on the crystal and become part of it. When the layer grew to the size of the crystal face, the growth step was destroyed. For continued growth it is therefore necessary for two-dimensional nucleation to occur at an appreciable rate. At low supersaturations, the growth rate would be expected to be controlled by the rate of nucleation.

In 1949, Frank[2] observed the differences between the predicted rate for two-dimensional nucleation and the actual growth rates at low degrees of supersaturation, and suggested that allowances for crystal imperfections must be made in order to describe the experimental results satisfactorily. He suggested that screw dislocations would adequately account for the results observed. (As its name implies, a "screw dislocation" is a spiral growth which continues round a central point of dislocation in a similar manner to the thread around the centre stock of a screw nail.) Frank's hypothesis has since been supported by a considerable amount of further experimental work, as well as by further theoretical work on screw dislocations. A fuller summary of Frank's theory will be found in the now historic Faraday Society Discussion to which we have referred above, and in a more recent review by Frank,[3] which includes work on both ideally perfect and imperfect crystals. The latest theoretical information on crystal growth is conveniently summarised in the proceedings[4] of the International Conference on Crystal Growth which was held in Cooperstown, New York, in 1958.

In the present discussion, we propose to confine ourselves to examining the possible effects of surface-active materials, which are adsorbed at the interfaces between the parent phase and the newly-formed discontinuous phase.

Every precipitation process in a liquid medium involves, to a greater or less degree, the two stages of nucleation and the growth of solid or liquid particles. These are often accompanied or followed by two other phenomena: aggregation (which has already been discussed in Section B of the present chapter), and particle digestion.

Nucleation can be defined as the formation of the smallest particles

[1] Gibbs, *Collected Works*, Yale University Press, 1928, **I,** p. 325.

[2] Frank, *Discussions of the Faraday Society*, 1949, **5,** 48.

[3] Frank, *Advances in Physics*, 1952, **1,** 91.

[4] Doremus, Roberts, and Turnbull, *Growth and Perfection of Crystals*, Chapman and Hall, 1959.

(nuclei) of the substance being precipitated which can act as centres for further deposition of solute from a supersaturated solution under the prevailing conditions of concentration, temperature, pressure, etc. These nuclei are large enough to have the essential characteristics of a new phase, *viz.*, an interfacial tension against the parent phase and, in the case of a solid, a definite crystal structure. It was first recognised by Gibbs[1] that the existence of what we have called the interfacial tension, between the parent phase and the new phase which is being formed, means that precipitation cannot occur until particles of a certain minimum size (*i.e.*, nuclei) are formed : a corollary is that a supersaturated solution will always be present in the initial stages of every precipitation process. The thermodynamical necessity for the existence of such a supersaturated solution, and the effect of the interfacial tension on the degree of supersaturation which is necessary, can be demonstrated as follows.

Consider the formation of a single, small particle of a pure liquid or solid, at constant temperature and pressure, from a surrounding solution, the whole process being assumed to be reversible. If n is the number of moles in the new, one-component phase represented by the particle, and A_1, A_2, etc., are the areas of the different types of interfaces present between the new phase and the parent solution, then we can write for the change in the total free energy of the particle

$$dG = \left(\frac{\partial G}{\partial n}\right)_{A_1, A_2 \ldots} dn + \left(\frac{\partial G}{\partial A_1}\right)_{n, A_2 \ldots} dA_1 + \left(\frac{\partial G}{\partial A_2}\right)_{n, A_1 \ldots} dA_2$$

Since $\left(\dfrac{\partial G}{\partial n}\right)_{A_1, A_2}$ can be considered to be the chemical potential of the material in such a particle which is so large that $\left(\dfrac{\partial G}{\partial A_1}\right)_{n, A_2 \ldots} dA_1$ and $\left(\dfrac{\partial G}{\partial A_2}\right)_{n, A_1 \ldots} dA_2$ are negligible compared with $\left(\dfrac{\partial G}{\partial n}\right)_{A_1, A_2 \ldots} dn$—*i.e.*, it is the chemical potential of the substance in bulk at the prevailing temperature—and $\left(\dfrac{\partial G}{\partial A_1}\right)_{n, A_2 \ldots}$ etc., are the interfacial tensions of the different interfaces, we can write

$$dG = \mu_b dn + \gamma_1 dA_1 + \gamma_2 dA_2 + \ldots$$

For a particle of a *liquid*, which can be assumed to be a sphere, and which will present only one type of interface to the parent solution, this equation becomes

$$dG = \mu_b dn + \gamma dA.$$

---

[1] Gibbs, *Collected Works*, Yale University Press, 1928, **I,** pp. 252 ff.; see also the summary by Volmer, *loc. cit.*, p. 14 ff., which in addition describes later work.

Since $n = \dfrac{V\rho}{M} = \dfrac{4}{3}\pi r^3 \dfrac{\rho}{M}$, and $A = 4\pi r^2$, where V is the volume of the particle, r is its radius, ρ is its specific gravity, and M is the molecular weight of the single component of which it is composed, it can be shown by simple algebra that

$$\frac{dG}{dn} = \mu_b + \frac{2M\gamma}{r\rho}$$

Since $\dfrac{dG}{dn}$ is the chemical potential of the component in particles of radius r, which we can call μ_r, this equation can be re-written in the form

$$\mu_r - \mu_b = \frac{2M\gamma}{r\rho}. \tag{39}$$

If the activity coefficient of the solute in the parent phase is substantially the same at the two concentrations which correspond to μ_r and μ_b, then this becomes the well-known equation

$$ln\,\frac{L_r}{L} = \frac{2M}{RT\rho}\,\frac{\gamma}{r} \tag{39a}$$

in which L is the solubility of the substance in bulk, and L_r is its solubility in spherical, isotropic particles of radius r.

For solid, crystalline particles the situation is of course more complicated. Let us however consider the case of a parallelepiped (Figure 26), with edges of lengths a, b, and c, there being three types of interface present at which the thermodynamical interfacial tensions are γ_1, γ_2, and γ_3, respectively. We will suppose that the three crystallographic angles α, β, and ε are constant. The general equation for the free energy change accompanying particle growth now becomes, since $A_1 = 2bc \sin \alpha$, $A_2 = 2ac \sin \beta$, and $A_3 = 2ab \sin \varepsilon$,

$$dG = \mu_b dn + 2\gamma_1 \sin \alpha \, d(bc) + 2\gamma_2 \sin \beta \, d(ac) + 2\gamma_3 \sin \varepsilon \, d(ba) \tag{40}$$

In order to find relations between dn and $d(bc)$, $d(ac)$, and $d(ab)$, we can note that, in the first place,

$$n = \frac{V\rho}{M} = \frac{\rho}{M}\,2abc\,\sqrt{\begin{array}{l}\sin\left(\dfrac{\alpha+\beta+\varepsilon}{2}\right)\cdot\sin\left(\dfrac{-\alpha+\beta+\varepsilon}{2}\right)\\[2mm]\cdot\sin\left(\dfrac{\alpha-\beta+\varepsilon}{2}\right)\cdot\sin\left(\dfrac{\alpha+\beta-\varepsilon}{2}\right)\end{array}}$$

$$= \frac{\rho}{M}\,2abc\phi \tag{41}$$

where ϕ is a constant which is characteristic of the crystallographic system.

Secondly, we can make use of the theorem of the equilibriated crystal, developed by Gibbs,[1] who shows that a crystal which grows under strictly

---

[1] Gibbs, *loc. cit.*, p. 321.

equilibrium conditions assumes a constant shape characterised by the fact that the expression

$$\frac{\Sigma(\gamma_j l_{ij} \cosec \omega_{ij} - \gamma_i l_{ij} \cot \omega_{ij})}{A_i}$$

shall have the same value for each face of the crystal. This expression represents the summation around the i'th face for all the faces j which are contiguous with it, l_{ij} being the length of each common edge and ω the angle between the i'th face and each neighbouring face. For the case which we are considering, this theorem leads to the simple condition that

$$\gamma_1 \, bc \sin \alpha = \gamma_2 ac \sin \beta = \gamma_3 ab \sin \varepsilon \tag{42}$$

Combining equations (40), (41), and (42), and assuming that γ_1, γ_2, and γ_3 are constants, we find that the chemical potential μ_n of the material in a

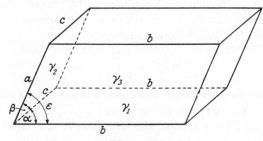

Figure 26

Equilibrium crystal shape : Generalised case of a parallelepiped

Crystallographic angles: α, β, ε.
Lengths of edges: a, b, c.
Interfacial tensions: γ_1, γ_2, γ_3.

crystal containing n moles is related to the bulk chemical potential by the equation

$$\mu_n - \mu_b = 2 \left(\frac{M}{\rho\phi}\right)^{\frac{2}{3}} \left(\frac{2\gamma_1 \sin \alpha \cdot \gamma_2 \sin \beta \cdot \gamma_3 \sin \varepsilon}{n}\right)^{\frac{1}{3}} \tag{43}$$

If the activity coefficient of the solute in the parent phase is again substantially the same at the two concentrations which correspond to μ_n and μ_b, this becomes

$$\ln \frac{L_n}{L} = \frac{2}{RT} \left(\frac{M}{\phi\rho}\right)^{\frac{2}{3}} \left(\frac{2\gamma_1 \sin \alpha \cdot \gamma_2 \sin \beta \cdot \gamma_3 \sin \varepsilon}{n}\right)^{\frac{1}{3}} \tag{43a}*$$

Since all the quantities on the right-hand side of equations (39), (39a), (43), and (43a) are positive, μ_r and μ_n must be greater than μ_b; *i.e.*, a small

---

* There is of course nothing novel about our equations (39) to (43a), inclusive, all of which are either derived, or implicitly stated, in the work of Gibbs and others. The authors would however acknowledge a private communication from Mr. A. J. Hailwood, which was of very considerable help in deriving equations (40) to (43a) in the present treatment.

particle, either liquid or crystalline, will have a higher solubility than the same material in the mass. The first particles formed (the nuclei) can therefore grow only in a "supersaturated" solution. It will also be noted that a reduction in the interfacial tension, γ, in equations (39) and (39a), or in any one or more of the interfacial tensions in equations (43) and (43a), will reduce the difference $(\mu_r - \mu_b)$ or $(\mu_n - \mu_b)$. In other words, the presence of a surface-active agent which is adsorbed, either on a liquid droplet or on one or more of the faces of a crystalline particle, has an effect which can be expressed by any of the following equivalent statements:

(a) the extra solubility due to very fine particle size is reduced,

(b) the degree of supersaturation required to initiate crystallisation is decreased,

(c) smaller particles or droplets become capable of existence and can act as precipitation nuclei.*

The *quantitative* value of equations (39)–(43) is limited by the fact that the *thermodynamical* interfacial tension γ is used, and in the case of a solid particle this takes no account of possible internal stresses or stretching tensions (*cf.* Chapter 3, p. 91). Further approximations are also introduced by the facts that the density ρ of a very small crystal or droplet will differ from that of the material in bulk, and that the interfacial tension will also be different. It has been estimated by Benson and Shuttleworth,[1] however, that the interfacial tension of a cluster of thirteen molecules will differ from that of a bulk phase by less than 15%. The qualitative validity of arguments based on these equations seems to be adequate for our purposes.

Having shown that the general effect of an adsorbed solute on the solubility of small particles is qualitatively the same for both isotropic and crystalline precipitates, let us for the sake of simplicity consider only the case of the isotropic precipitate in greater detail. Suppose we have a homogeneous solution containing a concentration C of solute, C being greater than L, and the temperature and pressure being constant. As the result of the random association of dissolved molecules (or ions)—which may be encouraged by such mechanical devices as special forms of agitation, the introduction of a foreign body, etc.—particles of all sizes will be formed up to a maximum effective radius r_x, the solubility of which will be L_x. These particles cannot however act as nuclei, and hence precipitation

---

* It may be of interest to note here that, for the solubility of a small particle to be appreciably greater than that of the substance in bulk, it seems to be necessary that its radius be about a micron or less. Let us suppose that the molecular weight of the precipitating substance, a liquid, is 300, that its specific gravity is unity, the temperature 300° K., and that the interfacial tension 100 dynes/cm. and that the crystal is free from internal strains; an increase of 10% in the solubility over that of the substance in bulk demands a particle radius of only 0·8 microns.

[1] Benson and Shuttleworth, *J. Chem. Phys.*, 1951, **19**, 150.

cannot begin under the particular conditions prevailing, until L_x becomes equal to or smaller than C, *i.e.*, until the condition is satisfied that

$$r_x \geq \frac{2M}{RT\rho} \frac{\gamma_x}{ln \left(\frac{C}{L}\right)}. \tag{44}$$

If now at a given value of C a surface-active agent is added, which by definition will decrease γ_x, it follows from (44) that the number of particles, if any, which are large enough to act as nuclei will be increased. The presence of the surface-active agent will therefore increase the number of effective nuclei in the initial stages of precipitation, provided always that the surface-active agent is not adsorbed in such a way as to interfere too greatly with the deposition of solute. If such an interference becomes the preponderating mechanism, which might for example be the case if closely packed interfacial films were formed in which the individual molecules had a low mobility, then the effect of the surface-active agent, which cannot usefully be considered in terms of the interfacial free energies, is to "poison" the nuclei and hence to decrease their effective number at the beginning of the precipitation.

It is almost impossible to separate the nucleation process from growth of the precipitate, but some light is thrown on the process by several papers. Giddings and Eyring[1] have examined nucleation in the course of a more general study of multibarrier kinetics. This treatment depends on the fact that there is a series of successive free energy barriers to be overcome in a given process. Giddings and Eyring work out the general solution for the steady-state rate of such a process, and introduce mathematical approximations which simplify the problem. When this method is applied to nucleation, it shows that it is controlled by passage over all the various energy barriers involved, and not by passage over the single highest barrier, as assumed by Volmer and Weber.[2] Application of multibarrier kinetics leads to the same results as those obtained by Becker and Döring.[3]

Schlichtkrull[4] has shown that, when insulin crystals are grown in the absence of distorted, twin-like crystals, surface nucleation provides the best explanation of the particle size distribution which is obtained. This was borne out by the reduction in nucleation when the insulin was crystallised in a paraffin-covered enclosure or in the presence of "Tween 80" (*cf.* p. 473), and by the increased rate of nucleation when the surface of the solution was increased, for example, by foaming.

As we have seen, the particle growth stage of a precipitation, which begins as soon as an appreciable number of nuclei have been formed, is

[1] Giddings and Eyring, *J. Phys. Chem.*, 1958, **62**, 305.
[2] Volmer and Weber, *Z. phys. Chem.*, 1925, **119**, 277.
[3] Becker and Döring, *Ann. der Physik.*, 1935, **24**, 719.
[4] Schlichtkrull, *Acta Chem. Scand.*, 1957, **11**, 439.

partly concurrent with nucleation and can in fact usually be considered as competing with the nucleation process for the available solute. Thus if at any instant during the particle growth stage we consider two species of particles having radii r_1 and r_2, r_1 representing the minimum size which can act as a nucleus under the conditions momentarily prevailing, and r_2 being a larger and, on the average, older species, then it follows from equation (39a) that

$$ln \frac{L_1}{L_2} = \frac{2M}{RT\rho} \left(\frac{\gamma_1}{r_1} - \frac{\gamma_2}{r_2} \right) \tag{45}$$

where L_1 and L_2 are the solubilities of the two species. If conditions are such that $\gamma_1 = \gamma_2$, then we can write

$$ln \frac{L_1}{L_2} = \frac{2M\gamma_2}{RT\rho} \left(\frac{1}{r_1} - \frac{1}{r_2} \right) \tag{45a}$$

from which it follows that, the solubility of the smaller particles being always greater, deposition on the larger particles is continually favoured. If now a surface-active agent is added which does not interfere with the deposition of solute, and which is so rapidly adsorbed that the interfacial tensions of the different species, though reduced, are independent of age, so that γ_1 and γ_2 remain equal, then it is apparent from (45a) that the ratio L_1/L_2 will be diminished; *i.e.*, deposition on the larger particles will not be favoured to the same extent as in the absence of the agent. In such a case, therefore, the presence of the surface-active agent will favour the formation of a finer precipitate, since (a) it increases the number of effective nuclei in the early stages of precipitation, and (b) it reduces the tendency, under comparable conditions, for material to be preferentially deposited on the larger (older) particles than on the fresh nuclei formed in the later stages of the precipitation.

Many examples of this type of effect have been observed. Packter[1] has examined the effect of a number of surface-active agents on the particle size of insoluble silver, copper, and lead salts. Polypeptides, polysaccharic acids, polyhydroxylic non-ionic agents derived from lauric acid and polyethylene glycol and from heptyl alcohol and ethylene oxide, and certain colloidal polyelectrolytes, were all found to reduce the particle size of crystals deposited from supersaturated solutions of these salts. It is also well known that stable sols of many insoluble metal salts can be prepared by mixing dilute solutions of the reactants in the presence of surface-active agents, which reduce the particle size of the precipitate and also act as deflocculating agents and protective colloids. It is interesting to note that Lucchesi,[2] who studied the rate of formation of sparingly soluble barium, lead, and strontium sulphates by measuring the changes in conductivity of the solutions during precipitation, found that the rate depended on the

---

[1] Packter, *J. Chem. Soc.*, 1957, 2359; *Z. phys. Chem.* (Leipzig), 1957, **207**, 210.
[2] Lucchesi, *J. Coll. Sci.*, 1956, **11**, 113.

order of addition of the reagents. The rate of formation of lead sulphate was faster when lead ions were added to sulphate ions than *vice versa*. Addition of sulphate ions to a solution containing barium ions gave a slower rate of formation than the reverse case, but at sulphate ion concentrations greater than 0·004 M this effect appeared to be reversed. Lucchesi suggests that this indicates that the electrokinetic potential at the solid surface plays an important part in the precipitation process. This may play a part in the rate of crystallisation in the presence of ionic surface-active agents.

In considering equation (45), however, it is worth examining a further possible case, *viz.*, that a surface-active agent is present which does not interfere with deposition, but which is adsorbed sufficiently slowly that the interfacial tension of the nuclei (γ_1) is not reduced to the same extent as the interfacial tensions of the larger particles, the surfaces of which will be, on the average, older. Under such conditions it is possible for a surface-active agent actually to increase the ratio L_1/L_2 and hence to increase still more the tendency for the larger particles to grow more rapidly than the smaller particles. In such an event the total effect of the surface-active agent in the precipitation process might be in the direction of either a coarser or a finer precipitate, since it would tend on the one hand to increase the number of nuclei at each stage of the process, but on the other hand would encourage still more the preferential deposition of solute on the larger particles once they were formed. The fact that there is an appreciable time effect in the lowering of the interfacial tension, however, increases the likelihood of the latter mechanism predominating and of the surface-active agent yielding a coarser precipitate.

Attention has already been drawn to the fact that surface-active agents can sometimes "poison" precipitation nuclei by mechanically interfering with, or even preventing, the deposition of solute, and thus diminishing the number of useful nuclei which are present at any instant. The effect of such an adsorbed material, which cannot be explained in terms of the thermodynamics of surfaces, will also usually continue into the crystal growth stage, which will be retarded thereby; consequently the total effect of the agent on the precipitation process may not be predictable. In general, however, a finer precipitate seems to result from these conditions, presumably because the poisoning effect on each particle increases with time, thus requiring the formation of a greater number of successive crops of nuclei, in order to complete the precipitation, than would be needed in the absence of the surface-active agent.

This effect is shown rather well by the action of sodium polymethacrylate and the ammonia adduct of an *iso*butylene-maleic anhydride copolymer on the precipitation of calcium carbonate, as reported by Williams and Ruehrwein.[1] Turbidity measurements showed that the time before

---

[1] Williams and Ruehrwein, *J. Amer. Chem. Soc.*, 1957, **79**, 4898.

precipitation occurred is prolonged in the presence of these polyelectrolytes. The rate of precipitation decreases, as well as the quantity of calcium carbonate precipitated, with increasing concentrations of both agents. It is possible that the repression of precipitation was caused by sequestration of the calcium ions, and in the case of sodium polymethacrylate, calculations from the experimental results showed that the number of moles of calcium carbonate which were prevented from being precipitated by each equivalent of polymeric ion was a constant. For the *iso*butylene-maleic anhydride polymer this number was much higher and was not constant, suggesting that this polymer inhibited crystal growth to such an extent that many small crystals of calcium carbonate could not be filtered and were therefore not recovered. Photographs of the crystals suggest that adsorption of the polymeric ion on calcium carbonate may be responsible for both the marked distortion and the delayed precipitation. In the case of sodium polymethacrylate, the constant nature of the sequestering effect would not explain the difference in the induction period before precipitation occurred.

The digestion stage in a precipitation process refers to the growth of the larger particles at the expense of the smaller ones, caused by the greater solubility of the latter. The effect of this mechanism during the precipitation, when relatively large amounts of fresh solute are being deposited, may be negligible, but digestion phenomena may become more important towards the end of a precipitation process, and may be decisive in determining the stability of a disperse system obtained by controlled precipitation.* If an adsorbed surface-active agent interferes sufficiently with the deposition of solute, it may effectively stop a digestion process and stabilise a considerably more finely divided precipitate than could otherwise be obtained. This point is very well illustrated by a paper by Perry[1] on one aspect of the digestion or "ripening" of silver halide crystals. He investigated the effect of gelatine, polyacrylamide, polyvinyl alcohol, polyvinylamine, and substituted polyvinyl acetal on the crystallisation of mixed halides, and found, in agreement with earlier workers, that two different types of ripening could be distinguished: digestion of the type which we have described above ("Ostwald ripening") and "coalescence ripening," which is characterised by the co-existence of two size classes of crystals. In the presence of the substituted polyvinyl acetal, coalescence ripening occurs, but it does not take place with polyvinyl alcohol, gelatine, or polyacrylamide. Polyvinylamine alters the crystal habit substantially, as is shown by the electron micrographs. If the surface-active agent does not

---

* It should be noted that digestion processes usually stop when the precipitate reaches a certain size, presumably because the thermodynamical driving force arising from the interfacial free energies has then become too small, *e.g.*, L_1/L_2 in equations (39a), (43a), and (45a) has become sensibly unity.

[1] Perry, *J. Coll. Sci.*, 1959, **14**, 27.

interfere too greatly with deposition, on the other hand, then there are again several theoretical possibilities, depending on whether or not the interfacial tensions of the larger and smaller particles are lowered to the same extent by the agent. If the lowering in the interfacial tension remains the same for all the species, under the conditions prevailing, then equation (45a) predicts that the surface-active agent will simply decrease the fractions L_1/L_2, L_2/L_3, etc. (where $r_1 < r_2 < r_3$, etc.,), and hence diminish the decrease in free energy accompanying the process of digestion. Under practical conditions, involving finite times, such a diminution in the thermo-dynamical driving force behind the process might be decisive in stopping a digestion process. The possibilities become more varied if the surface-active agent lowers the interfacial tensions of the different species by differing amounts during digestion, though it seems likely that the interfacial tension γ_1 of a smaller, dissolving particle (the surface of which is contracting) would usually be lower than that (γ_2) of a larger, growing particle. If such a condition obtained, equation (45) predicts that the surface-active agent would diminish L_1/L_2, *i.e.*, it would again act against the process of digestion.

The foregoing argument also applies qualitatively to the precipitation and digestion of anisotropic solid particles. When however we come to consider the effect of surface-active agents in the latter connection, it becomes necessary also to examine their effect on crystal shape.* If a surface-active agent is more strongly adsorbed on certain faces of a growing crystal than on others, then its effect can be considered in terms of the relative changes in interfacial tensions, or alternatively of mechanical inter-ference with the deposition of solute. If the adsorbed surface-active agent does not interfere greatly with deposition, then we can apply the Gibbs concept of the minimum interfacial free energy. If for example we again consider the case of the parallelepiped, and assume that the crystallographic angles are unaffected by the adsorption, but suppose for example that γ_1 is lowered proportionately more than γ_2 or γ_3, it follows from equation (42) that bc will be increased relatively to ac and ab—*i.e.*, a crystal shape will be encouraged in which the relative area is increased of those surfaces the interfacial tension of which is decreased by the adsorption of a surface-active material. The effect of a surface-active agent may be even more striking, in that it may permit the formation of a face which would other-wise be thermodynamically unstable. The relevance of this minimum inter-facial free energy criterion depends *inter alia* on the ratio of the surface of a crystal to its mass; thus Volmer supports the widely held view that it can be applied only to crystals which are less than about one micron in diameter.

---

* It will be appreciated by those acquainted with the extensive literature on the subject, that the term "surface-active solute" in the present connection includes dye-stuffs and many other types of solutes which are outside the scope of the present book.

If the action of a surface-active agent which is preferentially adsorbed on one type of crystal face is simply that it prevents or seriously hinders the deposition of solute on that face, then the result in terms of crystal shape will in general be similar, and the area of that face will be increased relatively to the areas of the other faces. This statement may at first sight appear to be paradoxical, but it follows quite simply from the fact that those faces in a polyhedron on which relatively more material is deposited will tend to diminish relatively in area.

The effect of surface-active agents on crystal shape is well illustrated by some hitherto unpublished results by Fysh,[1] in which adipic acid was allowed to crystallise from aqueous solutions, under carefully standardised conditions, in the presence of a cationic and an anionic surface-active agent (cetyltrimethylammonium bromide and sodium oleyl-*p*-anisidide-3-sulphonate, respectively). Under the experimental conditions, in which a 10% solution of adipic acid was allowed to cool with stirring from 85° c. to 20° c. over a period of approximately one hour, it was found that the crystals obtained in the absence of surface-active agent were the usual flat, hexagonal plates, with prominent (001) faces. If as little as 0·0001% of cetyltrimethylammonium bromide, calculated on the original mother liquor, was present during the precipitation, then markedly thinner plates were obtained, though without any great diminution in the average crystal size. As the concentration of this agent was increased, the plates obtained became still thinner, and also smaller and more imperfectly formed. The anionic agent, on the other hand, had the opposite effect: beginning at 0·0025%, the plates obtained became thicker, passing through the prism shape at 0·01% to needles at higher concentrations (0·1%). At the higher concentrations the average crystal size decreased, but much less markedly than when cetyltrimethylammonium bromide was present. The faces on the ends of the elongated prisms and needles were positively identified as the (001) faces which were prominent in the hexagonal plates obtained in pure water. Both surface-active agents were effective only during crystal growth. Thus if a hexagonal plate was placed in a saturated solution of adipic acid containing sodium oleyl-*p*-anisidide-3-sulphonate, no change in crystal shape occurred if the temperature was kept constant; if however the solution was cooled or evaporated, so that fresh deposition of adipic acid took place, the crystal developed into a prism, and eventually a needle, during growth. This effect follows closely that previously observed by Wells[2] on the growth of crystals in different solvents.

These results are explained by Fysh on the assumption that the anionic agent is adsorbed amphipathically on those regions of the crystal surfaces containing $—[CH_2]_4—$ chains, this surface-active agent being repelled by the hydrated, anionic COOH groups. It is significant that the (001) faces,

[1] D. Fysh, private communication.
[2] Wells, *Phil. Mag.*, 1946, **37**, 184.

which are prominent on the flat hexagonal tablets obtained in pure water, consist entirely of COOH groups, while the side faces contain both COOH groups and —$[CH_2]_4$— chains. It therefore follows that the anionic surface-active agent, being adsorbed on the side faces of the crystal but not on the initially prominent (001) faces, should favour the propagation of the former, giving prisms or needles instead of plates.

The effect of the cationic surface-active agent (cetyltrimethylammonium bromide) is considered by Fysh to be due to a strong chemisorption on those portions of the surface containing COOH groups. A salt linkage is postulated between these groups and the quaternary ammonium groups of the surface-active agent; a less powerful amphipathic adsorption may also occur where there are —$[CH_2]_4$— chains in the surface. On this explanation, adsorption should be greatest on the initially prominent (001) faces, hence the cationic surface-active agent should encourage the growth of a still more plate-like crystal, as in fact happens.

Fysh's explanation, which is in good agreement with the facts, is of course a general one. It applies equally well to explanations based on the Gibbs concept of the minimum total interfacial free energy, or on the idea of mechanical interference with deposition by adsorbed layers on the faces of the crystals, both types of explanation demanding an increase in the relative areas of those faces on which the surface-active compound is adsorbed.

Fysh's suggestion that the changes in habit of adipic acid crystals are due to differences in the adsorbability of the two types of surface-active agents on the end faces and side faces, respectively, has been followed up quantitatively in an important paper by Michaels and Colville.[1] These workers studied the effect of an anionic agent (sodium tetrapropylbenzene sulphonate) and a cationic agent (dodecyltrimethylammonium chloride) on the rate of deposition* on the 001 face ("C" face) and on the 110 and 010 faces ("AB" faces, or "side faces" in Fysh's terminology), in both nucleation-and-growth and growth-from-seed experiments. They found, in agreement with Fysh, that the cationic agent reduced the rate of deposition on the C face much more than on the AB faces, favouring the formation of plate-like crystals, in both types of growth, while the anionic agent had the reverse effect. In the absence of either surface-active agent, they found that the rates of deposition were in the order $110 > 010 > 001$, *i.e.*, slower on the face with a higher surface density of —COOH groups.

Michaels and Colville carry out an interesting theoretical analysis of

---

* We use the phrase "rate of deposition *on* a face," in the present connection, rather than "rate of growth *of* a face," because the latter is often applied to the rate at which the *area* of a crystal face increases. The geometry of crystals means that those faces on which deposition is *hindered*, relative to other faces, will actually increase in area *more* rapidly, relatively speaking, and *vice versa*.

[1] Michaels and Colville, *J. Phys. Chem.*, 1960, **64**, 13.

their results. For the nucleation-and-growth processes, they use an expression derived from the theory of two-dimensional nucleation (*cf.* p. 187):

$$R = Ke^{-\beta/\ln S}$$

where R is the rate of deposition in milligrams/min. cm.^{2}, S is the supersaturation ratio in the solution, K is a proportionality constant, and β is a constant which depends on the absolute temperature and the edge-free-energy of the two-dimensional nucleus. This equation was found to agree quite well with the data on rates of deposition which were calculated from the changes of crystal size and shape with time: by plotting log R against $1/\ln S$, straight lines were obtained, from which K and β could be calculated, the results being given in Table 5

Table 5

Rate constants for crystallisation of adipic acid, in the presence of surface-active agents

(Michaels and Colville, *J. Phys. Chem.*, 1960, **64**, 13.)

Addition	A (110) Face		B (010) Face		C (001) Face	
	β	K	β	K	β	K
None	0·35	1·05	0·60	1·35	0·39	0·22
0·137 mmol./litre sodium tetra-propylbenzene sulphonate .	0·37	0·76	0·63	0·90	0·38	0·20
0·364 mmol./litre dodecyltri-methylammonium chloride .	0·36	0·96	0·61	1·15	0·39	0·15

As Michaels and Colville point out, the fact that the value of β for each face is unaltered by the presence of either surface-active agent, suggests that the agents do not alter the free energy of two-dimensional nucleation. The reductions in K values suggest that the adsorbed agents reduce the frequency of nucleation on each face, possibly by blocking a fraction of the surface. It will be observed that, on the A and B faces (which contain —CH_2— as well as carboxy groups) the anionic agent reduces the value of K more than does the cationic agent; on the C face (which is made up of carboxy groups) the reverse holds true. This suggests, in agreement with Fysh's hypothesis, that the anionic agent is amphipathically adsorbed, while the cationic agent is chemisorbed with reversed orientation.

Michaels and Colville make estimates, from the values of β, of the γ's (thermodynamical interfacial tensions in our nomenclature) of the three types of faces. Although, as they point out, the absolute values which they obtain appear to be much too low, the relative values are clearly in the order $\gamma_C > \gamma_A > \gamma_B$. When these relative values are considered in terms of the requirement of minimum interfacial free energy, which we have discussed earlier in the present chapter, the rate of growth of the areas of the three faces should be in the order B-face > A-face > C-face, so that the order of rate of deposition on the faces (R values under comparable conditions) should be C-face > A-face > B-face. In fact, the experimental values for rates of deposition are almost entirely in the order A-face > B-face > C-face. This deviation of the C-face from the expected order is explained very reasonably by Michaels and Colville by hydration of the carboxy groups in the C-face, which presents an energy barrier to the deposition of adipic acid molecules, and to a lesser extent by the postulate of electrostatic repulsion between anionic groups.

Michaels and Colville found that both the surface-active agents studied by them had on the whole a much greater retarding effect on the nucleation-and-growth process than on growth-from-seed, although the same qualitative picture emerged in both cases of the effect of the surface-active agents on crystal habit. They explain this on the assumption that in the latter process at least one other type of nucleation can occur, *viz.*, propagation from dislocations, and that this process is less affected by surface-active material than is two-dimensional nucleation. They also observed that, in the growth-from-seed experiments, the relative differences in deposition rates became less marked as the concentration of either surface-active agent was increased. They interpret this in terms of a self-limiting adsorption mechanism, assuming that (a) the fractional retardation in R caused by the surface-active agent is proportional to the fraction of the face covered by adsorbed agent, and (b) the adsorption of the agent obeys the Langmuir isotherm. This leads to the equation

$$R = R_0 \left(1 - \frac{\theta_s bC}{1 + bC} \right)$$

where R is the rate of deposition on the face in question in the presence of a concentration C of surface-active agent, R_0 is the rate of deposition when $C = 0$, θ_s is the fraction of the surface covered when it is saturated with surface-active agent, and b is the constant in the Langmuir adsorption isotherm. The values obtained by applying this equation to the experimental data for growth-from-seed are highly instructive. (See Table 5.)

It will be noticed that the θ_s values for the anionic agent on both types of face are the same, but that the saturation value for the cationic agent is greater on the C-face. This, and the fact that the intensity constant b is considerably greater for the cationic agent, is considered by Michaels and Colville to be further evidence that the anionic agent is physically (amphipathically) adsorbed, while the cationic agent is chemisorbed.

The importance of Michaels and Colville's paper to the whole question of just how surface-active agents affect crystallisation processes is self-evident; one of its most interesting features is that (at least under the

Table 5

Adsorption constants for surface-active agents on adipic acid crystal faces, calculated from retardation of the rate of deposition

(Michaels and Colville, *J. Phys. Chem.*, 1960, **64**, 18)

Surface-active Agent	Average Values on			
	A and B Faces		C Face	
	θ_s	b	θ_s	b
Sodium tetrabutylbenzene sulphonate . .	0·73	4·9	0·73	0·72
Dodecyltrimethylammonium chloride . .	0·67	21·4	0·83	25·5

experimental conditions used by them), the effect of the two surface-active agents on adipic acid can be more adequately explained on a *kinetic* picture, than on the basis of the simple thermodynamics of surfaces. It is to be hoped that similar studies will be made of other crystallisation processes.

The effect of surface-active materials (in the widest sense) on crystal habit is very widespread; Whetstone[1] has found, for example, that soluble dyestuffs can cause considerable changes in the habit of inorganic salts.

The formation of silver halide sols in the presence of cationic detergents has been studied by Matijevic and Ottewill.[2] The sols which they used were negatively charged, and the effect of dodecyltrimethylammonium bromide, dodecylpyridinium chloride, dodecylpyridinium bromide, dodecylpyridinium iodide, and dodecylquinolinium bromide was examined by spectrophotometric, micro-electrophoretic, and electron microscopic techniques. "Sensitised" coagulation occurred at a critical concentration of the surface-active compound lying between 10^{-5} and 10^{-6} moles/litre. Matijevic and Ottewill suggest, from these results, that the nuclei must grow to a critical size before adsorption of the surface-active agent can occur, and that the difference in size of the head groups of the various agents which they examined would require different critical particle sizes. This adsorption was considered to be the cause of the coagulation. Periodic fluctuations of coagulation and stabilisation were observed when the concentrations of the surface-active agents were altered. This was considered to be due to the alteration of the surface area of the crystals attendant upon their reduction

---

[1] Whetstone, *Trans. Faraday Soc.*, 1955, **51**, 973, 1142; *J. Chem. Soc.*, 1956, 4841.
[2] Matijevic and Ottewill, *J. Coll. Sci.*, 1958, **13**, 242.

in size, in combination with the adsorption of a second layer of surface-active material on the particles, so that discharge of the ζ-potential (which leads to coagulation) is followed by the formation of a *positive* charge which again renders the dispersion stable. It is also interesting to note that, when the critical micelle concentration was reached, the agents all acted as protective colloids and the rate of formation of the silver halide particles was reduced.

This apparent difference in behaviour between single surface-active ions and materials of a highly colloidal nature as protective colloids is quite striking, and we have referred to it previously (p. 178). Similar effects were observed by McCartney and Alexander,[1] when they examined additives in the crystallisation of calcium sulphate dihydrate. They found that the rates of nucleation and of crystal growth were markedly reduced by colloidal materials which have regularly spaced, ionised carboxyl groups on the chain structure, such as keratin, gelatine, polyacrylic acid, and carboxymethyl cellulose. These additives slow down the crystallisation, which McCartney and Alexander suggest is due to their adsorption on the crystals. It might be expected that, with the extremely small quantities of the additives involved, nucleation would continue until all the additive was used up, when crystal growth could occur. They suggest that the additive does not allow the nuclei to grow to the critical size, so that the nuclei redisperse and the stabilising material is then free to interact with other embryos. This is consistent with the fact that such additives do not significantly reduce the rate of solution of calcium sulphate dihydrate. The crystal habit was modified by the adsorption of these anionic polymers to different degrees. When a solution of calcium sulphate, which contained enough polyacrylic acid to prevent crystallisation at 30°, was heated to 70°, a deposit of crystals appeared which grew extremely rapidly to needles which were visible to the naked eye. These needles were curved and highly imperfect, and it appears that the polyacrylic acid cannot quite prevent nucleation when the solution is heated. Once a few nuclei are formed, the excess solute is rapidly deposited on them. "Teepol" (a sulphated olefin), cetyltrimethylammonium bromide, a number of dyestuffs, and several of the lower aliphatic alcohols, all had no effect on either the rate of crystallisation, or on the crystal habit.

F. Foam Formation and Foam Destruction

The formation of foams is of technical importance, *per se*, in fire-fighting and in the formation of foamed concrete and plastics, which are discussed in Chapter 9, and is an ancillary phenomenon in many detergent processes (Chapter 8). Problems in the prevention or destruction of foams

---

[1] McCartney and Alexander, *J. Coll. Sci.*, 1958, **13**, 383.

are also encountered very widely. There is a considerable literature on the subject, including four well-known monographs,[1] to which reference should be made for more detailed information.

The theoretical background to foams and foaming has been examined recently in a very useful review by Kitchener and Cooper.[2] They point out that the rather contradictory theories which have been advanced in the literature probably arise from attempts to make too extended generalisations from insufficiently diversified experiments. The physical nature of the foaming process is so obviously complicated that it is extremely unlikely that one simple factor can be found to explain all the recorded observations.

The foaming properties of solutions have been shown to be broadly dependent on the surface activity of the solutes, and it is now well established that pure liquids do not foam. The standard of purity required completely to avoid foaming on water is extremely high, and it was the failure to appreciate this fact which led to the publication of a number of papers which were contradictory and confusing. The really persistent foams are formed only in the presence of highly surface-active solutes, such as soaps, synthetic detergents, and soluble proteins, but transient foams can be produced on water by very small quantities of impurities, such as saponin at 0·0005% (5 p.p.m.).

Kitchener and Cooper divide foams into three classes: unstable, metastable, and solid. Unstable foams, as their name implies, persist for only a short time, and collapse independently of the occurrence of drainage. Metastable foams, on the other hand, are those in which drainage of liquid from between the bubbles eventually stops, and the foam would persist indefinitely if it could be completely protected from disturbing influences. Vibration, draughts, evaporation, dust, and other external influences can be largely prevented, but in the case of three-dimensional foams this is insufficient to confer lasting stability, since gas diffuses from the smaller to the larger bubbles, and after a time the structure becomes mechanically unstable and suddenly re-arranges itself. The shock of this rearrangement tends to rupture the very thin lamellae in a well drained, metastable foam. All foams are thermodynamically unstable, with the possible exception of the third class, *viz.*, the solid foams, which are characterised by the fact that their stability is due to one or more chemical processes, which occur during or just after the formation of the foam.

The main factors which have to be considered in foam technology are the differences in physical properties between foaming and non-foaming solutions, and what mechanism or mechanisms render certain liquid

---

[1] Bikerman, *Foams, Theory and Industrial Applications*, Reinhold, 1953; Manegold, *Schaum*, Strassenbau, Heidelberg, 1953; de Fries, *Foam Stability*, Rubber-Stichting, Delft, 1957; Mysels, Shinoda and Frankel, *Soap Films*, Pergamon Press, 1959.

[2] Kitchener and Cooper, *Quart. Rev.*, 1959, **13,** 71.

lamellae metastable. These two questions are related but are not directly connected, since many solutions foam fairly readily but do not give persistent foams.

The stabilising mechanisms in foams have been considered mainly in terms of the properties of the thin liquid films which separate the dispersed gas. Most of the theories proposed to explain the persistence of foams were advanced about a hundred years ago: the concept of surface elasticity by Gibbs and Marangoni, and that of surface viscosity by Plateau. Gibbs showed that, when a film containing an adsorbed surface-active solute is stretched locally, the adsorption equilibrium is disturbed, and the amount of surface-active agent in unit area of the surface is instantaneously decreased. This leads to an "elasticity" effect, since the surface tension immediately rises and tends to counteract further expansion. Gibbs's arguments apply to static conditions, and under dynamic conditions the magnitude of the elasticity effect is even greater, since a rapidly expanding surface has a tension greater than the equilibrium value. This latter effect was pointed out by Marangoni about ten years before Gibbs's theory was enunciated. Many experiments have been carried out on the surface ageing of surface-active agents over short periods of time (10^{-3} to 10^{-2} seconds), and give strong support to Marangoni's theory. Dynamic surface tension values and their significance are discussed in Chapter 3, p. 114. Sutherland,[1] for example, has shown that adsorption of surface-active materials occurs much more rapidly than can be accounted for by diffusion alone, and has suggested that convection to the surface is important. A quantitative treatment of the Marangoni effect would require fairly detailed information about the hydrodynamics of the system under investigation. Another possible factor contributing to the stability of foams has been proposed by Ewers and Sutherland,[2] who suggest that a spreading monolayer drags with it a significant quantity of underlying solution, which effect would rapidly repair any thinning spots in the lamella caused by any slight local disturbance.

The surface viscosity of the lamellae is another important factor in increasing the life of foams. This suggestion was first put forward by Plateau, and although the experiments which he did to prove his hypothesis were not completely rigorous, his main postulates have since been completely substantiated. Several workers[3] in recent years have constructed surface viscometers which enable the surface viscosities of soluble films to be determined absolutely. It has been found that the surface viscosity of solutions of sodium dodecyl sulphate is increased considerably when a small amount of dodecyl alcohol is added. Other physical properties of the surface

---

[1] Sutherland, *Reviews of Pure and Applied Chemistry* (Australia), 1951, **1**, 35.

[2] Ewers and Sutherland, *Australian Journal of Scientific Research*, 1952, **A5**, 697.

[3] Ewers and Sack, *Australian Journal of Chemistry*, 1954, **7**, 40; Davies, *Second Congress*, 1957, **I**, 220.

films have also been found to be dependent on the presence of very small quantities of impurities, and this discovery has cast considerable doubt on much of the earlier work. For the case of sodium dodecyl sulphate containing added dodecyl alcohol, a close correlation has been demonstrated between surface viscosity and the stability of foams produced from these solutions. Increasing the surface viscosity slows down the drainage in the lamellae and thus increases the life of the foams.

Not all metastable foams, however, exhibit high surface viscosities. Derjaguin and Titijevskaya,[1] by studying the stability of very thin metastable "black" films, have deduced that electrical repulsion between the ionic double layers formed by adsorption on the two sides of each lamella is the chief stabilising mechanism. The theory of the electrical double layer is not sufficient to explain the limiting thickness of 120 Å. when sodium chloride is added to a solution of sodium oleate, and Derjaguin and Titijevskaya suggest that hydrated layers are built up under the adsorbed layer of sodium oleate. The existence of solvent layers of such a considerable thickness (60 Å). has not yet been proved, and more work will be needed to clear up this point.

Kitchener and Cooper mention several other factors in their paper which have been suggested as being of importance in the stabilisation of foams. The concentration of solute is important, presumably because a maximum elasticity effect must operate, and other factors, such as synergistic effects of mixed surface-active agents, the presence of solid particles, temperature fluctuations, and evaporation, also affect the stability of foams.

The importance of synergistic effects has only been fully appreciated fairly recently. Sawyer and Fowkes[2] have studied the interaction of anionic detergents with polar aliphatic compounds in foam formation. They found that the pure surface-active agents had a greater "susceptibility to foam stabilisation," the greater the surface tension at concentrations above the critical micelle concentration. The polar aliphatic compounds with straight chains containing eight to fifteen carbon atoms were the most effective additives, and this effectiveness was greater the more the critical micelle concentration was depressed by the additive. The effect increased with increasing surface activity of the additives, and the most stable foams contained 60% to 90% of additive in the adsorbed layers; this result was found experimentally and confirmed theoretically by calculations of the composition of the monolayers, by a thermodynamical argument which treats the monolayer as a separate phase. In treating the equations which arise, the activity coefficient of water in the monolayer is assumed to be so high that the mole fraction of water is neglibibly small; the reference solutions are taken as solutions of detergent without additive, and of additive without detergent, and it is also assumed that the heat of mixing

[1] Derjaguin and Titijevskaya, *Second Congress*, 1957, **I**, 211, 254.
[2] Sawyer and Fowkes, *J. Phys. Chem.*, 1958, **62**, 159.

of like hydrocarbon groups of the detergent and additive in the monolayer is so small that their activity coefficients are equal. Monsanto[1] claim that the addition of the metal or ammonium salts of the sulphated triethylene glycol ether of 2-butyl-1-octanol, and similar compounds, to sodium N-dodecyltaurine has a synergistic effect on the lathering power of this detergent, especially in the presence of oils, fats, and greases. These effects may be due to alterations in the surface structure of the adsorbed films, such as a change from gaseous to liquid, and to solubilisation of oils by mixed micelles.

The importance of the structure of the surface layer in foams is also shown by the work of Walling, Ruff, and Thornton[2] on the relative adsorption of calcium and sodium ions by foams stabilised by anionic agents. Their experiments indicate that calcium ions are strongly adsorbed preferentially in the surface layer, and also in the micelles. The addition of even small quantities of divalent ions (Ca^{++}, Mg^{++}, and Zn^{++}) leads to considerably "wetter" foams, in which the drainage rate was increased from 90 to 106 grams per hour, and to a closer packing of the sodium palmitoyl-N-methyltaurine in the surface layer, as judged by chemical and physical analyses of the foams. They suggest that their results point to a possible explanation for the difference in foaming behaviour of synthetic detergents in hard and soft water, even when the detergents are completely stable in hard water.

The opposite problem, *viz.*, the destruction or retardation of the formation of foams, is also of considerable importance. The technical literature contains hundreds of examples of compositions which are claimed to inhibit or destroy foams. These substances must in general possess properties which are the opposite of those needed for foam stabilisation or production: *i.e.*, they must eliminate or appreciably diminish the surface elasticity effect, increase the speed of drainage in the lamellae, decrease the stability of the interfacial films, wet out solid stabilisers into the liquid medium, and so on.

It seems likely that reductions in surface elasticity are achieved by the anti-foaming agent displacing the foaming agent from the interface. In order to do this, the anti-foaming agent, if it is a liquid, must have a low intrinsic surface tension and must be able to spread when it is applied to the foam lamellae. Since foams have very large interfacial areas, and it is advantageous to maintain a high surface concentration of any anti-foaming agent, low solubility of the anti-foaming agent is also a desirable property. The great versatility of the silicone fluids as anti-foaming agents is due to their low solubility in aqueous media, their very low surface tensions (*ca.* 20 dynes/cm.), and their high spreading pressures on water. Thanks to

[1] Monsanto Chemical Co. and Brown, U.S.P. 2,673,842.
[2] Walling, Ruff, and Thornton, *J. Phys. Chem.*, 1957, **61**, 486.

this combination of properties, very small quantities (of the order of 1 to 100 parts per million) are frequently effective.

Not all types of foam can be destroyed or prevented by one single type of anti-foaming agent, and many of these agents work on quite different principles. Ross and his co-workers[1] have shown, for example, that tributyl phosphate and methylisobutyl carbinol have an anti-foaming action on "Nacconol NRSF" (an alkylated aromatic sulphonate) foams by increasing the rate of drainage of liquid from the foam lamellae. Although at higher concentrations methylisobutyl carbinol destroys the film-stabilising action of the foaming agent, the tributyl phosphate acts *only* by increasing the drainage from the lamellae.

Many cases are also known in which foams which are stabilised by finely divided, partly wetted solids, are broken by the addition of wetting-out agents which cause the particles to be wetted by the liquid; in such cases the formation of fresh foam will also usually be hindered.

---

[1] Ross and Young, *Ind. Eng. Chem.*, 1951, **43**, 2520; Ross and Cutillas, *J. Phys. Chem.*, 1955, **59**, 863.

PART II

TECHNICAL APPLICATIONS OF SYNTHETIC SURFACE-ACTIVE AGENTS

CHAPTER 5

TECHNICAL WETTING-OUT AND WATER-PROOFING PROCESSES

In Chapter 4 we have defined wetting—considered as a fundamental inter-facial process—as any phenomenon in which one fluid phase is displaced, completely or in part, by another fluid phase from the surface of a solid or liquid, the displacement not being due to mutual solution. "Wetting" in this physical sense plays an essential part in many technical processes in which surface-active agents are used, as we shall see in the present and succeeding chapters. We shall also see that in many cases (*e.g.*, at certain stages of detergent processes) both the fluid phases involved in a wetting phenomenon are liquids. When however we come to consider the technical applications of surface-active agents, it becomes very convenient to talk of "wetting" in a more restricted sense. We propose in fact to use the phrase "wetting-out processes" to denote only those in which the desired end is the displacement of a gas (usually air) by a liquid (usually an aqueous solution) from the surface of a solid. A wetting-out agent will accordingly be defined as a surface-active agent which assists such a process, and not as a substance which necessarily promotes a wetting in the broader physical sense. To take a familiar example, surface-active agents such as isopro-pylated naphthalene sulphonates are very effective wetting-out agents, assisting as they do in the displacement of air by aqueous solutions from textile materials or foliage. This does not mean, however, that these par-ticular agents are necessarily effective in promoting the displacement, by aqueous solutions, of oils or fats from textiles. This latter phenomenon, which is one stage of the process of detergency, must be considered to be a wetting process in the broader physical sense, and can be analysed thermo-dynamically in the same general way, but it is more convenient to exclude such effects from the present chapter on wetting-out processes.

We propose, similarly, to define water-proofing as the achievement of an opposite effect to wetting-out processes, in which water or an aqueous solution is either displaced from the surface of a solid, or made to wet the surface less completely, the other fluid phase involved being a gas, almost invariably air.

Technical wetting-out agents, even on this restricted definition, find an extremely large number of applications. They are used for ensuring the complete removal of air from textiles (usually as a preliminary to some further treatment), for promoting the displacement of air from powdered solids (usually, but not always, as a first step towards obtaining a disper-sion), for increasing the efficiency of contact pesticides, for ensuring that

211

vegetation and other surfaces are completely and uniformly covered by
pest-control or germicidal sprays, for laying dust in roadways, and for
improving the efficiency of aqueous sprays which are used to remove dust
particles in air-conditioning equipment. It is obviously impossible to cover
all the possible technical wetting-out processes in the present chapter; on
the other hand we feel that it would be a mistake to confine our attention
to a few of the best-known examples, such as the wetting-out of textiles
or of foliage. We propose instead to attempt a compromise by considering
technical wetting-out processes under the following general headings, based
on the geometry of the systems involved, with specific illustrations wher-
ever possible:

(a) Technical wetting-out processes occurring at *isolated surfaces*:

    (*i*) spreading of bulk liquid masses;
    (*ii*) adhesion of spray droplets on impact with solid surfaces;
    (*iii*) adhesion of small solid particles on impact with liquid surfaces.

(b) Wetting-out of *porous solid bodies*:

    (*i*) wetting-out of textiles and other coherent porous masses;
    (*ii*) displacement of air from solid powders, etc., the structure of
which changes radically during the process.

A. Technical wetting-out processes at isolated surfaces

1. SPREADING OF BULK LIQUID PHASES

The simplest possible wetting-out process is that in which a fairly
extensive, smooth solid surface, which is substantially free from a capillary
structure, is brought into contact with a bulk of liquid in such a way that
adhesion is certain to occur. The desired result, and hence the criterion by
which the efficiency of a wetting-out agent is judged, may be one or more
of the following, *viz.*, (a) that spontaneous spreading of the liquid shall
occur, (b) that the spreading brought about by other forces (*e.g.*, gravity)
shall be impeded as little as possible, or (c) that a film of the liquid which
has already been formed (*e.g.*, by spreading, spraying, or immersion) shall
not recede from the surface. The simplest of these possibilities is obviously
the first, and we have seen in Chapter 4 that it will take place if the spreading coefficient S (Equation 1, Chapter 4) is positive (there being accordingly
no measurable contact angle), and that a wetting-out agent can help the
process by lowering the interfacial tensions liquid-air and/or solid-liquid.
In practice, however, the effect of forces such as gravity must nearly always
be considered. Thus if we are applying a water-paint or distemper to a
smooth wall, the initial spread will be the resultant of the brush-work put
into the job (favourable!), the effect of gravity (helping spreading at some
points, acting against it at others), and the interfacial tensions acting along

the lines at which the wall, the liquid medium, and the air meet. A wetting-out agent which alters the value of the spreading coefficient from negative to positive will obviously promote spreading, but this is not usually an essential criterion—*i.e.*, it may suffice if the contact angle is lowered considerably without actually disappearing (*cf.* Chapter 4, Equation 2). Such a lowering of the contact angle is due primarily to adsorption of a surface-active agent at the solid-liquid interface; it will be further favoured by adsorption at the liquid-air interface if the solid-air interfacial tension is then greater than the solid-liquid interfacial tension (*cf.* Chapter 4, Equation 2). It is therefore not surprising that suitable wetting-out agents for such spreading processes will be found in general to lower the surface tension of the aqueous medium (more correctly, the *dynamic* surface tension at the appropriate age), and in addition to lower the *advancing* contact angle (measured inside the liquid).

This conclusion is borne out by model experiments with horticultural wetting-out agents on artificial surfaces which have been reported by Martin[1] and by Evans and Martin.[2] In these experiments, the object of which was to devise rapid sorting tests for commercial wetting-out agents, small drops of the solutions were carefully placed on the "model" surfaces (cellulose acetate, cellulose nitrate, shellac, or paraffin wax), and the final areas of spread obtained were compared with the surface tensions of the solutions and the contact angles. The best correlation was given by the relation

$$A = \frac{k}{\sqrt{\gamma_{AW}(1 - \cos \theta_A)}} \tag{1}$$

where A is the area of spread, k is a constant, γ_{AW} is the *static* surface tension of the solution, and θ_A is the advancing contact angle. This equation predicts of course that the area of spread will be greater the smaller γ_{AW} and θ_A, increasing without limit as θ_A approaches zero.

It is interesting to note that if one combines the relation used by Padday for the direct determination of spreading coefficients

$$S = -\tfrac{1}{2}\rho g h^2 \qquad \text{(Equation 4, Chapter 4)}$$

(where ρ is the density of the liquid, g is the acceleration of gravity, and h is the height of the sheet of liquid) with the well-known equation for the spreading coefficient at finite contact angle

$$S = \gamma_{AW}(\cos \theta - 1) \quad \text{(Equation 1a, Chapter 4)}$$

noting that the volume of the liquid, which is given approximately by Ah, is constant, one obtains equation (1).

Another approach is to recall that the work which must be supplied to

---

[1] Martin, in *Wetting and Detergency*, Harvey, London, 1937, p. 117.
[2] Evans and Martin, *J. Pomology*, 1935, **13**, 261.

the system in order to bring about spreading over a *plane* surface, creating
A cm.^{2} of each of the interfaces solid-water and air-water,* and destroying
A cm.^{2} of air-solid interface, is given by

$$w = A\gamma_{AW} + A\gamma_{WS} - A\gamma_{AS}$$

where the γ's are the three interfacial tensions air-liquid, liquid-solid, and
air-solid, respectively. If we assume that the process is carried out reversibly, and that there is a finite (and reproducible) advancing contact angle
θ_A, then we can substitute for γ_{AS} the expression $(\gamma_{WS} + \gamma_{AW} \cos \theta_A)$ (*cf.*
Chapter 4, Equation 2), and obtain

$$w = A\gamma_{AW}(1 - \cos \theta_A)$$

or
$$A = \frac{w}{\gamma_{AW}(1 - \cos \theta_A)} \tag{2}$$

There would appear to be two main possible sources of this work w, at
constant temperature, pressure, and composition, *viz.*, kinetic energy
supplied when the drop is placed on the surface, and the potential energy
due to the hydrostatic pressure of the drop. The latter case is covered
adequately for our purposes by equation (1), the relationship of which with
the equations for the spreading coefficient we have just noted. The former
will be rather complicated, the kinetic energy which is available depending
on the course of wetting as well as on the manner in which the liquid is
applied. It is obvious, however, that equation (2) predicts that, other
things being equal, the area of spread will again be favoured by a low
(dynamic) surface tension and a low contact angle.

Martin (*loc. cit.*) points out that equations such as (1) inevitably raise
the question of whether static or dynamic values should be used for the
surface tension (and, we might add, for the contact angle). Unfortunately,
there are still insufficient experimental data for a really satisfactory answer,
and little more can be done at present than to point out that the question
of surface age is always relevant. It is probably true to say that, unless very
rapid evaporation is taking place, the static values will usually be usable
in analysing cases of wetting-out by bulk spreading in horticulture and
agriculture. This will apply especially if appreciable concentrations of
electrolytes are present, which will tend to suppress slow surface-ageing
effects (*cf.* Chapter 3, Section B–2), and if the criterion of wetting-out is the
extent of spreading during a long time interval.

A secondary factor which may be important in cases of wetting-out by
spreading is the action of a wetting-out agent in preventing recession. This
factor will of course predominate if we are dealing with the maintenance of

---

* This is only approximately true of the air-water interface, which has an appreciable
curvature, which may alter during spreading. For areas of spread which are not too
small, however, the errors involved in this assumption are probably not serious.

a liquid layer which has already been spread over the surface of the solid. Both the surface tension of the solution and the contact angle will again be important, with the differences that the ages of the various interfaces will usually be greater, and that the receding contact angle will be the relevant one. The velocity of adsorption at the air-liquid and solid-liquid interfaces will therefore be even less important than in the cases in which the liquid advances, equilibrium values becoming more useful indications of the effectiveness of different surface-active agents. Such measurements of the prevention of recession form the basis of the well-known "card test" for evaluating agricultural and horticultural sprays, in which a waxed card is immersed in the solution and then withdrawn, wetting-out efficiency being judged by whether or not the card remains wetted. Although this test may be useful in the preliminary sorting of surface-active agents, it does not of course furnish a physically accurate "model" for the great majority of technical wetting-out processes—its most serious defect is that it usually involves the use of an artificial surface.

The distinction between wetting-out processes on plane surfaces which are determined by the extent of initial spreading, and those which are determined by the degree to which recession is prevented, is discussed very clearly in the paper on plant pest-control by Martin (*loc. cit.*), who refers to these two effects as "spreading" and "wetting," respectively. Both are usually operative in practical horticultural spraying processes, determining respectively the initial degree of "wetting-out" (our terminology), and the retention of spray.

An important recent paper by Somers[1] indicates that, even when wetting-out is complete, surface-active agents can, by virtue of their *solution* properties, cause considerable differences in the retention of fungicides which are applied as aqueous sprays. Somers determined the retention of "Burgundy mixture" which had been applied to broad leaf beans and to laurel leaves, using a non-ionic agent (isooctyl-*o*-cresol condensed with ten mols of ethylene oxide), a cationic agent (cetylpyridinium chloride), and three anionic agents (sodium dinonyl- and dioctylsulphosuccinates, and sodium dodecyl sulphate). In all cases, the receding contact angle had disappeared, complete "run-off" conditions being obtained. He found that the non-ionic agent gave a high retention, which remained constant with increasing concentration of agent, while the cationic agent gave a similar effect, though at a lower retention figure. The anionic agents, on the other hand, gave a *decreasing* retention figure as their concentration was increased, this effect being particularly noticeable with the two sulphosuccinates. The decrease in retention began as the concentration exceeded the critical micelle concentration. Possible explanations are that the anionic micelles have a solubilising action on the waxes in the surface, that they

---

[1] Somers, *Second Congress*, 1957, **III**, 183.

sequester cupric ions, or (we would further suggest) that the agent has, above its critical micelle concentration, a pronounced deflocculating action on the particles of insecticide, which reduces their tendency to adhere to the plant surface. (One might, for example, expect the anionic agents to have a marked deflocculating action at higher concentrations by forming an adsorbed double layer on the particles of the basic copper salt, as discussed in Chapter 3, p. 142.) Whatever the exact explanation of these effects—and the explanations given here are not mutually exclusive—they draw attention to the possibility of side effects when wetting-out agents are used, since the agents may be colloidal electrolytes as well as being simply "surface-active."

We have tacitly assumed so far in the present section that a bulk liquid phase was spreading on a smooth surface. It is doubtful whether this condition is ever fully satisfied in practice; even in the apparently simple case of the surface of a leaf, the surface is traversed by veins and usually covered by hairs. Although the complete displacement of air from such a surface will involve capillary penetration, it seems to us that for many practical purposes (*e.g.*, if the object is only to apply a protective deposit fairly extensively over the surface of a leaf) wetting-out can be most usefully considered as a spreading phenomenon on a composite, isolated surface, the effect of "compositeness" being allowed for by Cassie and Baxter's treatment. Thus we have seen in Chapter 4 that the latter authors showed that the effective advancing contact angle θ'_A, for example, on a composite surface was given by

$$\cos \theta_A' = f_{13} \cos \theta_A - f_{123} \text{ (Equation 11, Chapter 4)}$$

where θ_A is the true advancing contact angle (on a smooth surface), and f_{13} and f_{123} are the areas of actual solid-liquid and air-liquid interface, respectively, per unit area of apparent solid-liquid interface. We can show that the analogous equation to (2) in the present chapter, for the case of a composite surface, is

$$w' = A\gamma_{AW}(1 - \cos \theta_A') = A\gamma_{AW}(1 - f_{13} \cos \theta_A + f_{123}) \qquad (2a)$$

where w' is the work which must be expended in spreading the liquid over an apparent area A of the composite surface, the apparent advancing contact angle θ_A' being finite (but not necessarily the true contact angle θ_A —*cf.* Chapter 4, p. 142). Equation (2a) again predicts that wetting-out will be favoured by a low surface tension of the solution and a low contact angle (either true or apparent), but it also suggests that

(a) spreading will usually be more difficult on the composite rough surface, since $(f_{13} \cos \theta_A - f_{123})$ will usually—though not invariably—be smaller than $\cos \theta_A$;

(b) compositeness due to roughness may cause a spreading process, which would have occurred spontaneously on a smooth surface, to require the expenditure of energy on a rough surface, since we have seen in Chapter 4 that it is possible for $\theta_A{}'$ to be finite even when θ_A is not;

(c) if a wetting-out agent displaces air from a composite surface, thus increasing f_{13} at the expense of f_{123}—which seems a very likely occurrence —then it will still further favour the spreading process by decreasing the value of w' in equation (2a).

Similar arguments also apply to the spreading of very small quantities of liquids on solid surfaces. "Anti-dimming" compositions became very well known during the war for use with gas-mask eye pieces. Here the problem is to obtain a high degree of wetting (probably complete spontaneous spreading) of a surface, which is usually contaminated with a layer of grease, by very small drops of water which have condensed from the vapour phase. It seems likely that a contact angle equal to or approaching zero is needed. This requirement is in practice not difficult to fulfil, since the wetting-out agents can be used at quite high concentrations, the actual amount of water present usually being quite small. The agents are normally applied to the transparent surface before condensation occurs, and it is therefore important that they should have good "re-wetting" properties (see p. 235). Anti-dimming agents are frequently applied from an impregnated cloth or sponge,[1] which again differentiates this use from most applications of wetting-out agents.

2. ADHESION OF SPRAY DROPLETS ON IMPACT WITH SOLID SURFACES

Surface-active agents can affect the efficiency of spraying operations (*e.g.*, in agriculture, horticulture, or public health work) in four ways: by altering the fineness of the spray, by increasing the proportion of impingeing drops which adhere to the surface of the solid, by promoting the spreading of adherent drops, and by preventing the recession of adherent drops or films of liquid from the surface. The last two of these four mechanisms have been discussed in the preceding paragraphs, in which we saw that the function of a wetting-out agent was to diminish the advancing and the receding contact angles, and the liquid-air interfacial tension, as much as possible. The surfaces involved are relatively old (probably at least a few seconds). These requirements imply of course that the agent should be strongly adsorbed at the liquid-air and liquid-solid interfaces—but they do not necessarily imply rapid adsorption. The function of a wetting-out agent in the first of the above four mechanisms (formation of the spray) seems on the other hand to be to make the spray finer by lowering the liquid-air interfacial tension very rapidly—*i.e.*, during the very small fraction of a second in which the drops are being formed. It must be noted, however, that it may be preferable in some cases to avoid forming too fine

---

[1] See, for example, Kingan and Sadd, B.P. 574,707 and B.P. 574,736, who describe such materials which have been inpregnated with dialkylsulphosuccinates or partial esters of polyglycerols with fatty acids.

a spray, in order to obtain a greater spraying range or to increase the kinetic energy with which the drops strike the surface.

The intermediate stage of the process, during which the drops impinge on the surface, is complicated by the fact that the drops may bounce off again after impact. In order to clarify the *desiderata* of a surface-active agent during the impingement stage of a spraying process, we can divide it into two steps or phases:

(*i*) an "impact," during which the liquid is advancing across the surface of the solid, which may be followed, provided that the advance does not proceed too far, by

(*ii*) a "rebound," during which the liquid tends to recede, and the droplet may even leave the surface altogether, breaking up as it does so.*

The rebound may be caused by an elastic recoil in the solid substrate, as well as by any tendency for the deformed liquid drops to oscillate between the oblate and prolate spheroid shapes. The hydrodynamics of the impingement are obviously complicated, but it seems reasonable to suppose that an efficient wetting-out agent should, at this stage of a spraying process

(a) *decrease* the work of adhesion air-to-solid (against the liquid) during the impact phase, and

(b) *increase* the work of adhesion liquid-to-solid (against air) during the rebound (if any).

The first of these two requirements means that W_{AS} should be as small as possible in the equation

$$W_{AS} = \gamma_{AL} + \gamma_{LS} - \gamma_{AS} \tag{3}$$

where the γ's refer to the interfacial tensions air-liquid, liquid-solid, and air-solid, respectively (*cf.* Chapter 4, Equation 5), *i.e.*, that the wetting-out agent should lower both the air-liquid and liquid-solid interfacial tensions, but preferably not the air-solid interfacial tension.

The second requirement means that W_{LS} should be as large as possible in the equation

$$W_{LS} = \gamma_{AL} - \gamma_{LS} + \gamma_{AS} \tag{4}$$

i.e., that the agent should lower the liquid-solid, but preferably neither the air-liquid nor the air-solid interfacial tensions.

Assuming that a well-defined contact angle exists under these highly dynamic conditions, we can write equations (3) and (4) in the following forms:

$$W_{AS} = \gamma_{AL}(1 - \cos\theta_A) \tag{3a}$$

and

$$W_{LS} = \gamma_{AL}(1 + \cos\theta_R) \tag{4a}$$

---

* See, for example, the interesting photographs by Ollivier, *Ann. chim. phys.* (8), 1907, **10**, 289, reproduced in Bikerman's *Surface Chemistry*, Academic Press, 2nd Edition, 1958, p. 363; and the recent paper by Gallily and La Mer, *J. Phys. Chem.*, 1958, **62**, 1295.

where θ_A and θ_R are the advancing and receding contact angles *measured in the liquid phase in both cases* (*cf*. Equation 6, Chapter 4), it being of course assumed that finite, stable values are obtained. Low values for W_{AS} and high values for W_{LS} would both be favoured by low values of the contact angles, both advancing and receding, but again the *desiderata* as regards the surface tension of the liquid phase would be contradictory, wetting being favoured by a *low* surface tension during the impact phase, and a *high* surface tension during the rebound (if any). Although this contradiction may need careful study, both experimental and theoretical, in processes in which the liquid of a relatively coarse spray does not readily wet a solid surface, it seems to us that its importance diminishes greatly as soon as a wetting-out agent is introduced into the argument: *i.e.*, the greater the extent of spreading during the impact phase, the less important is the "rebound" stage. It seems reasonable to conclude, therefore, that wetting-out by the adhesion of spray droplets (especially of aqueous solutions) to solid surfaces will be favoured by wetting agents which give low air-liquid interfacial tensions (especially low dynamic values), as well as low solid-liquid interfacial tensions. This means of course that the wetting-out agent should be strongly and rapidly adsorbed at these two interfaces.

We have been assuming that the desired end in a wetting-out process is as complete a coverage of the surfaces being sprayed as possible. As Martin (*loc. cit.*) and other workers have noted, however, the weight of spray retained by foliage does not always correlate completely with the degree to which the spray wets out the surfaces involved. It is in fact established that intermediate degrees of wetting-out frequently give higher retentions than either complete wetting or very poor wetting. This is presumably due to the fact that intermediate values for the advancing contact angle and the surface tension ensure the adhesion of a high proportion of impingeing drops (*cf*. equations 3 and 3a), but that at the same time the receding contact angle and surface tension remain large enough to ensure that the drops remain on the leaves in the form of lenses, rather than draining off again. This point is obviously of practical importance when the object of a spraying operation is to obtain a heavy deposit rather than a high degree of cover.

3. THE WETTING-OUT OF DUST PARTICLES ON LIQUID SURFACES

The wetting-out of an isolated solid particle which has come in contact with the surface of a large volume of liquid is in one sense a case of what Osterhof and Bartell have called immersional wetting (*cf*. Chapter 4, p. 138), in which the work of immersion $W_{i,SL}$ should be as large as possible (algebraically speaking) in the equation

$$W_{i,SL} = \gamma_{AS} - \gamma_{LS} \quad (\textit{cf}.\ \text{Equation 7, Chapter 4}).$$

This equation, which however refers only to the initial and final states of the complete process of immersion, suggests simply that a wetting-out agent will favour a process of immersional wetting if the solid-liquid interfacial tension is lowered as much as possible, and the solid-air interfacial tension as little as possible, the air-liquid interfacial tension apparently being irrelevant. It is important to recall, however, that this total process of immersion will occur in successive stages in most practical cases—thus Osterhof and Bartell have pointed out that the wetting of a solid cube is analysable into successive steps of adhesion, immersion, and spreading—and that the nature of these stages will depend on the shape of the dust particles and on the mechanical conditions obtaining.

Suppose for example that we are concerned with the behaviour of particles of dust which are falling on to the surface of an aqueous solution of a wetting-out agent. The individual particles coming in contact with the surface of the liquid will usually be subjected to effects such as gravity, mechanical agitation, or air currents, some of which will fluctuate, at times favouring adhesion and at other times tending to carry the particles away from the interface again. The further any particle has sunk into the solution, the less likely is it that it can be removed again by disturbing mechanical effects; the function of a wetting-out agent is therefore to influence the interfacial tensions in such a way that they will favour rapid sinking. Adapting to our purposes the well-known treatment of Coghill and Anderson[1] for the floating needle, we can see that, if a spherical particle of radius r comes in contact with the surface of a solution then the effect of the interfacial tensions can be treated as equivalent to that of an upward force (opposing sinking) given by

$$f = l\gamma \sin(\alpha - \theta_R')$$

where l is the length of the line of contact solid-air-solution, γ is the surface tension of the solution, θ_R' is the receding contact angle measured in the air, and α is the angle between the horizontal and the tangent to the circle at the point of contact. It can be shown by simple geometry that $l = 2\pi r \sin \alpha$, whence it follows that

$$f = 2\pi r \gamma \sin \alpha \sin(\alpha - \theta_R') \tag{5}$$

It follows from (5) that, if $\theta_R' < \alpha$, f is positive, and the interfacial tensions act against wetting, their effect being less adverse if θ_R' is large and the surface tension of the solution is as small as possible. Since $\theta_R' + \theta_A = 180°$, where θ_A is the advancing contact angle measured in the solution, this means that θ_A should be as small as possible. If however $\theta_R' > \alpha$, then f is negative, and sinking is helped by the resultant of the interfacial tensions. If we can assume in this case that the absolute value of f is an approximate measure of the extent to which the interfacial tensions will accelerate the sinking, then it follows that the wetting-out process is favoured by a surface-active agent which lowers the advancing

---

[1] Coghill and Anderson, *J. Phys. Chem.*, 1918, **22**, 245.

contact angle (measured in the solution), but with as small a lowering as possible in the surface tension of the wetting solution.

B. The wetting-out of porous masses

1. Textiles and other coherent structures

Perhaps the best known—and certainly one of the most important—of the applications of technical wetting-out agents is in promoting the displacement of air from textiles by aqueous solutions, usually as a preliminary to further treatment such as scouring, dyeing, or mercerisation. The importance of securing an adequate degree of contact between textile materials and treating baths, especially in a reasonably short time, has been fully discussed elsewhere,[1] and seems to be so generally appreciated as to require no elaboration here. Two facts which should, however, be made clear are that textile wetting-out processes are fairly complex capillary phenomena, and that we cannot speak of one single textile wetting out process. It is in fact necessary to distinguish explicitly between two quite different general types, in order not only to appreciate the functions of textile wetting-out agents, but also to assess the relative merits or significance of the various wetting-out tests which have been proposed.

In the first of these two types (*wetting-out by sinking or capillary rise*), a piece of cloth is placed on the surface of a solution, without being immersed, the solution penetrates freely into the system of tortuous capillaries in the textile, and wetting is assessed by such criteria as the time of sinking, or the height of climb or amount of imbibition which occurs in a given time. The rate and completeness of wetting-out are determined by what happens at the advancing menisci in the capillary system, and of course by the viscosity of the solution. We have already seen in Chapter 4 that such a process will be favoured in general by a surface-active agent which lowers the advancing contact angle as much (and as rapidly) as possible, but with the minimum possible lowering of the surface tension of the solution. (This is borne out by the experimental results reported by Durham and Camp,[2] who found that the rate of advance was greater at higher values of the surface tension.) If, of course, a wetting-out agent lowers the advancing contact angle from a value greater than 90°, to one appreciably less than 90°, thus causing the capillary forces to work with rather than against the wetting-out process, then this effect will predominate, and a large lowering of the surface tension may not be noticeably disadvantageous. It will be evident, however, that one cannot expect a correlation between the wetting-out power of a series of wetting-out agents, and their tendency to lower the

---

[1] See, for example, Horsfall and Lawrie, *The Dyeing of Textile Fibres*, Chapman and Hall, London, 1946, pp. 378 ff., and Chwala, *Textilhilfsmittel*, Springer, 1939, pp. 103 ff.

[2] Durham and Camp, *Second Congress*, 1957, **IV**, 3.

surface tension of water (especially *static* surface tension values). Unfortunately, insufficient data are available for any comprehensive attempt at correlating wetting-out power, as judged by criteria such as sinking times,* with dynamic values of surface tensions and advancing contact angles, at different surface ages. In the absence of such data, it seems safer to base tentative conclusions about the mechanism of this type of wetting process on appropriate work with pure liquids, in which surface-ageing effects will be small. Thus, for example, the work of Eley and Pepper with pure liquids, which is discussed in Chapter 4, (p. 157) suggests that it is in fact correct to picture the pressure difference across the advancing menisci as the driving force behind the wetting-out process. There may of course be other influences at work, either for or against the wetting-out process, such as gravitational forces and buoyancy effects, but these will not be directly influenced by the presence of surface-active agents and can therefore be left out of account in the present discussion. This pressure difference in the capillaries is opposed by the effect of the viscosity of the medium (*cf.* Chapter 4, equation 31), though the concentrations of wetting-out agents normally used ($< 0.2\%$) will have a negligible effect on the viscosity of the solution. The *desiderata* just quoted, *viz.*, a low advancing contact angle, associated with a minimum lowering of the surface tension, appear therefore to apply to this type of wetting-out process. In terms of the individual interfaces, this means that a good wetting-out agent should be strongly and rapidly adsorbed at the interface between the fibre and the solution, thus lowering the fibre-solution interfacial tension as much as possible, but that it should lower the solution-air interfacial tension only in so far as that may be necessary to ensure a small value for the advancing contact angle, in particular a value less than 90°.

Trommer[1] has pointed out that capillary wetting of this "sinking" type can be accompanied by spreading wetting of the type discussed in Section A–1 of the present chapter. He found that with solutions of some agents the capillary wetting of a floating canvas square was accompanied or preceded by a superficial wetting. He accordingly devised a test for capillary wetting-out (which he termed "penetration") in which the wetting solution was poured into a hole in a steel plate which had been placed on several layers of cloth. The time was measured for the solution to penetrate through the cloth, as determined by an electrical conductivity method. This method is of interest where it is desired to determine capillary wetting-out (our terminology) without any spreading, and it also appears to be more quantitative than the ordinary surface sinking test.

. The second (and it seems to us the more important) type of wetting-out

---

* For a description of the method in practice, see for example Auerbach, *Textilber.*, 1926, **7**, 681, and Kind and Auerbach, *ibid.*, 1926, **7**, 775. Their theoretical treatment cannot however be recommended.

[1] Trommer, *Amer. Dyes. Reporter*, 1950, **39**, P811, P830.

process is that in which a textile or other porous mass is *completely immersed* in the wetting-out solution. The theory of this process, which involves both advancing and receding menisci, and the escape of air bubbles through the solution, has been shown in Chapter 4 (p. 151) to be rather complicated. If, however, we assume that substantially complete wetting-out of the textile must be achieved, then we can adopt the special argument developed in Chapter 4 which suggests that an effective wetting-out agent should not only lower the advancing contact angle, but that it should also lower the surface tension of the solution as much as possible, both characteristics again referring to dynamic values. This means of course that the surface-active agent should be strongly and rapidly adsorbed at both the interfaces solution-fibre and solution-air.

The importance of what we might term the "dynamic factor" in the wetting-out of textiles has been made clear in papers by Bartholomé and Schäfer,[1] Lange,[2] and Schäfer.[3] Bartholomé and Schäfer proposed the theoretical equation

$$\gamma_{H_2O} - \gamma = \frac{F}{F\sqrt{\pi}/2cLkT\sqrt{Dt} + 1} \tag{6}$$

where γ_{H_2O} is the surface tension of pure water and γ that of a surface of a solution of a surface-active agent at time t from its formation, F is the equilibrium spreading pressure, *i.e.* $(\gamma_{H_2O} - \gamma_\infty)$, where γ_∞ is the surface tension at equilibrium, L is the constant of a two-dimensional equation of state, k is Boltzmann's constant, and D is the diffusion coefficient of the surface-active agent. This equation can be re-written in the form

$$\gamma_{H_2O} - \gamma = \frac{a}{b/\sqrt{t} + 1}$$

where a and b are characteristic constants for a given solution of the surface-active agent. This expression was differentiated by Lange to obtain

$$-\left(\frac{d\gamma}{d\sqrt{t}}\right)_{t=0} = a/b$$

Lange used the quantity a/b as a single parameter for characterising the wetting-out power of a solution. He measured the surface tension-time curves for eleven (unnamed) wetting-out agents by the method of Addison and Hutchinson,[4] and their wetting-out power by a method described by Schwen.[5] (This latter method is based on the same principle as the well-known Draves test, which we discuss later, the time being measured for a

[1] Bartholomé and Schäfer, *Textilber.*, 1950, **31**, 487.
[2] Lange, *Koll. Z.*, 1951, **121**, 120.
[3] Schäfer, *Z. Elektrochemie*, 1955, **59**, 273.
[4] Addison and Hutchinson, *J. Chem. Soc.*, 1948, 930.
[5] Schwen, *Textilber.*, 1950, **31**, 627.

totally immersed specimen to lose its buoyancy to the point at which it sinks.) Lange then plotted the surface tension against $\sqrt{t}$, obtaining a/b from the limiting slope at $t = 0$; these values correlated well with the wetting-out times for the different agents at 0·1 and 0·2%. Lange found that a was much less dependent on concentration than was b, from which he argued that the sinking time t_s for a given agent should be given approximately by

$$\log t_s = -2 \log C + \text{const.}$$

a relation which had been empirically known for some time. This also led to the prediction that the limiting slope of the $\log t_s - \log C$ curves should be 2, which was substantiated by Lange's results.

The importance of Lange's work seems to us to be two-fold: it demonstrates that there is a correlation between *dynamic* surface tension values and wetting-out behaviour, and it confirms the argument (which we have given in Chapter 4,) that a *low* dynamic surface tension should favour *immersional* wetting.

The wetting of a completely immersed textile mass is the basis of most practical wetting-out tests. In the well-known Herbig[1] method, for example, a skein of yarn is given a standard complete immersion, removed from the solution, centrifuged in order to remove excess water, and then weighed, the wetting-out effect being expressed in terms of the percentage gain in weight of the specimen. Variations on this theme have been described by a number of authors. Thus Seck and Lachmann[2] immersed small skeins for ten seconds and then simply drained them for 50 seconds before weighing; it seems clear however that centrifuging is preferable in that it gives a more standardised and reproducible removal of externally adhering water, the extent of removal being more nearly independent of the surface tension of the solution. An elegant method is that of Ruperti,[3] who suspends an immersed, weighted specimen from a floating hydrometer. The hydrometer can be calibrated so as to read off directly the volume of air remaining in the cloth, which is observed at different times. Similarly, Draves and Clarkson[4] submerged a test skein by attaching it to a weight; the time was then noted at which the skein had become so wetted that it sank.

The Herbig method has also been further studied by Lenher and Smith,[5] who obtained improved results by increasing the time of wetting, and decreasing substantially the time interval between wetting and centrifuging. This latter was accomplished by tipping the wetting-out solution,

[1] Herbig and Seyferth, *Textilber.*, 1927, **8**, 45, 149. This paper contains a critical historical summary of previous work.

[2] Seck and Lachmann, *Textilber.*, 1926, **7**, 851.

[3] Ruperti, *Textilber.*, 1926, **7**, 936.

[4] Draves and Clarkson, *Amer. Dyestuffs Reporter*, 1931, **20**, 201.

[5] Lenher and Smith, *Amer. Dyestuffs Reporter*, 1933, **22**, 689, and *Ind. Eng. Chem.* (*Anal. Ed.*), 1933, **5**, 376. Both papers give useful reviews of earlier work.

containing the immersed skein of unbleached cotton, directly into the basket of the centrifuge. These authors compared the results of their wetting-out tests with (static) surface tension measurements by the capillary rise method. Although there was a general agreement between wetting-out power and decrease in the static surface tension, there was no quantitative correlation. Lenher and Smith suggest that this was due to their wetting-out test being determined by the fibre-solution interfacial tension, the sinking time test being determined by the solution-air interfacial tension. As will be apparent from our earlier argument, this suggestion does not seem to us to be valid; we suggest that the most likely explanation for the lack of complete correlation lies principally in the different rates of adsorption of the different wetting-out agents at the relevant interfaces, which would appear in the wetting-out tests, but not in static surface tension measurements.

An important paper on the use of the Herbig test is that of Evans,[1] who examined a series of surface-active agents at different temperatures and concentrations. He made the interesting observation that the wetting-out power of solutions of three C_{16} surface-active agents (sodium cetyl sulphate, cetylpyridinium bromide, and sodium hexadecane sulphonate) was considerably affected by temperature, rising steeply between 20° and 40° c., whereas two C_{12} agents (sodium dodecyl sulphate and sodium dodecane sulphonate) showed a much smaller dependence on temperature over the range 20° to 60° c. Evans therefore studied the effect of concentration at a temperature (50° c.) at which all the agents were exhibiting their full effect. He found that each agent gave a straight line when the logarithms of the Herbig readings were plotted against the logarithms of concentrations. From these log-log plots he was able to read off the concentration of each agent required to give a certain degree of wetting, for which purpose he chose a Herbig value of 70%. Although, as Evans points out, this value is quite arbitrary, it seems to be an appropriate one for assessing general wetting power, since it lies approximately halfway between the highest and the lowest Herbig values which he recorded. Assigning to one particular surface-active agent (sodium cetyl sulphate) the standard value of 100, Evans then calculated the "Wetting Index" for the other agents from

$$W_E(70\%, 50° \text{ c.}) = 100 \, C_s/C_x$$

in which we use $W_E(70\%, 50° \text{ c.})$ to denote Evans's wetting index at (for example) 50° c. and an arbitrary Herbig value of 70%, C_s is the concentration of the standard agent (*e.g.*, sodium cetyl sulphate) required to give this figure of 70% at 50° c., and C_x is the concentration of the agent being characterised which gives the same result. Evans's results on this basis are given in Table 7 (see following page).

---

[1] Evans, *J. Soc. Dyers Colourists*, 1935, **51**, 233.

Table 7
Relative wetting-out power of typical surface-active agents
(Evans, *J. Soc. Dyers Colourists*, 1935, **51**, 233)

Agent	For Herbig figure of 70% at 50° c.	
	Concentration (%) read from log-log plot	"Wetting Index"
Sodium cetyl sulphate . . .	0·024	100
Sodium dodecyl sulphate . . .	0·031	77
Sodium hexadecane sulphonate .	0·033	73
Sodium dodecane sulphonate . .	0·043	56
Cetylpyridinium bromide . .	0·080	30

It is important to note that certain "sinking" tests, notably that of Draves and Clarkson, which is widely used in the United States, belong to the class which we have chosen to call *immersion* tests, rather than to our class of "sinking" tests. The process involved in the Draves test is basically the same as in the Herbig test and its modifications, *viz.*, the displacement and escape of the air which is trapped in a submerged specimen, which involves receding menisci in the "capillaries" and escaping bubbles at their outlets, as well as advancing menisci. Where the Draves test differs from the "centrifuge" tests is in the method of determining how much air has been displaced in a given time. It is therefore interesting to note that Lenher and Smith[1] found significant differences between the results of the two tests, as applied to olive oil soap and four synthetic surface-active agents. It seems to the present authors that Lenher and Smith's preference for the centrifuge test is justified, on the grounds *inter alia* of the greater uniformity of mechanical treatment, its applicability to wider ranges of concentration, and the more quantitative criterion of degree of displacement of air. All these points are discussed by Lenher and Smith; thus they point out that the loss of buoyancy in a submerged textile specimen is not an accurately determinable quantity. The usefulness of the Draves test is however illustrated by an important paper by Caryl,[2] containing Draves tests by Vitalis, in which the wetting-out power of a series of esters of sulphosuccinic acid (including a number of the "Aerosol" products) is correlated with their molecular structure.

It seems to be generally agreed that wetting-out tests which are based on the principle of complete immersion of the specimen, especially those in which the externally adhering water is removed by centrifuging, and the degree of wetting-out is expressed as the gain in weight, are more reproducible and accurate than tests in which a floating specimen is allowed to

---

[1] Lenher and Smith, *Ind. Eng. Chem. (Anal. Ed.)*, 1933, **5**, 376.
[2] Caryl, *Ind. Eng. Chem.*, 1941, **33**, 731.

sink. This superiority is especially marked in dilute solutions, and is probably due to the fact that local irregularities in structure or wettability can have a greater effect in the sinking test. What is perhaps even more important, it seems that in most cases the immersion test is to be preferred on the grounds of relevance to practice. This is especially the case where materials are fed mechanically into a processing solution. At the same time, however, the fact should not be overlooked that the two types of test differ in their nature as well as in precision, and that in certain applications of surface-active agents the sinking test may be the more relevant.

Edelstein and Draves[1] have made a valuable comparative study of the behaviour of four wetting-out agents in four different tests: (i) the "yarn bundle" test, in which the sinking time is determined for a skein placed on the surface, (ii) a similar test in which a canvas square is used, (iii) the Draves test, and (iv) a similar test, in which a canvas square is used. (It will be noted that the first two of these tests are true "sinking" tests in the sense used by us, while the third and fourth are immersion tests.) They found that the curves for logarithm of concentration against logarithm of sinking time were not entirely parallel for different agents in any one test, the comparison among different agents depending on the criterion of sinking time chosen. There was also a divergence in the behaviour of different agents when different weights were used in the Draves test. For a given product, however, the slopes of the $\log t_s - \log C$ curves given by different tests were remarkably similar. Edelstein and Draves point out that the most suitable test will depend on the circumstances of the case, and recommend that full $\log t_s - \log C$ curves should be used whenever possible in order to obtain the full picture of any test.

Shapiro[2] confirmed Edelstein and Draves's results on the parallelism of the $\log t_s - \log c$ curves obtained for the same wetting-out agent with different weights in the Draves test. He recommended the use of woven tape in place of a skein of thread, on the grounds of greater convenience and accuracy; this tape can also be used in tests of re-wetting (*cf.* p. 235). Shapiro considered the buoyancy effect in the Draves test, in which not all of the air is displaced from the sample at the time when it sinks, and recommended the use of a buoyancy balance to follow the displacement of air with time, instead of simply timing the occurrence of sinking.

It may at first seem to be surprising, in view of the fundamental physical differences between immersion and sinking tests, that they show a considerable degree of correlation as, for example, in the work of Edelstein and Draves referred to above. It is also general knowledge that the different wetting-out tests will generally distinguish technically effective wetting-out agents from "duds." The most likely explanation would seem to lie in the importance in all these tests of *lowerings of the advancing contact angle.*

[1] Edelstein and Draves, *Amer. Dyes. Reporter*, 1949, **38**, P343.

[2] Shapiro, *Amer. Dyes. Reporter*, 1950, **39**, P38, P62.

This point, which will be apparent in the arguments which we have given above, is made very clearly in an important paper by Fowkes,[1] who determined rates of wetting-out by both the Draves tests (immersional) and the "yarn bundle" test (sinking). Fowkes considered the wetting-out process microscopically, pointing out that, as penetration into the cloth occurs, the meniscus can advance only where a yarn is out of alignment with its fellows, and comes nearer to the yarns which are already wetted, so that the meniscus can leap across. If d'' represents the maximum distance between yarns at which this jump can occur, and d' is the average distance between yarns in the direction of wetting, then a fraction y of all the d values will be equal to or less than d'', given for a given hydrostatic pressure by

$$y = a\,e^{-(d'-r\cos\theta_A)/d''}$$

where r is the radius of the yarn, θ_A is the (advancing) contact angle on the yarn,* and a is a constant. If the sinking time t_s is inversely proportional to y, then we have

$$\log t_s = 2\cdot303\left(-\log a + \frac{d'}{d''} - \frac{r}{d''}\cos\theta_A\right) \tag{7}$$

in which it is at once obvious that the sinking time t_s will decrease as the advancing contact angle θ_A decreases, and that the contact angle is the parameter determining the sinking time which is influenced by the presence of a surface-active agent. Fowkes also draws attention to the importance of depletion of surface-active agent by adsorption at the textile-water interface, which he finds to be greater with non-ionic than with ionising surface-active agents. He concludes that wetting-out tests like the Draves test are in fact determined by the contact angle and the extent of depletion.

Fowkes states that it is *empirically* true in some cases that

$$\cos\theta_A = 1\cdot68 - 0\cdot035\gamma \tag{8}$$

where γ is the air-liquid interfacial tension. If this is combined with equation (7), one obtains the empirical relation

$$\log t_s = A + B\gamma$$

where A and B are constants. The theoretical significance of equation (8) is by no means clear, especially since γ is the *equilibrium* surface tension, and it is the dynamic tensions which should be decisive; possibly the expression is empirically true in some cases because of some special relationship between the equilibrium and dynamic boundary tensions. An alternative approach might be to use Young's equation in the form

---

* It should be noted that this may well be an advancing contact angle on a rough or on a composite surface, as discussed in Chapter 4, p. 139.

[1] Fowkes, *J. Phys. Chem.*, 1953, **57**, 98.

$$\cos \theta_A = (\gamma_{AF}{}^\star - \gamma_{LF}{}^\star)/\gamma_{AL}{}^\star$$

where $\gamma_{AF}{}^\star$, $\gamma_{LF}{}^\star$, and $\gamma_{AL}{}^\star$ are the *dynamic* boundary tensions air-fibre, liquid-fibre, and air-liquid, respectively, at the appropriate surface ages, and combine it with Fowkes's equation to obtain

$$\log t_s = K - k(\gamma_{AF}{}^\star - \gamma_{LF}{}^\star)/\gamma_{AL}{}^\star \tag{9}$$

where K and k are constants. If θ_A is less than $90°$, $\gamma_{AF}{}^\star > \gamma_{LF}{}^\star$, and $\log t_s$ will clearly diminish with $\gamma_{AL}{}^\star$.

It remains to be seen whether or not equations such as (9) will prove to be of any use in interpreting the increasing amount of data on dynamic surface tensions. (One problem, of course, is to decide the *ages* of the surfaces in question—*i.e.*, which values of the dynamic boundary tensions to use—and whether or not the dynamic boundary tensions can be treated even approximately as constants.) In the mean time, however, it seems quite clear that, except in special cases, the lowering of the *equilibrium* surface tension is not a reliable guide to the wetting-out power of an aqueous solution, a fact which has been appreciated for some time.*

It has been tacitly assumed so far in the present chapter that, at an advancing meniscus, wetting-out agents lower the solid-liquid and air-liquid interfacial tensions (and hence the contact angle), but do not affect the *solid-air* interfacial tension at an advancing meniscus. This is probably true in the great majority of cases, since it seems unlikely that they could leave an aqueous solution and spread over the solid-air interface in advance of the meniscus.† It is interesting to note in this connection, however, that it has been proposed to pre-treat solid masses, which are to be wetted out by aqueous solutions of surface-active agents, with the vapours of compounds such as *sec.*-octyl, nonyl, or decyl alcohols.[1] Presumably in this case any lowering of the fibre-air interfacial tension is more than offset by a lowering of the fibre-solution interfacial tension, to which perhaps interfacial complex formation between the water-soluble surface-active agent and the alcohol (*cf.* Chapter 6, p. 253) may be contributing.

The present discussion has so far been limited to the wetting-out of textile fabrics with fairly dilute aqueous solutions, in which the great majority of surface-active agents are readily soluble. It is however sometimes necessary to wet out textiles with fairly concentrated solutions of electrolytes, the best known examples being the strong caustic solutions, which may for example contain between 22% and 26% of sodium hydroxide,

---

* See, for example, Lenher and Smith, *Ind. Eng. Chem.* (*Anal. Ed.*), 1933, **5**, 376; *Amer. Dyes. Reporter*, 1933, **22**, 689; Seck, *Textilber.*, 1927, **8**, 359.

† The situation will naturally be quite different at a receding meniscus. There, as we have already noted, the solid-air interface will almost certainly be contaminated with surface-active material, and this may contribute materially to the difference between advancing and receding contact angles.

[1] Shell Development Co., James, and Barritt, U.S.P. 2,501,337. See also Bataafsche Petroleum Mij., Dutch P. 63,219.

which are used for mercerising cotton. The general physical mechanism involved has already been discussed, *viz.*, the wetting-out of a completely immersed textile fabric, which is favoured by a surface-active agent which lowers both the surface tension of the aqueous medium and the advancing contact angle at the menisci in the "capillaries" in the fabric. The presence of the high concentration of caustic hydroxide, however, raises special problems which are worth a brief discussion. For fuller accounts of mercerising processes, which contain further details of the use of surface-active agents, the reader is referred to the books by Chwala,[1] Diserens,[2] and Horsfall and Lawrie.[3]

The chief problem which arises in selecting wetting-out agents for mercerising baths is of course that of solubility, ordinary agents such as the alkylated naphthalene sulphonates or the long-chain alkyl sulphates, for example, being salted out by the caustic alkali present. Two general methods have been used to overcome this defect in the considerable number of efficient commercial products which are available: the use of mixtures of ordinary wetting-out agents with "solubilisers" such as the substituted phenols, and the selection of specially soluble surface-active agents, which usually contain substantially smaller hydrocarbon residues than do ordinary wetting-out agents. The mixtures and special agents are described more fully in Part III. It seems likely that, as suggested by Chwala, the mixtures form what he calls "hydrotropic" solutions in the mercerising baths, by which we understand him to mean that mixed micelles of some sort are formed, leading to an increased solubility (*cf.* Chapter 2). This would appear to be a reasonable explanation for the fact that phenols, mixtures of cresol with polyether alcohols, or more complicated mixtures of phenols, hydroaromatic hydrocarbons, and diethylene glycol monobutyl ether, for example, will increase the solubility of sulphated oils or alkylated naphthalene sulphonates in mercerising liquors.[4] It seems quite possible that highly soluble, complex mixed micelles are formed, diminishing the chemical potential of the sulphated oil or alkylated naphthalene sulphonate at a given concentration, and thus increasing the amount which will dissolve.

The manner in which a solubilised surface-active agent will act as a wetting-out agent is of course largely a matter for conjecture. One would not expect it to lower the equilibrium value of the surface tension of the solution as much as would the unsolubilised agent, since the micelle would not be expected to be adsorbed at the air-solution interface. It could,

[1] Chwala, *Textilhilfsmittel*, Springer, Vienna, 1939, pp. 299–320.

[2] Diserens, *Neue Verfahren in der Technik der chemischen Veredlung der Textilfasern*, Birkhäuser, Basle. vol. 1, 1948, pp. 606–655.

[3] Horsfall and Lawrie, *The Dyeing of Textile Fibres*, Chapman and Hall, 1946, 2nd Ed., pp. 55–59.

[4] *Cf.* Oranienburger Chem. Fabrik, F.P. 659,538; I.G., F.P. 687,616; Sandoz, B.P. 374,214.

however, give a lower dynamic surface tension if it acted as a "reservoir" of rapidly available amphipathic ions or molecules in the solution, and the complex micelles might moreover be adsorbed at the fibre-solution inter-face and thus lower the advancing contact angle, which would be distinctly favourable to wetting. Finally, it seems likely that some at least of the added solubilisers might themselves act at the air-solution and/or the fibre-solution interface, since it is known that phenolic bodies themselves have some wetting-out power in mercerising liquors.

The specially selected mercerising wetting-out agents such as the lower alkyl sulphates (butyl to heptyl)[1] can probably be assumed to act in con-centrated sodium hydroxide solutions in much the same way as do the longer chain sulphates (*e.g.*, sodium dodecyl sulphate) in dilute aqueous media. Presumably the hydrophobe-hydrophile "balance" in a short-chain sulphate is more favourable in the mercerising liquor than it is in water, on account of the fact that the polar group is less highly hydrated in the concentrated electrolyte solution. As a result, a molecule which is much too "water-soluble" in water, is appreciably amphipathic in caustic soda solu-tion. It is unfortunate that there are not surface tension data available to check this point. It is however noteworthy that it has been proposed to add solubilisers (*e.g.*, the monoethyl ether of 1 : 3-butylene glycol) even to these lower alkyl sulphates.

In view of the fact that a low surface tension is desirable for rapid wetting-out when a fabric is immersed in a solution, it is interesting to note with Chwala (*loc. cit.*, p. 304) that the surface tensions of mercerising liquors which contain no wetting-out agents are substantially higher (*ca.* 100 dynes/cm.) than that of pure water (73 dynes/cm.).

2. THE WETTING-OUT OF POWDERS

The wetting-out of a powder by a liquid medium, not necessarily aqueous, is very similar, up to a point, to the wetting-out of a coherent mass such as a textile fabric. Thus there are the same two possible general types of process: wetting by sinking or capillary rise (favoured by a low advancing contact angle but a high surface tension), and the wetting-out of a quantity of powder which is completely immersed in a liquid (favoured by a low advancing contact angle and, on the whole, by a low surface tension also). It therefore appears to be permissible to apply again the general physical pictures which we have considered in the preceding section, provided that a further interfacial phenomenon is not neglected, *viz.*, deflocculation of the solid particles during the wetting-out process. It will be seen in Chapter 7, p. 275, that the wetting-out of a powder is very often only a preliminary, though a necessary one, to a deflocculation stage of a dispersion process; the point which we would make here is that the

---

[1] I.G., B.P. 354,946.

occurrence of deflocculation and dispersion during the wetting-out of a powder may considerably assist the latter process.*

Suppose that we are mixing a dry powder into a relatively large volume of a liquid (in order, for example, to prepare a fluid dispersion), and that the prevailing conditions, including the presence of a wetting-out agent, allow wetting-out of the powder to occur by one or both of the two types of processes which we have considered. At any instant the advance of the liquid into the powder will be impeded by the viscous effects in those parts of the "capillaries" which already contain liquid (*cf.* Chapter 4, Equation 31). If now the wetting-out agent or some other constituent of the wetting medium is an effective deflocculating agent, then those portions of the powder into which liquid has already penetrated will disintegrate more easily and disperse into the bulk of the liquid. The result is to shorten considerably those parts of the "capillaries" which are filled with liquid, thus reducing the viscous drag on the penetration process.

A similar conclusion is reached if we consider the addition of a small volume of a liquid medium to a relatively large bulk of powder, in order for example to obtain a plastic or doughy mass. If the solid particles are in a deflocculated state as they become wetted, then they will pack together more closely, less liquid will be required to fill the interstices, and more liquid will be available for wetting the rest of the powder. It is even possible that this close packing will directly favour capillary penetration by reducing the effective capillary radii in neighbouring capillaries (*cf.* Chapter 4, Equation 31).

A very large number of synthetic surface-active agents find application in the wetting-out of finely divided dyestuff powders, pigments, agricultural and horticultural pesticides, rubber chemicals, and other powders, and it does not seem worth while to attempt an enumeration of examples here. It may however be of interest to describe a more unusual development, which illustrates this very wide applicability of synthetic wetting-out agents, *viz.*, their addition to the calcium chloride solutions which are used to consolidate the coal dust on mine roadways. The use of deliquescent salts such as calcium chloride to lay dust is of course well known. A serious difficulty in applying the method to the coal dust in mine roadways arose from the fact that coal dust is not readily wetted by water or by solutions of calcium chloride, even when it is mixed with the limestone dust which is introduced to prevent dust explosions; consequently a proper "consolidation" of the dust with the aqueous solution was not usually achieved. As the result of prolonged practical trials, which were initiated by Tideswell

---

* It is important to note that the word "wetting" is often applied loosely to the dispersion of pigments in oils. Tests such as that for "oil-absorption," in which one determines the amount of oil needed to give a fluid dispersion of a pigment powder, are usually not greatly influenced by the extent of removal of air, *i.e.*, by wetting out, and should not, it seems to us, be described as "wetting" tests.

and his collaborators in the Safety in Mines Research Board, with collaboration from industry, the value of surface-active agents in solving this wetting-out problem has been fully demonstrated. A selection of relevant papers and publications on the details and history of these trials is given below;[1] it will suffice here to refer to the method as officially recommended by the Ministry of Fuel and Power.[2]

The recommended method is based on maintaining a moisture content of about 10% in the coal dust in a mine roadway, by spreading the appropriate amount of flake calcium chloride. The exact usage will depend on such factors as the prevailing relative humidity of the air. A satisfactory mechanical consolidation can be achieved only if the resulting saturated solution of calcium chloride is uniformly distributed through the dust; consequently a prior wetting-out of the dust with water is recommended. This wetting-out must occur to a depth of at least one inch, and in order to ensure this, the addition of a wetting-out agent to the water is advised. Examples of suitable agents given are "Lissapol N," "Calsolene Oil HS," "Perminal COL," and "Perminal W," made by I.C.I., at concentrations of 3% to 5%, and "Teepol," made by Shell, at 5%. The solution of wetting-out agent is put down by spraying lightly and repeatedly over the surface of the roadway, at the rate of four gallons for each hundred square feet of roadway. After an interval of half an hour, water is put on as a coarse spray, intermittently if necessary, until a penetration of one inch has been achieved. After a further interval of one hour, most of the flake calcium chloride is spread over the surface, after which six to twenty-four hours are allowed to elapse in order that deliquescence may occur. The surface of the roadway is then consolidated mechanically, and the rest of the calcium chloride is added a few days later. The consolidated surface is stable for periods of six months to a year, provided that excessive fresh falls or spillage of dust are avoided; otherwise it may be necessary to retreat the surface periodically, though with smaller quantities of wetting-out agent and calcium chloride.

The wetting-out process involved in the above procedure could involve as many as four distinct wetting phenomena (physically speaking): an initial adhesion of spray droplets to a rough surface, a spreading over this surface, a capillary penetration into the dust, and the escape of air bubbles from capillary openings through the aqueous medium. The wetting-out times involved are very long, especially compared with those obtaining in the wetting-out of textiles; consequently static values of the relevant interfacial tensions and contact angles will probably be applicable. It seems

---

[1] Tideswell and Wheeler, *Trans. Inst. Mining Engineers*, 1934, **87**, 1; Hay and Tideswell, *Trans. Inst. Mining Engineers*, 1936, **90**, 213; Price, *Trans. Inst. Mining Engineers*, 1937, **93**, 252; 24th Annual Report of the Safety in Mines Research Board for 1945, H.M. Stationery Office, 1947, p. 12; 25th Annual Report, p. 14; Griffiths and Webb, *Iron and Coal Trades Review*, August 23rd and 30th, and September 20th, 1946.
[2] Ministry of Fuel and Power, Safety Circular No. 164, H.M. Stationery Office, 1948.

likely that the critical and decisive step in the whole wetting-out process will be a capillary penetration, the other three possible wetting phenomena being relatively unimportant, especially if the spraying is carried out as recommended in the Ministry of Fuel and Power Circular.* This means that the most important *desideratum* of a surface-active agent is that it should give a low advancing contact angle, with the smallest possible simultaneous lowering of the surface tension of the solution. Alternatively expressed, it should lower the solid-liquid interfacial tension rather than the liquid-air interfacial tension. It seems likely *a priori* that the lowering of the advancing contact angle is the most important measurable criterion—in particular, the advancing contact angle should be small enough to ensure that spontaneous capillary penetration becomes possible. The view that the solid-liquid interface is the important one, rather than the liquid-air interface, seems to us to derive some empirical support from the fact that it is advisable to use fairly concentrated solutions (3% to 5%) during the critical first spraying operation. Since much lower concentrations (0·2% to 1%) of these wetting agents will suffice to give the maximum lowering of the static surface tension, it seems reasonable to surmise that the favourable effect of still further increasing the concentration of surface-active agent is due to an adsorption at some other interface, for example, the solid-liquid interface.

Two further properties of a surface-active agent are probably important in determining its usefulness in the consolidation of mine roadways: its solubility and surface-activity (*i.e.*, its "compatibility") in saturated solutions of calcium chloride, and its deflocculating effect on the dust particles. The supreme importance of "compatibility" requires no elaboration, and we have already noted in the present section that the wetting-out of a large amount of powder by a small amount of liquid will be favoured if the wetted particles are in a deflocculated condition and therefore pack closely together. In the present case, moreover, a high degree of deflocculation is desirable *per se* and quite apart from its effect on the wetting-out process, since the consolidated surface should preferably be plastic and coherent. This means that the deflocculating power of the surface-active agent in a saturated solution of calcium chloride, as well as in water, will be significant.

It seems to be quite generally appreciated that, although many wetting-out agents have some foam-stabilising power, there is no fundamental connection between the two properties. This is clear from considering the fundamentals of the two processes (*cf.* Chapter 4, p. 144, and Chapter 4,

---

* The appropriate passage reads: "Preferably the solution should be sprayed lightly and repeatedly over the dust within reach rather than as a heavy spray steadily traversing the floor: this allows the dry surface dust to become damp and receptive of more solution before the layer of liquid becomes deep enough to flow away along channels." (Ministry of Fuel and Power, Safety Circular No. 164, H.M. Stationery Office, 1948, p. 4.)

p. 204), wetting-out power being determined by the dynamic values of certain boundary tensions, and foaming power chiefly by the formation of mechanically stable films at the gas-liquid interface. Foaming is, in fact, disadvantageous in many wetting-out processes, so that agents of low foaming power may be preferred, such as polyethenoxy agents in the wetting-out of phenothiazine powders.[1] Where, of course, a foam is stabilised by the presence of incompletely wetted solid particles, foaming and wetting-out properties are diametrically opposed, and wetting-out agents may be useful as foam-breakers.

3. "WETTING-BACK" PROCESSES

We have already noted that, except for the special case of pre-treatment of porous materials with substances in vapour form, the discussion in the preceding sections was confined to wetting-out processes in which a surface-active agent was present in the wetting-out medium, so that it was unnecessary to consider the solid-air interface as being important. When however the wetting-out agent is present in the material being wetted, a fresh *desideratum* may arise, *i.e.*, that the surface-active agent should lower the solid-air interfacial tension as little as possible. This will apply if the surface-active agent is present as an adsorbed film at the solid-air interface, rather than as a separate solid phase, since a lowering of the solid-air interfacial tension means that all the criteria of efficient wetting-out are adversely affected. Thus the spreading coefficient (Chapter 4, Equation 1) will become smaller, algebraically speaking; the contact angles (Chapter 4, Equation 2) will become larger; the work of adhesion liquid-solid (Chapter 4, Equation 5) will become smaller—to summarise, the free energy which becomes available from the disappearance of solid-air interface, and which favours *all* possible types of wetting, suffers a diminution.

This argument may apply to many "wetting-back" processes, *i.e.*, processes in which a textile or a powdered solid, for example, which has previously been impregnated with a solution of a wetting-out agent and then dried, is brought into contact with an aqueous solution, frequently containing no wetting-out agent. It will be especially applicable if the wetting-out agent is strongly adsorbed during the impregnation, and the adsorbed layer has an orientation which favours wetting-back. It is a common experience, however, especially in the wetting-back of textiles, that an agent which is useful in an ordinary wetting-out procedure is of little value for wetting-back. This may be due to the fact that adsorption occurs with orientation in the reverse sense, *i.e.*, the amphipathic molecules are adsorbed with their polar heads turned to the substrate and their hydrophobic structures orientated outwards, and this orientation persists through the drying operation. In such a case the solid-air interfacial tension

---

[1] Du Pont and Littler, U.S.P. 2,540,131.

will be smaller during the wetting-back process, and the solid-liquid interfacial tension will be greater than if the same agent were used in an ordinary wetting-out process. It seems to us, however, that a more frequently valid explanation is one to which Schwartz and Perry[1] draw attention, *viz.*, that when the impregnating solution of the wetting-out agent is dried out of the textile in the first place, it should not form a large number of water-repellent particles in the interstices. This tendency for amphipathic compounds to come out of solution as crystals on which hydrophobic faces are prominent, is familiar to most workers with these substances; it is presumably due to the fact that surfaces composed of paraffin chains would be expected to have lower interfacial tensions (against air) than those composed predominantly of polar groups, so that the former would be thermodynamically favoured (*cf.* Chapter 4, p. 196). As Schwartz and Perry point out, therefore, wetting-out agents which will form liquid or highly amorphous deposits at the solid-air interface are in general preferable for wetting-back processes. Even if the amphipathic molecules in the surface of such an amorphous deposit are orientated with their paraffin chains outwards, they can reorientate themselves very quickly when they come in contact with water.

C. Water-proofing processes

We have defined a "water-proofing" process in the introduction to the present chapter as a treatment which renders the surface of a solid more difficult to wet by water, the competing fluid phase being understood to be air. The most important and best-known technical applications of such treatments are in the textile field, in which our definition will be seen to exclude methods which depend on closing the interstices of a fabric with materials such as rubber and oxidised vegetable drying oils, and to refer only to water-proofing techniques which normally leave a fabric with an open structure.* Although an account of all the methods of water-proofing textiles would take us outside our present subject, certain cationic surface-active agents have become so important in modern water-proofing processes that it is necessary to examine their use for this purpose.

The general physical principle behind all the methods of water-proofing textiles which come within our definition is of course to modify the surfaces of the yarns, either by a chemical attack or by the deposition of films of special hydrophobic substances, so that the contact angle (measured inside the aqueous phase) is appreciably increased. Whether it is the advancing or the receding contact angle which matters, or both, depends on how the fabric and the water come into contact with each other. If, for example, the

---

* The word "*Hydrophobierung*," which has been used by Chwala and other writers in German to define this type of water-proofing process, makes this distinction clear.

[1] Schwartz and Perry, *Surface-Active Agents*, Interscience, 1949, p. 323.

water-proofed fabric is expected to support a column of water, then it can be seen at once that the penetration of water into the fabric, which is a system of complicated, irregular capillaries, will be opposed by the inter-facial tensions if the advancing contact angle can be made greater than 90°. The extent of this resistance to penetration can be expressed approximately by the pressure difference across the meniscus of largest radius r', in an equation of a form such as the following:

$$\Delta p = \frac{2\gamma_W \cos \theta_A}{r'} \quad \text{(Equation 18, Chapter 4).}$$

This pressure difference reaches a maximum, if we are considering water-proofing rather than wetting, when the advancing contact angle θ_A reaches 180° (more correctly, when the contact angle measured inside the air phase disappears), and when the surface tension of the water γ_W is as large as possible. In practice, however, the receding contact angle θ_R may also be significant, especially if the system consisting of the fabric and the column of water is subjected to vibration or mechanical attrition, flexing, etc. Thus if a certain meniscus is momentarily displaced downwards by an intermittent mechanical effect, which is then removed, the extent to which the situation will be restored by the meniscus returning to its original position, will depend on how nearly the value of the receding contact angle approaches that of the advancing contact angle. Since such fluctuating mechanical effects will usually be present in practice, so that the receding contact angle as well as the advancing angle will be significant, it follows that the surface condition produced by a water-proofing treatment should be as stable as possible to contact with water. This means that the water-repellent film should not only continue to adhere to the solid substrate, but that the molecules of which it is composed should not reorientate themselves on contact with water so as to present hydrophilic groups to the water phase. This fairly obvious conclusion will hardly come as a surprise to the practical man.

A property which is often required of a water-repellent fabric is that it should "shed" drops of rain which impinge upon it. The process involved in this "shedding" can be considered as taking place in three steps: an impact, a possible rebound, and a possible capillary penetration into the fabric. The impact and rebound stages are essentially those which have been discussed in Section A—2 of the present chapter, but with the opposite *desiderata*, *i.e.*, a high work of adhesion air-fibre is favourable during impact, and a low work of adhesion water-fibre is favourable during the rebound (if any).* It will be seen from equations (3), (3a), (4), and (4a) that this is tantamount to requiring a high surface tension of the

---

* A recent paper by Gallily and La Mer, *J. Phys. Chem.*, 1958, **62**, 1295, on the adhesion of very fine droplets of glycerol to a water-repellent surface, reveals that the percentage of adhesions at first increases with droplet velocity, and then passes through a maximum and decreases.

water, a high water-fibre interfacial tension, and a low air-fibre interfacial tension during impact, and a low surface tension, high water-fibre interfacial tension, and a low air-fibre interfacial tension during the rebound. If it is permissible to use contact angles, these requirements become, respectively,

(*i*) a high surface tension, and a value for cos θ_A which is as negative as possible (*i.e.*, θ_A greater than 90° and as near 180° as possible);

(*ii*) a low surface tension, and a value for cos θ_R which is as negative as possible, it being noted that the work of adhesion water-fibre becomes zero as θ_R approaches 180°.

The third stage of the process is essentially the same capillary penetration which was discussed in the last paragraph but one. It will therefore be clear that two *desiderata* apply throughout the process of impingement of water drops on a water-proofed fabric, *viz.*, high advancing and high receding contact angles, measured inside the aqueous phase, and that it is particularly desirable that both contact angles should exceed 90° if possible. The requirements as regards the surface tension of the water are apparently contradictory. It seems to us, however, that the question of whether on balance the surface tension should be high or low is academic. Thus the surface tension of the rainwater could only be altered, practically speaking, in one direction: it could be decreased by introducing surface-active agents into the fabric, which would slowly dissolve out. Any advantage which such an addition might cause at the "rebound" stage of impingement would be more than offset by the disadvantages at the other two stages, and above all by the fact that such additions would almost certainly decrease the contact angles. The need for removing water-soluble surface-active materials from water-proofed fabrics needs no elaboration for the practical proofer.

It is important to note that the contact angles which determine the impact and rebound stages of drop-impingement processes, and probably the capillary penetration of water-proofed textiles as well, are not the "true" contact angles which obtain on perfectly plane, "pure" surfaces, but are the apparent contact angles which are encountered on composite surfaces. It follows from this fact, which has been established by Cassie and Baxter in the papers discussed in Chapter 4 (pp. 139–142), that fabric structure is of considerable importance in determining the water-repellency of textiles (as well as of most of the water-repellent surfaces which occur in nature). It is also the explanation of the experimental fact that very high effective contact angles are possible on textiles, even when the "true" contact angles are relatively low, since the effective composite "solid-liquid" interfaces may in fact contain quite high proportions of air-liquid interfaces (*cf.* Equation 11, Chapter 4). A practical conclusion to be drawn is that a water-proofing treatment should not only give high values for the "true" advancing and receding contact angles, but that it should preferably not cause any matting of the fabric or any other change in structure which will decrease the proportion of true air-liquid interface in the apparent fibre-liquid interface. Furthermore, as Cassie and Baxter have made clear, the extremely high water-repellency of many naturally occurring surfaces is made possible by their special structures, and is no evidence that these surfaces necessarily contain substances of extremely high waterproofing power.

The effect of fabric structure on water-repellency has been considered in more detail by Segall,[1] who deals particularly with the "break-down" of water-repellency, *i.e.*, the conditions under which drops of water can force their way through the fabric pores. Segall visualises a fabric as consisting of a system of capillaries, the walls of which are composite surfaces made up of fibres and intervening air. If P is the hydrostatic pressure-resistance of the fabric, and P_y is the pressure required to force water between the fibres on the surface of the yarns which make up the walls of the capillary pores, then the best resistance to break-down is obtained when the fabric is so designed that P and P_y are approximately equal. Under these conditions, the water which is forced into the pores will spread out laterally between the yards, and recovery will be possible. If however $P_y > P$ (as will happen if the effective diameters of the capillaries are considerably greater than the distances between the yarns which make up the capillary walls), water can force its way through the capillaries, and break-down occurs. Segall concludes that the highest level of water-resistance will be obtained from fabrics with the smallest possible pore size, consistent with this condition that P and P_y are approximately equal.

The importance of surface structure in determining the effective contact angle should of course not be over-emphasised; *i.e.*, it would be quite incorrect to say that the intrinsic water-repellency of the surface plays a negligible rôle in comparison with the structure of the surface. It is obvious, for example, that for a given surface structure the value of the apparent contact angle θ_R' or θ_A' in Equation 11, of Chapter 4 will be increased by any increase in the true contact angle θ_R or θ_A, which may be brought about by a special water-proofing treatment. Even if θ_R' or θ_A' were already 180°, an increase in the true contact angle is still advantageous to water-repellency, as becomes clearer if we re-formulate the problem in terms of the three interfacial tensions instead of using contact angles. If we denote by W_{AS}' and W_{LS}' the works of adhesion air-solid and liquid-solid, respectively, on a composite surface on which f_{13} and f_{123} are the areas of actual solid-liquid and air-liquid interface per unit area of apparent solid-liquid interface, then it follows that

$$W_{AS}' = \gamma_{AL}(1 + f_{123}) + \gamma_{LS}f_{13} - \gamma_{AS}f_{13}$$
$$= \gamma_{AL}(1 + f_{123}) + f_{13}(\gamma_{LS} - \gamma_{AS})$$

[1] Segall, *Textile Research J.*, 1952, **22**, 736.

and
$$W_{LS}' = \gamma_{AL}(1 - f_{123}) - \gamma_{LS}f_{13} + \gamma_{AS}f_{13}$$
$$= \gamma_{AL}(1 - f_{123}) - f_{13}(\gamma_{LS} - \gamma_{AS})$$

If now the surface of the solid is so treated that it becomes intrinsically more water-repellent, without any change in γ_{AL}, f_{13}, or f_{123}, i.e., if $(\gamma_{LS} - \gamma_{AS})$ becomes larger algebraically speaking, then the work of adhesion air-solid is increased and the work of adhesion liquid-solid is decreased. Both changes favour water-repellency, irrespective of whether or not a finite apparent contact angle exists, the only possible qualification being that the increase in water-repellency will be negligibly small if the term $f_{13}(\gamma_{LS} - \gamma_{AS})$ remains negligible compared with the terms $\gamma_{AL}(1 + f_{123})$ and $\gamma_{AL}(1 - f_{123})$. If moreover the water-proofing treatment increases f_{123} (which it might do by reducing the extent of displacement of air from the composite solid-liquid interface), then W_{AS}' can be further increased and W_{LS}' decreased.

The foregoing discussion will perhaps have made clear that "chemical" water-proofing treatments are complementary rather than competitive to methods which are based on altering the structure of a surface, at least in the case of open fabrics, and that the essential rôle of any "chemical" treatment is to modify the fibre-air interface in such a way that the true contact angles (both advancing and receding) are increased without altering the surface tension of the water phase. More generally expressed, the treatment should increase, algebraically speaking, the quantity $(\gamma_{LS} - \gamma_{AS})$. The older methods of achieving this result relied on depositing a layer of an insoluble, hydrophobic substance on the surfaces of the fibres. It is well known, for example, to impregnate fabrics with solutions of waxes in organic solvents, or alternatively to treat them with soap solutions and then with solutions of multivalent metal salts, especially aluminium salts, so that very thin layers of "aluminium soaps" are deposited. A logical combination of these two principles was to emulsify paraffin wax, for example, in the aqueous soap solution, so that the final deposit consisted of a mixture of wax and aluminium soap. Ingenious emulsion systems are also available in which paraffin wax and aluminium salts are present together, thus enabling textiles to be water-proofed in a single treating bath. Such treatments continue to be of great technical value, but they do not properly belong in the present monograph.*

A well-known defect of the treatments just described is that the hydrophobic deposits are removed by washing and dry-cleaning. Modification of the fibre surface by chemical attack has therefore been extensively studied, although such treatments usually involve the use of either an organic solvent or gaseous medium. The aim is to form a layer of molecules in the

---

* This also applies to more recent developments, such as the use of organic titanium compounds (see Speer and Carmody, *Ind. Eng. Chem.*, 1950, **42**, 251) or of basic zirconium salts (see Bayer, D.R.P. 928,343) as water-proofing agents for textiles.

surface of the fibre, which shall be integral with the fibre chemically, and which shall contain hydrophobic groups which are suitably orientated away from the fibre. The methods used, in which for example the hydroxyl groups in the cellulose micelles are reacted with fatty acid chlorides or with chloromethyl ethers of fatty alcohols, are also outside our subject: they are discussed in Chwala's book, and in the sections on cellulose fibres in the *Annual Reports on the Progress of Applied Chemistry* of the Society of Chemical Industry. A further development of this principle, in which cationic surface-active agents are applied to textiles from aqueous media and then decomposed on the fibres, chemical interaction between the agent and the fibre almost certainly occurring, is however of direct relevance.

The cationic, water-soluble, durable water-proofing agents are typified by the original product of this class, "Velan PF"* of I.C.I., in which the effective agent is stearamidomethylpyridinium chloride,

$$C_{17}H_{35}{\cdot}CONHCH_2\overset{+}{N}\langle\ \rangle,\ Cl^-$$

The treatment of viscose fabrics with "Velan PF," which has been described by Weston,[1] will illustrate the modern technique. An aqueous solution of the agent is prepared by wetting the commercial product (which contains sodium chloride) with ethyl alcohol at 30–40° c. and dissolving with enough water at the same temperature to give a solution containing between 2% and 10% of the commercial product. Sodium acetate is then added in order to prevent tendering of the cloth by hydrochloric acid during a subsequent baking (see below), after which the cloth is padded through this solution, which is described as "opaque, slightly opalescent, and highly surface-active." The cloth is dried, baked at a temperature between 120° and 150° c. in a well-ventilated oven, and finally washed off and dried. According to Weston, stearamidomethylpyridinium chloride decomposes in the presence of water to give methylolstearamide, which is only moderately hydrophobic:

$$C_{17}H_{35}{\cdot}CONHCH_2\overset{+}{N}\langle\ \rangle,\ Cl^-$$
$$+\ H_2O \rightarrow C_{17}H_{35}{\cdot}CONHCH_2OH\ +\langle\ \rangle N{\cdot}HCl$$

---

* See also "Zelan A" (du Pont). The impression that "Velan PF" is stearyloxymethylpyridinium chloride,

$$C_{18}H_{37}OCH_2\overset{+}{N}\langle\ \rangle,\ Cl^-$$

(*cf.* Chwala, *loc. cit.*, p. 405, and Schwartz and Perry, *Surface-Active Agents*, Interscience, 1949, p. 179) appears to have been due to a mistaken identification of the product with the compounds described in B.P. 466,817 of I.C.I., Reynolds, Walker, and Woolvin. This error now appears to be perpetuated in much of the technical literature!

[1] Weston, Lecture to the Eleventh International Congress of Pure and Applied Chemistry, Imperial College of Science and Technology, London, 21st July, 1947.

17

In the absence of excess water, on the other hand, a more powerfully hydrophobic substance is formed, which is probably methylene distearamide,

$$C_{17}H_{35}\cdot CO\cdot NHCH_2NH\cdot OC\cdot C_{17}H_{35}$$

This explains the need for drying in a well-ventilated oven and baking at a fairly high temperature. Treatment of fabrics with "Velan PF" not only renders them water-repellent, but also gives them a softer "handle."

The chemistry of water-proofing with "Velan" has also been studied by Davis,[1] who concludes that stearamidomethylpyridinium chloride decomposes first to methylolstearamide, which is then capable of either condensing with the hydroxyl groups in the surface of the cellulose during the baking operation to form linkages of the type

$$>CH\cdot O\cdot CH_2NH\cdot OC\cdot C_{17}H_{35} \qquad (I)$$

or of condensing with itself to form successively the compounds

$$C_{17}H_{35}\cdot CO\cdot NHCH_2OCH_2NH\cdot OC\cdot C_{17}H_{35} \qquad (II)$$

and $$C_{17}H_{35}\cdot CO\cdot NHCH_2NH\cdot OC\cdot C_{17}H_{35} \qquad (III)$$

both of which are hydrophobic. Davis considers that product (I) is preferred up to a total of about 1% to 2% of stearamidomethylpyridinium chloride calculated on the fabric, but that any excess above this figure decomposes to (II) and (III). This picture is in good general agreement with that drawn by Weston, who points out that part of the product is so tenaciously held by the fabric that it cannot be removed by solvent extraction or other physical means, so that he also adopts the theory of the ether linkage with hydroxyl groups in the cellulose. He considers that this chemically bound material acts as a sort of "mordant" for the rest of the deposit. Finally, it should be noted that "bulk" properties of the rayon fibre, such as its solubility in cuprammonium solution or its moisture regain, are not materially affected by treatment with "Velan."

Schuyten, Weaver, Frick, and Reid[2] investigated the mechanism of water-proofing with "Velan" by applying stearamidomethylpyridinium chloride and several possible intermediates to cotton and then heat-curing, with the following results:

(*i*) Distearamidomethane (III) gave good water-repellency, but the effect was completely destroyed by extraction with boiling chloroform.

(*ii*) Methylolstearamide gave good water-repellency. The deposit was extractable with chloroform if no acid catalyst was present during the heat-curing; with a catalyst present, it was not completely extracted. No

[1] Davis, *J. Soc. Dyers Colourists*, 1947, **63**, 260.
[2] Schuyten, Weaver, Frick, and Reid, *Textile Research J.*, 1952, **22**, 424.

formaldehyde was formed when the chloroform-extracted cloth was treated with hot 5% sulphuric acid; consequently it was concluded that the deposit remaining after chloroform extraction could not have been stearamido-methyl cellulose (I).

(*iii*) Stearamidomethyl acetate gave good water-repellency, which survived extraction with chloroform. There were small yields of nitrogen and formaldehyde when the extracted cloth was treated with 5% sulphuric acid, indicating that a small amount of stearamidomethyl cellulose (I) was formed.

(*iv*) Stearamidomethylpyridinium chloride itself gave a good water-repellency, which survived extraction with chloroform. The extracted material gave appreciable yields of nitrogen and formaldehyde with 5% sulphuric acid.

Schuyten, Weaver, Frick, and Reid therefore concluded, in agreement with Davis, that some 1 to 2% of the stearamidomethylpyridinium chloride reacts with the cellulose, involving about 1 in 150 of the anhydroglucose units, but (unlike Davis) they conclude that methylolstearamide is not an intermediate in the water-proofing process.

The facts and theories in the preceding paragraphs suggest at once that the mechanism of water-proofing with "Velan" and similar products consists of the following steps:

(a) The stearamidomethylpyridinium chloride is adsorbed from aqueous solution by the fabric, during the "padding" operation. It seems fairly certain that the agent is present to a large extent in a micellar or even coarser colloidal form, though it is not possible to suggest with any reasonable certainty which particular species is (are) actually adsorbed.

(b) The adsorbed stearamidomethylpyridinium chloride, and the surplus of this compound which is present in the mechanically held interstitial solution, decomposes to methylolstearamide, this process possibly beginning during the drying, after which the adsorbed methylolstearamide reacts with the cellulose to form compound (I), (Davis), *or alternatively,*

(c) The adsorbed stearamidomethylpyridinium chloride reacts directly with the cellulose, perhaps partly *via* the intermediate stearamidomethyl acetate, to give (I) (Schuyten *et al.*).

(d) Simultaneously with or subsequent to stage (b) or (c), the methylol-stearamide which was formed by decomposition of the unadsorbed stear-amidomethylpyridinium chloride will condense to compounds such as (II) and (III), which contain two paraffin chains, and which will form one or more separate "bulk" phases. These phases will, however, be evenly spread over the fabric, and they will have a high work of adhesion to the chemically modified surface resulting from stage (b) or (c).

(e) The chemically modified surface formed during (b) or (c) will not be removable by washing or by extraction with organic solvents. The hydro-phobic phase(s) deposited during (d) will be more difficult to remove than a hydrophobic phase which has been deposited on an unmodified cellulose surface, but it will be possible to remove it by severe physical treatments such as solvent extraction.

The foregoing picture, which is essentially a collection of suggestions by previous authors, is of course only tentative, but it can probably be applied in general terms to describe the mode of action of other soluble water-proofing compounds such as the condensation product of thiourea and methylolstearamide,[1] or stearoyloxymethylpyridinium chloride,[2]

$$C_{17}H_{35}\cdot COOCH_2\overset{+}{N}\langle\bigcirc\rangle, Cl^-$$

Other chemical types are considered in Part III.

A development which is really outside the scope of the present book, but which is of such technical and scientific interest as to demand some mention, is the use of silicones (polysiloxanes) as water-proofing agents for textiles, ceramic materials, etc. The chemistry of silicones has been reviewed in Rochow's well-known book,[3] while their use as water-proofing agents has been discussed by Hunter, Gordon, Barry, Hyde, and Heidenreich,[4] by Dennett,[5] by Fortess,[6] by Weltzien and Hauschild,[7] and by Watt.[8] The silicones are applied, either as aqueous emulsions or as solutions in chlorinated organic solvents, in the form of lower polymers ("silicone oils"), which are obtained, for example, by the reaction between methyl dichlorosilane or dimethyl dichlorosilane, and water:

$$2\left[\begin{array}{c} H \\ | \\ Cl{-}Si{-}Cl \\ | \\ CH_3 \end{array}\right] + 3H_2O \rightarrow HO{-}\overset{\displaystyle H}{\underset{\displaystyle CH_3}{Si}}{-}O{-}\overset{\displaystyle H}{\underset{\displaystyle CH_3}{Si}}{-}OH$$

$$\text{or}\quad 2\left[\begin{array}{c} CH_3 \\ | \\ Cl{-}Si{-}Cl \\ | \\ CH_3 \end{array}\right] + 3H_2O \rightarrow HO{-}\overset{\displaystyle CH_3}{\underset{\displaystyle CH_3}{Si}}{-}O{-}\overset{\displaystyle CH_3}{\underset{\displaystyle CH_3}{Si}}{-}OH$$

These "oils" are further polymerised *in situ* on the fibre to give polymers of general structure such as

---

[1] S.C.I., B.P. 527,012.
[2] Warwick Chemical Company, B.P. 560,448.
[3] Rochow, *An Introduction to the Chemistry of Silicones*, John Wiley and Sons, 1946.
[4] Hunter, Gordon, Barry, Hyde, and Heidenreich, *Ind. Eng. Chem.*, 1947, **39**, 1389.
[5] Dennett, *Amer. Dyes. Reporter*, 1950, **39**, 63.
[6] Fortess, *Ind. Eng. Chem.*, 1954, **46**, 2325.
[7] Weltzien and Hauschild, *Textilber.*, 1956, **37**, 199, 316, 449, 575, 695.
[8] Watt, *J. Textile Inst.*, 1957, **48**, T175.

$$\ldots \underset{\underset{\text{CH}_3}{|}}{\overset{\overset{\text{CH}_3}{|}}{\text{Si}}}\text{—O—}\underset{\underset{\text{CH}_3}{|}}{\overset{\overset{\text{CH}_3}{|}}{\text{Si}}}\text{—O—}\underset{\underset{\text{CH}_3}{|}}{\overset{\overset{\text{CH}_3}{|}}{\text{Si}}}\text{—O} \ldots \text{("dimethylpolysiloxanes")}$$

or $\quad \ldots \underset{\underset{\text{CH}_3}{|}}{\overset{\overset{\text{H}}{|}}{\text{Si}}}\text{—O—}\underset{\underset{\text{CH}_3}{|}}{\overset{\overset{\text{H}}{|}}{\text{Si}}}\text{—O—}\underset{\underset{\text{CH}_3}{|}}{\overset{\overset{\text{H}}{|}}{\text{Si}}}\text{—O} \ldots \text{("H-polysiloxanes")}$

or mixtures of the two types. Various catalysts are used, and the molecular weight can be controlled by a suitable choice of the ratio of dimethyl-polysiloxane to H-polysiloxane, the latter being more reactive, and by the use of trimethylchlorosilane as a chain stopper. It seems to be established that the lower polymers are not actually adsorbed by the fibre, but are either deposited as a separate liquid phase from aqueous emulsions, or simply mechanically held by the textile substrate when the silicones are "padded" on from solution. Weltzien and Hauschild support the opinion, from analyses of films made on mercury surfaces, that the polymers are not entirely linear, but that appreciable cross-linking occurs through Si—O—Si bridges. They also conclude that fixation is essentially mechanical and that there is no chemical linkage with the fibre.

The two properties of polysiloxane films which make them of particular interest for water-proofing textiles are their low solubility in dry-cleaning solvents, and the fact that their surface tensions against air are probably appreciably lower than their interfacial tensions against water. Fox, Taylor, and Zisman[1] found that the surface tensions of silicone oils were as low as 15·7 dynes/cm., where the corresponding interfacial tension against water was 39·9 dynes/cm. If similar values obtain for the boundary tensions of the higher polymers, then it is at once apparent from Young's equation that the contact angle (measured in the water) will be greater than 90°, and in fact the two boundary tension values just quoted suggest a contact angle of about 110°, which is in reasonable agreement with the observed values. This contact angle is a little higher than that usually found for water on smooth paraffin wax surfaces (*ca.* 105°), and this is consistent with the water-proofing efficiencies reported by Weltzien and Hauschild, which range from slightly inferior to a paraffin wax emulsion on cotton, to superior on cellulose acetate and "Perlon." Obviously the water-proofing efficiency is a function of the structure of the treated surface, as well as of its intrinsic water-repellency.

Most of the tests which are at present used for measuring the water-repellency of treated fabrics can be related to the physical picture of the

---

[1] Fox, Taylor, and Zisman, *Ind. Eng. Chem.*, 1947, **39**, 1401.

spray-impingement process which we have already considered. In the well-known Bundesmann test,[1] for example, a spray of drops of water falls on the cloth samples, which are fastened on slowly revolving, tilted cups. The under sides of the cloth samples are swept by rotating wiper arms, which simulate the flexing and rubbing which are present when a water-proofed garment is worn in practice. Water-proofness is judged by the amount of water which, under standard conditions, penetrates the specimens of cloth and collects in the cups. The American "Drop-Penetration" test is broadly similar, except that the wipers are absent, while in the "Impact Penetration Test" the water which penetrates through the cloth (which again is not flexed) is absorbed by a piece of blotting paper which is placed immediately underneath the test specimen and is weighed before and after the exposure. In the du Pont "Rain Test," water is sprayed against a vertical test specimen which is backed by a blotter, but the hydrostatic head behind the spray is varied, emphasis being laid on determining the extent of penetration at different spray intensities. All these tests are more or less quantitative—many of our readers will also be familiar with simpler spray tests in which the extent of wetting or penetration is judged visually after the test specimen has been exposed to a standard shower. The hydrostatic pressure test is, as its name implies, based on a different physical principle, the pressure being determined at which water just penetrates the test fabric. The literature on these methods of testing is very extensive; a useful summary has been published by Slowinske and Pope.[2]

Any comparison of the relative merits of these different tests resolves itself at once into an examination of their relevance to the particular use to which a water-proofed fabric is to be put, though even for a given use preferences will be found to vary. If for example we consider only the testing of fabrics which are to withstand prolonged exposure to rain, we find that Slowinske and Pope give a reasoned argument for preferring their "Rain Test" to the Bundesmann test, and it in fact seems clear that their use of varying spray intensities has much to recommend it. Landsberg, Kelly, and Sinski[3] concluded, as the result of correlating extensive "rain room" practical tests with laboratory tests by the du Pont, drop-penetration, and Bundesmann tests, that all three tests were equally reliable, that all three were preferable to the hydrostatic pressure test, and that the results by all three tests could be expressed by an equation of the form

$$\log Y = a + b \log X$$

where Y is the "rain room" value, X the laboratory test value, and a and b are constants. They preferred the du Pont and drop-penetration tests to

[1] Bundesmann, *Textilber.*, 1935, **16**, 128. See also the report by Lawrie *et al.*, *J. Text. Institute*, 1942, **33**, S49–S52.

[2] Slowinske and Pope, *Amer. Dyes. Reporter*, 1947, **36**, P108.

[3] Landsberg, Kelly, and Sinski, *Textile Research J.*, 1949, **19**, 505.

the Bundesmann test simply on the grounds that the last-named was more complicated and showed no compensating advantages. For many purposes,* however, it seems to us that the supporters of the Bundesmann test are right in stressing the relevance to practice of the flexing and rubbing which the test specimen receives from the wiper arms. Perhaps the ideal water-repellency test will represent a combination of these and other tests; for our present purpose it is probably sufficient to point out that both the mechanical durability of a water-repellent finish, and its continued resistance to impact from drops of different sizes, are almost certainly as important as the extent to which it initially promotes the "shedding" of drops of rain.

Reference has already been made to the fact that water-proofing treatments which are based on the principle of making the surfaces of the yarns water-repellent, rather than of blocking the interstices, do not prevent circulation through open fabrics. An interesting demonstration of this permeability to water vapour of "Zelan" treated fabrics has been published by Stearn and Cooper.[1] Finally, the reader may be interested in an account of the testing of water-proofed fabrics for the American Army, under severely practical conditions, by Simpson.[2]

---

* An example of such a case is probably the simulation of the conditions under which raincoats are used by the average civilian in the British Isles.

[1] Stearn and Cooper, *Amer. Dyes. Reporter*, 1944, **33**, 150.

[2] Simpson, *Amer. Dyes. Reporter*, 1946, **35**, 243.

CHAPTER 6

THE PREPARATION OF EMULSIONS: DEMULSIFICATION

In Chapter 4, Section D ("Mechanical Phase-Subdivision Processes"), we have indicated very briefly the two possible functions of surface-active agents in the preparation of emulsion* systems, *viz.*, the lowering of the interfacial tension at the interfaces between the dispersed droplets and the continuous phase, and the formation of interfacial protective films. The first of these two effects makes easier the initial process of mechanical phase-subdivision, and reduces the degree of thermodynamical instability of the resulting disperse system; the second stabilises the emulsion, which stabilisation may also increase the efficiency of the preceding stage by reducing re-aggregation or coalescence. A given surface-active agent may in practice discharge either or both of these functions. The aim of the present chapter is accordingly to describe methods for the preparation and destruction of emulsions, but only in enough detail to clarify the use of the synthetic surface-active agents which are described in Part III of the present book. A full account of the theory and technology of emulsions is unnecessary, particularly in view of the treatises already available, the most important of which is that of Clayton and Sumner.[1] A useful short summary of the factors which influence the stability of emulsions has been given by Sherman.[2]

A. Emulsion techniques—General

Methods of emulsification can be conveniently classified, from the point of view of the emulsifying agents used, into the "mayonnaise" procedure and the self-emulsifiable oil technique; a further general principle—the formation of surface-active agents or complexes at the interface—is applicable to both methods but seems to merit separate consideration.

---

* By an emulsion we mean of course a dispersion of one liquid in another liquid, the two being immiscible—or incompletely miscible—under the conditions obtaining. In the vast majority of cases one of these liquids will be water or an aqueous solution; consequently it is a convenient usage to refer generally to the "water" and to the "oil" phases, and to classify emulsions as being of the "oil-in-water" or "water-in-oil" types.

[1] Clayton's *The Theory of Emulsions and their Technical Treatment*, 5th edition by C. G. Sumner, Churchill, London, 1954. See also Berkman and Egloff, *Emulsions and Foams*, Reinhold, 1941. The symposium organised by the International Society of Leather Trades Chemists in London in 1934, published under the title *Technical Aspects of Emulsions*, Harvey, 1935, is also of considerable value. A revised version edited by Bennett, entitled *Emulsion Technology*, Chemical Publishing Co., 1946, is particularly to be recommended.

[2] Sherman, *Research*, 1955, **8**, 396.

1. THE MAYONNAISE METHOD

In this technique, the surface-active agent is dissolved in the continuous phase, and the liquid to be emulsified is then added, with stirring. Frequently (one might almost say traditionally), this addition is made gradually in a "batch-wise" fashion, and the emulsion first obtained may then be passed through a "valve homogeniser" or subjected to disruption in a colloid mill (see below). There is however an increasing tendency for the mixing and emulsification to be carried out in a single operation, and more or less continuously. A further refinement which is frequently used is two-stage homogenisation (*cf.* Clayton and Sumner, *loc. cit.*, p. 557), in which an emulsion is passed two or more times through the homogenising valve or colloid mill, presumably in order to distribute the emulsifying agent, which will not be instantaneously adsorbed at the interfaces, more uniformly around the globules and thus reduce the tendency to aggregation ("clumping") or coalescence.

It seems fairly certain that the most important function of a surface-active agent in the mayonnaise method is to act as a protective colloid by forming a stable interfacial film which prevents coalescence (*cf.* Chapter 4, p. 177), a point which is made very clearly in Clayton and Sumner's book. Although macromolecules are especially effective for preventing coalescence, they are not essential. The protective colloid power of the simple paraffin chain salts in oil-in-water emulsions depends to a considerable extent on their concentration in the aqueous medium. Cockbain and McRoberts[1] found that the ability of cetyltrimethylammonium bromide and sodium laurate to prevent film rupture increased with concentration up to the critical micelle concentration, after which it fell; a similar general picture emerges for sodium dodecyl, hexadecyl, and octadecyl sulphates from the work of Osipow, Birson, and Snell.[2] These latter authors found that the logarithm of their stability parameter (optical density of the emulsion after standing, or percentage survival of larger drops which were projected against an oil-water interface) was a linear function of $\sqrt{c/c_M}$, where c is the concentration of emulsifying agent, and c_M is the critical micelle concentration. There is an increasing amount of evidence that protective films which prevent coalescence are fairly thick: according to van den Tempel,[3] they should be at least 100 Å. thick, and Sata, Harisaki, and Tunoda[4] conclude, from adsorption measurements on non-ionic amphipathic agents at the benzene-water interface, that the stabilising layers are multimolecular. The situation may be complicated in the case of mixed emulsifying agents, however, by competition for the interface. Thus

---

[1] Cockbain and McRoberts, *J. Coll. Sci.*, 1953, **8**, 440.

[2] Osipow, Birson, and Snell, *J. Amer. Oil Chemists' Soc.*, 1957, **34**, 34.

[3] Van den Tempel, *J. Coll. Sci.*, 1958, **13**, 125.

[4] Sata, Harisaki, and Tunoda, *Koll. Z.*, 1959, **162**, 134.

Osipow, Snell, and Ferencz[1] find that sucrose monostearate is a good stabiliser for emulsions of mineral oil in water, while the distearate and glyceryl monostearate are not. In mixtures of these agents, the two last-named agents tend to displace the sucrose monostearate from the interface as their concentrations increase, thus reducing emulsion stability. The logarithm of the stability parameter is a linear function of $c_1/(c_1 + c_2)$, where c_1 is the concentration of sucrose monostearate and c_2 is the concentration of sucrose distearate. These findings show an interesting similarity to those reported by Blair on the demulsification of petroleum emulsions (see p. 266), and illustrate very clearly the fact that emulsion stability is far from being determined by the adsorption thermodynamics of the system.

A further important function of an emulsifying agent is to deflocculate the system, *i.e.*, to hinder clumping or clustering of the droplets. Although the reduction in the interfacial tension, which will normally accompany adsorption at the oil-water interface, may also be advantageous *per se*, it will generally be less important than the two effects just described, provided that an efficient emulsifying machine is used. These generalisations hold particularly well with oil-in-water emulsions, in which the surface-active material should give externally hydrated films of the condensed liquid or solid type; the films should be rapidly formed but preferably desorbed as slowly as possible, and they should be stable to applied stresses, and preferably self-healing. (See the work of Schulman and co-workers, which is discussed below.) The presence of a high electrokinetic potential is nearly always desirable, but it is probably not essential: it probably does not play an appreciable part in the stabilisation of emulsions by non-ionising surface-active agents.

It is not surprising, in view of the requirements listed above, that glue, gelatine, casein, gums, and other water-soluble macromolecules have always been important in the preparation of emulsions by the mayonnaise method (*cf.* Clayton and Sumner, *loc. cit.*, p. 148 ff.). Synthetic water-soluble polymers have also been used: to give only two examples, the I.G.[2] used alkyl ethers of cellulose (*e.g.* dimethyl cellulose) for preparing emulsions for the treatment of leather, and also stated[3] that sulphonated polystyrene has emulsifying properties. In addition to the many disclosures and claims on the use of simpler synthetic surface-active agents, which will be found in Part III (*cf.* also Clayton and Sumner, *loc. cit.*, p. 148 ff., and Berkman and Egloff, *loc. cit.*, p. 178 ff.), special mention should be made of the use of mixtures of protective colloids with simpler synthetic compounds. The I.G.[4] patented mixtures of glue, or other gelatinisable colloids, with alkylated

[1] Osipow, Snell, and Ferencz, *J. Amer. Oil Chemists' Soc.*, 1958, **35**, 65.
[2] I.G., B.P. 318,070 = F.P. 666,039.
[3] I.G., B.P. 367,416.
[4] I.G., B.P. 258,551.

aromatic sulphonates, a subsequent variation by the same patentee[1] being the use of alkyl celluloses (*e.g.*, dimethyl cellulose) in place of the glue. I.C.I., Hailwood, Shepherdson, and Stewart[2] claim that the emulsions so obtained are improved, especially as regards their convenience in use, if a liquefying agent for the glue (*e.g.*, urea, thiourea, an alkali metal nitrate, or dextrine) is also added. The effects of the glue and of the alkylated aromatic sulphonate in such a mixture may be simply additive, the former acting as a protective colloid, while the latter improves the ease of emulsification and the emulsion stability by reducing the interfacial tension and increasing the electrokinetic potential (which is negative in sign). Such an explanation implies of course that molecules of the sulphonate, and molecules or micelles of the glue, are present together in a mixed interfacial film: it is therefore interesting to speculate as to whether or not interfacial complexes of enhanced emulsifying power are also formed (see below).

The mixed emulsifying agents just described are intended for use only in neutral or alkaline media, since glue and gelatine, for example, are precipitated by alkylated sulphonic acids on the acid side of their iso-electric points. It is therefore interesting to note that I.C.I., Hailwood, and Todd[3] describe the preparation of acid-stable, positively charged emulsions of the oil-in-water type by using mixtures of glue or gelatine with cationic surface-active agents (*e.g.*, octadecyl or dodecylpyridinium bromide). The procedure used is essentially the mayonnaise technique.

2. SELF-EMULSIFIABLE OILS

It is frequently desired to make oil-in-water emulsions "on the spot" by simply mixing an oil with water, without the use of special machinery, and preferably without having to measure out a special emulsifying agent. To meet this requirement, self-emulsifiable oils* have been developed which form fine emulsions (which are frequently at or beyond the limit of resolution in a light microscope), apparently spontaneously, when they are mixed with water. The first step towards developing such products was the use of oils containing fatty acids, which could be emulsified in alkaline aqueous solutions, the emulsifying agent being the soap which was formed *in situ* at the oil-water interface. This procedure is commonly called the "nascent soap" technique. A further development was the preparation of oils which contained water soluble soaps, the soap being solubilised in the oil by the addition of a phenol. The well known disinfectant "Creoline" is of this type, consisting of 45–60% neutral tar oil, 10–15% of phenols, and

---

* The widely-used expression "miscible oils" is not, strictly speaking, correct if an emulsion is obtained, since a two-phase system is involved. The term is also likely to lead to confusion with those textile "oils" which are genuinely water-soluble, such as Turkey Red Oil.

[1] I.G., B.P. 268,387.

[2] I.C.I., Hailwood, Shepherdson, and Stewart, B.P. 323,720 = U.S.P. 1,873,580.

[3] I.C.I., Hailwood, and Todd, B.P. 393,276.

30–40% of rosin soap.* This type of self-emulsifiable oil, which is extensively used in horticultural sprays, cutting oils, emulsions for oiling textiles, as well as for disinfectant compositions, has been scientifically studied by Woodman,[1] who found that amyl alcohol could be used in place of the phenolic solubiliser. Mention should also be made of the proposal by Sajitz and Pott[2] to use aromatic alcohols (*e.g.*, benzyl alcohol) in place of the phenolic ingredients, and to extend the "soap" constituent to include sulphonated fatty acids and sulphonated aromatic or hydroaromatic hydrocarbons.

The range of oil-soluble surface-active agents which can be used for making self-emulsifiable oils is now very large indeed. Many sulphonated vegetable, animal, and mineral oils are sufficiently soluble in the oils to be emulsified, even as their sodium salts, while the triethanolamine salts of fatty acids are frequently used for this purpose. The polethenoxy surface-active agents were early recognised as being particularly suitable for use in making self-emulsifiable oils, because many of them are soluble in both oil and aqueous media.[3] They can also be mixed with oil-soluble sulphonates, as in the proposal of Monsanto, Kaberg, and Harris[4] to add sodium dodecylbenzene monosulphonate and octylphenol condensed with ten to twelve moles of ethylene oxide to the oil to be emulsified. Some of the mixtures of agents which have been proposed for making self-emulsifiable oils probably also make use of the principle of forming interfacial complexes (see p. 253): examples are mixtures of sorbitan fatty acid esters with sorbitan fatty acid esters which have been condensed with ethylene oxide,[5] and mixtures of these two types with the further addition of oil-soluble sulphonates.[6]

Reference has already been made to the practical convenience of making emulsions by the self-emulsifiable oil technique. Two other features of the method are also worth special mention, *viz.*, that it is possible that some of the very finest emulsions made in this way are approaching a state of thermodynamical stability, in which the state of dispersion is determined by the composition, temperature, and pressure, and not by the history and mechanical treatment, and secondly, that a given emulsifying agent is usually more effective if it is introduced *via* the oil phase or made *in situ*,

---

* See Thorpe's *Dictionary of Applied Chemistry*, Longmans, Green, and Co., 1939, vol. III, p. 419. According to Ullmann's *Enzyklopädie der technischen Chemie*, Urban and Schwarzenberg, 1929, vol. III, p. 584, these emulsions were known in 1887. If the soaps and phenols are present in sufficient excess, oils are obtained which are apparently genuinely miscible: *i.e.*, they give clear solutions in water. Many well known disinfectants are of this type, or are on the rather ill-defined borderline between micellar solutions and emulsions.

[1] Woodman, *J. Soc. Chem. Ind.*, 1933, **52**, 4 (T); see also the article in *Emulsion Technology*, Chemical Publishing Co., 1946, p. 166.

[2] Sajitz and Pott, B.P. 266,746 = U.S.P. 1,817,205.

[3] *Cf.* I.G., B.P. 380,431, and the article by Schulz, *Fette u. Seife*, 1938, **45**, 146.

[4] Monsanto, Kaberg, and Harris, U.S.P. 2,447,475.

[5] Standard Oil Development Co. and Leland, U.S.P. 2,470,405.

[6] Standard Oil Development Co., Sproule, and Dixon, U.S.P. 2,565,403.

rather than being dissolved in the aqueous phase. The first of these points has already been discussed on pp. 180–181, and its practical importance requires no comment. The second fact is very widely appreciated by emulsion technologists, and is probably due to a more rapid diffusion of the emulsifying agent(s) towards the interface from the oil medium, in which the agents will generally be more nearly in molecular solution.

The nascent soap procedure is not of course confined to the emulsification of mobile oils: Anode Rubber Co.[1] have proposed to use it in dispersing rubbery or plastic masses. It has also been used in what is in effect the mayonnaise procedure, in combination with a water-soluble protein; thus Whatmough[2] dissolved a fatty acid in the oil phase and added a water-soluble protein and an alkali to the aqueous phase.

3. INTERFACIAL COMPLEXES

An important contribution to the theory of emulsification was the development by Schulman and his colleagues[3] of the concept of enhanced emulsification by interfacial complexes. We have seen in Chapter 3, p. 87, that the formation of an interfacial complex between an oil-soluble and a water-soluble surface-active compound, respectively, would be expected to give a greater decrease in the interfacial tension with increasing concentration. This decrease in interfacial tension (*cf.* Alexander and Schulman, *loc. cit.*) would of course be expected to increase the ease of emulsification, as Schulman and Cockbain have pointed out. Their theory goes further, however, in suggesting that interfacial complex formation also has a marked stabilising effect on an emulsion, by virtue of the mechanisms which in the present book we have chosen to call deflocculation and protective colloid action.

The theory of Schulman and Cockbain is based on their observations that (a) the emulsifying power of water-soluble paraffin-chain salts (*e.g.*, sodium cetyl sulphate, sodium oleate, sodium elaidate, sodium palmitate, cetyltrimethylammonium bromide) is increased by the presence in the oil phase of amphipathic molecules* such as cetyl alcohol, oleyl alcohol,

---

* Broadly speaking, these experimental observations were anticipated by Schrauth (*Chem.-Ztg.*, 1931, **55**, 17), and Lindner (*Seifensieder Ztg.*, 1934, **61**, 833), and by Speakman and Chamberlain (*Trans. Faraday Soc.*, 1933, **29**, 358) in their work on the scouring of wool. Another interesting earlier reference is the proposal by Deutsche Hydrierwerke (D.R.P. 565,057, published 25th November, 1932) to use as emulsifying agents combinations of *inter alia* soap substitutes with fatty alcohols containing more than one hydroxyl group. In none of these earlier publications, however, is either the theory of Schulman and Cockbain or their systematic experimental work anticipated.

[1] Anode Rubber Co., B.P. 296,685.

[2] Whatmough, B.P. 280,096 = U.S.P. 1,663,323.

[3] Schulman and Cockbain, *Trans. Faraday Soc.*, 1940, **36**, 651, 661; Alexander and Schulman, *ibid.*, 1940, **36**, 960. For the earlier work which led to the theory, see in particular Schulman and Rideal, *Proc. Roy. Soc. B.*, 1937, **122**, 29, 46; Cockbain and Schulman, *Trans. Faraday Soc.*, 1939, **35**, 716. Summaries of the theory will be found in the books by Clayton and Sumner (p. 275 ff., 311 ff.), and by Berkman and Egloff (pp. 101 ff.).

elaidyl alcohol, or cholesterol, and (b) the order of effectiveness of the different combinations of surface-active compounds is in general the same as the order of their tendency to form stable complexes at air-water interfaces, as shown by the work with the Langmuir trough. This tendency towards improved emulsifying power is considerably affected by steric influences in the non-polar portions of the molecules: thus the combinations sodium cetyl sulphate-elaidyl alcohol (*trans* isomer of oleyl alcohol), sodium cetyl sulphate-cetyl alcohol, and sodium elaidate-cetyl alcohol, are superior to the combinations sodium cetyl sulphate-oleyl alcohol or sodium oleate-cetyl alcohol. The forces holding the molecules together in a complex are thus assumed to be of two kinds: van der Waals forces of attraction between the non-polar portions, and polar interactions between the head groups.

Schulman and Cockbain suggest that the complexes favour the formation of emulsions of the *oil-in-water* type by virtue of the following effects:

(*i*) a lowering of the interfacial tension, owing to the fact that the interfacial excess is increased;

(*ii*) the formation of a condensed liquid film, which prevents coalescence, but which is sufficiently mobile to recover quickly from any distortion;

(*iii*) an increase in the electrokinetic potential on the droplets, due to the fact that a larger number of surface-active ions are now packed into the interface.

Schulman and Cockbain postulate that the first of these effects is also operative in promoting the formation of *water-in-oil* emulsions, but that the second and third are different; *i.e.*, the interfacial film should now be of the condensed solid type, possessing considerable rigidity, and the interface should be uncharged electrokinetically.

It is interesting to note that Schulman and Cockbain found that the emulsifying power of gelatine was also increased by the addition to the oil phase of oil-soluble amphipathic compounds which are known to form complexes with insoluble proteins at the air-water interface. The most effective additions were (in decreasing order of effectiveness): cholesterol, oleic acid, oleyl alcohol, elaidic acid, stearic acid, cetyl alcohol.

Results which confirm those of Schulman and Cockbain have also been reported by Jellinek and Anson,[1] who used sodium stearate in the aqueous phase and glyceryl monostearate in white mineral oil, and by Cockbain and McRoberts[2] with a combination of cholesterol and sodium laurate in emulsions of medicinal paraffin in water.

It will of course be appreciated that Schulman and Cockbain's theory applies primarily to combinations of oil-soluble amphipathic compounds with ionising water-soluble surface-active agents, and that it may require

---

[1] Jellinek and Anson, *J. Soc. Chem. Ind.*, 1949, **68**, 108.

[2] Cockbain and McRoberts, *J. Coll. Sci.*, 1953, **8**, 440.

modification, perhaps only in emphasis, when it is applied to non-ionising surface-active agents such as the type $Alkyl.[OCH_2CH_2]_nOH$. Thus the presence or absence of electrokinetic potentials may well prove to be unimportant in determining the stability of emulsions containing such agents, though in our opinion it would be unwise to assume this until it has been experimentally verified. A more general criticism which might be advanced against the theory is that it does not directly prove the existence of intermolecular complexes. Thus the emulsification and interfacial tension results could, taken in isolation, be explained by the independent coexistence in the interfacial phase, of the oil-soluble and water-soluble surface-active species, respectively. On such a picture each species would contribute independently (except insofar as activity coefficients were mutually affected) to the lowering of the interfacial tension, the total lowering by both species together being greater than that by either alone.*

It seems clear to the present writers, however, that the interfacial tension and emulsification results of Schulman and his colleagues cannot be considered in isolation, but against the general background of the work of the Rideal school and others on interactions in unilayers. When due account is taken of the parallelisms with the behaviour of films at the air-water interface, and when the highly specific effect of the structure of the surface-active molecules (especially those pointing to steric influences) are considered, the theory advanced by Schulman and Cockbain becomes the most reasonable explanation of the facts so far reported. The theory is also supported by further experimental work, among which may be mentioned that of Matalon,[1] who found that the spontaneous emulsification of medicinal paraffin in water, the oil and water phases containing cholesterol and sodium dodecyl sulphate, respectively, was enhanced by the presence of small amounts of electrolyte (NaCl or $CuSO_4$) in the aqueous phase. When only sodium dodecyl sulphate was present, small amounts of electrolyte had no effect. This suggests very definitely that a new surface-active species is formed when both surface-active materials are present, the formation of this complex being favoured by the presence of electrolyte.

As mentioned above, acceptance of the theory that interfacial complexes are formed in many emulsion systems does not, of course, exclude the possibility that independent adsorption of both the water-soluble and the

---

* We are indebted to Mr. A. E. Ambler for drawing our attention to this possible criticism. He has also pointed out to us that different meanings might be attached to the phrase "interfacial complex." In the present treatment we have considered that it refers to a distinct species, having its own properties such as a partial surface pressure in the interfacial film, but in equilibrium with the two amphipathic molecular species. Between this picture of an interfacial complex, and the other extreme of completely independent co-existence, there are of course intermediate stages such as a very marked mutual lowering of activity coefficients in the interfacial phase, which might be considered as types of interfacial complex formation.

[1] Matalon, *Trans. Faraday Soc.*, 1950, **46**, 674.

oil-soluble agents may also occur in other emulsions. Such a case has in fact been reported by Cockbain and McMullen.[1]

The practical importance of the concept of interfacial complexes in emulsion systems is obvious from the results described by Schulman and Cockbain and by Speakman and Chamberlain. It is worth noting that, although most of the emulsions described by these workers were made by what is essentially the mayonnaise method, though with relatively gentle agitation, interfacial complexes may also be valuable in the preparation of emulsions by the self-emulsifiable oil technique, provided that the water-soluble agent can be made soluble in the oil. It even seems possible that the Schulman-Cockbain theory is applicable to at least some of the older self-emulsifiable oils containing soaps or sulphonated surface-active agents, along with solubilisers such as phenols, aliphatic alcohols, or aromatic alcohols (*cf.* Sajitz and Pott's patent[2]). The fact that benzyl alcohol, for example, will solubilise soaps in oil media suggests that complex formation is occurring, and it would not be surprising if such complexes had a suitable configuration and hydrophobe-hydrophile ratio which made them more surface-active, at the particular interface in question, than either benzyl alcohol or soap alone.

B. Emulsifying machinery

We have already noted that the preparation of emulsions by the self-emulsifiable technique is designed to avoid the use of special machinery, any reasonably efficient mixing device being suitable. In the mayonnaise method, on the other hand, mechanical conditions are frequently critical, success depending to a large extent on the emulsifying machine which is available. In view of the full descriptions of such machines in the books by Clayton and Sumner and by Berkman and Egloff, as well as in the article by Johnson,[3] it is proposed to describe them here only in general terms.

1. HIGH-SPEED STIRRERS

Stirrers, with which the contents of the emulsifying vessel are violently agitated, are often used. It is a matter of common experience that a high degree of turbulence is needed: baffles may be inserted in the vessel for this purpose, and propeller agitators may also be arranged with this end in view. Propellers are also frequently set so as to force streams of the oil and the aqueous phase against each other across the interface. A serious problem which is often encountered with high-speed stirrers, especially when an oil is being added slowly to an aqueous solution, is frothing. A voluminous foam will decrease the effective capacity of the mixing vessel, reduce the

[1] Cockbain and McMullen, *Trans. Faraday Soc.*, 1951, **47**, 322.

[2] Sajitz and Pott, B.P. 266,746 = U.S.P. 1,817,205.

[3] Johnson, in Bennett's *Emulsion Technology*, Chemical Publishing Co., 1946, p. 88.

degree of disruption of the oil droplets by decreasing the effective shearing forces, and sometimes even reduce the stability of the emulsion. Such difficulties are sometimes overcome by immersing the stirrer to a sufficient depth.

2. COLLOID MILLS

These mills are of very great value in making emulsions by the mayonnaise method. It is usually advantageous to mix the oil and aqueous phases beforehand, and to feed a coarse emulsion into the colloid mill, in which the larger droplets are broken up by the intensive shearing forces (*cf.* Chapter 7, p. 273). One characteristic of the colloid mill which requires mention, however, is the extremely short time during which the droplets in each portion of the emulsion are subjected to disruption. Thus it is not unusual for a colloid mill of the plate type, for example one with a rotor which is 12 inches in diameter, working at a clearance of 6/1000 inch, to deliver 100 gallons of emulsion per hour. This means that, on the average, the material in the milling space changes twelve times in every second. An emulsifying agent, especially one containing a protein or other macromolecular colloid, may therefore be adsorbed too slowly to stabilise completely the emulsion which is being formed: *i.e.*, a certain degree of coalescence or flocculation may occur, or the emulsion may break altogether. Although further passages through the mill may improve matters, it may be necessary to select a special surface-active agent, the use of nascent soaps, which diffuse rapidly to the interface, being a well-known remedy.

3. VALVE HOMOGENISERS

Homogenisers are used after a preliminary emulsification in a mixing vessel, colloid mill, or other device. In the design of these machines which is most often encountered, the coarse emulsion is pumped, under considerable pressure, against a spring-loaded valve which fits into an accurately-ground seating. The valve is thus forced partly open, the emulsion streaming at a high velocity through the annular opening. The droplets are disrupted, partly by the simple "sieving" action and partly by the intense shearing forces which are set up in the annulus. Although the rate of adsorption of the surface-active agent is usually important, it does not appear to be so critical as with colloid mills. "Two-stage homogenisation" (*i.e.*, two passages through a homogenising valve, or two homogenising valves working in series) is widely used.

4. OTHER DEVICES

Many other emulsifying devices resemble the three types just described. Mention might be made here of special mixing pumps, centrifugal emulsifiers ("emulsifying bowls"), ultrasonic generators, slotted mixers of the

"Ultra-Turrax" type, mixing jets (including those in which ultrasonic vibration occurs), and turbulent flow devices in which a coarse emulsion is made to flow along a tube at a speed greater than the critical velocity for turbulence.[1]

5. RELATIVE MERITS OF EMULSIFYING MACHINES

The relative merits of these different types of emulsifying machinery cannot be usefully compared in general terms, since so much depends on the properties of the particular emulsion (*e.g.* viscosity) and of the interface involved (interfacial tension, type of interfacial film which is formed, velocity of formation of the interfacial film), and on the uses to which the emulsion is to be put. It is probably true in the majority of cases, however, that colloid mills will tend to give a larger proportion of very fine droplets, while valve homogenisers will usually give more nearly homodisperse systems—this means of course that these two types of machines are in general complementary rather than competitive. In our opinion, the relative merits of different emulsifying machines for a particular composition, or the relative merits of different surface-active agents for use with an available machine, can only be settled after experimental trial with particular reference to the following factors:

(a) the required rate of production (which involves the viscosity—or consistency—of the emulsion as a whole);

(b) the shearing forces set up in the machine, and the time during which they act;

(c) the possible occurrence of unfavourable effects such as excessive foaming or local over-heating in the machine;

(d) the degree of lowering in the interfacial tension required for successful emulsification under the mechanical conditions obtainable;

(e) the type of interfacial film required to stabilise the emulsion, its mechanical properties (*e.g.*, resistance to mechanical disruption), its chemical stability, and the possibility of the formation of interfacial complexes;

(f) the speed with which the interfacial tension falls and the interfacial film is formed (or re-formed), with particular attention to the phase(s) through which the surface-active agent(s) must diffuse in order to reach the interface.

To this list might be added a requirement which appears to be common to all emulsification procedures, though it is usually automatically satisfied, *viz.*, that the emulsifying agent, etc., must be so chosen that the surfaces in the emulsifying machine are preferentially wetted by the liquid which constitutes the *continuous* phase of the emulsion. If this condition is not

---

[1] South Metropolitan Gas Co., Stanier, and Davis, B.P. 393,934.

satisfied, the emulsion formed may be of the wrong type or (what is much more likely) a considerable amount of coalescence may occur.*

C. Water-in-oil emulsions: Multiple emulsions

Although the preceding discussion has been chiefly concerned with oil-in-water emulsions—and most of the emulsifying agents to be described in Part III of the present book yield that type—many of the arguments apply also to water-in-oil emulsions. Thus the formation of water-in-oil emulsions is favoured by a lowering in the interfacial tension, by a protective colloid action arising from the formation of stable interfacial films (including films which are stabilised by interfacial complexes), and by a high degree of deflocculation of the dispersed droplets in the continuous phase. The differences between the two types arise from the fact that the continuous (oil) phase in a water-in-oil emulsion is normally a liquid of low dielectric constant, which is a substantially non-ionising solvent. The presence of an electrokinetic potential across the interface is therefore unnecessary or, if we accept the view of Schulman and Cockbain, actually undesirable. Schulman and Cockbain have also suggested that interfacial films of the solid type are more efficient than are condensed liquid films, for stabilising water-in-oil emulsions. This suggestion seems to us to receive some indirect support from the fact that finely divided solids are often very effective water-in-oil emulsion stabilisers. Sherman[1] found that the interfacial films of sorbitan sesquioleate in water-in-oil emulsions were of the viscous type, approaching solid films in appearance; they were formed by a two-stage adsorption process which lasted for many days, the interfacial viscosity rising to a maximum and then falling to a constant value after thirty or forty days. These results suggest that with some water-in-oil emulsifying agents a decay of stabilising action with time may have to be reckoned with. Sherman[2] has also found that the stabilising films in water-in-oil emulsions can have a very marked effect on the flow properties of the emulsions. He examined emulsions having equal phase volume ratios and closely similar particle sizes, in which dilute aqueous glycerine solutions were emulsified into mineral oil with the help of ten non-ionic emulsifying agents: lecithin, sorbitan sesquioleate, mono-oleate, and trioleate, the mono-oleate of a polyethylene glycol of molecular weight 200, diglycol monolaurate, propylene glycol mono-oleate, blown soya oil, glyceryl polyricinoleate, and polyethylene glycol polyricinoleate. He found considerable differences in flow properties, which he attributed to differences in the physical nature

---

* See, for example, the results of Dvoretskaya, *Koll. Zh.*, 1948, **10**, 334 (*Chem. Abs.*, 1949, **43**, 7776), who found that emulsions of water and benzene, kerosene, or transformer oil were of the oil-in-water type when they were made in glass, but of the water-in-oil type when they were made in a dry plastic test-tube.

[1] Sherman, *J. Coll. Sci.*, 1953, **8**, 35.

[2] Sherman, *J. Coll. Sci.*, 1955, **10**, 63.

of the interfacial films formed by the different surface-active agents, especially as regards their globular resistance to deformation when the emulsion was subjected to shearing, and secondly, to differences in the effective volumes of disperse phase, due to differing amounts of precipitation of the agents at the interfaces. These results of Sherman's, quite apart from their intrinsic technological interest, also underline the fact that the properties of an emulsion are very far from being fully defined by the phase volume ratio.

The principal difference between oil-in-water and water-in-oil emulsions on the preparative side is that the emulsifying agent is almost always added to a water-in-oil emulsion by the mayonnaise* technique, *i.e.*, to the continuous phase, there being so far as we are aware no inverse counterpart in practice to the self-emulsifiable oil technique for making oil-in-water emulsions. The reason for this fact is probably simply that the technical advantages of the self-emulsifiable oil—*e.g.*, convenience in transport and in use, rapid diffusion of the surface-active agent to the interface—disappear when the internal phase is aqueous. The nascent soap principle is, however, still important, as shown by the well known use of a fatty acid in the continuous oil phase and calcium or barium hydroxide in the aqueous phase. Similar emulsifying machines are also used, though it is probably generally true to say that less severe mechanical agitation is usual in the preparation of water-in-oil emulsions—this may be due partly to the higher intrinsic viscosity of the continuous (oil) phase in many cases, and partly to the less robust interfacial films in most water-in-oil emulsions.

Albers and Overbeek[1] have recently studied the stability of water-in-oil emulsions, both experimentally and theoretically. The emulsions used were of water in benzene, stabilised with barium, manganese, calcium, zinc, aluminium, nickel, cadmium, strontium, ferric, magnesium, lead, and cupric oleates, calcium didodecylsalicylate, and the magnesium, barium, and zinc salts of a petroleum sulphonate. The stabilities of the emulsions, which ranged from a few hours to several months, were observed at 15% vol./vol. concentrations of disperse phase, and compared with ζ-potential measurements, which were done by electrophoresis on samples diluted with benzene. All the ζ-potentials were found to be positive. The stability of the emulsions did not increase with increasing ζ-potential: there was, in fact, a rough correlation in the opposite sense. This result is in agreement with the view of Schulman and Cockbain (*cf.* p. 254) that the formation of water-in-oil emulsions is favoured by the *absence* of a high ζ-potential, since such a potential will tend to give a more expanded interfacial film. Considerable

---

* Although we are aware that "mayonnaises" are in fact oil-in-water emulsions, the generalised use of "mayonnaise technique" to describe any emulsification process in which the agent is added to the continuous phase, seems to us to be too useful to be abandoned in the present connection.

[1] Albers and Overbeek, *J. Coll. Sci.*, 1959, **14**, 501, 510.

further light is thrown on this point by Albers and Overbeek's chemical analyses of the material actually adsorbed in the interfacial films in these emulsions, which show considerable changes in composition from the original agents, and suggest that the more efficient water-in-oil emulsifying agents undergo considerable hydrolysis in the interface. This leads to the picture that cupric, magnesium, and ferric oleates, for example, all three of which are among the best of the water-in-oil emulsifying agents studied by Albers and Overbeek, are present in the interface as insoluble basic metal oleate complexes (*e.g.*, Mg—Ol—OH or $CuOlHCO_3 \cdot CuCO_3$) the formation of these complexes being accompanied by decreases in the potential.

Albers and Overbeek also consider the question of why the considerable ζ-potentials (100 mv. and greater) in many of these emulsions are unable to stabilise them, although previous theoretical work had suggested that they would be ample. They point out that the ionic double layers in feebly ionising media such as benzene will be much thicker than in water (several microns, instead of 10^{-3} to 10^{-2} microns). Such a diffuse layer can prevent the adhesion of two particles *considered in isolation*, but Albers and Overbeek show that it would be expected to fail in more concentrated emulsions. In these more concentrated emulsions, the multiple inter-particle interactions lower the effective energy barrier to such an extent that flocculation will occur, and the effect of gravity is also shown to be capable of overcoming the stabilising electrical energy barriers. Albers and Overbeek's theoretical treatment is admittedly only approximate, but it gives a decisive qualitative or semi-quantitative answer, and it seems to us that it will prove to be of considerable value to workers investigating the fundamental properties of non-aqueous disperse systems, especially at the concentrations which are usually encountered in technology.

Emulsifying agents are usually classified into those which favour the formation or stabilisation of oil-in-water emulsions (for example, the alkali metal, ammonium, or hydroxyalkylamine salts of fatty acids, alkyl sulphates or alkane sulphonates with long paraffin chains, and alkylated aromatic sulphonates), and those which preferentially stabilise water-in-oil emulsions (for example, multivalent metal salts of fatty acids, lanoline, oxidised vegetable oils, water-insoluble cellulose ethers). For practical purposes it is important to note that emulsifying agents will often stabilise *either* type, depending on such factors as the phase volume ratio and the method of mixing. This happens most frequently with materials such as glue or gelatine, or with finely divided solids such as bentonite, carbon black, or silica, but it is not unknown with simpler amphipathic molecules. The question of which type (or types) of emulsion will be stabilised by a given surface-active agent is a complex one, which is discussed in Clayton and Sumner's book (see especially Chapters 6 and 7). It is relevant here to recall the general rule to which we have referred in Chapter 4, p. 181, *viz.*, that the continuous phase will tend to be that one in which the individual surface-active units of the emulsifying agent (molecules, colloidal micelles, or solid particles of microscopic dimensions) are preferentially, but not exclusively, soluble or wettable. It may happen, however, that the lateral cohesive forces between the units which make up an interfacial film (*e.g.*, protein molecules) are so powerful that we can no longer consider the individual molecules or micelles, but must treat the entire interfacial film around each droplet as a single unit. The likelihood of the agent showing a pronounced preference for one type of emulsion will in such an event be greatly reduced, if not eliminated. It seems to us that this concept receives support from the well-known observation that interfacial films in emulsion systems can be so stable that they survive the rupture—for example by severe mechanical treatments—of the droplets in an emulsion, and can afterwards be observed as very fine "foils."

There are of course two other possible explanations for the fact that an emulsifying agent will sometimes stabilise either type of emulsion. If the emulsion stabiliser is a finely divided solid, then that liquid in which the contact angle is smaller, at the line at which the two liquids and the solid phase meet, will be the continuous phase. The existence of a hysteresis factor in the contact angle, however, means that the contact angle of the liquid with which the solid first comes in contact will be decreased, owing to the fact that it is under those conditions a *receding* contact angle. Consequently it is quite feasible for this hysteresis factor to determine on which side of 90° the contact angle shall lie, and for the type of emulsion which is stabilised to depend on which liquid first wets the solid. The second explanation, which is widely accepted, is that a given emulsifying agent may contain more than one effective emulsifier, and that the emulsifiers present tend to stabilise opposite types of emulsions. This explanation is of course more likely to be valid with agents such as glue, or colloidal clays such as bentonite, than it is with simpler amphipathic molecules. It will be appreciated that none of the three possibilities discussed necessarily excludes the others in particular cases.

Two fairly recent approaches to the problem of why so many emulsifying agents tend to give emulsions of one particular type would appear to us to show considerable promise. Sumner[1] has suggested that the type of emulsion is determined by the relative permeability of the interfacial film to the two liquids, the liquid (1) to which the film is more permeable becoming the continuous phase. On this picture, if two droplets of liquid (1) approach close to each other, then (1) is capable of diffusing across the two-phase boundaries, establishing contact between the two droplets and leading to their coalescence.

This idea that emulsion type is determined by the relative rates of coalescence of the two different types of droplets, oil-in-water and

[1] Sumner, *J. Applied Chem.*, 1957, **7**, 504.

water-in-oil, has been developed in an important paper by Davies.[1] He gives a quantitative kinetic treatment, according to which an oil-in-water emulsion will be formed if $Rate_2/Rate_1 \gg 1$, and a water-in-oil emulsion if $Rate_2/Rate_1 \ll 1$, where $Rate_2$ is the rate of coagulation of the water-in-oil emulsion, and $Rate_1$ is the rate of coagulation of the other type. The ratio of these two rates is, in fact, given by

$$Rate_2/Rate_1 = \frac{A_2}{A_1} \exp \frac{0.24\,\psi_0^2 + \theta\Sigma E_h - 600\,n\theta}{RT} \tag{1}$$

where A_2 and A_1 are hydrodynamic collision factors of the water-in-oil and oil-in-water types, respectively (which includes the volume of disperse phase and the viscosity of the continuous phase), ψ_0 is the electrical potential at the interface, θ is the fraction of the interface occupied by the interfacial film, ΣE_h is the total energy barrier due to the water of hydration at the interface, and n is the number of $-CH_2-$ groups in the hydrocarbon chain of the emulsifier (which is assumed to be a straight-chain amphipathic molecule). It will be apparent that the first two terms in the numerator of the exponential term measure the tendency towards an oil-in-water emulsion, while the third term in the numerator gives the tendency towards the water-in-oil type, and that the effect of the phase volume ratio is included in A_2/A_1.

Davies also relates his treatment to the concept of the hydrophilic: lipophilic balance (HLB), developed by Griffin,[2] according to which each paraffin chain surface-active compound is characterised by the quantity

$HLB = \Sigma$(hydrophilic group numbers)

$$- n\text{(group number per } CH_2 \text{ group)} + 7$$

the "group numbers" being measures of the hydrophilic or oleophilic power of the groups. Davies combines this expression with (1) to obtain (for the case that $A_1 = A_2$, *i.e.* that the viscosities and phase volumes of the oil and aqueous phases are equal)

$$\ln (Rate_2/Rate_1) = 2.2\theta(HLB - 7) \tag{2}$$

the hydrophilic group number for a single hydrated group being given by $E_h/1260$, and for a charged group by $1.9 \times 10^{-4} \cdot \psi_0^2/\theta$.

Davies's treatment indicates that the hitherto empirical "HLB" concept has a theoretical basis, and clarifies a number of interesting practical points. Thus equation (2) predicts that neither type of emulsion is favoured if either $HLB = 7$, or θ is very small, and the effect of hexadecyl alcohol in

---

[1] Davies, *Second Congress*, 1957, **I**, 426.

[2] Griffin, *J. Soc. Cosmetic Chem.*, 1949, **1**, 311; 1954, **5**, 4; "Emulsions," in Kirk and Othmer's *Encyclopedia of Chemical Technology*, Interscience, 1950, **5**, 692.

increasing the stability of emulsions made with sodium hexadecyl sulphate (Schulman and Cockbain) is interpreted in terms of an increase in E_h and θ in equation (1). It will be very interesting to see the results of applying Davies's treatment to still further emulsion systems.

Several examples are quoted by Clayton and Sumner of the formation of *multiple emulsions*, in which the droplets of the discontinuous phase are themselves small continuous phases, containing still smaller emulsified droplets: this can be repeated, if not *ad infinitum*, at least five times. An illustration of how multiple emulsions of the water-in-oil-in-water type have been made for a particular technical purpose, is afforded by a British patent issued to I.C.I.[1] This specification, which is concerned with emulsions containing dispersed pigments and synthetic resin binders for colouring textiles, claims that the water-in-oil-in-water type of emulsion combines some of the advantages of each of the two simpler types. The general principle used for obtaining the multiple emulsions, as explained on p. 4 of the Complete Specification, is to make a water-in-oil emulsion first, and then to emulsify it in water, avoiding the use in the same emulsion of emulsifying agents which show marked preferences for emulsions of opposite types. Thus "if a water-in-oil-inducing emulsifying agent is used in making the original two-phase water-in-oil emulsions, then an emulsion stabiliser is used in its conversion to the three-phase emulsion; if an oil-in-water-inducing emulsifying agent is to be used in the final step in making the three-phase emulsion, then an emulsion stabiliser is used in making the original two-phase water-in-oil emulsion; alternatively, emulsion stabilisers may be used in the manufacture of both the two-phase and the three-phase emulsions." The specification defines "emulsion stabilisers" as substances (*e.g.*, glue, gelatine, casein, polyvinyl alcohol, or water-soluble cellulose ethers) which "do not tend to induce the formation of either kind of emulsion but rather to stabilise emulsions of both kinds."

D. Demulsification

The destruction of emulsion systems, of which the most important industrial example is the breaking of crude petroleum emulsions, is discussed *inter alia* by Berkman and Egloff and by Clayton and Sumner, both books giving an exhaustive bibliography. As these and other writers have pointed out, there are many possible ways of breaking emulsions, including special mechanical treatments, heat treatments, electrical deposition, freezing, exposure to supersonic vibrations, filtration through a filter medium which is preferentially wetted by the discontinuous phase of the emulsion, and the addition of surface-active agents or other special chemicals. We propose to confine the present discussion to a very brief summary of the ways in

---

[1] I.C.I., Dawson, Douglas, and Moilliet, B.P. 555,289.

which surface-active agents may break emulsions. Although the behaviour of different emulsion systems is highly specific, so that it is quite impossible to give universally applicable demulsification recipes, it is nevertheless possible to outline a coherent general picture.

It has been appreciated for some time that a surface-active agent (or other specially added chemical, especially one which forms or destroys a surface-active compound in the emulsion) may break an emulsion through one or more of the following mechanisms :[1]

(a) by flocculating the emulsion to such an extent that coalescence of the droplets is no longer prevented by the interfacial film;

(b) by removing the emulsifying agent from the interface, either by precipitation or decomposition, or by rendering it highly soluble in, or completely wetted by, one of the liquid phases;

(c) by tending to form an emulsion of the opposite type (oil-in-water or water-in-oil) to that already present.

Flocculation is most often used for breaking oil-in-water emulsions, especially flocculation by electrolytes. Thus the addition of acids or of calcium, magnesium, or aluminium salts to negatively-charged emulsions (stabilised by soaps, sulphonated oils, or long-chain alkyl sulphates) is very well known. Surface-active agents containing surface-active ions, of opposite charge to those which stabilise the emulsion, can also be used in the same way; in all these cases the purely flocculating effect is likely to be accompanied by precipitation of the emulsifying agent. It is worth noting that the methods which will reversibly flocculate solid dispersions, by precipitating the surface-active agent present in an insoluble form (*e.g.*, the acidification of dispersions containing mixtures of glue and anionic surface active agent—*cf.* Chapter 4, p. 176) will usually break an emulsion irreversibly, owing to the fact that the insolubilised interfacial films are unable to prevent coalescence of the liquid droplets.

Displacement of an emulsifying agent into either phase of an emulsion is a quite general demulsification mechanism, though it can be complicated in practice. Thus we have seen that the emulsifying power of finely divided solids is due to the fact that a finite contact angle is formed, as the result of the composition and history of the system, at the line at which the two liquid phases meet the solid, the contact angle preferably not departing too far from 90°, and the liquid in which the contact angle is acute being usually the continuous phase. If now a surface-active agent is added which causes the solid to become markedly more wetted by either of the liquids, the stability of the emulsion may be so reduced that it will break: if complete transfer of the solid into one phase is achieved, the collapse may be extremely rapid. The same general mechanism of displacement from the interface can also operate in the destruction of emulsions which are

---

[1] See especially Berkman and Egloff, *loc. cit.*, p. 270.

stabilised by *soluble* emulsifying agents. Thus it is well known that an emulsion which is stabilised by a soap can usually be broken by adding acid or a calcium or magnesium salt. If the calcium or magnesium soap which is formed is sufficiently soluble in the oil phase, its removal into the oil may contribute to the demulsification. This effect is probably more important when acid is added than when a divalent metal salt is used, since the possibility of the free fatty acid being surface-active is less than that of the alkaline earth soap.

Perhaps the best known method for destroying emulsions is the use of the antagonistic effect between emulsifying agents which tend to give emulsions of opposite types.[1] This method is based on the fact that, as an emulsion is inverted from one type to the opposite, the stability passes through a minimum at the phase-inversion point. This principle will be particularly effective if the emulsion to be broken is stabilised by an agent which exhibits a very marked preference for that particular type of emulsion, the stability in such a case at the phase-inversion point being usually negligibly small.

Blair[2] has drawn attention to a fourth possible mechanism by which surface-active materials can break water-in-oil emulsions, *viz.*, by displacing thick and mechanically stable interfacial films by films of smaller molecules which have a higher spreading pressure but are less effective interface stabilisers. The emulsions in question are relatively coarse water-in-crude petroleum systems, with disperse droplets 10 to 100 microns in diameter, but they are very stable. This stability is not attributed to a monomolecular interfacial layer, but to the presence of very thick layers of colloidal materials (possibly from the resin and asphaltene fraction in the oil, possibly porphyrins or porphyrin-like substances) which stabilise the emulsions mechanically. The interfacial tensions in these emulsions are surprisingly high, typical values lying between 20 and 33 dynes/cm. The emulsifying agents are quite distinct from the finely divided solids which can also contribute to the stability of petroleum emulsions, since the former are not eliminated by filtration. The action of demulsifiers (for example, the product prepared by acylating a mixture of one mole each of the mono- and diglycerides of ricinoleic acid with three moles of phthalic anhydride[3]) is attributed by Blair and his co-workers in the Petrolite Corporation to the greater spreading pressure of the demulsifier at the oil-water interface. As a result, the stabiliser is displaced from the interface, and although the system is now thermodynamically less unstable, the *steric* stabilising mechanism has been destroyed, and coalescence can occur. This picture is in

---

[1] *Cf.* Berkman and Egloff, *loc. cit.*, pp. 219 ff.

[2] Blair, Lecture to Surface Activity Group of the Society of Chemical Industry, London, on 12th October, 1959; published in *Chemistry and Industry*, May 14, 1960, p. 538.

[3] Tretolite Co. and Roberts, U.S.P. 1,977,146.

good agreement with the results of estimates of the "spreading force" (*i.e.*, the surface pressure at the oil-water interface), and with force-area curves at both the air-water and the oil-water interfaces of the typical demulsifier mentioned above and of other similar agents. The force-area curves suggest that the demulsifiers give highly expanded interfacial films, which are probably only about 10 to 20 Å. thick. It was also possible to observe visually the displacement of the stabilising films by the demulsifier, since the stabilising film is made visible by the presence of finely divided adventitious solid matter in the interface (reminiscent of the lycopodium powder of classical surface chemistry!). As Dr. Blair pointed out in the discussion after his lecture, the alternative hypothesis that the emulsion stabiliser is removed from the interface by a solubilisation mechanism (*i.e.*, formation of a complex with the demulsifier) appears to be unlikely, if only because of the very large excess of stabiliser over the amount of demulsifier which is capable of breaking the emulsion.

Blair is of the opinion that the ability of a demulsifier to spread strongly at the oil-water interface in question, yielding a film of the expanded type, is a necessary, but not a sufficient condition for demulsification to occur. Where such an agent fails to demulsify, other factors are evidently operative, and Blair suggests that at least part of the answer may lie in the *dynamics* of the process, *i.e.*, in failure for displacement of the emulsifier by a demulsifier of higher spreading pressure to take place within the available time.

This approach to elucidating the action of demulsifying agents seems likely to be a fruitful one, and can probably be usefully applied to explaining results such as those of Pincus, Ockert, and Kinney[1] on the breaking of water-tar emulsions, which are formed during the manufacture of water gas, with a number of surface-active agents. A more specific case where it seems to us that the theory of Blair and co-workers should be applicable is in the use of cetyltrimethylammonium bromide for breaking the *oil-in-water* emulsions which are formed during the extraction of penicillin from an acid culture medium, as described by Hastings[2]. The medium will contain various proteins (including, in many cases, difficulty soluble proteins from Indian corn, such as zein), and these materials could be expected to stabilise the emulsion. Owing to the acid pH of the medium (*e.g.*, phosphoric acid may be added to a pH value of 2·1), it is necessary to add a surface-active agent which is not precipitated by the proteins, and a cationic agent meets this requirement. A compound like cetyltrimethylammonium bromide would be expected to give a much more expanded film than the stabilisers, and thus fits in with Blair's picture. It is of course possible that finely divided solids also contribute to the emulsification, and that the cationic agent wets them into the aqueous phase.

---

[1] Pincus, Ockert, and Kinney, *Ind. Eng. Chem.*, 1951, **43**, 521.
[2] Distillers Co. and Hastings, B.P. 610,649.

It will of course be evident that, in many cases of demulsification by surface-active agents, several of these mechanisms may operate simultaneously. If for example we gradually add a water-soluble surface-active agent such as sodium oleyl sulphate to the familiar emulsions of water in medicinal paraffin, stabilised with a calcium or magnesium soap, an unstable region is encountered in which the emulsion breaks. The explanation most often advanced is that there is an antagonistic effect between the calcium or magnesium soap and the sodium oleyl sulphate, which strongly favour the formation of water-in-oil and oil-in-water emulsions, respectively. It seems to us to be implicitly assumed in this explanation that both types of surface-active agent are present together in the interface as independent species, which may not be true. The possibility cannot be excluded, moreover, that displacement of the calcium or magnesium soap from the interface by solubilisation into the aqueous phase is also contributing to the demulsification, since sodium oleyl sulphate is known to have "lime-soap-dispersing" properties (*cf.* Chapter 8, p. 302). To take a converse case, it is well known that sufficiently high concentrations of calcium, magnesium, and aluminium salts will break emulsions of the oil-in-water type which are stabilised by water-soluble alkyl sulphates. Precipitation of the emulsifying agent by the multivalent metal salt is an obvious explanation, but it is inadequate if the emulsion starts to break before the limit of solubility of the aluminium cetyl sulphate, for example, is reached. (It will be recalled that the multivalent metal salts of the alkyl sulphates are considerably more soluble in water than are the corresponding multivalent metal soaps.) In such a case it seems likely that a further contributory factor to the breaking of the emulsion will be flocculation of the emulsion droplets, and perhaps also the antagonistic effect between the sodium salts and the multivalent metal salts of the surface-active agent.

CHAPTER 7

THE DISPERSION OF SOLIDS IN LIQUID MEDIA

A. Introduction

PROCESSES for the preparation of dispersions of solids in liquid media are of considerable importance to the users of materials such as vat dyestuffs, pigments, insoluble chemicals for the compounding of rubber latex, and insoluble fungicides, pesticides, and medicinals (to give only a few examples), which are applied in media in which they are insoluble. The successful carrying out of a process for dispersing such solids requires that suitable conditions of wetting, deflocculation, etc., should exist at the interfaces between the solid particles and the liquid medium. These conditions can sometimes be fulfilled by a suitable choice of the liquid medium or of the solid to be dispersed, and many dispersion processes have been devised on this basis. Some of these processes, such as the preparation of oil or tempera paints, for example, are of very great antiquity. In many cases, however, it has been found necessary to make special additions in order to disperse solids in liquid media, and the use of gums, soluble proteins, and other natural surface-active materials is well known in classical colloid science, as well as in more traditional fields such as the apothecary's art. The advent in more recent times of large numbers of new chemical compounds which required dispersion in particular media, which coincided with the appearance of synthetic surface-active agents and of improved mechanical contrivances, has led to an immense development in the technique of preparing dispersions, especially in aqueous media. It is probably true to say that the present-day dispersion technologist is nearly always presented with problems in which the nature of both the substance to be dispersed and the dispersion medium are already fixed, and he is expected to achieve the required result by a suitable choice of mechanical procedure and of a surface-active agent, the latter sometimes having been specially synthesised for the purpose.* This does not imply, of course, that he will necessarily use only synthetic surface-active agents—the continued popularity of materials such as glue and dextrine in aqueous media, sometimes in admixture with synthetic surface-active agents, or of "bodied" linseed oil

---

* One of the main achievements of classical colloid science was to establish that the colloidal state is not simply an inherent property of certain materials, but that any solid can be obtained in that state if it is sufficiently finely dispersed in a medium in which it is insoluble. It would be unsafe to conclude that a realisation of this principle was essential for the development of present-day industrial dispersion technology, though it is interesting to speculate on how far the inventor(s) of D.R.P. 222,191, for example, which was filed on 5th March, 1909, and which is discussed in greater detail below, were directly influenced by contemporary developments in "pure" colloid science.

in oily media, is noticeable even in fairly recent patent literature—but there is no doubt that the advent of the synthetic products has brought about a revolutionary improvement in dispersion technique. In certain respects the techniques used in industry are far in advance of those described in textbooks of colloid chemistry, a fact which we shall attempt to make clear in the following sections.

Although technical dispersions are prepared by the same general methods as are the sols of pure colloid chemistry, *viz.*, controlled precipitation ("condensation"), and mechanical disintegration, it is necessary to note certain important differences. In general the technical dispersion must be obtained at much higher concentrations of the dispersed substance, but at lower ratios of surface-active agents to dispersed material, the dispersion must be more stable, and the technique used must be economically feasible; on the other hand it is not always necessary to obtain a dispersion of sub-microscopical fineness (one, for example, in which the particles are all smaller than 0·2 μ), particle sizes up to 10 μ or more being frequently quite permissible in industry. The economic criterion just mentioned means that the most effective (and scientifically the most interesting) dispersion techniques have tended on the whole to be developed for dispersing relatively expensive substances. Partly for this reason, and partly on account of the authors' own background, most of the processes described below are taken from the literature of the dyestuffs and related fine chemicals industries. It will, we hope, be appreciated that they are intended only as examples of general methods, a comprehensive collection of published dispersion recipes being quite out of the question in the present book.

B. Mechanical methods for preparing dispersions

Mechanical methods for dispersing solids directly in liquid media involve one or both of two general principles, in which (a) the solid particles in the liquid medium are broken up (crushed, sheared, or rubbed) between two external surfaces, or (b) disruption occurs in the liquid as the result of mutual attrition between the particles themselves. In either case the present of a surface-active agent may help by reducing the breaking strain of the individual particles, and/or by preventing re-aggregation (*cf.* Chapter 4, p. 179 ff). Dispersions in liquid media can also be obtained indirectly by mechanical means, *e.g.*, by a preliminary fine grinding in air, by grinding the solid in one liquid and then transferring it by preferential wetting to another liquid medium ("flushing"), or by grinding the solid with a second solid which can then be dissolved away: surface-active agents are frequently used in these indirect processes in order to ensure adequate wetting and deflocculation in the eventual dispersion medium. At least one of these general methods, direct or indirect, is involved in each of the following techniques.

1. BALL-MILLING

Perhaps the simplest of all mechanical dispersion contrivances is the ball mill, which usually consists of a cylindrical vessel, revolving about a horizontal axis. The "comminutor" (porcelain or metal balls, pebbles, etc.) should fill approximately half the volume of the mill,[1] and the dispersion charge (*i.e.*, the mixture of liquid medium, solid to be dispersed, and surface-active agent) should slightly more than fill the interstices between the comminutor particles. The angular velocity at which the mill is rotated should be such that the comminutor and charge can cascade, but preferably not so great that the balls are carried up and fall freely on the charge below. (At still greater angular velocities—above the so-called "critical speed"— the balls and charge will be carried around the periphery of the mill without either falling or cascading, and substantially no milling at all will take place.) The importance of obtaining a cascading effect, which is due to the fact that wet ball-milling processes require a rubbing rather than a crushing action for the production of fine particles, has been pointed out by Klein-feldt,[1] and more explicitly by Bergl and Reitstötter.[2] It is worth noting that the action required for efficient dry ball-milling appears to be rather different.

The mechanical efficiency of a "classical" ball or pebble mill which depends on a cascading effect is determined by three principal factors: the size of the balls or pebbles, the viscosity (usually not a "Newtonian" viscosity) of the paste being milled, and the difference in density between the balls or pebbles and the paste. Other things being equal, the milling effect is generally greater the smaller the balls or pebbles, the greater the viscosity (provided that this is not achieved by partial flocculation of the paste), and the greater the difference in density between balls and paste. In practice, however, the improvements which can be effected by varying these factors are severely limited. As the size of the balls or pebbles is decreased, and the viscosity of the paste is increased, a limit is soon reached at which cascading ceases. The use of balls of higher density (*e.g.*, of iron or steel) is common practice in preparing dispersions in non-aqueous media, such as paints and varnishes, but iron and ordinary steel cannot be used with aqueous dispersions because of rusting, and non-corroding metals such as stainless steel may be too expensive in many processes. Mills are therefore made in which free cascading is replaced by vibratory or shaking motions, so that more nearly optimal conditions can be used; it is also claimed that these mills frequently give more efficient milling in cases in which cascading would be feasible.

The general principle of milling by attrition between comminutor

---

[1] *Cf.* Kleinfeldt, *Chem. Met. Engineering*, 1923, **29,** 436, and Rogers, *Ind. Eng. Chem.*, 1927, **19,** 139.

[2] Bergl and Reitstötter, *Koll. Z.*, 1928, **46,** 53.

particles is also used in devices in which a positive agitation is imparted to the mill contents. Thus the Anode Rubber Company[1] feed the paste which is to be dispersed into a vessel containing a charge of small, hard particles (*e.g.*, quartz or flint pebbles), which are stirred with a paddle. Such a device is marketed as the Szegvari "Attritor."[2] "Dispersing agents" (non exemplified) may be present. Similarly, British Dyestuffs Corporation, Hailwood, and Shepherson[3] dispersed a number of insoluble solids (*e.g.*, indanthrone, indigo, and the insoluble acetate silk dyestuff 1-amino-2-methylanthraquinone) by simply stirring them in the form of a thick paste with a comminutor, such as sand or a finely-divided metal, which was harder than the material to be dispersed. The use of deflocculating agents (*e.g.*, lignin sulphonic acid derivatives for aqueous media) was also recommended; separation of the comminutor was effected by dissolving it or by differential sedimentation. More recently, mills of this type have been described in which the mixture of comminutor (sand) and dispersion are agitated in a cylindrical vessel by means of rotating discs,[4] or of spoked annular rings.[5] With such an arrangement, the charge is not churned up, and the paste to be milled is fed continuously into one end of the cylindrical vessel and withdrawn at the other. It has also been proposed to use a soluble comminutor such as borax,[6] which can be separated from the paste by dilution as well as by sedimentation. The advisability of "sand-milling" at high concentrations has been emphasised by Howell,[7] who recommends proportions such as 675 parts of water, 125 parts of deflocculating agent (sodium salt of a naphthalene sulphonic acid-formaldehyde condensate), 417 parts of phthalocyanine pigment, and 2,080 parts of fine sand, the mixture being milled in a cylindrical vessel as recommended by Hochberg.

It seems to be generally agreed that, for efficient milling in the normal type of ball mill, the solid : liquid ratio of the charge should be as high as possible, provided always that the charge is not so viscous as to interfere seriously with cascading. This frequently provides a further reason—in addition to the need for preventing re-aggregation and lowering of the breaking strain of the particles—for deflocculating the charge as completely as possible by the addition of a surface-active agent. The deflocculating agent must however satisfy other conditions, among the most important being that it shall not form a stable froth or foam which will make discharging of the mill unduly difficult. This requirement is probably one reason for the widespread use of the lignin sulphonic acids and of the

---

[1] Anode Rubber Co., Klein, and Szegvari, B.P. 293,071.
[2] *Paint Manufacture*, 1959, p. 57. (No author given.)
[3] British Dyestuffs Corporation, Hailwood, and Shepherdson, B.P. 293,896 = U.S.P. 1,837,772.
[4] Du Pont and Hochberg, U.S.P. 2,581,414 = B.P. 686,234.
[5] Du Pont, Hochberg, and Bosse, B.P. 810,005.
[6] Du Pont, Ehrich, and Stratton, U.S.P. 2,816,114.
[7] Du Pont and Howell, U.S.P. 2,816,115.

aromatic sulphonic acid-formaldehyde condensates,[1] neither type being characterised by a particularly high surface-activity at the water-air interface. It is unsafe, however, to generalise too broadly about the suitability of surface-active agents for wet ball-milling processes, the most effective agents frequently being specific to the particular system involved.

2. "COLLOID"-MILLING

The so-called "colloid mills" of Plauson and others have been fully discussed in the scientific, technical, and patent literature.[2] Although many of these mills are exceedingly useful, especially for breaking down aggregates of solid particles (their use for making emulsions, for which they are frequently of outstanding value, is discussed in Chapter 6), it seems to us that Chwala[3] and Travis[4] are quite correct in maintaining that the name "colloid mill" is a misnomer, since dispersions of colloidal fineness are not obtained. The term is however well established by usage to describe mills in which relatively thin layers of a fluid dispersion are sheared between two surfaces, at least one of which is moving with a highly angular velocity. In a common embodiment of this principle, a circular plate (say 6 in. to 18 in. in diameter) is rotated at speeds up to several thousand revolutions per minute, at a distance of a few thousandths of an inch from a similar but stationary disc. The suspension is fed into the clearance near the axis of rotation, and is carried outwards between the discs by the centrifugal pressure set up. In other mills of this general type, the suspension may be ground between a rotating cone and a closely fitting, tapered annulus. A useful survey of available mills is given in Clayton and Sumner's book.

Surface-active agents fulfil much the same functions in colloid-milling as in ball-milling processes, and the two methods are frequently mentioned together in patents on dispersing agents or techniques.

3. PLASTIC-MILLING

Roller mills, in which a dispersion of a solid in a liquid medium is subjected to a shearing action between two or more rollers, or between a single roller and a closely fitting pressure bar, are well known in the paint industry, for example. If the suspension being ground is fluid, then the grinding principle involved is similar to that in the colloid mill, disruption of the solid particles being due to shearing between two external surfaces moving relatively to each other, separated by a very narrow clearance. It is worth noting that there is nearly always a shearing as well as a crushing action in such mills: thus in a multiple-roller mill the rollers which are in

---

[1] See for example Dewey and Almy, B.P., 414,932.

[2] *Cf.* Travis, *Mechanochemistry and the Colloid Mill*, Chemical Catalog Co., 1928, and the comprehensive review by Chwala, *Koll. Z.*, 1930, **52**, 367; 1930, **53**, 137, 267; 1931, **54**, 117, 243, 358; **55**, 122, 251, 371; **56**, 117.

[3] Chwala, *Kollchem. Beih.*, 1930, **31**, 237.

[4] Travis, *loc. cit.*, pp. 149 *ff.*

contact move with different peripheral velocities. If now the consistency of the dispersion is progressively increased, especially if the liquid medium is "tacky," it becomes possible to mill with increasingly greater clearances. In the limiting case of a stiff, plastic mass, it becomes unnecessary, if not inconvenient or impossible, to use a machine which operates with a narrow clearance. The milling is now most effectively done in a kneading machine, the solid particles being broken down by a shearing action within the plastic mass itself, *i.e.*, by the process of plastic-milling.

Plastic-milling processes are usually carried out nowadays* in strongly constructed mixers of the Werner-Pfleiderer, Baker-Perkins, Bekens Duplex, or Banbury types, though roller mills are also used.[1] The stiffness of the mass (which is best judged by the power consumption of the mixer) should be as great as possible, and it is frequently advantageous to achieve this by using a viscous or gelatinous liquid medium, as well as by adjusting the ratio of solid to liquid. Thus Cabot[2] recommends the use of a linseed oil jelly for dispersing titanium dioxide in turpentine by plastic-milling, while Calco Chemical Corporation[3] use dextrine in the dispersion of certain pigments and vat dyestuffs in aqueous media by plastic-milling. A further requirement, which is absolutely essential for a successful working of the process, is that the solid particles should be in a highly deflocculated condition, and hence also completely wetted-out, in the liquid medium. A number of surface-active agents have been recommended for this purpose. British Dyestuffs Corporation[4] mention *inter alia* sulphite cellulose lye (lignin sulphonic acids) and naphthalene sulphonic acid-formaldehyde condensation products, as well as gum arabic, rubber, and cellulose acetate, the two last-named substances being, of course, used with non-aqueous media in which they are soluble. It is noteworthy that this patent specification does not specify that the medium itself be highly viscous or gelatinous, even allowing for the presence of the "dispersing agent," but only that a mixture of solid, dispersing agent, and dispersion medium should be worked under conditions "such that at the beginning of the operation there is formed a viscous paste of a consistency which is capable of setting to a

---

* We are indebted to Mr. W. A. Silvester for drawing our attention to the passages in Mitchell's *Inks : Their Composition and Manufacture*, Griffin, London, 1937, pp. 26–37, which indicate that the plastic-milling principle has been used by the Chinese for over 2000 years in the manufacture of so-called Indian ink. The plastic mass, which consists of carbon black, glue, and water, is pounded in a mortar until it becomes "pliable," the state of subdivision obtained being extremely fine.

[1] *Cf.* Einstein's Electro Chemical Process Ltd. and Pigache, B.P. 377, 995; Redd, *Paint, Oil, and Chemical Review*, 1950, **113**, No. 6, 14, 18; Barkman, *ibid.*, 1950, **113**, No. 16, 30, 34, 36, 38. These last two papers give useful practical descriptions of the plastic-milling of paints, enamels, and lacquers, Barkman also reviewing other methods. It should be noted that Redd uses "wetting" to denote what we call deflocculation.

[2] Cabot, B.P. 246,874.

[3] Calco Chemical Corp., Crossley, Kienle, and Royer, B.P. 473,058 and B.P. 474,827.

[4] British Dyestuffs Corporation, F.P. 649,551.

permanent form." Similarly, British Dyestuffs Corporation, Adams, and Shepherdson[1] describe a plastic-milling process in which specially treated lignin sulphonic acids are used. Calco Chemical Corporation[2] also use lignin sulphonic acids and the condensation products of naphthalene sulphonic acids and formaldehyde.

It seems clear that the function of the deflocculating agent in a plastic-milling process may be wider than in either ball-milling or colloid-milling: the agent may not only reduce the breaking strain of the particles and decrease their tendency to re-aggregate, but its presence may also be necessary in order to obtain a plastic mass. The necessity for a high degree of deflocculation is due, we suggest, to two reasons: (a) the mass being worked or kneaded must be coherent rather than crumbly, so that the shear exerted by the mixer blades will be properly transmitted through the plastic mass, and (b) in a deflocculated, plastic mass the solid particles will tend to assume a very close packing, so that any shearing action will result in a considerable amount of mutual attrition and disruption between inter-locking particles in different planes of shear. This effect of a deflocculating agent will of course be complementary to that of a solute which simply increases the viscosity of the interstitial medium, and it may be possible for the same substance to act in both capacities.

Although plastic-milling processes give rise to special problems on the large scale (for example the mixers used must be very robust), it seems to the writers that the method has not received the attention which it deserves in textbooks on the preparation of colloidal solutions. Thus the claim implied in expressions such as "colloidised vat dyes" in B.P. 474,827 can be fully justified if enough of a suitable surface-active agent is present during the milling, and if the mechanical conditions are sufficiently severe; *i.e.*, plastic-milling is capable of producing truly colloidal (submicroscopical) dispersions by what appears to be a purely mechanical method.

4. DRY PULVERISATION

It is frequently sufficient, for technical purposes, simply to incorporate a finely powdered solid into a liquid medium without a special dispersion technique, provided that a highly efficient pulverising machine has been used. In such a case it is necessary, however, to ensure complete wetting (*i.e.*, removal of air) and adequate deflocculation, for which purposes it may be necessary to add one or more deflocculating and wetting agents, either before or after pulverisation. The wetting stage of the dispersion process will usually approximate to the process of capillary penetration discussed in Chapter 5 (p. 231). The chief function of the wetting agent (*e.g.*, an alkylated aromatic sulphonate) will be to reduce the contact angle, especially when we are considering insoluble *organic* compounds, on which

---

[1] British Dyestuffs Corporation, Adams, and Shepherdson, B.P. 301,549, Example 4.
[2] Calco Chemical Corp., Crossley, Kienle, and Royer, *loc. cit.*

the initial contact angle of water can often be seen to be obviously greater than 90°. The deflocculating agents will be similar to those used in ball-milling, colloid-milling, and plastic-milling processes, though again they may be specific to the particular solid or liquid involved. The function of these wetting and deflocculating agents will of course be quite different from that of the so-called "grinding aids" which are extensively used in dry ball-milling processes. One function of the grinding aids, apart from a possible lubricating action, has been shown by Berry and Kamack[1] to be to prevent re-aggregation of the material being ground. They found that a limiting surface area was approached during the dry ball-milling of il-menite, this limiting surface area increasing with increasing additions of naphthenic acid. Although Berry and Kamack do not mention the possibility, it seems to us that, having regard to the work of the Rehbinder school, Röttig, Eichborn, and others (*cf.* Chapter 4, p. 182), there is a strong *prima facie* case for the hypothesis that the grinding aids also help in the primary disruption process, in addition to their other effects.

A dispersion technique which is of particular historical interest in the development of classical colloid science is to grind a dry mixture of the solid to be dispersed with a second solid (usually present in considerable excess) which is soluble in the dispersion medium or can be washed away. Von Weimarn[2] and Pihlblad[3] used this principle for preparing the first truly "colloidal" sols which were obtained by purely mechanical means, the second solid (sugar or urea) being a non-electrolyte and hence having no flocculating action on the sol. Similarly, Neugebauer[4] dispersed a number of solids, including some medicinals, by grinding them with glucose. The more usual industrial practice today is to use a salt or other electrolyte, which is subsequently washed away, the material to be dispersed (for example, a phthalocyanine pigment) being left in a flocculated, readily filtered form.[5] The resulting press-cake can, if desired, then be treated with a deflocculating agent, with or without a paste-milling treatment. Alternatively, a deflocculating agent such as sodium dodecyl sulphate, sulphite cellulose lye, or a sodium benzylsulphanilate, can be added at the dry-milling stage, the purpose presumably being to obtain a more uniform distribution of surface-active agent throughout the dispersed solid.[6] It has also been proposed to add liquid grinding aids during the dry-grinding operation, such as oleic or linoleic acid, or mixtures of polymerised linoleic acid and linseed oil.[7]

---

[1] Berry and Kamack, *Second Congress*, 1957, **IV**, 196.
[2] Von Weimarn, *Koll. Z.*, 1912, **11**, 315.
[3] Pihlblad, *Z. phys. Chem.*, 1913, **81**, 420.
[4] Neugebauer, *Koll. Z.*, 1927, **43**, 65.
[5] I.G., B.P. 457,526 and B.P. 470,079; S.C.I., B.P. 566,325.
[6] S.C.I., B.P. 566,325.
[7] I.C.I., Moilliet, and Todd, B.P. 569,402.

5. INTENSIVE MIXING

Dispersions can sometimes be prepared, with the help of surface-active agents, simply by intensive mixing. In such a case the material to be dispersed is already present in sufficiently small particles, which may be aggregated but certainly are not tightly agglomerated or sintered. Some carbon blacks are in this condition. A careful study of the factors governing the dispersion of carbon black in aqueous medium by intensive mxing has been published by Dannenberg and Seltzer.[1] They showed that complete wetting-out was essential, and determined wetting times in solutions of "Aerosol OT" (sodium dioctylsulphosuccinate). The amount of deflocculating agent ("Marasperse CB," a partially desulphonated lignin sulphonic acid) which was needed depended on the total surface area and on the composition of the carbon black, increasing with the soluble ash content. The results obtained also depended on the mechanical treatment given to the dispersion in a "Waring Blendor" or with a propeller agitator.

C. Dispersion by controlled precipitation ("condensation" method)

The so-called "condensation" method is undoubtedly the most effective of the techniques of classical colloid science for preparing disperse systems, and it is also of considerable importance in modern industrial practice. The essential features of the method arc too well known to require detailed comment here: the substance to be dispersed should be formed (or precipitated) fairly suddenly in a medium in which it is highly insoluble, and a protective colloid should be present if a dispersion of appreciable concentration is to be prepared. The function of the protective colloid, apart from preventing aggregation, is essentially to interfere with deposition of the precipitating substance on the nuclei and other small particles formed, which (*cf.* Chapter 4, p. 191) results in the formation of a large number of very small particles. In view of this mechanism of action, it is not surprising to find that macromolecules generally, and soluble proteins in particular, are very extensively used for this purpose, in industry as well as in fundamental colloid investigations, and that synthetic surface-active agents are less important here than they are in the preparation of dispersions by mechanical methods. A few examples are however worth considering; others will be found in Part III of the present book.

Perhaps the earliest reference to the use of a synthetic surface-active agent in the condensation method for dispersing solids is in D.R.P. 222,191,[2] published in 1910, in which azoic pigments were coupled, or indoxyl was oxidised to indigo, in the presence of lignin sulphonic acids. This technique was later extended by the same patentee to include the dispersion of indigo

---

[1] Dannenberg and Seltzer, *Ind. Eng. Chem.*, 1951, **43**, 1389.
[2] Badische, D.R.P. 222,191.

and other vat dyestuffs by oxidising the leuco compound in the presence of
the same agent,[1] or of a number of other surface-active agents, the most
important being condensation products of naphthalene-2-sulphonic acid
and formaldehyde, cresol sulphonic acid-formaldehyde condensates, and
benzylsulphanilic acid.[2] The actual precipitation procedures given by the
"Badische" in the examples varied considerably: thus the vat dyestuffs
were oxidised by air, and a slow oxidation (*e.g.*, 48 hours) is recommended,
while the azoic couplings represent fairly rapid precipitations. The claims
for concentrations of dispersion attained (*e.g.*, over 6% of indigo in Example
1 of D.R.P. 265,536) and fineness of dispersion are impressive, and the
ratios quoted for surface-active agent to dyestuff being dispersed (*e.g.*,
1 : 2) are not excessively high. It is interesting to note that, although it is
claimed that many of the suspensions will completely pass a filter, the
flocculation by acid of a dispersion of thioindigo containing lignin sulphonic
acids is also described[3]: the precipitate is filtered off and washed with
water until deflocculation begins, when it is worked up into a paste (presumably with more lignin sulphonic acid?). This very instructive series of
patent specifications, which are not easily available, is abstracted quite
fully in Friedländer.[4]

It is probably difficult to over-emphasise the specificity of surface-active
agents to the particular system involved when considering the preparation
of dispersions by controlled precipitation. An illustration of this point,
which may also be of interest as exemplifying dispersion by controlled
precipitation from a mutual solvent (*i.e.*, a solvent for the substance
to be dispersed, which is also miscible in the dispersion medium), is
furnished by B.P. 561,838.[5] Here the biologically active insoluble compound
tetraethylthiuram monosulphide is dispersed in water by first dissolving it
in a water-miscible solvent (*e.g.*, industrial alcohol), to which is added the
condensation product of polyglycerol and a fatty acid; the solution gives
a fine dispersion when it is poured into water. In this case the successful
preparation of the dispersion depends on using a suitable surface-active
agent, the object of the invention being to devise a dispersion technique
which does not require special apparatus.

A mutual solvent which is extensively used in the dispersion of insoluble
dyestuffs and pigments by controlled precipitation is sulphuric acid, though
oleum and chlorosulphonic acid are also used. Perhaps the most striking
(though certainly not the oldest) examples of the value of this procedure
are afforded by the phthalocyanine pigments, which are readily soluble in
cold, concentrated sulphuric acid, but insoluble in water. If for example a

[1] Badische, D.R.P. 265,536.
[2] Badische, D.R.P. 274,970.
[3] Badische, D.R.P. 265,536, Example 3.
[4] Friedländer, *Fortschritte der Teerfarbenfabrikation*, 1913, **10**, 407; 1915, **11**, 323, 325.
[5] I.C.I., Collie, Kay, and Moilliet, B.P. 561,838.

solution of copper phthalocyanine in sulphuric acid is poured into water, with thorough agitation, the pigment is precipitated with great suddenness from a very highly supersaturated solution, so that it is obtained in a very finely divided, as well as relatively pure, form.[1, 2] Owing to the powerful flocculating action of the sulphuric acid, however, the primary particles are heavily flocculated and can therefore be isolated by filtration. Imperial Chemical Industries[3] report further that the state of dispersion can be improved if a deflocculating agent (*e.g.*, a naphthalene sulphonic acid-formaldehyde condensation product, or lignin sulphonic acid or its derivatives) is present in the sulphuric acid and in the water into which the acid solution is drowned. The same authors also recommend a final milling with these agents, for example in a ball mill, after the precipitated pigment has been filtered off and washed free from acid.

The controlled precipitation principle can also be combined with a mechanical disintegration technique. An interesting patent is that of Courtaulds, Tallis, and Field,[4] who obtain a dispersion by carrying out a reaction, which yields an insoluble substance in a liquid medium, in a ball mill. Surface-active agents may also be present. In the example given, diethylene triamine and phenyl isothiocyanate are caused to react in aqueous medium in the presence of "Igepon T" (sodium salt of oleyl-N-methyltaurine), the mixture being ball-milled during and after the reaction.

D. The stabilisation of dispersions in industry

Attention has already been drawn in Chapter 4, Section B, to the fact that many aqueous dispersions obtained in industry are coarse enough for the particles to settle against the action of the Brownian motion, and that clays are formed in such cases if the particles are in a sufficiently highly deflocculated condition. Stewart and Bunbury[5] have pointed out that it is possible to overcome this claying in a concentrated aqueous dispersion, and yet to obtain dilutions which are deflocculated, by using suitable mixtures of deflocculating ("dispersing") agents and ordinary electrolytes such as sodium chloride. This effect depends on the fact that the deflocculating power of a satisfactory surface-active agent increases more rapidly at low concentrations than does the flocculating power of an inorganic electrolyte; consequently a concentrated dyestuff paste, for example, which is heavily flocculated (and therefore stable) may become completely deflocculated when it is simply diluted with water. This behaviour in the presence of electrolytes is obviously an important property of deflocculating agents

[1] Scottish Dyes Limited, Thorpe, Linstead, and Thomas, B.P. 389,842.
[2] I.C.I., Heilbron, Irving, Linstead, and Thorpe, B.P. 410,814.
[3] I.C.I., Davies, Hailwood, and Todd, U.S.P. 2,213,693.
[4] Courtaulds, Tallis, and Field, B.P. 536,687.
[5] Stewart and Bunbury, *Trans. Faraday Soc.*, 1935, **31**, 214.

which are to be used in dispersed aqueous pastes: it is particularly important that the antagonistic* action of a deflocculating agent and an electrolyte should be reversible, and that the former is not thrown irreversibly out of solution by the latter. Thus a dispersion containing a soap or a water-soluble salt of an alkyd resin could be stabilised against the formation of clay by adding aluminium sulphate, but the dispersion would not become spontaneously deflocculated when it was diluted with water.

The most effective means of rendering aqueous dispersions stable is undoubtedly to convert them into dispersible powders, which obviously cannot clay, and which are also free from instability to freezing, evaporation, or shaking received in transport. The simplest method for preparing dispersible powders is to add suitable surface-active agents to as concentrated aqueous pastes as possible, and then to remove the water by evaporation. Thus for example dispersible powders of insoluble dyestuffs for acetate silk have been made by drying down an aqueous paste of the dyestuff in the presence of the condensation product of naphthalene sulphonic acid and formaldehyde,[1] while the use of lignin sulphonic acids for the same purpose has also been disclosed.[2] Special methods of drying may be used: thus Trutzer[3] proposed the use of spray driers in order to remove the dispersion medium with the minimum loss of state of dispersion.

In view of the fact that plastic-millings are carried out in the presence of relatively small amounts of water, it is not surprising to find the method used for making dispersible powders, by drying the stiff mass obtained after kneading, in several of the references already cited. It has also been proposed to prevent aggregation of the particles during the conversion of a dispersed paste to a dispersible powder by converting the surface-active agent present in the paste to a water-insoluble form, and then adding substances to the dry powder which will re-generate a water-soluble agent when the powder is added to water. Thus dispersible powders of the well-known anthelmintic phenothiazine (thiodiphenylamine) have been prepared by drying down a finely divided aqueous paste containing a water soluble salt of a volatile base such as ammonia and an insoluble alkyd (glyceryl phthalate) resin of sufficiently high acid value (at least 50 mg. KOH/gm.). The resulting powder is not wetted by water, but it becomes wettable and dispersible if a basic substance such as sodium carbonate is mixed with it: other surface-active agents, for example sodium oleyl-*p*-anisidide-2-sulphonate, can also be added in the dry form in order to help the ultimate

---

* This antagonism is probably analogous to the well-known phenomenon of "ionic antagonism" in inorganic sols, in which the flocculating power of a cationic species, for example, is reduced by the presence of a multivalent anion.

[1] British Dyestuffs Corporation, Baddiley, Shepherdson, Swann, Hill, and Lawrie, B.P. 224,077.

[2] S.C.I., B.P. 300,299.

[3] Trutzer, D.R.P. 422,803.

dispersion into water. It is claimed that dispersible powders containing as much as 95% of phenothiazine can be made by this method.[1]

E. Preparation of dispersions in non-aqueous media

The preceding sections have been principally concerned with the preparation of dispersions of solids in aqueous media. When we come to consider dispersions in non-aqueous media, certain differences arise which require comment. In the first place suitable surface-active agents for use in non-aqueous media are even more highly specific to the systems involved, and there do not appear to be any agents of comparable ubiquity to that of the lignin sulphonic acids or the naphthalene sulphonic acid-formaldehyde condensates, for example, in aqueous media. Secondly, many non-aqueous dispersion media, such as paint vehicles or rubber, have such powerful deflocculating properties in themselves (presumably due to surface-active materials already present), that the addition of a special surface-active ingredient is often unnecessary.

The high degree of specificity of deflocculating agents for pigments in oil media means that the worker in this field must rely to a very large extent on empirical sorting tests when seeking a "dispersing agent" for a particular system. A number of useful summaries and proposals have nevertheless been published.[2]

The usefulness of these summaries of *ad hoc* information is considerably increased if they are read against the background of several more fundamental papers. Bowman and Hughes[3] have drawn a clear distinction between wetting-out and deflocculation, and point to the importance of steric effects (*cf.* Chapter 4, p. 168) in the stabilisation of dispersions in non-aqueous media, especially by dissolved macromolecules. They do not think that electrokinetic potentials generally play much part in stabilising these systems, but suggest that dipole potentials are important. (The use of the word "potentials" in this connection is perhaps unfortunate, and may have been one reason for the criticism of this paper in the subsequent discussion. Their suggestion that dispersion stability is enhanced by interactions between adsorbed dipoles seems reasonable, but the suggestion that electrophoresis is due to dipole potentials seems questionable.) Another valuable paper is Zettlemoyer's[4] extensive survey of information on the pigment-vehicle interface, which also defines and clarifies many

---

[1] I.C.I., Collie, and Moilliet, B.P. 550,930.

[2] See the papers by Jarrett, *J. Oil and Colour Chemists' Assn.*, 1948, **31**, 261; Gardner, *American Paint Journal*, 1951, **35**, No. 32, 73, 76, 80; No. 33, 76, 78, 80, 82, 84; Degussa and Weihe, D.R.P. 907,130; Bingham, *Official Digest of the Federation of Paint and Varnish Production Clubs*, 1956, **28**, 418; Bass, *Paint Manufacture*, 1957, **27**, 5.

[3] Bowman and Hughes, *J. Oil and Colour Chemists' Assn.*, 1951, **34**, 412.

[4] Zettlemoyer, *Official Digest of the Federation of Paint and Varnish Production Clubs*, 1957, **29**, 1238.

practical problems in this field. The explanation of the flocculating action of water in many non-aqueous dispersions is particularly interesting. Finally, Dintenfass's[1] paper on the adsorption of surface-active compounds from toluene solutions on to a range of inorganic pigments is worth special study. The adsorbability of the agents was found to be a function of their polar groups and not of their hydrocarbon residues, the agents being classifiable into a number of types based on the nature of the polar group : carboxylic acids, hydroxy compounds (both aliphatic and phenolic), primary amines, metal soaps (calcium, magnesium, barium, etc.), and secondary amines. Agents from different classes were found to be adsorbed independently of each other, while agents from the same class were competitively adsorbed; this led to the hypothesis that the surfaces of the pigments were in each case heterogeneous, different sites being available to different types of surface-active molecules.

One field of application of synthetic surface-active agents in non-aqueous media which is worth special discussion is the improvement of the ease of dispersion in such media of solids (*e.g.*, synthetic pigments) which have been synthesised or isolated in an aqueous medium. It is a very well known fact that, if an aqueous paste is simply dried down, the resulting powder may be difficult to disperse in an "oil" (*e.g.*, a paint vehicle), and that this difficulty may be due as much to an irreversible aggregation among the particles, giving what is called a bad "texture," as to the absence of adequate wetting and deflocculation in the oil. Surface-active agents find application in two ways in this problem : firstly, in obtaining powders of improved texture and dispersibility in "oils" of various kinds, and secondly, in promoting the direct transfer (without an intermediate drying) of the particles from an aqueous to a non-aqueous medium in the so-called "flushing" process. Both types of application are based on treating the solid particles, while they are still suspended in the aqueous medium, with a surface-active agent (or combination of agents) which will render the surfaces of the particles "hydrophobic" and "oleophilic."

The fact that dry particles which have become covered with an oil-attracting adsorbed film will wet and deflocculate more readily in many oil media needs no elaboration. The way in which such a surface modification may improve the texture of a powder is perhaps not so self-evident, apparently involving two mechanisms, *i.e.*, flocculation (in the water), and surface dehydration. The fact that the treated solid particles are water-repellent means that they will be heavily flocculated in water, and hence that they will adhere to each other to form a bulky, open structure, which will reduce the tendency for shrinkage to occur during drying. The water-repellency of the particles also means that their surfaces will be "dehydrated," *i.e.*, that their work of adhesion to water will be reduced.

---

[1] Dintenfass, *Koll. Z.*, 1957, **155**, 121.

Consequently, as the films of water between the particles are removed by evaporation, the tendency for the particles to be drawn together, which is due to the high work of adhesion and to the high work of cohesion of water itself, will be diminished, and this fact will also diminish the degree of shrinkage of the paste.

The presence of a water-repellent, oil-attracting surface film on the solid particles in an aqueous paste will obviously also favour their transfer to an oil medium with which the paste is mixed. It should be noted, however, that the preferential wetting by the oil must be very marked indeed, *i.e.*, that the contact angle measured in the oil phase at the triple-phase line solid-water-oil must be small. If this condition is not satisfied, for example if the contact angle is in the region of 45°, a "clean" transfer will not occur, but rather the formation of an emulsion of the water-in-oil type, in which the partially wetted solid acts as an emulsifying agent.

There are two general methods of treating aqueous pastes with surface-active agents in order to obtain dry powders of improved dispersibility in non-aqueous media. In the first, a water-soluble surface-active agent is added, and, after allowing it to become adsorbed on the solid particles, a precipitant is added which will convert it to a water-insoluble, oil-soluble form. This principle has of course been used for very many years in the treatment of lakes and pigments with agents such as the barium and calcium rosinates, and other examples will be found in the patent literature. Hamburger[1] co-precipitated white lead pigments with insoluble soaps (*e.g.*, lead palmitate) in order to improve oil-dispersibility. British Dyestuffs Corporation[2] treated a number of finely divided pigments in aqueous media with soluble rosinates or naphthenates, which were then precipitated with barium salts: the use of organic amine precipitants (none exemplified) is also recommended. The treated pigments were filtered off and dried, and were claimed to have greatly improved dispersibilities in oil media. The principle can be extended by also having present some of the vehicle, preferably in emulsified form, in which the pigment is ultimately to be dispersed. Thus Imperial Chemical Industries[3] recommend precipitating colouring matters such as vat dyestuffs, barium chromate pigments, or azoic pigments in the presence of an emulsified vehicle such as linseed or castor oil, the emulsifying agent (*e.g.*, ammonium oleate) being precipitated with acid or a metal salt, either during or after the precipitation of the pigment.

The second general method for improving the oil-dispersibility of dry powders is based on the use of an amphipathic surface-active agent which is adsorbed in the reverse sense, with the polar group attached to the solid phase, and the hydrophobic grouping(s) orientated towards the aqueous

[1] Hamburger, B.P. 2405/1912.
[2] British Dyestuffs Corporation, F.P. 654,745.
[3] I.C.I., Hailwood, Shepherdson, and Stewart, B.P. 326,516.

medium. A good example of this technique, which is of considerable scientific interest (*cf.* Chapter 4, p. 175), is furnished by the method of du Pont[1] who treat aqueous dispersions of pigments with water-soluble cationic surface-active agents, which cause flocculation. The pigment is then filtered off and dried. Sloan and Patterson give a comprehensive (and, incidentally, quite generally useful) definition of suitable cationic agents in this patent and the related specification U.S.P. 2,192,954 (see below): they include *inter alia* salts of alkyl amines, and quaternary ammonium, ternary sulphonium, and quaternary phosphonium compounds, each containing only one polar group and a hydrocarbon chain with at least eight carbon atoms.*

The "flushing" technique, in which an aqueous paste is mixed with a non-aqueous, water-immiscible liquid vehicle in a suitable mixer (*e.g.*, of the Werner-Pfleiderer type) until the particles are transferred to the non-aqueous medium by preferential wetting, has been used for some time in the manufacture of white lead paints. Sanderson[2] and Bischof[3] described such procedures at the beginning of the century. Bischof points out the advantage of starting with an excess of oil and gradually adding the rest of the aqueous white lead paste, the water which separates being removed after each addition. It seems likely that the preferential wetting by the oil medium was helped by the formation of chemisorbed layers of lead "soaps" on the surface of the pigment particles, which is borne out by Ramage's[4] proposal to add metallic soaps. A more recent proposal for the formation *in situ* of a water-insoluble adsorbed film is that of du Pont and Martone[5] to treat an aqueous pigment paste (*e.g.*, of copper phthalocyanine) with a water-soluble deflocculating agent, such as a naphthalene sulphonic acid-formaldehyde condensation product, and then with a precipitant such as a calcium, ferric, or aluminium salt, before mixing the paste with the oil medium. Perhaps the most interesting method, at least scientifically, for improving the ease of flushing of pigments is du Pont, Sloan, and Patterson's[6] addition of water-soluble cationic surface-active agents to the aqueous pigment paste. It seems fairly clear that the surface-active agent renders the pigment more oil-wettable by virtue of being chemisorbed with the paraffin chains orientated outwards (*cf.* again Tomlinson's results, quoted in Chapter 4, p. 175).

* It is interesting to note in this connection that cationic surface-active agents have been found to make bentonite oleophilic (Jordan, *J. Phys. Chem.*, 1949, **53**, 294).

[1] Du Pont, Sloan, and Patterson, U.S.P. 2,192,956.
[2] Sanderson, B.P. 11,522/1898.
[3] Bischof, B.P. 2774/1900.
[4] Ramage, B.P. 13,422/1913.
[5] Du Pont, and Martone, B.P. 546,785.
[6] Du Pont, Sloan, and Patterson, U.S.P. 2,192,954 = B.P. 499,334.

CHAPTER 8

DETERGENT PROCESSES

A. Introduction

MODERN detergents represent one of the major achievements in the field of synthetic surface-active agents. The achievement is all the more striking when we consider on the one hand the complexity of detergent processes and the strict demands made on detergent products, and on the other hand the chemical skill and ingenuity which has been brought to bear on the many technological problems involved. One of the best historical summaries will be found in Chwala's[1] book, which describes how synthetic detergents were developed from the early attempts to overcome fat shortages, through present position at which detergents and special detergent mixtures can be "made to measure" for many purposes. The problem of greatest scientific interest is undoubtedly the relation between detergent action and the chemical structure of the detergent molecule, though it must be admitted at the outset that the information available is largely empirical, except when limited to broad generalisations (*e.g.*, that a detergent molecule must contain both polar and non-polar groups, sufficiently separated). Before this problem can be satisfactorily solved, it is evident that the mechanism of detergent processes must be properly understood. In the present chapter we shall therefore attempt to analyse in some detail detergent processes themselves, after proposing some general definitions and indicating briefly the scope and technical importance of scouring processes.

Broadly speaking, we can define a detergent process as any procedure for removing liquid and/or solid "dirt"* from the surface of a solid (the substrate) by means of a liquid (the detergent medium). For the present purpose, however, we propose to confine ourselves largely to processes in which the detergent medium is an aqueous solution, and to exclude those cases in which the dirt is water-soluble. Even with this limitation, the scope of detergent processes is fairly broad, as the following examples, which are grouped according to the nature of the substrate, will show:

(a) processes for removing liquid and/or solid dirt from approximately plane surfaces: *e.g.*, de-greasing of metals, glass, and ceramic ware (including dish-washing), cleansing or de-waxing of painted surfaces and wood-work;

(b) processes for removing liquid and/or solid dirt from porous or

---

* The well-known definition of dirt as "matter in the wrong place" is particularly appropriate here—especially if the "dirt" (*e.g.*, raw wool fat) is itself of considerable commercial value.

[1] Chwala, *Textilhilfsmittel*, Springer, Vienna, 1939.

fibrous masses: *e.g.*, scouring of raw wool and cotton, removal of spinning oils from textile fabrics, de-greasing of leather, laundry and domestic washing, de-sizing of textiles.

It is quite generally recognised that every case of detergent action is a complex process, involving a number of constituent phenomena. It is equally important to note that detergent processes may differ considerably with regard to the nature as well as to the relative importance of the constituent phenomena. Thus emulsification will obviously be a necessary step in the removal of wool fat from a mass of raw wool fibre, whereas it may hardly occur at all when a film of grease is flushed from a polished surface. In order to simplify the discussion, therefore, we propose to consider detergent processes in terms first of *fundamental detergent phenomena*, which are always present, and then of *ancillary detergent phenomena*, which are not necessarily involved in all detergent processes, though they may be essential in individual cases.

We also propose in general to assume that the detergent is introduced into the system *via* the aqueous medium. This will not always be true: thus a "nascent soap" may be formed at the interface by reaction between a fatty acid in the dirt and an alkali in the water, or an interfacial complex may be formed in the interface, between an oil-soluble amphipathic compound in the "dirt" and a water-soluble surface-active agent in the detergent medium.* Such occurrences will not invalidate the arguments to be presented, though it is important to note that they are in general highly favourable; this is strikingly demonstrated in the work of Speakman and Chamberlain.[1]

B. Fundamental phenomena in detergent processes

1. INITIAL WETTING-OUT

It is fairly obvious that, before any detergent process can take place, both the substrate and the dirt (liquid and/or solid) must be brought into direct contact with the detergent medium: *i.e.*, air must be substantially completely displaced from the solid surfaces, both clean and dirty, either before or during scouring. It should be noted that, in the majority of cases, the clean substrate will be much more readily wetted by aqueous solutions than are those to which dirt is adhering; consequently the speed or completeness of this preliminary wetting-out process will usually be largely determined by what happens on the soiled portions of the substrate, and on how they are distributed. Subject to this *proviso*, the wetting-out which precedes (or sometimes, chronologically speaking, accompanies) most

---

* It is common practice to add such materials to textile lubricating oils, in order to facilitate their subsequent removal by scouring.

[1] Speakman and Chamberlain, *Trans. Faraday Soc.*, 1933, **29**, 358.

detergent processes, has already been considered in its essentials in Chapter 5. The most important property of the detergent at this stage is therefore that it should lower the interfacial tension (or tensions) between the aqueous medium and the different types of dirt present, as rapidly as possible. As we shall see below, this condition will almost certainly be automatically satisfied by any efficient detergent.

It may also be desirable for the air-solution interfacial tension to be lowered rapidly, if a case of simple spreading wetting is involved, or if a porous mass has been immersed in the detergent solution. Although most detergents will also satisfy this requirement to some extent, the possibility exists that it may sometimes be desirable to add a so-called "wetting-out agent" in order to accelerate the wetting-out stage of the process. Thus we have seen in Chapter 5 that an essential property of many wetting-out agents seems to be that they lower the surface tension of water as rapidly as possible. One of the most important characteristics of a detergent, on the other hand, is that it lowers the dirt-water interfacial tensions, with the result that detergents tend to have larger hydrophobic groups than those in efficient wetting-out agents.*

2. Displacement of the Liquid Dirt Phase

This process can be considered as the recession (*cf.* Chapter 4, p. 133) of an "oil" medium, which is displaced by the advancing aqueous detergent medium, or as the converse case of wetting (it being noted that a gaseous phase such as air is *not* involved). The importance to detergent processes of such a wetting or recession, which is essentially determined by the interfacial tensions obtaining at the interfaces substrate-solution (*S–W*), substrate-oil (*S–O*), and oil-solution (*O–W*), appears to have been first recognised by Hailwood in 1932,[1] and has been treated both theoretically and experimentally by Adam.[2] The following is based largely on the treatment by these two workers.

If we consider a substrate such as a textile fibre in isolation (so that we are dealing with spreading wetting in a substantially non-capillary system), then it follows from equation (1) in Chapter 4 that it can occur spontaneously only if the spreading coefficient S in the following relation is positive:

$$S = \gamma_{SO} - \gamma_{SW} - \gamma_{OW} \tag{1}$$

---

* It should be noted however that the addition of a special wetting-out agent to a detergent solution is no guarantee that the wetting-out power will be increased in proportion, since mixed micelles of the two surface-active agents may be formed. If now the detergent forms micelles more readily than does the wetting-out agent (which will usually be true), this will have the effect of depressing the critical concentration for micelle formation of the wetting agent, the activity of which (in the thermodynamical sense) will accordingly be decreased.

[1] See the acknowledgment in the following reference, p. 125.
[2] Adam, *J. Soc. Dyers Colourists*, 1937, **53**, 121.

If however S is not positive, it may still be possible to detach the oil by mechanical action, provided that the work of adhesion oil-substrate is not too great, this work of adhesion W_{OS} being given by

$$W_{OS} = \gamma_{SW} + \gamma_{OW} - \gamma_{SO} \tag{2}$$

If a definite contact angle is present, (2) can be re-written

$$W_{OS} = \gamma_{OW}(1 + \cos \theta) \tag{2a}$$

θ being the contact angle measured inside the oil phase.

The conclusions to be drawn from equations (1) and (2) are of course that the recession of an oily dirt from an isolated substrate is favoured by the presence of a detergent which lowers the interfacial tensions substrate-solution and oil-solution, *i.e.*, which is adsorbed at these two interfaces, but that the detergent should preferably not be adsorbed at the oil-substrate interface. In general one would not expect the detergent to find its way to this last-named interface in any appreciable amount, since it will usually be more soluble in water than in oil, and the aqueous phase is generally present in much greater amount than is the oil, but the possibility cannot be ignored.

The nature and importance of the displacement process has been demonstrated experimentally by Adam,[1] and again by Palmer.[2] Adam followed photographically the behaviour of coloured lanoline and of "black oil," on the surface of individual wool fibres, in the presence of increasing concentrations of sodium cetyl sulphate. As the concentration of detergent increased, the film of oil receded until, at $0 \cdot 02\%$ of active agent, displacement was complete: expressed alternatively, a finite contact angle (measured in the oil) appeared and steadily increased as the concentration of detergent increased, finally reaching $180°$ and apparently disappearing again. In addition to showing that spontaneous spreading occurs in a technically important case, Adam's results also seem to us to suggest that the sodium cetyl sulphate may have lowered the interfacial tension substrate (fibre)-solution. Thus an examination of Figure 18 in Chapter 4, and of Young's equation

$$\gamma_{SW} = \gamma_{SO} + \gamma_{OW} \cos \theta \tag{3}$$

shows that it is not possible for θ to change from a value less than $90°$ to one above $90°$ (*i.e.*, for a detergent to reverse the relative wetting power of the detergent medium and the oil, on a given substrate) unless either

(*i*) γ_{SW} *decreases*—*i.e.*, the detergent is positively adsorbed at the substrate-solution interface, *or*

(*ii*) γ_{OS} *increases*—*i.e.*, the detergent finds its way into the oil phase and is *negatively adsorbed* at the substrate-oil interface,

and the second of these alternatives seems to be by far the less probable.

[1] Adam, *loc. cit.*

[2] Palmer, *J. Soc. Chem. Ind.*, 1941, **60**, 56, 60.

Adam's results are also of course in agreement with a lowering by the detergent of the interfacial tension oil-solution. Robinson[1] has shown in a relevant case that this lowering is most striking, sodium cetyl sulphate at 0·04% decreasing the interfacial tension between aqueous solutions and lanoline (at 60° c.) from over 10 to about 0·07 dyne/cm. Many other examples of lowerings of oil-water interfacial tensions by detergents will be found in the literature.

These observations of the phase-displacement process, which Adam refers to as "rolling off," have been confirmed and extended by a number of workers. A useful summary of much of this work, as well as of the general theory of detergent action, has been published by Adam and Stevenson.[2] Their paper contains a number of photomicrographs which illustrate the various effects very well. An interesting point is Stevenson's observation that, in general, anionic detergents have a greater "rolling-up" power than a typical non-ionic (*sec.*-octylphenol condensed with ethylene oxide), but that the latter agent is a better emulsifying agent for the oily dirt under the relatively mild mechanical conditions prevailing. This illustrates the fact that different surface-active agents often vary in their relative efficiencies in the different component phenomena in detergency.

Further work in the last ten years has also revealed that the displacement process is frequently complicated by the formation of bubbles inside the oil being displaced, and of gelatinous masses and "myelenic" growths at the oil-water interface. The bubbles were first observed by Powney,[3] who thought that they were bubbles of air which had been displaced by the detergent solution from the inside of the yarns. Powney accordingly suggested that the degree of internal wetting of the cloth was an important factor in detergency, and the explanation of the fact that prolonged soaking of the cloth favours subsequent removal of dirt. Stevenson[4] later showed that these bubbles are not air, but are small aqueous droplets, formed by osmosis of water from the detergent solution to electrolytes which are present at or near the oil-fibre interface. He found that these droplets could materially help the removal of liquid dirt.

The formation of gelatinous or myelenic growths, which is referred to in the summary by Adam and Stevenson, has been considered in some detail by Stevenson[5] and by Harker,[6] who between them have published a really magnificent collection of photographs which show the removal of several oils from a series of fibres of different "polarities." These photographs will repay careful study. Stevenson shows that complex formation between

---

[1] Robinson in *Wetting and Detergency*, Harvey, London, 1937, p. 146.
[2] Adam and Stevenson, *Endeavour*, 1953, **12**, 25.
[3] Powney, *J. Textile Inst.*, 1949, **40**, T519.
[4] Stevenson, *J. Textile Inst.*, 1951, **42**, T194; 1953, **44**, T12.
[5] Stevenson, *J. Textile Inst.*, 1953, **44**, T12.
[6] Harker, *J. Textile Inst.*, 1959, **50**, T189.

detergents and oil-soluble fatty acids or fatty alcohols, either at the interface *or in the bulk oil phase*, is of considerable importance. Interfacial
complex formation (as we have seen in Chapter 3, p. 87, and Chapter 6,
p. 253) can give exceedingly low interfacial tensions—so low that spontaneous emulsification can occur. This probably accounts for the very low
values obtained by Robinson at the lanoline-water interface in the presence
of sodium cetyl sulphate, to which we referred above. Stevenson suggests
that spontaneous emulsification is essential for the removal of oils from
"oleophilic" fibres. If complex formation occurs in the bulk of the oil, gels
and myelenic growths or anisotropic droplets are formed, and these are
readily removed. This bulk complexing is considered by Stevenson to be
an important mechanism in detergent action, which is related to solubilisation (*cf.* Chapter 2 and he suggests that non-ionic detergents generally act
more in this way than by the "rolling-off" mechanism.

Harker, who confirms Stevenson's observations on the formation of
aqueous droplets inside the oil phase by osmosis, and on complex formation,
considers the effect on detergent processes of the polarity* of the soil and
fibre, respectively, with reference to four combinations:

(A) non-polar oil on non-polar fibre (*e.g.*, medicinal paraffin on
   polythene);
(B) polar oil on polar fibre (*e.g.*, fatty acid on wool);
(C) non-polar oil on polar fibre (*e.g.*, medicinal paraffin on wool);
(D) polar oil on non-polar fibre (*e.g.*, fatty acid on polythene).

He considers that a genuine phase-displacement or rolling-off process (which
he terms "true detergency") will definitely occur only in case (B), when the
oil can be seen to collect into spheres and become emulsified by slight
mechanical action. This will occur, for example, in the clear-cut observations of "rolling-off" by Adam and others. This may also occur sometimes
in case (C), but Harker is definitely of the opinion that, where a really
non-polar fibre is involved, as in cases (A) and (D) above, efficient removal
of the oil can only be achieved by complex formation, which may necessitate
adding suitable polar substances to the oil. (This is of course well known
in the preparation of textile lubricating oils.)

Lawrence[1] has recently suggested that all cases of *spontaneous* removal
of *at least partially polar* dirt (our italics) must be explained in terms of
penetration and complex formation of this type, leading to solubilisation
if the ratio of detergent to oily dirt is large enough. In Lawrence's view,
spontaneous detergency of polar dirt "has nothing to do with surface

---

* It seems to us that it is better to describe fibres in this connection as "polar" and
"non-polar" than as "hydrophilic" or "hydrophobic," in spite of the wide-spread use of
the latter expressions. We agree with those who prefer to use "hydrophilic" and "hydrophobic" to describe wettability by water, as characterised by works of adhesion, contact
angles, etc., the non-aqueous phase being either a gas or a water-immiscible liquid.

[1] Lawrence, *Nature*, 1959, **183,** 1491.

forces, but results from cryoscopic forces and diffusion processes in the ternary soap/water/polar dirt system."

It seems to us that complex formation, leading to the formation of readily dispersible gels, myelenic figures, or liquid droplets, must be considered as an important mechanism in many detergent processes. In a sense it represents the transition between Adam's "rolling-off" mechanism, and detergency by solubilisation, which we discuss later in the present chapter. It is of course clear that it does not rule out the "rolling-off" mechanism, which can be seen to occur in many cases, and which explains such things as the need for a considerable degree of agitation in most technical detergent processes, or the specificity of different substrates. The "rolling-off" mechanism, probably supplemented in many cases by penetration into the liquid dirt phase, is still usefully interpreted in terms of Young's equation and the work of adhesion concept.*

The relevance of the substrate (and hence of the substrate-oil and substrate solution interactions, interpreted in terms of the two interfacial tensions) in displacement processes is well illustrated by the results of Fineman and Kline[1] on the removal of paraffin oil containing carbon black from plane surfaces by a non-ionic detergent of the alkylphenol-ethylene oxide condensate type. Large differences were observed in the ease of removal of this dirt from glass, nylon, and several metals. The differences, which were not due to differences in the extent of exhaustion of the detergent by adsorption, were readily explained in terms of works of adhesion. Perhaps the most interesting observation in this work, however, was the effect of the substrate on the fineness of the dispersed particles of dirt after removal: very fine particles were formed when the dirt was displaced from steel, much coarser ones on displacement from glass, and still coarser particles when the soil in bulk was dispersed, all these results being obtained under carefully controlled mechanical conditions. Fineman and Kline suggest that the differences are due to differences in works of adhesion, relative to the work of cohesion of the soil. This suggestion can perhaps be expressed more clearly as follows. Suppose that we have initially unit areas of steel (S) and of glass (G), respectively, covered by equal volumes of the oil (O), and that both liquid layers are completely removed, under identical mechanical conditions, by detergent solutions (W) of identical composition, so that the oil-water interfacial tension γ_{OW} is the same in both cases. The increase in interfacial free energy in the first case will be given by

$$\Delta G_S{}^S = A_1\gamma_{OW} + \gamma_{SW} - \gamma_{OW} - \gamma_{SO} = (A_1 - 2)\gamma_{OW} + W_{aS}$$

---

* Harker in fact uses this approach in interpreting some of the cases of displacement described in his paper, though some of the details are rather puzzling, such as the statement that complete wetting of the fibre implies that its interfacial tension against the detergent solution is *zero*.

[1] Fineman and Kline, *J. Coll. Sci.*, 1953, **8**, 288.

where A_1 is the total area of emulsified oil droplets, and W_{aS} is the work of adhesion oil-steel (in competition with the solution), and in the second case

$$\Delta G_S{}^G = A_2\gamma_{OW} + \gamma_{GW} - \gamma_{OW} - \gamma_{GO} = (A_2 - 2)\gamma_{OW} + W_{aG}$$

where A_2 is again the total area of emulsified oil droplets, and W_{aG} is the work of adhesion oil-glass, in competition with the solution. If now the processes are carried out under conditions sufficiently near to reversibility that we can write as a reasonable approximation

$$\Delta G_S{}^G \approx \Delta G_S{}^G \approx 0,$$

$$(A_1 - 2)\gamma_{OW} + W_{aS} \approx (A_2 - 2)\gamma_{OW} + W_{aG}$$

whence $(A_1 - A_2) \approx (W_{aG} - W_{aS})/\gamma_{OW}$.

In so far as this equation is a valid approximation, it follows that, if W_{aG} is greater than W_{aS}, then $A_1 > A_2$; i.e., a finer emulsion will be formed when the oil is scoured from the steel. It will be noted that we have used works of adhesion of oil in competition with the solution; a similar conclusion is reached if works of adhesion against air are used, along with the work of cohesion of the oil.

The rôle of the substrate in detergent processes has also been considered, from the kinetic point of view, in the paper by Fava and Eyring[1] to which we have referred in Chapter 3. They postulate that adsorption of detergent by the fabric is a necessary step in the process of detergency, according to the following scheme:

$$\text{fabric-dirt} + \text{detergent} = \text{fabric-detergent} + \text{soil-detergent}$$

whence

$$- dS/dt = 2Sk_s \sinh b_s S$$

where S is the amount of soil (dirt) adsorbed in time t, and k_s and b_s are rate constants. If several soils and detergents are adsorbed at the same time, then the contributions to the rate of desorption, from the stresses due to each substance, should be additive, and the rate of desorption of dirt is given by

$$- dS/dt = 2Sk_s \sinh (b_s S + b_D D)$$

where D and b_D are the amounts of detergent adsorbed and the rate constants for adsorption of detergent, respectively. This leads to the postulate that the fundamental function of a detergent is to accelerate the desorption of dirt by increasing the stress on the adsorbent material, and to the corollaries that (other things being equal) detergency will be increased by increasing the adsorption of detergent by the fibre, or by adding substances, *which are not necessarily detergents*, which are capable of being rapidly adsorbed.

---

[1] Fava and Eyring, *J. Phys. Chem.*, 1956, **60**, 890.

This last suggestion by Fava and Eyring is, of course, implicit in Adam's thermodynamical analysis of the "rolling-off" phenomenon, and it has also been made on more empirical grounds by Feuell[1] and by Bartholomé and Buschmann[2] in explaining the favourable effect of carboxymethyl cellulose in many detergent processes. Bartholomé and Buschmann state that carboxymethyl cellulose is strongly adsorbed by the fibre and hence displaces the dirt. As we shall see below, there is considerable doubt as to whether carboxymethyl cellulose is actually adsorbed, and most of the evidence supports the view that it acts primarily as a protective colloid on the suspended dirt. Feuell accepts this latter view, but believes that carboxymethyl cellulose does have a small but definite effect in the actual displacement of medicinal paraffin (containing graphite) from cotton by solutions of the non-ionic detergent "Lissapol N." Since non-ionic agents appear to be in general less adsorbed by textiles than are anionics, it seems quite possible that carboxymethyl cellulose might have a significant effect with the non-ionics, but be "swamped" by the more powerful adsorption of the anionics.

Although it seems clear *a priori* that adsorption of detergent (or some other solute) at the fibre-solution interface should, if it is rapid enough, favour detergency, the question which remains to be answered is whether or not it will in fact contribute significantly to the "driving force" behind the phase-displacement process. If, for example, we take Fava and Eyring's experimental results for the maximum adsorption of sodium dodecyl-benzene sulphonate on cotton at 30° c., assume that the specific surface of cotton is 3×10^5 cm.^{2}/gm.,* that all this surface is available to the detergent, and that the area occupied by each adsorbed molecule in the saturated adsorbed layer is 30–50 Å^2., we can use the Volmer-Frumkin equation of state (*cf.* Chapter 3, Equation 26) to calculate the surface pressure exerted by the adsorbed detergent at the fibre-water interface. The value obtained is less than one dyne/cm., which would not appear to be highly significant in determining either the direction or the rate of the displacement process. This very tentative conclusion relates, of course, only to the particular case of this detergent on cotton, and leaves open the question of whether or not other detergents or detergent additives act in this way. It is also based on the assumption that the whole surface area of 3×10^5 cm.^{2}/gm. is available to the detergent.

It is also worth noting that the preceding arguments relate only to the possible role of lowerings of the fibre-solution interfacial tension in processes of *complete* displacement of "oily" dirt from smooth, homogeneous surfaces. In fact, complete displacement does not usually occur, and the

---

* See Vickerstaff, *The Physical Chemistry of Dyeing*, Oliver and Boyd, 2nd edition, 1954, p. 172.

[1] Feuell, *J. Textile Inst.*, 1949, **40**, T523.

[2] Bartholomé and Buschmann, *Textilber.*, 1949, **30**, 249.

majority of surfaces encountered in detergent processes (especially with natural fibres) are rough and possibly composite as well. It is therefore worth examining the case of a composite surface in terms of Cassie and Baxter's equation (p. 140). If we assume that a given textile fibre, for example, is so rough that the detergent solution cannot completely displace the oil from the pores, so that the apparent "substrate-solution" interface is in reality a composite of substrate-solution and oil-solution, then we must replace equation (1) in the present chapter by, for example, an expression of the form

$$S' = \gamma_{OS} - \gamma_{OW} - f_{SW}\gamma_{SW} - f_{OWS}\gamma_{OW} \tag{4}$$

where f_{SW} is the area of actual substrate-solution interface per unit area of apparent substrate-solution interface, and f_{OWS} is the area of *actual* oil-solution interface, per unit area of apparent substrate-solution interface, created by the advancing detergent solution. This expression suggests that, if f_{OWS} is sufficiently large relative to f_{SW}, then the value of γ_{SW} might be unimportant, and the rôle of a detergent in assisting a spontaneous apparent recession of oil might be solely to reduce the oil-solution interfacial tension. Similarly, it can be shown that, if f_{OWS} is large relative to f_{SW}, a lowering in γ_{OW} could explain a change in the apparent contact angle (measured in the oil) from less than to more than 90°. This explanation is of course valid only if a certain amount of oil, which may be very small, remains in the substrate after the displacement process, but, as we have already pointed out, this is in fact true of most textile scouring processes. It therefore seems to the writers that it cannot be dismissed without further evidence, and that a lowering of fibre-solution interfacial tensions in textile scouring processes cannot yet be taken to be established by observations on apparent contact angles.

The preceding discussion applies to recession processes on single fibres or other substrates which can be considered in isolation. In a loose mass such as raw cotton or wool, it is probably still permissible to apply the same argument, and to allow for the effect of neighbouring fibres during the subsequent stages of emulsification and re-deposition (see below). If however the porous mass is compact (*e.g.*, if a mass of textile fibres or a fabric has been heavily compressed, or felted), then it becomes necessary to treat the displacement of liquid dirt by the detergent medium as a case of capillary wetting. It seems unlikely that a process analogous to the capillary rise would occur, but rather that we would have one of the cases discussed in Chapter 4 (p. 153), in which one fluid (oil rather than air in the present instance) is displaced from a complicated system of capillaries which has been immersed completely in the detergent medium. If we consider the appropriate form of equation (23) in Chapter 4, for example, making the necessary substitutions of "oil" for "air," we can see that the displacement of the oil will certainly be favoured by a detergent which lowers the oil-solution interfacial tension, and will also be assisted if the detergent decreases the hysteresis factor between the advancing and receding contact angles.

3. Detachment of solid particles

In many detergent processes—perhaps in the majority of those involving textiles—the particles of solid dirt will be dispersed in an oil medium, and it may be possible substantially to ignore them except in so far as they affect the viscosity or interfacial properties of the oil. If however solid particles are present outside the oil phase, or if the latter is absent altogether, then their detachment must be treated as a fundamental detergent phenomenon. The action of a detergent during this process of detachment (which need not be spontaneous, since the system will usually be mechanically agitated) is analogous to that of a deflocculating agent. Thus if a surface-active agent is adsorbed at either or both of the interfaces dirt (solid) solution and substrate-solution, giving rise to hydrated sheaths and/or electrokinetic potentials (of the same sign), then the particles can be more easily detached. The analogy with deflocculation must not be carried too far, however, since the substrate and dirt are not identical nor mutually miscible (*i.e.*, there is a finite interfacial tension dirt-substrate); consequently there is not the same thermodynamical tendency towards coalescence.

Several papers in the past few years have dealt with the role of electrical potentials, especially the electrokinetic or ζ-potential,* in the detachment of solid particles during detergent processes. Electroendosmotic measurements of a number of fibre-solution ζ-potentials have been reported by, among others, Stanley,[1] von Stackelberg, Kling, Benzel, and Wilke,[2] and Kling.[3] The general picture which emerges from this work is that the effect of detergents on fibre-solution ζ-potentials is usually what would be expected from their electrochemical classification, anionic agents making the potential more negative, cationics making it less negative or even positive, and non-ionics having very little effect, if any. It appears to be generally accepted that, when ionogenic detergents are used, mutual repulsions are set up between the surface of the fibre and the charged particles of solid dirt, and that this repulsion helps detergency, so that there is a general parallelism between ζ-potential and the results of detergency tests.[4, 2] At the same time, it appears to be established that mutual electrostatic repulsion is not the only mechanism which leads to the displacement of particles of solid dirt, even with ionogenic detergents, but that surface

---

* See Chapter 4, p. 166.

[1] Stanley, *J. Phys. Chem.*, 1954, **58**, 533.

[2] Von Stackelberg, Kling, Benzel, and Wilke, *Koll. Z.*, 1954, **135**, 67.

[3] Kling, *Textilber*, 1955, **36**, 166.

[4] Kling and Lange, *Koll. Z.*, 1952, **127**, 19.

hydration, steric effects, and perhaps even displacement by the interfacial pressures exerted by adsorbed surface-active molecules at the fibre-solution and dirt-solution interfaces, also play a part. It also seems clear that, with non-ionic detergents, the ζ-potentials play no significant part at all.

It seems likely that the occurrence of *adsorption with reversed orientation* can severely limit the role of the ζ-potentials in the removal of solid particles. Doscher,[1] who found no correlation between detergent action and ζ-potential, pointed out that this type of adsorption causes the solid-liquid interfaces to become hydrophobic, and hence not only opposes detergency, but may be more decisive than changes in ζ-potential. It is also interesting to note the observation of von Stackelberg *et al.*, that with a relatively polar fibre (viscose) the negative ζ-potential was increased by a series of sodium alkyl sulphates only above the critical micelle concentration, whereas with less polar fibres such as cellulose acetate and "Perlon," there was an increase below the critical micelle concentration. This suggests that on viscose there is first an adsorption with reversed orientation, which does not increase the ζ-potential. This is then followed by the formation of a second, amphipathically adsorbed layer above the critical micelle concentration, which is ionisable and therefore makes the ζ-potential more negative. With a non-polar fibre, on the other hand, amphipathic adsorption would be expected to occur from the very beginning.

It follows from what has been said that, as demonstrated by Vold and Konecny,[2] measurements of the suspending power of surface-active agents on solid "dirt" are not a reliable test for detergent power.

A general picture of the theory of the removal of solid dirt from fibre surfaces has been published by Durham,[3] who considers the balance between the van der Waals attraction between fibre and dirt, and the forces of repulsion postulated in the theories of Born and of Verwey, Overbeek, and others, which we have discussed in Chapter 4, p. 162. Durham points out that it is the *total* potential differences between the phases (ψ_0), rather than the ζ-potential (which is the potential difference between the plane of slip in the liquid phase and the bulk of the liquid phase), which determines the electrostatic repulsion; for this reason alone one cannot expect a complete correlation between detergency and ζ-potentials. Durham also draws attention to the fundamental difference between the removal of solid particles and oil droplets, respectively, from the surface of the fibre,[4] and to the complexity of the whole detergent process, which means that no one physico-chemical phenomenon can fully explain it.

The determination of "adhesion numbers" by the method of von

[1] Doscher, *J. Coll. Sci.*, 1950, **5**, 100.
[2] Vold and Konecny, *J. Phys. Chem.*, 1949, **53**, 1262.
[3] Durham, *J. Applied Chem.*, 1956, **6**, 153.
[4] *Cf.* Utermohlen, *Textile Research J.*, 1949, **19**, 489.

Buzágh[1] is a useful means of investigating the relevance to a particular detergent process of the detachment of solid dirt particles from the substrate. It was used by Palmer and Rideal[2] with solutions of several surface-active agents: sodium dodecyl sulphate, cetyl pyridinium bromide, sodium cetyl sulphate, and sodium oleyl-N-methyltaurine ("Igepon T"). These authors obtained interesting correlations between the concentration of surface-active agent and the percentage of particles (*e.g.*, wax-coated carborundum or chalk) which did not become detached from waxed glass surfaces under carefully standardised conditions. The results indicated quite clearly, for the particular systems concerned, that the percentage which became detached increased with increasing concentration of the detergent until the critical concentration for micelle formation was reached, when the percentage again decreased. These results suggest that the surface-active agents in question were amphipathically adsorbed on the waxed surfaces, the decrease in efficiency above the critical micelle concentration being due to a regression of the chemical potential in the (mixed) detergent.

C. Ancillary phenomena (favourable) in detergent processes

1. EMULSIFICATION AND DEFLOCCULATION

A number of writers have referred to the importance or the necessity of efficient emulsification of liquid dirt, or of thorough deflocculation of solid dirt, in the scouring of textiles. Thus Robinson[3] points out that one would expect that the formation of a stable emulsion, during the initial process of displacement from the fibre, would facilitate the escape of oily dirt from the interstices in a mass of fibres. The same general argument no doubt applies to the removal of solid dirt. Although it was soon recognised that emulsifying and/or deflocculating power did not suffice in themselves to make a surface-active agent a good detergent, it seems to have been generally agreed since the early work of Donnan[4] and of McBain[5] that they were important criteria. Thus Götte[6] showed that the detergent power of sodium alkyl sulphate solutions, on artificially soiled cotton, ran closely parallel with the emulsifying power for the particular oily dirt involved, over a range of pH values. The minimum in the scouring power (at pH = 5) corresponded to the point of zero electrokinetic potential on the dirt particles, *i.e.*, to the pH at which the degree of deflocculation would be at a minimum. Götte further developed this idea of the importance of

[1] Von Buzágh, *Koll. Z.*, 1929, **47**, 370; 1930, **51**, 105, 230.
[2] Palmer and Rideal, *J. Chem. Soc.*, 1939, 573.
[3] Robinson, *Wetting and Detergency*, Harvey, London, 1937, p. 147.
[4] Donnan, *Z. phys. Chem.* A, 1899, **31**, 42.
[5] McBain, *Seifensieder Ztg.*, 1919, **46**, 138.
[6] Götte, *Koll. Z.*, 1933, **64**, 331.

the electrokinetic potential—which must be of the same sign as the electrokinetic potential of the fibres—by showing that a simple multivalent anion,
such as ferrocyanide, increased the detergent effect, whereas multivalent
cations (Al^{+++}, Ba^{++}) had the opposite effect. One would of course expect,
on the classical concept of ionic antagonism (Schultze-Hardy principle) that
multivalent anions would increase, and multivalent cations would decrease,
the negative electrokinetic potentials on both dirt and fibre. Urbain and
Jensen,[1] who measured the electrokinetic potentials of emulsions and of
carbon black suspensions, stabilised with a series of "soaps" with paraffin
chains varying in length from C_2 to C_{18}, obtained further evidence in support of this view, both the electrokinetic potential and the stability of the
disperse system increasing with increasing chain length. Urbain and Jensen
advance the interesting suggestion that the soap micelles contributed
directly to the deflocculating effect, functioning essentially as anions of
very high valency.

We have seen in Chapters 6 and 7 that the ease of emulsification of a
liquid (or of deflocculation of a solid) is generally increased by the addition
of a surface-active agent which lowers the interfacial tension between the
liquid (or solid) and the dispersion medium.[2] This is probably a further
reason for the practically universal coincidence of high detergent power on
textiles, and the property of lowering the interfacial tension between water-
immiscible liquids and aqueous media—it has already been pointed out
that a lowering of the oil-solution interfacial tension is favourable to the
initial displacement process. One of the most interesting contributions on
this point is that of Speakman and Chamberlain,[3] who found that the
depression of the interfacial tension and the ease of scouring by soap solutions, of mineral oil, was increased by the addition of a few per cent of
oleyl alcohol to the oil. At the same time, however, Speakman and Chamberlain showed that depression of the interfacial tension was not the only
factor involved, since the scouring efficiency passed through a maximum
at 6%–10% of oleyl alcohol, and then decreased again, whereas the interfacial tension continued to fall as the concentration of oleyl alcohol was
increased up to 100%. This was explained by an increase in the adhesion
of the mineral oil to the fibre : in terms of the present Chapter, equation (2),
the interfacial tension fibre-oil was decreased by adsorption of the oleyl
alcohol at that interface.

2. Solubilisation

The possibility that solubilisation of dirt by detergent solutions plays a
part in detergent processes has been examined *inter alia* in papers by

[1] Urbain and Jensen, *J. Phys. Chem.*, 1936, **40**, 821.
[2] Adam, *J. Soc. Dyers Colourists*, 1937, **53**, 124.
[3] Speakman and Chamberlain, *Trans. Faraday Soc.*, 1933, **29**, 358.

Hartley[1] and by McBain,[2] to which reference is recommended for reviews of earlier work and opinions. It seems to the present writers that such a mechanism, being relatively specific, is not likely to be important in all detergent processes, but that it must always be borne in mind in considering individual cases of detergent action. Thus Hartley points out that it is unlikely to be relevant in wool-scouring processes, since (a) the amount of oil removed is usually far too great to be dissolved by the amount of detergent present, and (b) detergents are often used at concentrations below the critical concentration for micelle formation.* Where however a detergent is applied at a high concentration and then rinsed off—for example in hand-washing, as pointed out by Hartley, or in some methods of laundering—solubilisation may be important.

The above argument applies only to detergent compositions which consist essentially of water-soluble amphipathic compounds only. Where solubilised "fat solvents" are present in detergent solutions, however, the ability of the complex micelles to dissolve dirt may be an essential property of the detergent composition. Detergent mixtures containing fat solvents are discussed more fully in Part III of the present monograph; as illustrations may be quoted Friesenhahn's[3] early proposal to add cyclohexanol to soap solutions, the resulting mixtures being optically empty, and the work of Engler and Dieckhoff referred to in the article by McBain.[4]

Solubilisation—though in the opposite sense to that usually meant—also plays a major part in the action of non-ionic and other detergents in *dry-cleaning* solutions. Here the "oily" dirt is removed by solution in a solvent such as trichloroethylene, and the problem is to ensure the removal of water-soluble dirt. An interesting summary of dry-cleaning with solvents containing surface-active agents and water has been published by Fulton, Alexander, Lloyd, and Schwartz,[5] who describe how increasing the detergent concentration up to as much as 4% enables more water to be added, with a correspondingly more efficient removal of water-soluble dirt, without excessive sorption of water by the cloth. The fact that, as reported by these authors, the presence of the detergent greatly reduces the vapour pressure of the water in the system, suggests that water and detergent are present in some form of association complex—perhaps a mixed micelle with the water and the polar groups of the amphipathic molecules preferentially orientated inwards.

---

* Thus for example the critical concentration of sodium cetyl sulphate corresponds to an approximately 0·03% solution, calculated as effective agent, while this compound has marked detergent power at much lower concentrations.

[1] Hartley, in *Wetting and Detergency*, Harvey, London, 1937 p. 153.

[2] McBain, in *Advances in Colloid Science*, **I**, Interscience, 1942, p. 99.

[3] Friesenhahn, D.R.P. 365,160 (published 9th Dec., 1922).

[4] McBain, *loc. cit.*, p. 138.

[5] Fulton, Alexander, Lloyd, and Schwartz, *American Society for Testing Materials Bulletin*, 1953, **No. 192,** 63.

3. FOAMING

A number of writers have suggested that detergent processes are favoured by the formation of foams or lathers, and have pointed to correlations, general or detailed, between the foaming and the detergent power of certain series of surface-active compounds. (The identification of cleansing and lathering power is of course almost traditional in the popular mind.) Much of this "evidence" seems to the present authors to be unconvincing. Thus Volz[1] examined a number of detergents qualitatively in hand-washing tests, and found a general correlation between foaming and cleansing power. Such evidence—quite apart from its lack of precision—is purely circumstantial, and shows only that those chemical structures which are highly surface-active at the interfaces dirt-solution and substrate-solution, are also capable of stabilising foams. (It is worth noting in this connection that the air-solution interface appears in only one of the fundamental detergent phenomena, *i.e.*, in certain types of initial wetting processes.) The need for this scepticism is demonstrated by the work of other authors. Götte[2] scoured cotton with a series of sodium alkyl sulphates (dodecyl to octadecyl), and showed that the apparent general correlation between foaming and detergent power broke down on closer examination, since maximum foaming power decreased with increasing temperature, while detergent power increased. Similarly, Nüsslein[3] found, with soaps and alkoyl-N-methyltaurines of different chain lengths, that the optimum foaming power corresponded to a lower chain length in the alkoyl group than did optimum scouring power on textiles. Both sets of observations agree with Götte's suggestion that foaming power is related to the presence of ionic aggregates, to which it is obvious to add the suggestion that detergent power is determined by the molecularly dispersed portion of the surface-active agent. It seems to us that such evidence eliminates foaming as a *fundamental* phenomenon in detergent processes.*

It seems to be well established, however, that many processes of detergency are significantly helped by what we might term "dirt-entrainment" in foams. This effect appears to have been first recognised by Reumuth,[4] who published some interesting photographs which show how finely-divided solids, such as carbon black or rust, can be drawn into and "sequestered" by foams stabilised by soaps or by sodium alkyl sulphates. The phenomenon was further studied by Stevenson,[5] who showed that oily

---

* An example of where foaming is actually undesirable is in the rinsing of dishes. The so-called "rinse additives" (*cf. Chemical Week*, 1960, **86**, No. 8, 89) are non-ionic agents of low foaming power—which also give low receding contact angles on the surfaces in question.

[1] Volz, *Textilber.*, 1933, **14**, 505.
[2] Götte, *Koll. Z.*, 1933, **64**, 327.
[3] Nüsslein, *Textilber.*, 1938, **19**, 582.
[4] Reumuth, *Textilber.*, 1932, **13**, 599.
[5] Stevenson, *J. Textile Inst.*, 1951, **42**, T194. See also Adam and Stevenson, *Endeavour*, 1953, **12**, 25.

dirt collects at the junctions between foam lamellae. This is due to the fact that the curvature is greatest, and hence the pressure inside the liquid smallest, at these junctions. Adam and Stevenson also point out that foam can help at the stage of removal of dirt from the fibre, by introducing a certain rigidity into the system, so that the effect of mechanical agitation is greater, and by actually breaking up oily dirt by drawing it into the regions of lower hydrostatic pressure at the junctions between lamellae. (This latter effect will, of course, be greater the smaller the oil-water interfacial tension.)

D. Ancillary phenomena (unfavourable) in detergent processes

1. EXHAUSTION OF DETERGENTS BY ADSORPTION OR DECOMPOSITION

It is of course obvious that any phenomenon which decreases the active concentration of the detergent during a detergent process will have an unfavourable effect. This exhaustion may be caused by adsorption on the dirt or on the substrate, or by decomposition or precipitation by the detergent medium. It is of course an inescapable fact that some detergent will be lost through adsorption by the dirt which is being removed, but losses through adsorption by the fibre are not inevitable if it is true that either (a) lowerings of the fibre-solution interfacial tensions are unnecessary in order for liquid dirt to be displaced, (b) removal of oily dirt does not need to be complete, so that we are dealing with the scouring of a composite "fibre"-solution interface which actually contains a large amount of oil-solution interface (*cf.* p. 139), or (c) adsorption of detergent by solid particles alone is sufficient to detach them from the fibre. Some colour is lent to these possibilities by the fact that highly efficient non-ionic detergents have been shown to be much less strongly adsorbed than anionics or cationics.[1] It has even been reported that, under certain conditions, no measurable adsorption of non-ionic detergents can be detected, even though their detergent efficiency increased when their adsorption was increased by the presence of fatty acids in the fibre.[2]

The greater solubility of synthetic detergents, especially of the non-ionic types, in acid media, hard water, etc., is so well known as hardly to require comment. Apart, however, from the directly adverse effect of reducing the concentration of surface-active material, the precipitation (or excessive adsorption) of a detergent may have other unfavourable results. Thus lime soaps (which may be mixtures of calcium and magnesium oleates, palmitates, stearates, etc.), and fatty acids, are hydrophobic liquids or wax-like solids, which promote adhesion of dirt to fibre and must themselves be scoured off. Since it is often necessary to have soap present during a

---

[1] Weatherburn and Bayley, *Textile Research J.*, 1952, **22**, 797.
[2] McLaren, *J. Soc. Dyers Colourists*, 1950, **66**, 521.

scouring in hard water, detergents have been developed which are specially effective as "lime soap dispersing agents," examples being the sodium salts of oleyl-N-methyltaurine and of oleyl-*p*-anisidine sulphonic acid. Methods of studying their lime soap dispersing action have been described by, among others, Lottermoser and Flammer[1] and by Miles and Ross.[2] The latter authors demonstrated that the detergent power of sodium dodecyl sulphate is diminished in hard water by the presence of sodium laurate, and present evidence that a mixed calcium laurate-calcium dodecyl sulphate is formed, which has no detergent power—a mixed magnesium salt does not appear to be formed. An alternative method of preventing the deposition of lime soaps is the use of calcium and magnesium "sequestering" agents, such as sodium hexametaphosphate or the sodium salt of ethylene diamine tetraacetic acid. These agents, which are not themselves detergents, act as water-softeners, and are even capable of sequestering alkaline earth cations from lime soaps which have already been formed, an equivalent number of sodium ions being released.

A special phenomenon which occurs during the scouring of amphoteric fibres in acid media has been studied by Schöller,[3] who found that "Igepon T" (sodium oleyl-N-methyltaurine) was ineffective as a detergent under such conditions, whereas the non-ionising agent "Leonil O"[4] was highly effective. Schöller further observed that coloured wax emulsions which had been stabilised with "Igepon T" were adsorbed by wool in acid solutions, whereas emulsions stabilised with "Leonil O" were not. Bearing in mind the fact that "Igepon T" is itself soluble in the acid solutions, Schöller explains these results by postulating a chemisorption of "Igepon T" by means of salt linkages between the sulphonate groups in the detergent anions and the $NH_3{}^+$ groups in the wool. Such an adsorption would have the effect of covering the surface of the wool with a layer of amphipathic molecules having their paraffin chains oriented outwards, and thus of promoting the adhesion of an oily dirt to the substrate. (A similar mechanism probably explains the failure of cationic agents in alkaline media.[5]) No such adsorption is possible with the non-ionising detergent. Schöller's explanation is in agreement with his further observation that wool which had been treated with acetic anhydride, so as to acetylate the amino groups, could be scoured equally well with "Igepon T" and "Leonil O" in acid media. It is not of course implied that the absence of chemisorption in the reverse sense was the only reason for the superior detergent action of

---

[1] Lottermoser and Flammer, *Kolloidchem. Beih.*, 1937, **45**, 359.

[2] Miles and Ross, *Ind. Eng. Chem.*, 1943, **35**, 1298.

[3] Schöller, *Textilber.*, 1938, **19**, 57.

[4] According to Brandner, Lockwood, Nagel, and Russell, F.I.A.T. Final Report No. 1141, p. 65, this is the condensation product of a mixture of C_{18} to C_{21} fatty alcohols with twelve to fifteen molecular proportions of ethylene oxide.

[5] *Cf.* Powney and Wood, *Trans. Faraday Soc.*, 1941, **37**, 220; Bertsch, *Z. angew. Chem.*, 1934, **47**, 424; 1935, **48**, 52.

the non-ionising agent; it seems likely that a further contributory cause was the greater stability of the emulsified or suspended dirt against the flocculating effect of hydrogen ions—*cf.* Nüsslein's[1] statement that it is possible to scour textiles with non-ionising detergents in saturated solutions of aluminium sulphate.

2. REDEPOSITION OF SOLID OR LIQUID DIRT

The prevention of redeposition of suspended dirt—liquid, solid, or mixed—is so important in many detergent processes that it almost merits classification as a "fundamental" phenomenon in detergency. The occurrence of redeposition in scouring baths has been known for some time, as has the fact that deposition of emulsified oil,[2] or of suspended carbon black[3] can occur when they are brought into contact with textile fibres. Detergents reduce this tendency to varying degrees, but it was early observed that dispersions prepared with *cationic* surface-active agents were capable of adhering very tenaciously to textile fibres.[4] The tendency for carbon black suspensions to redeposit on cotton has also been studied as a function of the concentration of surface-active agent (sodium dodecyl sulphate), and shown to go through a sharp minimum well below the critical micelle concentration, and then through a maximum near the critical micelle concentration.[5] It has also been suggested that the adverse effect of calcium ions on the scouring efficiency of anionic detergents is due to increased redeposition, rather than to any effect on the dirt-displacement process.[6]

The theory of the redeposition of dirt from detergent baths has been considered by Durham,[7] in terms of electrical repulsions and van der Waals attractions between suspended dirt and the fibre. The ζ-potential was used as an approximate measure of electrical repulsion, while the attractive forces were calculated theoretically (*cf.* Chapter 4, p. 163). As a measure of stability, Durham used the term $(\zeta/\psi_0)^2$, where ψ_0 is the calculated surface potential needed to overcome the van der Waals attraction, account being taken of the curvature of the fibre surface. Durham found a qualitative correlation between stability and the term $(\zeta/\psi_0)^2$, but concluded that other factors were also operative, such as mechanical barriers due to solvated layers, and barriers due to the steric effect of adsorbed ions. These other factors would be expected to become even more important—probably almost exclusively so—in the case of non-ionic detergents.

[1] Nüsslein, *Textilber.*, 1938, **19**, 582.

[2] Dunbar, *J. Soc. Dyers Colourists*, 1934, **50**, 309.

[3] Powney and Noad, *J. Textile Inst.*, 1939, **30**, T157.

[4] Bertsch, *Z. angew. Chem.*, 1934, **47**, 424; 1935, **48**, 52.

[5] Vold and Phansalkar, *Rec. trav. chim.*, 1955, **74**, 41.

[6] Porter, *Second Congress*, 1957, **IV**, 103.

[7] Durham, *Second Congress*, 1957, **IV**, 60. See also Durham, *J. Applied Chemistry*, 1956, **6**, 153.

Shuttleworth and Jones[1] have published some interesting electron photomicrographs which indicate that, when carbon black is deposited on cotton, adhesion is due to simple sorptive forces, and not to the "micro-occlusion" which has sometimes been thought to occur. They also show that the tendency for deposition to occur is greater the smaller the carbon black particles, *i.e.*, the greater the ratio of surface to mass.

Undoubtedly the most striking example of the importance of reducing the redeposition of suspended dirt is furnished by the action of carboxy-methyl celluloses (sodium cellulose glycollates) when they are added to synthetic detergents. These agents have been found greatly to improve the efficiency of detergents, especially for scouring cotton, and they were widely used in Germany during the last war.[2] The generally held view is that agents of this type have very little effect, if any, on the initial displacement of dirt, but act by hindering redeposition.[3] It has also been reported that the suspending power of ordinary soap, which is reduced when the solutions are made alkaline, is restored by adding carboxymethyl cellulose[4]; this is in agreement with the view that a protective colloid is needed to prevent redeposition, in this case either an "acid soap" or carboxymethyl cellulose.

Although it seems to be agreed that carboxymethyl celluloses are adsorbed by suspended dirt, there is an apparent conflict of evidence as to whether or not it is also adsorbed by textile fibres. Nieuwenhuis[5], in a useful review of the use of carboxymethyl celluloses in detergent processes, reports that positive adsorption occurs. He also concludes, from an investigation of a range of carboxymethyl celluloses, that there is an optimum degree of substitution of the cellulose, lying between 0·50 and 0·60. Stüpel,[6] on the other hand, found no adsorption, except under acid conditions (which are, of course, irrelevant in the present connection), and similar results were reported by Porter.[7] This question has also been investigated very carefully by Stawitz, Klaus, and Krämer,[8] who used a radio-tracer technique for observing the behaviour of carboxymethyl cellulose, of a degree of substitution of about 0·7, on cotton, cellulose acetate, "Perlon," and wool. Within their experimental error they found no true positive adsorption (*i.e.*, no decrease in the concentration of the solution in contact with the fibre), but they did detect a trace of mechanically "occluded" carboxymethyl cellulose, which was not washed off.

---

[1] Shuttleworth and Jones, *Second Congress*, 1957, **IV**, 52.

[2] Brandner, Lockwood, Nagel, and Russell, *F.I.A.T. Final Report, No.* 1141, "Synthetic Detergents and Related Surface Active Agents in Germany." See also F.P. 805,718.

[3] Viertel, *Textilber.*, 1947, **28**, 345.

[4] Bayley and Weatherburn, *Textile Research J.*, 1950, **20**, 510.

[5] Nieuwenhuis, *J. Polymer Sci.*, 1954, **12**, 237.

[6] Stüpel, *Koll. Z.*, 1956, **145**, 140.

[7] Porter, *Second Congress*, 1957, **IV**, 151.

[8] Stawitz, Klaus, and Krämer, *Koll. Z.*, 1957, **150**, 39.

This apparent conflict of evidence has been very objectively reviewed by Nieuwenhuis and Tan,[1] who point out that the discrepancy may be due to the fact that Stawitz *et al.* used unbleached, solvent-extracted cotton, whereas Nieuwenhuis used bleached cotton. (It will also be observed that the carboxymethyl celluloses used in the two cases were of different degrees of substitution.) Nieuwenhuis and Tan also point out that the effect of carboxymethyl cellulose varies with the substrate, being effective in the scouring of bleached cotton, for example, but not with unbleached, solvent-extracted cotton. They suggest that the latter still contains some tenaciously held wax. They make the very important point, however, that the fact that the efficiency of carboxymethyl cellullose varies with the fibre is *not* evidence for a fibre-carboxymethyl cellulose interaction; it could equally well be that different fibres differ in their interactions with the dirt-carboxymethyl cellulose complex. Their final conclusion, that the question is still open as to which type of interaction is involved, seems to be inescapable at present.

The nature of these possible interactions has been considered by Fong and Ward,[2] and by Stillo and Kolat.[3] Fong and Ward report that carboxymethyl cellulose increases the ζ-potentials of both cotton and carbon black, whereas polyvinyl alcohol and polyvinyl pyrrolidone, both of which are effective retarders of re-deposition, do not. Stillo and Kolat invoke the theories of Mackor and van der Waals and of Verwcy and Overbeek (*cf.* Chapter 4, p. 163), in considering their data on ζ-potentials and anti-re-deposition efficiencies. They find no correlation between the two, and suggest that, with the range of polymers which they studied, carboxymethyl cellulose acted principally by a ζ-potential effect, while the action of the two non-ionic polymers was due to two steric effects: (*i*) a decrease in the non-electrical attractive forces due to the interposition of the adsorbed layer, and (*ii*) an increase in the non-electrical repulsive forces due to the decrease in configurational entropy which must result if re-deposition occurs. Stillo and Kolat have an open mind on the question of whether or not carboxymethyl cellulose is adsorbed by both cotton and carbon black.

E. Evaluation of detergents

Tests for detergent power are usually carried out for one or more of the following purposes: (a) to determine the best conditions (mechanical arrangements, substrate-to-medium ratio, temperature, pH, nature and concentration of the detergent, etc.) for doing a particular cleansing operation; (b) to compare different surface-active compounds for general detergent power as critically as possible; (c) to study the mechanism of

---

[1] Nieuwenhuis and Tan, *Second Congress*, 1957, **IV**, 12.
[2] Fong and Ward, *Textile Research J.*, 1954, **24**, 881.
[3] Stillo and Kolat, *ibid.*, 1957, **27**, 949.

detergent processes, with particular emphasis on the correlation of chemical structure and detergent efficiency. For the first of these purposes it seems to be generally agreed that the test should be carried out with the actual dirty material itself, and as far as possible under the actual operating conditions to be used.[1] The opinion has even been expressed[2] that artificially soiled materials are useless for all detergent tests. It seems to the present authors that this last view goes rather too far—though the need for caution in interpreting results with artificially soiled materials cannot be over-emphasised[3]—and that much useful information can be obtained from the published results with such materials. This is especially true of some of the more scientific investigations of detergent mechanisms. The references given below are intended to be illustrative rather than exhaustive: other relevant papers are cited in the monographs by Valko,[4] by Chwala,[5] by Lindner,[6] by Stüpel,[7] and by Niven.[8] Useful reviews of methods of testing detergents have also been published by, among others, Harwood and Wagg[9] and Wagg.[10]

The mechanical aspect of detergent testing has of course received a great deal of attention, rotating cylindrical vessels containing steel balls (which some workers prefer to have rubber-coated) having been frequently used.[11] A popular embodiment of this principle is the "Launderometer." A less drastic action, which in our opinion is preferable if small differences in detergent power are being studied in a series of related compounds, was used by Götte,[12] who placed the detergent medium and the cloth to be scoured in a 3·5-litre glass vessel, which was rotated about a radial axis so that the contents were thrown back and forth from top to bottom. Other workers have relied on carefully standardised stirring.[13] An interesting recent proposal has been to use an ultrasonic generator (cone transducer

---

[1] See for example Crowe *et al.*, *Amer. Dyes. Reporter*, 1943, **32**, 237.

[2] Franz, *Textilber.*, 1935, **16**, 277.

[3] *Cf.* Kling, *Z. angew. Chem.*, 1934, **47**, 425, and other speakers in the subsequent discussion.

[4] Valko, *Kolloidchemische Grundlagen der Textilveredlung*, Springer, Berlin, 1937.

[5] Chwala, *Textilhilfsmittel*, Springer, Vienna, 1939.

[6] Lindner, *Textilhilfsmittel und Waschrohstoffe*, Wissenschaftlicher Verlag, Stuttgart, 1954.

[7] Stüpel, *Synthetische Wasch- und Reinigungsmittel*, Kohlhammer, Stuttgart, 1954.

[8] Niven, *Fundamentals of Detergency*, Reinhold, 1950.

[9] Harwood and Wagg, *Reports of the Progress of Applied Chemistry*, 1951, **36**, 211.

[10] Wagg, *Second Congress*, 1957, **IV**, 35, 43.

[11] See for example Appel, Smith, and Christison, *Amer. Dyes. Reporter*, 1928, **17**, 731; Rhodes and Brainard, *Ind. Eng. Chem.*, 1929, **21**, 60; Snell, *ibid.*, 1933, **25**, 1240; Crowe *et al.*, *Amer. Dyes. Reporter*, 1943, **32**, 237; Holland and Petrea, *ibid.*, 1943, **32**, 534; Bacon, *ibid.*, 1945, **34**, 556; Nutting, *Amer. Dyes. Reporter*, 1950, **39**, No. 8, P260; Morrisroe and Newhall, *Ind. Eng. Chem.*, 1949, **41**, 423; Lambert and Sanders, *Ind. Eng. Chem.*, 1950, **42**, 1388.

[12] Götte, *Koll. Z.*, 1933, **64**, 222.

[13] *Cf.* Dunbar, *J. Soc. Dyers Colourists*, 1934, **50**, 309.

type) in contact with the soiled fabric, as a method of precisely controlling the power input.[1]

Although detergency tests are usually carried out on cloth specimens, either naturally or artificially soiled, the "chopped fibre" technique of Powney and Feuell[2] is now also well established. These authors used soiled single fibres, about 2 cm. long, which were made into a pad after scouring and examined with a reflectometer. The method, which is claimed to give more reproducible results than the scouring of woven fabrics, has been further developed by Wagg[3] and by Straw.[4]

The chief problem in "model" detergency tests, using artificially soiled materials, is undoubtedly the choice of a suitable representative "dirt." Most workers have used a combination of an oil or wax (*e.g.*, mineral oil fractions of varying types and degrees of purity, animal and vegetable oils, lanoline, etc.) with a solid such as carbon black which is readily visible.[5] The degree of scouring obtained can then be assessed visually or by means of a photoelectric device. This method is especially useful when it is desired to examine the behaviour of different compounds with mixed "dirts." For a more precise analysis of a detergent process, on the other hand, it may be preferable to use only a representative oil, and to assess the detergent action obtained by extracting the grease before and after scouring with a suitable solvent.[6]

Optical measurements can of course be carried out on either the test piece (reflectance), or the wash liquor (transmission), or on both. It is worth noting, however, that Barker and Kern[7] have reported that, although the results of the two types of measurement agree reasonably well when non-ionic detergents are used, there is a discrepancy when the detergent is a tallow soap.

A more recent development which shows great promise is the use of radioactive tracers in the dirt, which enables a direct measurement of the dirt remaining in the fabric to be carried out quickly, while avoiding the pitfalls of the optical methods. Osipow, Segura, Snell, and Snell[8] used this method for studying the scouring of synthetic dirt (a mixture of white petrolatum, mineral oil, palmitic acid, barium carbonate, and carbon black, tagged with C^{14}) from steel panels by means of emulsions of kerosene and pine oil, emulsified with triethanolamine oleate. In agreement with earlier work, it was found that unstable emulsions ("diphase systems"),

[1] Ludeman, Balog, and Sherrill, *J. American Oil Chem. Soc.*, 1958, **35**, 5.

[2] Powney and Feuell, *Research*, 1949, **2**, 331.

[3] Wagg, *J. Textile Inst.*, 1953, **44**, T658.

[4] Straw, *J. Soc. Dyers Colourists*, 1954, **70**, 288.

[5] See, however, Diamond and Levin (*Text. Research J.*, 1957, **27**, 787), who used zirconyl phosphate as the "dirt," deposited in the fabric by reaction *in situ*.

[6] *Cf.* Palmer, *J. Soc. Chem. Ind.*, 1941, **60**, 56, 60.

[7] Barker and Kern, *J. Amer. Oil Chem. Soc.*, 1950, **27**, 113.

[8] Osipow, Segura, Snell, and Snell, *Ind. Eng. Chem.*, 1953, **45**, 2779.

made by simply adding the ingredients to water, were more efficient cleaning agents than the more stable emulsions which were prepared by the "nascent soap" technique (*cf.* p. 251). Osipow *et al.* also found that one ingredient of their dirt, the palmitic acid, was preferentially removed, the radio-tracer technique allowing a separate determination of the removal of different constituents in the dirt. Further examples of the usefulness and good reproducibility of the radio-tracer method, as applied to textiles, have been described by Hemsley, Kramer, Ring, and Suter,[1] by Diamond and Levin,[2] and by Ehrenkranz and Jebe.[3]

It is generally appreciated that, besides the concentration of the detergent, factors such as the temperature, pH, and electrolyte content affect scouring processes and must be controlled; the effect of varying these factors frequently goes through a maximum. This is well illustrated in Götte's[4] series of papers, which constitute one of the classical contributions in this field, and in the papers by Rhodes and Bascom,[5] Dunbar,[6] Palmer,[7] and Aickin.[8] Sometimes the concentration and nature of the electrolytes which are present are completely beyond the control of the investigator, as in the war-time tests on available detergents in *sea water* (both natural and artificial) which have been described by Vaughn, Hill, Smith, McCoy, and Simpson.[9] Not unexpectedly, these workers found that the best detergents under these conditions (polyethenoxy and fatty amide sulphonate types) were those which were least liable to precipitation by the salts present.

F. "Detergent builders"

It has been known for many years that the efficiency of soap and of synthetic detergents can be considerably increased by the addition of electrolytes, especially of alkaline buffers. It is also well known that the efficiency of soaps in particular is increased by adding water-softening agents. More recently, electrolytes have been found which are so effective that the special expression "detergent builders"* has been coined to describe them, and it is probably true to say that the great majority of synthetic detergent compositions now contain such additives.

Although alkaline buffers such as sodium carbonate, sodium sesquicarbonate, sodium silicate, and borax have been added to detergent baths

---

* It seems to us to be preferable to restrict the use of this word to inorganic electrolytes, otherwise the whole concept becomes too broad to be easily handled.

[1] Hemsley, Kramer, Ring, and Suter, *J. American Oil Chem. Soc.*, 1955, **32**, 138.
[2] Diamond and Levin, *Textile Research J.*, 1957, **27**, 787.
[3] Ehrenkranz and Jebe, *Soap and Chemical Specialties*, 1958, **34**, No. 4, 47, 163.
[4] Götte, *Koll. Z.*, 1933, **64**, 222, 327, 331; 1933, **65**, 236.
[5] Rhodes and Bascom, *Ind. Eng. Chem.*, 1931, **23**, 778.
[6] Dunbar, *J. Soc. Dyers Colourists*, 1934, **50**, 309.
[7] *Cf.* Palmer, *J. Soc. Chem. Ind.*, 1941, **60**, 56, 60.
[8] Aickin, *J. Soc. Dyers Colourists*, 1944, **60**, 170.
[9] Vaughn, Hill, Smith, McCoy, and Simpson, *Ind. Eng. Chem.*, 1949, **41**, 112.

for many years, the most important builders at present are the "condensed phosphates," *i.e.*, salts of the acids which are obtained by eliminating water from orthophosphoric acid, H_3PO_4. A useful review of these materials has been published by Stüpel,[1] who attributes their first use in detergent baths to Agthe[2] in 1930. Well-known examples of condensed phosphates are sodium pyrophosphate ($Na_4P_2O_7$), sodium tripolyphosphate ($Na_5P_3O_{10}$), and sodium hexametaphosphate ($Na_6P_6O_{18}$). Stüpel points out that the constitution of many of these materials is not fully established, and that many of them are mixtures: for example, the well-known "Calgon" products are not all sodium hexametaphosphate. They can, perhaps, best be described as uni-multivalent electrolytes, some of which show some of the properties of colloidal electrolytes, and all of which have a tendency (though to varying degrees) to revert to ions of lower valency.

The mode of action of builders is undoubtedly a complex of a number of effects, many of which are specific to the system in question. It is therefore impossible to give a single, generalised picture of how they work   one can only attempt to enumerate the possible constituent phenomena, with an indication of where they are likely to be important. Further details will be found, for example, in the summarising article by Stüpel to which we have just referred, and in the books by Lindner[3] and by Niven.[4] The present evidence suggests that these constituent phenomena (which are not necessarily in the following order of importance) are as follows:

1. *Saponification and Water-softening*. Alkaline solutes such as soda ash or Na_3PO_4 are so well known to help the emulsification of greases which contain saponifiable matter, by a sort of "nascent soap" process, that this mechanism requires little comment. The same is also true of the action of the "Calgons" in removing concentrations of Ca^{++}, Mg^{++}, or Fe^{+++} ions which can cause precipitation, especially of the ordinary soaps. This latter effect is due to the "sequestering" action of the multivalent phosphate anions, which remove the metal ions by chelation.

2. *Swelling of the fibre*. Alkaline buffers (which must not, however, be too alkaline) are known to swell polar fibres such as wool or cotton, and it seems likely that this helps many detergent processes, for example, by making the fibres still more "hydrophilic" (*i.e.*, by reducing the fibre-solution interfacial tension), and/or by enabling the solution to make contact with the fibre, so that the "rolling-off" mechanism can begin. This may be one reason for the specificity of some combinations of builders and substrates.

3. *General increases in surface activity*. It is well known that electrolytes

---

[1] Stüpel, *Soap, Perfumery, and Cosmetics*, 1954, **27**, 65.

[2] Agthe, D.R.P. 506,338. See also I.G., B.P. 408,708; Henkel, B.P.'s 431,682; 435,475; 435,562; 443,487.

[3] Lindner, *Textilhilfsmittel und Waschrohstoffe*, Wissenschaftlicher Verlag, Stuttgart, 1954.

[4] Niven, *Fundamentals of Detergency*, Reinhold, 1950.

tend to increase the surface activity of amphipathic ions at many interfaces, in both the dynamic and static senses. Although it has been reported that sodium pyrophosphate did not decrease the surface tension, or the inter-facial tension against medicinal paraffin, of solutions of alkaryl sulphonates or non-ionic detergents,[1] simple electrolytes (such as sodium carbonate) are known to have this effect with anionic surface-active agents. We have seen in Chapter 3 that in such a case the electrolyte diminishes the potential gradient against which the surface-active ions must diffuse in order to reach the interface. There may well be an optimum valency for this effect, the anions of at least some of the condensed phosphates having perhaps too high a valency. It is worth noting, however, that Perry, Weatherburn, and Bayley[2] found that a series of builders, from orthophosphate to sodium hexametaphosphate, and including sodium metasilicate, had the expected effect of *increasing* the adsorption of sodium tetradecyl sulphate by cotton and by carbon black.

4. *Deflocculation*. It seems to be agreed that the most general effect of phosphate builders, especially of the more "highly condensed" types, is to deflocculate the suspended dirt, especially solid dirt. This mechanism, which reduces re-deposition of all types of dirt, and probably helps the detachment of solid dirt as well, appears to operate in the presence of non-ionic as well as of anionic detergents. It seems likely that increases in interfacial potentials (both dirt-solution and fibre-solution) are at least partly responsible. (It is worth recalling in this connection that the con-densed phosphates are used as deflocculating agents for inorganic solids in aqueous suspensions.)

G. Public health aspects of the use of synthetic detergents

A considerable amount of discussion has taken place during the past twelve years, on both sides of the Atlantic, on the question of how far the presence of synthetic detergents in domestic or industrial effluents is causing, or is likely to cause, troubles in sewage-disposal or water-purification plants. A sufficiently serious view was taken of the matter that in the United King-dom a special committee (the "Jephcott Committee") was set up by the Minister of Housing and Local Government in 1953 to investigate and report on the situation, while in the United States special efforts were made by the detergent manufacturers to co-operate in clearing up the problem.* A voluminous literature on the subject has rapidly developed, some of it contradictory, or pertinent only to local or special conditions. We propose

---

* See, for example, the article by Coughlin, *Soap and Chemical Specialties*, 1956, **32**, No. 2, 51, 67, 69, 71.
  [1] Sanders and Lambert, *Textile Research J.*, 1951, **21**, 680.
  [2] Perry, Weatherburn, and Bayley, *J. Amer. Oil Chemists' Soc.*, 1957, **34**, 493.

to confine ourselves here to a few selected papers which will perhaps give a general picture of the situation.

The report of the Jephcott Committee[1] considers first the possible effects of modern synthetic detergents when they come in contact externally with the skin, when they are taken internally (*e.g.*, from dishes or cutlery), and on plumbing and household appliances. The Committee's report is in general reassuring on these points: it is stated, for example, that there does not appear to have been a significant increase in dermatitis with the introduction of synthetic detergents,* that the amounts which are normally taken internally are negligible, and that damages to plumbing and household equipment appear to have been slight. The greater part of the Report is taken up with the possible effects of synthetic detergents in sewage works and in rivers and streams, with particular reference to

(1) primary purification processes in sewage works (sedimentation of solids, sludge filtration, etc.);

(2) secondary purification processes (aeration and biological degradation of organic matter);

(3) persistence of detergents in the final effluents.

The situation as described in the Report is, broadly, that the primary purification processes are not greatly affected, but that trouble is encountered during the secondary purification processes, chiefly through the formation of voluminous foams (especially in the activated sludge process, in which air is blown through the sewage), and to a less extent through a slowing down of the rate of oxygenation of water. The formation of foams, which may be several feet deep on occasion, is the most spectacular of these problems. These foams can be anything from a mere nuisance to a positive danger to the operatives, or to public health when they are blown about.

The adverse effect of synthetic detergents on the rate of oxygenation of water is perhaps more surprising. It has been studied by Gameson, Truesdale, and Varley,[2] and by Downing, Melbourne, and Bruce.[3] These latter workers studied the effect in glass vessels and in a wave tank, and found that the exchange coefficient with pure water was reduced by up to 60% by the presence of a mixture of seven proprietary detergents, at 0·1 to 15 parts per million of anionic detergent. The exchange coefficient first fell rapidly with concentration and then levelled off. With neat sodium dodecylbenzene sulphonate, the reduction varied from 25 to 40%, at less than

---

* A similar general picture emerges from the Plenary Lecture on the subject by Professor W. Schneider at the First International Congress of Surface Activity in Paris in 1954 (*First Congress*, p. 1299), and the paper by Bidaux (*ibid.*, p. 699). Schneider does, however, draw attention to the greater efficiency as grease removers of most modern synthetic detergents, and in this connection commends the ancient practice of anointing the skin with oil.

[1] *Report of the Committee on Synthetic Detergents*, H.M.S.O., 1956.
[2] Gameson, Truesdale, and Varley, *Water and Sanitary Engineering*, 1956, **6**, 52.
[3] Downing, Melbourne, and Bruce, *J. Applied Chem.*, 1957, **7**, 590.

one part per million. The addition of sewage effluent reduced the exchange coefficient of pure water, while the further addition of detergent (in the amounts mentioned above) caused a further, larger reduction.

This reduction of the rate of oxygenation of water can of course reduce the efficiency of a given sewage disposal unit, and (as pointed out by the Jephcott Committee and by Downing, Melbourne, and Bruce) can lead to a reduction in the rate of self-purification of rivers and streams, and to unfavourable effects on fish and animal life in the streams. The mechanism of the effect does not seem to be entirely clear: according to the Jephcott Report, it is more pronounced under intermediate conditions of aeration than when a water surface is either quiescent or vigorously agitated. This suggests that the barrier is greatest *during the attainment of adsorption equilibrium*, and that it is due to the presence of effects such as diffusion potentials (all these remarks apply only to anionic detergents), rather than to mechanical barriers to the diffusion of oxygen molecules. The results of work on retardation of evaporation or of mass transfer across interfaces,* on the other hand, would suggest that the affect may be at least partly due to the formation of barrier layers, especially by impurities in the detergents, or to more subtle effects on convection currents near the water-air interface.

The methods of foam destruction considered by the Jephcott Committee, on the basis of both British and American experience, include the use of the cheaper anti-foaming oils based on mineral oil, and the presence of a larger amount of suspended solids in the aerated mixtures. (The latter device tends to be specific, and appears to work better in the United States, where detergent concentrations in sewage are generally lower than in the United Kingdom.) The most obvious line of attack, however, on this and on the other problems in sewage disposal and water-purification, is the use of detergents which are themselves more sensitive to bacterial decomposition, even though by their nature synthetic detergents are more stable *chemically* than soap. The majority of the members of the Jephcott Committee envisage governmental control of the types of detergent which may be offered for sale, as the ultimate safeguard which might have to be introduced; in the meantime, they recommend a policy of careful observation of the situation, with emphasis on (quantitative) testing,† and further research on possible methods of foam-breaking.

Special precipitants have been described for removing synthetic anionic detergents or for counteracting their effects—and it is worth noting that, according to the Jephcott Committee, 95% of the synthetic detergents sold in the United Kingdom at that time were based on anionic surface-active agents. These precipitants include water-soluble salts of primary rosin

---

* See Chapter 9, p. 344.

† A useful summary of recommended methods for analysing for detergents in effluents has been published by the A.B.C.M.-S.A.C. Committee in the *Analyst*, 1957, **82**, 826.

amines,[1] or extra additions of aluminium sulphate.[2] The question of cost
arises, however, and in some cases of the permissibility of the precipitants.

The susceptibility of synthetic detergents to biological decomposition
appears to be influenced by the nature of the paraffin chain, straight-chain
alkyl sulphates or alkylated aromatic sulphonates being more readily
decomposed than their branched-chain analogues.[3] Polyethenoxy agents
containing a relatively small number of ether groups are also less stable
than the more "polymeric" ethylene oxide derivatives.[4] A useful summary
of information on this point, as well as of the problem as a whole in the
light of the work done at the Massachusetts Institute of Technology, has
been published by Sawyer.[5] He classifies synthetic detergents into biologically "soft" (*i.e.*, more easily decomposed) types, which are alkyl
sulphates or contain ester or amide groups, such as sulphated fatty monoglycerides or sodium oleyl-N-methyltaurine, and biologically "hard"
agents, which include the alkylbenzene sulphonates, the alkylphenol-
ethylene oxide condensation products, and the polyethylene glycols.
(Within each type there are considerable variations, and it would seem to
us to be premature to attempt too rigid a classification.) The conclusions
reached by Sawyer are, on the whole, in good agreement with those of the
Jephcott Committee.

As one result of the Jephcott Report, a Standing Technical Committee
on Synthetic Detergents was set up by the Ministry of Housing and Local
Government, with the task of watching the situation. This Standing Committee has issued three Progress Reports, published by the Stationery
Office in 1958, 1959, and 1960. The first states that the situation in the
United Kingdom appears to have become stabilised, in the sense that the
sales of synthetic detergents are reaching an apparent saturation level
(over 40,000 tons *per annum*), and that the degree of contamination of
sewage does not appear to be increasing. The second Progress Report
states that one experimental detergent has been prepared, following the
recommendations of the Jephcott Committee, which is technically satisfactory, and undergoes more rapid bacterial decomposition.

The Third Progress Report,[6] which has been published quite recently,
contains a summary of the valuable large-scale trials which were carried
out in the Luton-Harpenden area with the specially developed "biologically
soft" detergent, which is based on a straight-chain, as distinct from the
more usual branched-chain type of alkylbenzene sulphonate. Attempts

[1] Vaughn and Falkenthal, *Ind. Eng. Chem.*, 1956, **48**, 241.
[2] Beaver, *First Congress*, 1954, 1059.
[3] Hammerton, *J. Applied Chem.*, 1955, **5**, 517; Simpson, Bogan, and Sawyer, *Ind. Eng. Chem.*, 1956, **48**, 236.
[4] Simpson, Bogan, and Sawyer, *Ind. Eng. Chem.*, 1956, **48**, 236.
[5] Sawyer, *Sewage and Industrial Wastes*, 1958, **30**, 757.
[6] *Third Progress Report of the Standing Committee on Synthetic Detergents*, H.M.S.O., 1960.

were made, with the co-operation of the manufacturers and public author-
ities, to replace the old detergent by "soft" material in the shops in the
area, and to determine the effect of the change on the degree of decomposition of detergent at the sewage works, on the amount of detergent passing
into the River Lea, and on the amount of foam formed on the river. The
trials were beset with a number of difficulties: analytical problems were
encountered, the change-over to the new detergent was slower and less
complete than had been hoped, and 1959 was an unusually dry year, so
that concentrations tended to be higher than usual. In spite of these difficulties, however, the trials demonstrated that the adoption of the "soft"
detergent would lead to a higher degree of destruction, diminished contamination of the local river, and less foaming on the river.

Another contemporary public health problem, which arises in both
civil defence and industrial hygiene, is that of decontamination of articles
and persons from radio-active materials. The relative efficiencies of a
number of surface-active materials have been tested for this purpose. The
fact that the contaminant in question is radio-active is of course irrelevant
to the physico-chemical mechanism involved. In so far, therefore, as the
problem is to remove salts of yttrium and radio-active rare earth metals,
the function of a surface-active agent is to *sequester* the harmful multivalent cations, so that they can be washed away. Snell, Segura, Stigman,
and Snell[1] have reported that sodium hexametaphosphate (which is well
known to form soluble chelation complexes with ions such as Ca^{++}, Cu^{++},
and Fe^{+++}) is particularly useful for this purpose, and recommend its
addition to detergents which are to be used for decontamination. Their
article also gives a useful general summary of the place of surface-active
materials in the problem as a whole. It is also interesting to note the
parallel observation of Chandler and Shelberg[2] that the efficiency of
potassium laurate and potassium palmitate for removing yttrium trichloride from surfaces painted with U.S. "Navy Gray" paint rose sharply
just above the critical micelle concentrations. The samples of the two soaps
showed minima in their surface tension-concentration curves, suggesting
either the presence of impurities or partial hydrolysis, but it is quite
possible that either of these effects, which would increase the amount of
micellar solute present, would be distinctly favourable to the desired
sequestering of yttrium ions.

H. Fluorescent brightening agents

Although, strictly speaking, the so-called fluorescent brightening agents*
fall outside the scope of this book, a brief reference to them is needed, if

---

* These substances are also referred to as "white dyes" or "optical bleaches."
[1] Snell, Segura, Stigman, and Snell, *Soap and Sanitary Chemicals*, 1953, **29**, No. 10, 42.
[2] Chandler and Shelberg, *J. Coll. Sci.*, 1955, **10**, 393.

only to point out that they are not in fact detergents: *i.e.*, there is no evidence so far that they help in the removal of either solid or liquid dirt from textile materials. The function of these agents appears to be entirely an "optical" one: to absorb incident ultra-violet light and to re-emit it as visible light, usually blue-blueish white, which compensates for any yellowing of the substrate by a process of *additive* colour synthesis. Their action is therefore quite different from that of ordinary blueing, which corrects for yellowness by *subtractive* colour synthesis and consequently invariably decreases the total amount of reflected light.

Fluorescent brightening agents are mostly pale yellow substances which are soluble or dispersible in detergent solutions, and have an affinity for the fibre in question. Their use appears to have been first suggested by Krais[1] in 1929, but they have only achieved a widespread popularity since the Second World War, especially in domestic detergent mixtures. Summaries have been published by Landolt,[2] by Lesser,[3] by Caspar,[4] and by Siegrist.[5] Fuller accounts will be found in Diserens's well-known book,[6] and in the more recent monograph by Ühlein.[7]

I. General correlations between detergent action and the states of solution of surface-active agents

In Sections B, C, and D of the present chapter we have attempted to discuss the component phenomena, antagonistic as well as favourable, which make up detergent processes, and to show how surface-active agents can influence these phenomena by modifying the conditions at the various interfaces. A question of very great interest arises in this connection, which has been considered by a number of workers, *viz.*, how far these interfacial conditions are affected by the state of solution of a detergent, or more specifically, whether or not it is generally advantageous for the detergent compound to be present as micelles rather than as single ions. Partial answers have already been given, but a summary of the position would appear to be desirable.

It seems to be generally agreed that the individual amphipathic *ions* (or, in a non-ionising surface-active agent, the unassociated molecules) are the essential *surface-active* portion of the solute in a detergent solution.[8]

[1] Krais, *Textilber.*, 1929, **10**, 468.

[2] Landolt, *Amer. Dyes. Reporter*, 1949, **38**, 353.

[3] Lesser, *Soap and Sanitary Chemicals*, 1949, **25**, No. 11, 36.

[4] Caspar, *J. Soc. Dyers Colourists*, 1950, **66**, 177.

[5] Siegrist, *First Congress*, 1954, 512.

[6] Diserens, *Die neuesten Fortschritte und Verfahren in der Technik der chemischen Veredlung der Textilfasern*, **2**, pp. 654 ff., Birkhäuser, Basel, 1953.

[7] Ühlein, *Optische Aufheller*, Moser, Garmisch-Partenkirchen, 1957.

[8] *Cf.* Aickin, *J. Soc. Dyers Colourists*, 1944, **60**, 36; Palmer, *J. Soc. Chem. Ind.*, 1941, **60**, 56, 60; Hartley, *Trans. Faraday Soc.*, 1941, **37**, 131.

This point is discussed with great clarity by Preston,[1] from whose paper Figure 2, showing detergent efficiency and a number of physical properties as functions of the concentration of sodium dodecyl sulphate, is reproduced in Chapter 2. Preston points out that, over the critical concentration range, the concentration of molecularly dispersed amphipathic ions increases more and more slowly, until it becomes sensibly constant. The upper limit of the critical concentration range therefore coincides approximately with the maximum concentration of individual ions: since it also coincides with the attainment of maximum scouring power, it seems reasonable to conclude that washing is caused by the molecularly dispersed solute.*

Preston recognises that this conclusion, which is borne out by his experimental data on the effect of chain length in several homologous series of detergents, does not exclude the possibility that the micelles may play a part in some detergent processes by virtue of their solvent action. (See Section C—2 above.) It seems to us that other useful functions might also, in certain cases, be ascribed to the colloidal portion of the solute. Thus we have already noted Reumuth's suggestion that entrainment of dirt in a foam or lather may favour detergent action, and Urbain and Jensen's theory that micelles can contribute to the deflocculation of suspended dirt by acting as ions of very high valency. A further very reasonable suggestion is that advanced by Palmer,[2] that micelle formation might help the dynamics of detergent processes by accelerating the diffusion of surface-active compound to the various interfaces. A final, purely speculative point for consideration is that the colloidal matter in a detergent solution might favour the removal of dirt, or prevent its redeposition, by being adsorbed at the fibre-solution interface in such a way as to increase the "hydration" of the interface. The suggestion by Carter,[3] that sodium silicate prevents the deposition of solid dirt by forming a film on the cloth, has a bearing on this question. Unfortunately, we have not been able to find any data which allow this point to be settled.

Finally, it is worth recalling the evidence, which is discussed in Section

---

* It is important that Preston's phrase "washing is caused *by the fatty anions*" (our italics), should not be construed to mean that anions and cations are independently adsorbed at the relevant interfaces. The condition of electrical neutrality in the interfacial and in the bulk phases demands that each anion (*e.g.*, A^-) adsorbed must be accompanied by a cation (*e.g.*, Na^+), and *vice versa*. Usually both ions will come from the detergent solution, but in special cases one may be formed by a special chemical reaction. The effective surface-active component will be the whole compound (*e.g.*, NaA), and its mean activity $\sqrt{(a_{Na} \cdot a_A)}$ cannot decrease with increasing total concentration of solute in a solution of pure NaA, although it can become sensibly constant. One would therefore expect the detergent power, and other physical properties which are dependent on $\sqrt{(a_{Na} \cdot a_A)}$, to approach a constant value, but not to decrease, in a solution of the pure detergent. Where other components are also present, this does not necessarily apply (*cf.* the discussion on the minima in surface tension-concentration curves in Chapter 3).

[1] Preston, *J. Phys. Coll. Chem.*, 1948, **52**, 84.

[2] Palmer, *J. Soc. Chem. Ind.*, 1941, **60**, 56, 60.

[3] Carter, *Ind. Eng. Chem.*, 1931, **23**, 1389.

B–2 of the present chapter, that detergents can also function by penetration into liquid dirt, accompanied by the formation of complexes with polar ingredients of the dirt. This mechanism will also be favoured by a high concentration of molecularly dispersed surface-active material in the aqueous phase, as well as by a rapid transport to the interface, but it also raises the interesting question of the effect of the state of solution of the detergent *in the liquid dirt*. It remains to be seen how far definite correlations are found between these properties.

CHAPTER 9

SOME OTHER APPLICATIONS OF SURFACE-ACTIVE AGENTS

ALTHOUGH it has not been possible in the preceding chapters to mention all the uses of surface-active agents, it will be appreciated that many other applications are only further illustrations, broadly speaking, of those which have already been described. The use of wetting-out agents as "de-misting" agents on glass surfaces, and for improving the efficiency of water sprays for removing dust from air, are only further cases of the wetting-out processes discussed in Chapter 5. To take other examples, the use of detergents in the household, or the preparation of pharmaceutical emulsions, may raise special problems or *desiderata* such as the avoidance of toxic effects, but these two applications are not fundamentally different from those which have been considered in Chapters 8 and 6, respectively. There are however several specialised uses, without which no book on surface-active agents would be complete, which we propose to consider briefly in the present chapter.

A. Dyeing assistants

A number of the processes which have been described in the preceding four chapters are of importance in the dyeing of textiles. Thus for example wetting-out and scouring are often necessary preliminaries to dyeing, while "dispersing agents" are very widely used in obtaining insoluble dyestuffs of all types in the correct physical form for application. There are in addition several more specialised uses for surface-active agents in dyeing problems; such agents can be conveniently designated as "dyeing assistants." It is interesting to observe that certain of these special uses appear to be based more on the colloidal properties of aqueous solutions of the dyeing assistants, than on their surface-activity at macroscopic interfaces. The following examples will serve as illustrations; fuller accounts of these and other applications of dyeing assistants will be found in the books by Horsfall and Lawrie,[1] Diserens,[2] Chwala,[3] and Valko,[4] for example.

1. LEVELLING AND RESTRAINING AGENTS

An essential step in many dyeing processes is of course the adsorption of a water-soluble substance by a textile fibre. The water-soluble adsorbate

---

[1] Horsfall and Lawrie, *The Dyeing of Textile Fibres*, Chapman and Hall, 2nd Edition, 1946, pp. 378–415.

[2] Diserens, *Die neuesten Fortschritte in der Anwendung der Farbstoffe, Hilfsmittel in der Textilindustrie*, vol. II, Birkhäuser, Basle, 1949.

[3] Chwala, *Textilhilfsmittel*, Springer, Vienna, 1939.

[4] Valko, *Kolloidchemische Grundlagen der Textilveredlung*, Springer, Berlin, 1937.

may for example be a direct cotton dyestuff, an acid wool dye, or the water-soluble leuco form of a vat dyestuff. Adsorption by the fibre will in each case be due to one or more special mechanisms such as salt linkages between ionising groups in the dyestuff molecule and in the fibre, hydrogen bonds between special groups in the dyestuff and in the fibre, dipole interactions, and perhaps general amphipathic properties of the dyestuff molecules or ions. It is probably true to say, though not without danger of over-simplification, that salt linkages generally play a greater part in the dyeing of wool than in the dyeing of cellulose fibres; the theory of dyeing is discussed for example in the monographs by Valko (*loc. cit.*) and by Vickerstaff.[1] Whatever may be the exact causes of the affinity of a dyestuff for a fibre, however, a condition which is nearly always desirable *per se* is that the process

$$\text{Dyestuff (solution)} + \text{Fibre} \rightarrow \text{Dyed Fibre}$$

should go as far and as rapidly as possible to the right. This obvious requirement often leads, however, to an undesirable unevenness of dyeing, due to the fact that a very high proportion of the dyestuff is very rapidly adsorbed on the more accessible parts of the fibre, and that in the time available equilibrium is not established among the adsorbed dyestuff molecules on different parts of the fibre. The dyestuff which is first adsorbed may even block the channels into the fibre, so that other dyestuff molecules may be prevented from reaching vacant sites in the interior of the fibre. A further effect which may cause or contribute to uneven dyeing is that the receptivity for a given dyestuff of different regions of the fibre, or of different fibres in a mixture, may be different. Both of these unfavourable effects can often be diminished or eliminated by the use of suitable surface-active materials which act as "levelling agents."

When unevenness is due to an excessively rapid adsorption of dyestuff, levelling agents can restrain the process either by competing with the dyestuff for available sites on the fibre, or by reducing the chemical potential (and hence the effective concentration) of dissolved dyestuff by forming complex micelles with it in the aqueous solution. The "competition" mechanism is illustrated by the use of anionic surface-active agents in dyeing wool from acid dyebaths. The dyestuffs used are normally sulphonic acids, which form salt linkages with the $-NH_3^+$ groups; consequently agents such as sodium oleyl-*p*-anisidide sulphonate, sodium oleyl sulphate, oleyl-N-methyltaurine, or highly sulphonated oils can reduce the speed of dyeing by competing with the dyestuff anions for the $-NH_3^+$ groups. Although in theory the final equilibrium uptake of dyestuff must always be reduced by the presence of the levelling assistant, this disadvantage will often be small and in any case completely masked by the

---

[1] Vickerstaff, *The Physical Chemistry of Dyeing*, Oliver and Boyd, 2nd Edition, 1954.

improvement in the distribution of dyestuff on the fibre.* The mechanism of this type of levelling action has been investigated by Neville and Jeanson,[1] who studied the effect of pH and of the concentration of a sulphated fatty alcohol on the adsorption of the dyestuff Orange II by wool. They found that adsorption fell with increasing pH and with increasing concentration of anionic surface-active agent, both of which facts agree with the current theory outlined above. A similar picture emerges from the experiments of Flett and Hoyt[2] on the competition between "Nacconol NR" (a sodium alkylbenzene sulphonate) and the dyestuff Wool Orange A, from acid solution, for the adsorption sites on wool. Their results indicate that the competitive adsorption processes are reversible, the "Nacconol" stripping off dyestuff which had already been adsorbed by the fibre.

The possible importance of micelle formation in the retarding mechanism which we have just discussed will be at once apparent, since a micelle is in effect a large multivalent ion which would be expected to have a considerable affinity for cationically ionising groups on the fibre. Since the kinetics of adsorption are probably more important in this case than is the final equilibrium state, micelle formation might also be favourable to restraining action by accelerating the rate of transfer of surface-active anions to the fibre-solution interface. Thus for example the surface of a wool fibre would be expected to carry a positive electrokinetic charge in an acid solution, so that the diffusion of a multivalent micelle might be considerably accelerated. Even in a case of free diffusion, however, the resistance to diffusion of a micelle would increase only with the cube root of its aggregation number, whereas its mass would increase in direct proportion, so that the actual rate of transfer of material to the interface might increase in proportion to the two-thirds power of the aggregation number.

A levelling principle which is probably more frequently used in dyeing processes is to add a substance which forms a complex micelle with the dyestuff molecules or ions. A well-known example of this principle is the use of ethylene oxide condensates such as "Peregal O" or "Dispersol VL" for retarding the adsorption of leuco vat dyestuffs[3] or of direct dyestuffs[4] by cellulose. Valko[5] has shown by diffusion measurements that "Peregal O" causes the aggregation number of the leuco compound of the vat dyestuff Caledon Jade Green to increase from about three to about 420. Although these figures, which express average numbers without any reference to particle size distribution, are probably not strictly quantitative,

---

* To quote Horsfall and Lawrie (*loc. cit.*, p. 407), the surface-active agents in an acid dyebath "behave as if they were colourless acid dyestuffs." Alternatively, the dyestuff might perhaps be described as a coloured surface-active agent!

[1] Neville and Jeanson, *J. Phys. Chem.*, 1933, **37**, 1001.
[2] Flett and Hoyt, *Amer. Dyes. Reporter*, 1954, **43**, P335.
[3] Horsfall and Lawrie, *loc. cit.*, p. 406.
[4] Horsfall and Lawrie, *loc. cit.*, p. 402.
[5] Valko, *Trans. Faraday Soc.*, 1935, **31**, 254.

they clearly indicate that complex aggregates of some sort are formed. "Peregal O" and several cationic and anionic surface-active agents have also been shown by Valko[1] to increase the degree of aggregation of the direct cotton dyestuff Chicago Blue 6B (Chlorazol Sky Blue FF) and two acid wool dyestuffs. It is interesting to note that Valko's data suggest that a cationic agent ("Peregal OK") increased the degree of aggregation of the Chicago Blue 6B by up to about 1000 times, "Peregal O" considerably less, and that the anionic agents had very little effect. It is important to note that, as pointed out by Luck,[2] these increased "aggregation numbers" do not mean that the levelling agent simply causes the dyestuff to aggregate *with itself*. What is involved is an equilibrium of the type

Dyestuff (solution) + Agent (solution)

⇌ Dyestuff-Agent Complex (solution)

which is linked with other equilibria, such as that between dissolved and adsorbed dyestuff. It follows from Le Chatelier's principle that this last-named equilibrium will be displaced in the direction of *desorption* by the introduction of the levelling agent into the system. (Whether or not Luck is justified in treating the complex-formation as involving only one molecule of each reactant is perhaps debatable, but this does not in any way affect the qualitative validity of the argument.)

Although a reasonably good general picture can be proposed for the action of levelling agents in terms of "aggregation" or "sequestering" of the dissolved dyestuff, or of competition for sites on the fibre, it is obvious that the exact mechanism in each case is much more complicated. Since we are dealing with the kinetics of the dyeing process, it is important to note that, as Horsfall and Lawrie[3] point out, the complex micelles formed between the dyestuff and the surface-active agent, which act as reservoirs of available dyestuff, should decompose at the correct rate during dyeing. It is therefore not surprising that different dyestuffs behave quite differently with restraining agents, and that the more rapidly adsorbed dyestuffs are in general more affected by the addition of levelling agents. It is also interesting to note that the dyestuff anions can be displaced from the complex micelles, and thus released for adsorption, by the addition of anionic surface-active agents.[4] It does not appear possible, especially in the absence of precise information on the states of solution of the polyethenoxy surface-active agents, to suggest any sort of detailed picture of the structure of the complex micelles.

Although the "sequestering" mechanism described above has been studied chiefly with water-soluble non-ionic agents, it seems likely that it is

---

[1] Valko, *J. Soc. Dyers Colourists*, 1939, **55**, 173.
[2] Luck, *J. Soc. Dyers Colourists*, 1958, **74**, 221.
[3] Horsfall and Lawrie, *loc. cit.*, p. 406.
[4] Horsfall and Lawrie, *loc. cit.*, p. 407.

also responsible for the reported action of mixtures of cationic agents, such as cetyltrimethylammonium bromide, with the multivalent anionic agents obtained by condensing naphthalene sulphonic acids with formaldehyde.[1] (These latter agents are discussed in Chapter 10, p. 377.)

2. FIXING AGENTS

One of the chief limitations to the usefulness of the direct cotton dye-stuffs is their lack of fastness to contact with water, and in particular to scouring baths. This is due to the fact that the adsorption of a dyestuff such as Congo Red,

$$NH_2 \qquad\qquad\qquad\qquad\qquad NH_2$$

$$\text{—N} = \text{N—}\langle\ \rangle\text{—}\langle\ \rangle\text{—N} = \text{N—}$$

$$SO_3Na \qquad\qquad\qquad\qquad\qquad SO_3Na$$

is to a large degree reversible, so that desorption begins as soon as the dyed material is brought into contact with water. If however the adsorbed dyestuff is rendered insoluble or sparingly soluble on the fabric, then the fastness of the dyed fabric would be expected to be increased. It is on this principle that the so-called "fixing agents" for direct colours act. These agents, which are applied as aqueous solutions to the fabric after dyeing, are all cationic surface-active compounds: well known examples are the "Sapamines," which are long-chain amine salts, and "Fixanol C," which is cetylpyridinium bromide. Their application is described in the books by Horsfall and Lawrie, Chwala, and Diserens, to which we have already referred. It seems clear that they are primarily precipitants or "laking agents" for the dyestuffs; according to Chwala, Martina, and Becke,[2] the precipitation is a stoichiometrical double decomposition. It is understand-able that quaternary ammonium salts appear to be more effective, other factors being equal, than the amine salts, since the former are stronger bases, so that the "salt" of dyestuff anion and fixing agent cation is less likely to hydrolyse to free base and dyestuff on contact with water.

Although dyeings on cellulose which have been fixed with these agents are faster to water and to perspiration than the untreated dyeings, they suffer from several defects. The most serious is that the dyestuff anions in the insoluble "lake" are displaced by anionic detergents during washing treatments, so that the improved fastness largely disappears. It seems possible that solubilisation of the dyestuff-fixing agent complex in the micelles of the detergent may also contribute to this loss of fastness. There

[1] Geigy, Schwager, and Bindler, U.S.P. 2,482,942.
[2] Chwala, Martina, and Becke, *Textilber.*, 1936, **17**, 583.

is also a tendency for the shade of the dyestuff to be altered in the "hypso-chromic" direction (*e.g.*, reds become yellower) by the fixing treatment, and for the fastness to light to be diminished. The first effect suggests that the dyestuff-fixing agent complex may not be a simple "salt," even though the two constituents may happen to be present in equimolecular propor-tions, but that it may be a colloidal complex in which the dyestuff molecules are present in what is effectively a non-aqueous medium. This may also contribute to changes in light-fastness, though this is of course a matter of conjecture.

A more complex fixing agent, "Fibrofix," has been identified[1] with the condensation products of cyanamide with formaldehyde, which have been patented by Courtaulds.[2] This agent is claimed to give marked improve-ments in the fastness to washing of direct dyeings on viscose rayon[3, 4, 5]: *i.e.*, its complexes with direct dyestuffs are not readily broken down by soap.

3. STRIPPING AGENTS

A number of surface-active agents have been found to be useful in processes for "stripping" insoluble dyestuffs, such as vat dyestuffs and azoic pigments, from textile fabrics. When for example a vat dyeing is boiled in an alkaline solution of a reducing agent such as sodium hydro-sulphite, the dyestuff is reduced to the leuco form, and a certain amount of desorption occurs as the leuco dyestuff strives to attain a state of equi-librium between the adsorbed and the dissolved states. Since however the leuco dyestuff has a considerable degree of affinity for the fibre, desorption cannot be complete unless the stripping solution is changed a large number of times, and a considerable time interval is allowed after each change, which is not very practicable. If however a solute is present in the strip-ping bath which forms a complex with the leuco vat dyestuff (which is "anionic"), it may be possible to displace the equilibrium state so far in the direction of desorption that a high degree of stripping can take place in a limited time. Examples of suitable "stripping agents" are provided by those polyethenoxy agents which act as levelling agents for vat dyestuffs —the parallelism between the two processes is at once apparent—and by the mixture of cetyltrimethylammonium bromide with fatty compounds which is sold as "Lissolamine V." The difference in the mode of action of the two types of stripping agents seems to be that, while the polyethenoxy agents form water-soluble complex micelles with the leuco dyestuff, the

[1] Diserens, *Die neuesten Fortschritte in der Anwendung der Farbstoffe*, Birkhäuser, Basel, 1949, **2**, p. 89.

[2] Courtaulds and Tallis, B.P. 506,793.

[3] Wilcock and Tattersfield, *J. Soc. Dyers Colourists*, 1943, **59**, 119.

[4] Horsfall and Lawrie, *loc. cit.*, p. 411.

[5] Courtaulds, Whittaker, Wilcock, and Tattersfield, B.P. 515,847.

cetyltrimethylammonium bromide-fatty mixture precipitates the leuco vat dyestuffs irreversibly.[1]

Azoic dyestuffs are applied to textile fibres by a two-stage process in which the fabric is first immersed ("padded") in a solution of the sodium salt of an uncoloured "Brenthol" or "Naphthol" (*e.g.*, 2 : 3-hydroxynaphthoic anilide), a portion of which is adsorbed by the fabric, and then in a developing solution of a diazotised amine (*e.g.*, 2 : 5-dichloroaniline) or of a stabilised diazotised amine. The insoluble azoic pigment, in this case an orange red dyestuff of formula

is thus formed *in situ* on the fibre; it is so firmly anchored that its removal when the occasion demands is very difficult, even when an alkaline hydrosulphite solution is used to attack the azo group. When however the cationic surface-active agent cetyltrimethylammonium bromide ("Lissolamine A") is added to the alkaline hydrosulphite solution, azoic pigments are stripped from the fibre almost completely.[2] The mechanism of the action of cetyltrimethylammonium bromide has been studied by Rowe and Owen,[3] who found that it greatly increased the degree of decomposition of azoic pigments in bulk, the products obtained suggesting that fission was occurring at the azo group, and that it had a marked solubilising action on azoic pigments in alkaline media. Rowe and Owen therefore suggested that cetyltrimethylammonium bromide functions essentially as a "dispersing agent,"* rendering the azo groups in the insoluble pigment more open to attack by the alkaline reducing agent. This stripping process can therefore be analysed into two steps: a solubilisation (which is probably reversible), as the result of which part of the pigment passes into solution in the form of complex micelles with the cetyltrimethylammonium ions, the remainder of the pigment perhaps remaining on the fibre in a less markedly crystalline condition, followed by an irreversible decomposition of the pigment by the alkaline reducing agent. The surface-active material released by this reduction is presumably then free to solubilise a further quantity of pigment.

The fact that anionic surface-active agents are ineffective suggests that the cetyltrimethylammonium bromide and pigment molecules are held

---

* It seems to us that the expression "peptising agent" would be more appropriate in this connection.

[1] Horsfall and Lawrie, *loc. cit.*, p. 413.
[2] Lawrie, *J. Soc. Dyers Colourists*, 1933, **49**, 309.
[3] Rowe and Owen, *J. Soc. Dyers Colourists*, 1936, **52**, 205.

together in complex micelles at least partly as the result of salt linkages between the quaternary ammonium groups of the stripping compound and the anionic phenolate groups in the pigment. The pigment molecules may accordingly simply "adhere to" the micelles of cetyltrimethylammonium bromide, displacing adherent bromide and hydroxyl ions in the process, but the possibility cannot be excluded that salt linkages are formed at the outside of the micelles, with "solution" of the bulk of each pigment molecule in the interiors of the micelles.

4. SURFACE-ACTIVE AGENTS IN "PIGMENT-PAD-DYEING"

In the "pigment-pad-dyeing" process, which has become of considerable technical importance, a finely-divided suspension of a vat dyestuff in the "pigment" (*i.e.*, in the oxidised, water-insoluble) form is pumped through the material to be dyed, which is usually in the form of a "cheese" of wound thread, or a textile is "padded" through the suspension. The dyestuff is subsequently "fixed" by being reduced to the leuco form, when genuine adsorption from solution occurs. The dyestuff is finally oxidised back to the pigment form on the fibre. The process has been described by Richardson and Wiltshire,[1] and by Hampson.[2] Although the dispersed pigment dyestuff is not adsorbed by the fibre, in one version of the process it is deposited inside the mass of textile fibres by flocculation with electrolyte, which gives an "exhaustion" effect.

Surface-active agents are used in this process as deflocculating ("dispersing") agents for the vat dyestuff suspensions, and also as levelling agents to obtain an even adsorption of the leuco form of the vat dyestuff. Sulphated oils (see p. 424), and fatty alcohol-ethylene oxide condensation products, are widely used for this purpose. Bräuer[3] has suggested that the latter can also improve the exhaustion of the pigment form of the dyestuff because of their negative temperature coefficient of solubility (*cf.* Chapter 14, p. 477), which causes them to come out of solution as the temperature is increased, bringing the dyestuff particles with them.

A problem which can arise in the pigment padding of textile materials —and in a great many other industrial processes—is "migration" during drying: *i.e.*, if a textile which has been padded with a suspension of pigment dyestuff is subjected to a non-uniform drying operation, the particles of dyestuff are found to have "migrated" into those regions which first dried. It may not be generally appreciated that this is a classical phenomenon of colloid science, though perhaps one which has not received the attention which it deserves. It was first studied scientifically in 1919 by Bechhold,[4] and then investigated more fully by Kraus,[5] who named it the "Bechhold

[1] Richardson and Wiltshire, *J. Soc. Dyers Colourists*, 1947, **63**, 224.
[2] Hampson, *ibid.*, 1951, **67**, 369.
[3] Bräuer, *Textilber.*, 1953, **34**, 54.
[4] Bechhold, *Koll. Z.*, 1920, **27**, 229.
[5] Kraus, *ibid.*, 1921, **28**, 151.

capillary phenomenon." It is due to the fact that, if a liquid is evaporated from the menisci in one region of a system of inter-connected capillaries, there will be a compensating flow of liquid, driven by the capillary pressure, to this region, provided that the liquid strongly wets the walls of the capillaries. If the liquid contains a dissolved or dispersed material which has no affinity for the walls of the capillaries, there will be a transport of this material towards the region of evaporation. As every dyeing technologist is aware, the magnitude of the effect can be quite startling. It appears to be considerably more pronounced with water than with liquids of lower surface tension.

Kraus found that the Bechhold phenomenon was reduced or suppressed if the dissolved or dispersed material was adsorbed or deposited on to the walls of the capillaries, if the capillary walls were rendered hydrophobic by coating them with paraffin wax, or if the viscosity of the aqueous medium was increased by the addition of gelatine. The last of these remedies is the most useful technologically—apart from the obvious step of making drying conditions more uniform—and it has in fact been found that a number of water-soluble macromolecules, such as sodium alginate, water-soluble starch, or water-soluble cellulose derivatives, are much more effective than glue or gelatine, especially at low concentrations.[1]

B. Surface-active agents as bactericides

Synthetic surface-active agents have found a ready application in many fields of medical and pharmaceutical practice, but perhaps their most striking application has been as germicides, following the disclosure by Domagk in 1935 of the bactericidal potency of aqueous solutions of long-chain alkylbenzyldimethylammonium chlorides. Since then, literally hundreds of amphipathic substances have been tested for bactericidal action, and among the quaternary ammonium salts many of the most powerful modern bactericides have been found. Well-documented reviews of this subject have been given by Glassman, by Rahn and Eseltine, and by Lawrence.[2] The most up-to-date account is by Sykes.[3]

The use of certain dyestuffs, such as methyl violet and malachite green, as germicides appears to date from the last decade of the last century. The dyestuffs which were effective were all quaternary ammonium compounds, and later Jacobs and Heidelberger[4] also showed that numerous quaternary

---

[1] See, for example, Dierkes and Büstgens, *Textilber.*, 1956, **37**, 834.

[2] Glassman, *Bact. Rev.*, 1948, **12**, 105; Rahn and Eseltine, *Ann. Rev. Microbiol.*, 1947, **1**, 173; Lawrence, *Surface-Active Quaternary Ammonium Germicides*, Academic Press, 1949.

[3] Sykes, *Disinfection and Sterilization*, Spon, 1958.

[4] Jacobs and Heidelberger, *Proc. Nat. Acad. Sci.*, 1915, **1**, 226; *J. Biol. Chem.*, 1915, **20**, 659; Jacobs, *J. Exptl. Med.*, 1916, **23**, 563.

ammonium salts prepared by reacting hexamethylenetetramine with chloroalkyl compounds also possessed antibacterial properties. Many other antibacterial quaternary ammonium salts were examined by Browning and co-workers,[1] but it was not until 1935, when Domagk[2] showed that the introduction of a long paraffin chain greatly increased the germicidal activity of quaternary ammonium compounds, that an intense interest in the germicidal properties of surface-active agents in general was aroused. Some years earlier, however, Stanley and Adams[3] investigated the effect of the sodium salts of aliphatic acids on an organism which they refer to as *Mycobacterium leprae*. These authors studied several series of substituted and unsubstituted acids and came to the conclusion that, in any one series, the compounds which had the highest bactericidal efficiency were also those which were noted to be the most " soapy "—*i.e.*, had the greatest effect in depressing the surface tension of water. It is probably no exaggeration to say that since 1935 practically every surface-active agent which has been manufactured has been tested for bactericidal efficiency. It should be emphasised, however, that the application of the usual bactericidal tests, without modification, to solutions of surface-active agents introduces a number of extraneous effects, such as aggregation (or "clumping") of bacteria, adsorption, etc., due to the surface-activity of these compounds so that the precise method of test often has a great influence on the assessment of bactericidal efficiency. It has even been stated by Mallmann, Kivela, and Turner[4] that the quaternary ammonium compounds can be demonstrated to be either very effective or very ineffective bactericides by selecting the appropriate testing technique. Davies[5] has made a survey of the criticisms which have been levelled at the various methods and has devised a test procedure by which he appears to have eliminated the defects inherent in the commonly-used methods when applied to surface-active bactericides. Despite the uncertainties introduced by these defects some generalisations from the large amount of work published on the bactericidal properties of surface-active agents may, however, be drawn.

Both cationic and anionic agents exhibit bactericidal properties, but the non-ionogenic agents are practically without effect on most bacteria, even at high concentrations.[6] Although high bactericidal activity is therefore allied to surface-activity, the converse is not necessarily true. Cationic surface-active agents, when they are effective, are active against both Gram-positive and Gram-negative microorganisms, while the anionic

[1] Browning *et al.*, *Proc. Roy. Soc.*, 1922, **93B**, 329; 1926, **100B**, 293; *Brit. Med. J.*, 1926, **1**, 73.

[2] Domagk, *Deutsche med. Wochenschr.*, 1935, **61**, 829.

[3] Stanley and Adams, *J. Amer. Chem. Soc.*, 1932, **54**, 1548.

[4] Mallman, Kivela, and Turner, *Soap Sanit. Chemicals*, 1946, **22**, 130.

[5] Davies, *J. Hygiene*, 1949, **47**, 271.

[6] Hotchkiss, *Ann. N.Y. Acad. Sci.*, 1945, **46**, 479; Baker, Harrison, and Miller, *J. Exptl. Med.*, 1941, **74**, 611.

amphipathic electrolytes are in general effective only against the Gram-positive organisms, as has been shown for example by Birkeland and Steinhaus,[1] and by Baker, Harrison, and Miller.[2] The cationic agents appear to increase in potency with an increase in the pH of the medium, while decreasing the pH appears to increase the bactericidal effect of the anionic agents. Quisno and Foter[3] however find that the bactericidal efficiency of cetylpyridinium chloride is practically constant over the pH range from 2 to 10. This surprising departure from the usual behaviour of the quaternary ammonium compounds must be treated with some caution at present in view of the dependence of bactericidal results on the method of testing which we have mentioned previously. Since therefore the cationic agents have a more general usefulness, most of the commercially important surface-active bactericides belong to this class, and on account of the economics of production, practically all of them are quaternary ammonium salts. The anionic agents may however prove to be useful when action against only specific bacteria is desirable.

There can be no doubt that the bactericidal efficiency of the quaternary ammonium salts is intimately connected with the amphipathic character of the cation, and is almost independent of the nature of the anion. Shelton and co-workers[4] found that the bactericidal effect of alkyltrimethyl-ammonium bromides (I), the alkylpyridinium chlorides (II), and alkyl-methylpiperidinium bromides (III)

reached a maximum when the alkyl radical was cetyl, and that the cetyl compounds of (I) and (II) were approximately equal and somewhat superior to that of (III). Shelton and co-workers also showed that (*i*) substitution of the low molecular weight alkyl groups in the cetyl compounds by other low molecular weight groups such as ethyl, butyl, benzyl, acetoxyethyl, carbethoxymethyl, 2:3-dihydroxypropyl, etc., either reduced, or at best did not increase, the bactericidal potency, and (*ii*) the cetyltrimethyl-ammonium chloride, bromide, iodide, sulphate, nitrate, acetate, benzoate,

[1] Birkeland and Steinhaus, *Proc. Soc. Exp. Biol. Med.*, 1939, **40,** 86.
[2] Baker, Harrison, and Miller, *loc. cit.*
[3] Quisno and Foter, *J. Bact.*, 1946 **52,** 111.
[4] Shelton, van Campen, Tilford, Lang, Nisonger, Bandelin, and Rubenkoenig, *J. Amer. Chem. Soc.*, 1946, **68,** 753, 755, 757.

cyanide, and fluosilicate salts were of equal activity, while the laurate, salicylate, and *sec.*-orthophosphate salts were of somewhat lower activity. Similar results on the dependence of bactericidal potency on chain length have been reported by Hoogerheide[1] on the alkyltrimethylammonium bromides. He considers cetyltrimethylammonium bromide, on the basis of a comparison with several commonly used disinfectants, to be "one of the outstanding bactericidal and bacteriostatic agents." Kolloff, Wyss, Himelick, and Mantele[2] also found, with alkylpyridinium and alkyl-picolinium halides, that the maximum germicidal activity occurred with the cetyl compounds. Where only one of the hydrocarbon groups attached to the nitrogen atom is a long paraffin chain, the peak of the bactericidal efficiency occurs with 12, 14, or 16 carbon atoms. For example, in the alkylbenzyldimethylammonium chlorides, Valko and DuBois[3] showed that the lauryl and myristyl compounds were the most effective. Commercial products the active constituents of which are alkylbenzyldimethylammonium chlorides

$$\text{CH}_2-\overset{\overset{\displaystyle \text{CH}_3 \quad \text{CH}_3,}{|}}{\underset{\underset{\displaystyle \text{R}}{|}}{\text{N}}}{}^+, \ \text{Cl}^-$$

are, for example, "Zephirol" or "Zephiran" (Bayer) where R is the alkyl radical derived from coconut oil fatty acids, and "Triton K 12" and "Triton K 60" (Rohm and Haas) in which R is cetyl and dodecyl respectively. The high bactericidal efficiency of "Zephiran" has been reported by Dunn,[4] Maier,[5] and Freedlander.[6]

Many other series of quaternary ammonium salts have been the subject of study such as the N(β-acyloxyethyl)carbamylmethylpyridinium chlorides[7] (I), *p*-alkylphenoxyethoxyethyldimethylbenzylammonium chlorides[8] (II), and the dialkylbenztriazolium bromides[9] (III), all of which show a maximum when the bactericidal activity is plotted against the number of carbon atoms in the alkyl radical, R.

(I) $\text{R}-\overset{\overset{\displaystyle \text{O}}{||}}{\text{C}}-\text{O}-\text{CH}_2\cdot\text{CH}_2\cdot\overset{\overset{\displaystyle \text{H}}{|}}{\text{N}}\cdot\overset{\overset{\displaystyle \text{O}}{||}}{\text{C}}\cdot\text{CH}_2\overset{+}{\text{N}}\langle\ \rangle,\ \text{Cl}^- \qquad \text{R}=\text{C}_{11}\text{H}_{23}$

"Emulsol 605"
(Emulsol
Corporation)

[1] Hoogerheide, *J. Bact.*, 1945, **49**, 277.
[2] Kolloff, Wyss, Himelick, and Mantele, *J. Amer. Pharm. Ass.*, 1942, **31**, 51.
[3] Valko and DuBois, *J. Bact.*, 1945, **50**, 481.
[4] Dunn, *Proc. Soc. Exptl. Bio. Med.*, 1936, **35**, 427.
[5] Maier, *J. Bact.*, 1939, **38**, 33.
[6] Freedlander, *Proc. Soc. Exptl. Bio. Med.*, 1940, **44**, 51.
[7] Epstein, *Proc. Soc. Exptl. Bio. Med.*, 1943, **53**, 238.
[8] Rawlins, Sweet, and Joslyn, *J. Amer. Pharm. Ass.*, 1943, **32**, 11.
[9] Kuhn and Westphal, *Ber.*, 1940, **73**, 1109.

$$\text{(II) R}\langle\bigcirc\rangle\text{O·C}_2\text{H}_4\text{·O·C}_2\text{H}_4\text{—N}^+, \text{Cl}^-$$

CH_3 CH_3 ... CH_2

R = *p*-tertiary octyl
"Phemeride"
(Parke, Davis & Co.)

(III) with structure containing R—N, N, N$^+$, Br$^-$, R

Although the quaternary ammonium compounds have been the most popular surface-active bactericides from the commercial point of view, the bactericidal action of the sulphonium, phosphonium, and arsonium salts has also been investigated. Kuhn and Dann[1] studied the alkyldimethyl-sulphonium iodides and found them to have about one-third the activity of the corresponding quaternary ammonium salts, and in an extension of this work Jerchel[2] found in the alkyltriethyl and alkyldimethylbenzyl series that the phosphonium and arsonium salts were superior to the corresponding ammonium compounds.

As bactericides the quaternary ammonium salts have many qualities to recommend them. They have a pronounced detergent action and can thus be used in place of soap, giving a disinfectant as well as a cleansing effect. It is well known that these salts are adsorbed on many surfaces, as is demonstrated by the "greasy" film left on a glass vessel when it has been rinsed with an aqueous solution of the salt. It is claimed that these compounds also leave an invisible film on the skin. Miller, Abrams, Huber, and Klein[3] emphasise however that although the outer surface of this film is germicidal the inner surface is not and bacteria can survive under this film to be released when the film is broken for example by ordinary soaps, alcohol, or even by frequent dips into physiological saline or water. They, and other writers,[4] consider that an operation under aseptic conditions might be performed in the absence of surgical gloves only when the surgeon frequently dips his hands into a 1% solution of the quaternary ammonium compound during the operation. As Rahn[5] points out, the difference in the bactericidal properties of the two surfaces of the film is due to amphipathic

[1] Kuhn and Dann, *Ber.*, 1940, **73**, 1092.
[2] Jerchel, *Ber.*, 1943, **76**, 600.
[3] Miller, Abrams, Huber, and Klein, *Proc. Soc. Exp. Biol. Med.*, 1943, **54**, 174.
[4] Walter, *Surg. Gynec. Obstet.*, 1938, **67**, 683; Barnes, *Lancet*, 1942, **242**, 531.
[5] Rahn, *Proc. Soc. Exp. Biol. Med.*, 1946, **62**, 2.

adsorption—the cation being adsorbed on the skin with the polar head outwards and the paraffin chain in contact with the grease of the skin. Actual scrubbing with a solution of a quaternary ammonium compound results in a considerable reduction in the bacterial population of the skin, the reduction probably being caused by the combined germicidal and detergent action.

The fact that cationic agents are adsorbed by textiles makes them of particular interest for sterilising hospital blankets and sheets.* Anti-bacterial properties are imparted to the fabric, which persist for a few days after laundering.

The quaternary ammonium compounds are non-irritant to the skin and may even be applied to open wounds.[2, 3] Their germicidal activity is reduced in the presence of organic matter and although this reduction is claimed to be slight;[1, 2, 3, 4] these results were obtained with concentrations far in excess of the minimum bactericidal concentration. At these relatively high concentrations, therefore, they are effective for cleaning dirty and greasy bowls and surgical instruments but since these compounds are known[5] to be ineffective against spores, sterilisation of equipment is not likely to be achieved by this treatment alone. A one-minute rinse with a 1 in 5,000 dilution of "Zephiran" is very effective[6] in markedly reducing the number of bacteria commonly found on drinking glasses. This result has been confirmed for other quaternary ammonium compounds and since at the dilutions used for this purpose they are tasteless and odourless their use in food and drink establishments as a bactericidal rinse is strongly recommended. Other uses which may be mentioned are in the rinsing of milkcans and general dairy equipment, the washing of cows' udders, and washing shell eggs before dehydration.

The precise mechanism of the bactericidal action of these compounds has not as yet been completely elucidated, but several theories have been proposed, based on various biochemical studies. Surface-activity alone is not responsible since, as has been mentioned, the non-ionic amphipathic compounds have no bactericidal action, but it is an essential property of an effective bactericide in the class of compounds which we are considering as the many studies of the correlation of bactericidal power and the chain length of the amphipathic ion have shown. Valko[7] suggested that toxicity is the product of two factors, adsorbability and specific toxicity, the first

---

* A useful review of the work on this subject is given in the pamphlet *Interim Report on the Cleansing and Sterilisation of Hospital Blankets*, issued by the King Edward's Hospital Fund, 34 King Street, London, E.C.2., November, 1959.

[1] Williams, Clayton-Cooper, Duncan, and Miles, *Lancet*, 1943, **244**, 522.
[2] Barnes, *Lancet*, 1942, **242**, 531.
[3] Huyck, *J. Amer. Pharm. Ass.*, 1945, **34**, 5.
[4] McCulloch, Haugh, and Migaki, *J. Amer. Vet. Med. Ass.*, 1948, **112**, 283.
[5] Davies, *J. Hygiene*, 1949, **47**, 271.
[6] Krog and Marshall, *Amer. J. Pub. Health*, 1940, **30**, 341.
[7] Valko, *Ann. N.Y. Acad. Sci.*, 1945, **46**, 451.

step in the bactericidal action being the reversible ionic adsorption of the amphipathic ion by the bacteria. He cited as evidence the well-known dependence of the toxicity of both anionic and cationic compounds on the pH of the medium—when the pH is decreased, the adsorption of the relatively harmless hydrogen ions is increased and thus the ionic adsorption of the toxic anions is favoured and that of toxic cations is depressed. As further evidence, he referred to the de-toxicating action[1] of amphipathic anions, which he considered to be due to the reversal of the adsorption of the toxic amphipathic cations. This reversal of adsorption, he suggested, can be accomplished if the bacteria have been exposed to the bactericide for only a relatively short time, since the adsorption is quickly followed by other irreversible processes, which finally result in the death of the bacteria. Albert[2] considered a number of possible modes of action of antiseptics and agreed with Valko's ionic adsorption mechanism. He also suggested that the difference between a bacteriostatic and a bactericidal agent may be due solely to the amphipathic nature of the latter. The slight surface-activity of phenol, for example, is increased by introducing alkyl groups into the molecule (as in "Izal") or by introducing halogens and alkyl groups (as in "Dettol"). His results on a series of resorcinols, substituted in the 4-position with alkyl radicals (C_3–C_9), showed that the bactericidal activity against a Gram-negative organism is at a maximum when the alkyl chain has six carbon atoms, while against a Gram-positive organism the activity increases throughout the series. Baker, Harrison, and Miller[3] studied the effect of both cationic and anionic surface-active agents on the respiratory and glycolytic activity of Gram-positive and Gram-negative bacteria and con- cluded that those agents which depressed bacterial metabolism were also effective bactericides.

This process of cell lysis by surface-active agents has been further considered by several workers. Valko,[4] in a review which gives some inter- esting historical details of the discovery of the bactericidal properties of cationic agents, develops further his earlier opinion that the surface-active agent combines with proteins or other essential cell constituents, and that this can lead to destruction of the cell wall. He suggests that this adsorption can occur by an ion-exchange mechanism, for example, and he rejects the view that the agents act by lowering the interfacial tension between the solution and lipoid constituents of the cell walls. A review which contains more recent work is that of Salton.[5] This work has again demonstrated that cationic agents (cetyltrimethylammonium bromide or cetylpyridinium bromide) are more strongly adsorbed than are the anionics, but that both

[1] Valko and DuBois, *J. Bact.*, 1944, **47**, 15.

[2] Albert, *Lancet*, 1942, **243**, 633.

[3] Baker, Harrison, and Miller, *J. Exptl. Med.*, 1941, **73**, 249; 1941, **74**, 611.

[4] Valko, *First Congress*, 1954, 777.

[5] Salton, *Second Congress*, 1957, **IV**, 245.

types are capable of lysing the bacterial cell. Lysis is considered to be due to a "disorganisation" of the cell wall by the adsorbed surface-active material. This adsorption is probably preponderantly ionic (what Valko refers to as a "base-exchange" mechanism) in most cases involving cationic agents, but amphipathic adsorption (*cf.* Chapter 1, p. 6) can also occur, especially with anionic agents. Rather more subtle effects can also take place. Enzymatic degradation of the cell walls of *staphylococcus aureus* is stimulated by certain concentrations of cetyltrimethylammonium bromide, but inhibited by higher concentrations: here the agent may be sequestering both the enzymes and the naturally occurring enzyme inhibitors, the two effects varying to different extents at different concentrations of cetyltrimethylammonium bromide. Salton concludes that "most surface-active compounds react with the bacterial cell membrane and kill the organisms by releasing intracellular components and initiating the 'autolytic' breakdown of cellular nucleic acids, proteins, and structural elements. Lysis and digestion of the bacterial cells will depend in these instances on the activity of autolytic enzymes and will accordingly differ from one organism to another. Although the bacterial cell walls and capsules are the structural components having immediate contact with the molecules of surface-active compounds, it is evident that rapid penetration of these structures must occur before cell membrane damage releases the cell solutes."

Ruyssen and co-workers[1] have shown by a radio-tracer technique, using sodium dodecyl sulphate (labelled with S^{35}) and sodium desoxycholate (labelled with C^{14} in the carboxy group), that bovine red blood cells are haemolysed by these two agents when the amounts adsorbed are sufficient to cover only about one-third of the cell walls. This clearly indicates that a "spot-like" haemolysis occurs. By using cholesterol labelled with C^{14}, Ruyssen has also shown that haemolysis by sodium dodecyl sulphate is accompanied by extraction of cholesterol from the cells, in which micellar solubilisation probably plays a part.

Mixtures of cationic and non-ionic surface-active agents are used as combined bactericides/detergents, the mixtures of the two types frequently giving the optimum combination of bactericidal and detergent efficiency. (As pointed out in the makers' recommendations for the I.C.I. product "Vantropol BQ," for example, these mixtures should not be contaminated with *anionic* detergents, since the bactericidal action of the cationic agent will suffer thereby, presumably because of sequestration by the anionic micelles.) Moore and Hardwick,[2] in a review of surface-active agents as germicides and in germicidal mixtures, have reported that the addition of the non-ionic agent does more than merely introduce a more powerful detergent into the composition. They state that small additions of the non-ionic agent at first increase the bactericidal power of the cationic, by

---

[1] See Ruyssen, *Second Congress*, 1957, **IV**, 271.
[2] Moore and Hardwick, *Manufacturing Chemist*, 1956, **27**, 305.

increasing the penetration into the organism in question. There is, however, an optimum amount of non-ionic agent, beyond which bactericidal power falls because of the formation of mixed micelles between the two types of amphipathic molecules.

It is of course very well known to use anionic detergents as "carriers" (micellar solubilising agents) for ordinary disinfectants such as phenols and substituted phenols, and this principle has been used in a number of disinfectants, such as "Lysol," "Izal," and "Dettol." Work such as that of Alexander and Tomlinson[1] suggests that anionic surface-active agents, exemplified by dihexyl- and dioctylsulphosuccinates, can also help bactericidal action by opening up the bacterial structure. In this case again, however, there is an optimum concentration of anionic agent, above which the activity of the phenol diminishes because it is sequestered in mixed micelles.

It is implicit in what has been said so far that the bactericidal and/or bacteriostatic action of surface-active agents is due to the molecularly disperse material rather than to the micelles. It is therefore interesting to note that Armstrong[2] has found that the inhibition by sodium dodecyl sulphate of the aerobic fermentation of glucose by baker's yeast, becomes much more pronounced at about the critical micelle concentration. He also found that inhibition is enhanced by the presence of sodium chloride, and points out that this also suggests that it is the micelles of the amphipathic compound, rather than the individual ions, which are responsible for the inhibition of fermentation. There is of course no real conflict between these results and those discussed earlier in this chapter: it may well be that quite different phenomena are involved in different cases.

Hotchkiss[3] has criticised, as have other authors,[4] tests for bactericidal activity which can give only two results, *viz.*, 0% or 100% activity, since he considers that they are practically useless in any attempts to elucidate the mechanism of bactericidal action. He points out in this connection that one particular manifestation of surface-activity will not serve as a guide to bactericidal activity. When bacteria are killed as a result of the action of surface-active agents, Hotchkiss has shown by chemical analyses that compounds which were originally only present in the bacterial cell appear in the surrounding medium. Non-surface-active antiseptics such as hydrogen peroxide, potassium permanganate, organic mercurials, etc., if they were present in sufficient concentration to kill or completely to prevent growth, did not show this effect.

[1] Alexander and Tomlinson, *Research, Suppl. Surface Chemistry*, 1949, 317.

[2] Armstrong, *Nature*, 1957, **179,** 780; see also Wills, *Biochem. J.*, 1954, **57,** 109.

[3] Hotchkiss, *Ann. N.Y. Acad. Sci.*, 1945, **46,** 479.

[4] See for example, Glassman, *Bact. Rev.*, 1948, **12,** 105; Davies, *J. Hygiene*, 1949, **47,** 271.

Hotchkiss agrees with Valko that the first stage in the toxic action is ionic adsorption at the bacterial surface. This surface concentration, he believes, is sufficient to damage the cell membrane so that it becomes completely permeable. The contents of the cell thus escape into the surrounding medium, resulting in the death of the organism. Gale and Taylor[1] treated *Streptococcus faecalis* cells with cetyltrimethylammonium bromide, "Aerosol OT" (sodium dioctyl sulphosuccinate), or phenol and found that the cell wall was so affected that it allowed the amino-acids present in the cell to leak out. They consider the lytic action of these compounds to be sufficient to explain their bactericidal potency.

C. Flotation of ores

The practice and theory of flotation processes for separating minerals from unwanted residues has been so adequately treated elsewhere[2] that only a general outline will be attempted here. The basic principle which is usually involved is that valuable mineral constituents are present in aqueous suspensions as particles the surfaces of which are poorly wetted by the aqueous medium, while the particles of gangue are wetted more strongly, preferably completely. Provided that the particles of ore are sufficiently small and sufficiently water-repellent, they will adhere to the air-water interface—*i.e.*, they will "float"—while the particles of gangue will sink and can be suitably disposed of.* In order for the process to be economically feasible, however, it is preferable for the area of the air-water interface to be as large as possible; consequently it is usual to generate a foam in which the floating mineral particles are trapped. The foam containing these particles is then recovered, usually continuously, while the bulk of liquid containing the residues is run to waste. Surface-active materials can accordingly play two major rôles in flotation processes of this type: they may selectively render the surfaces of the mineral particles more hydrophobic—more precisely expressed, they may increase the contact angle of the aqueous medium against these particles without at the same time appreciably increasing the angle against the other particles present—and they

---

* The opposite principle is also used in practice, the gangue being removed by flotation and the desired mineral allowed to sink, but the physico-chemical principles involved are the same.

[1] Gale and Taylor, *J. Gen. Microbiol.*, 1947, **1**, 77.

[2] See, for example, Gaudin, *Flotation*, McGraw-Hill, Second Edition, 1957; Sutherland and Wark, *Principles of Flotation*, Australian Institute of Mining and Metallurgy, Second Edition, 1955; Schwartz and Perry, *Surface Active Agents*, Interscience, 1949, pp. 489–494. A useful summarising lecture on the subject was given recently by Fleming, *Chemistry and Industry*, 3rd Oct., 1959, p. 1230. We would like to thank Mr. E. J. Pryor, and the Chairman of the Annual Reports Committee of the Society of Chemical Industry, for the opportunity of reading the manuscript of an instructive summarising article by Pryor, which has been published by the Society of Chemical Industry in the *Reports on the Progress of Applied Chemistry*, 1959, **44**, 212.

may stabilise the foam which is being generated. Agents which fulfil these two functions, which cannot be considered entirely separately and may even be antagonistic, are termed "collectors" and "frothing agents," respectively, and are of very great technical importance.

The preceding sketch is of course not an historical summary of the development of flotation processes, which were originally evolved empirically. In recent years, however, the physico-chemical basis of technical flotation processes and of the action of flotation agents has become greatly clarified. It is clear, for example, that the contact angle need not be very large in order for flotation to occur, provided that it is finite and that the particles have small enough radii of curvature (see for example the case of the floating sphere which we have discussed in Chapter 5, p. 220). Owing to the fact that the particles of ore are usually initially completely wetted by water, and that they are then brought to the interface by vigorous mechanical agitation, it also appears that the relevant contact angle will generally be the receding one, though not always. The mechanism by which a collecting agent increases this contact angle, which we are defining as the angle measured inside the aqueous phase at the line of contact, appears in general to be one of chemi-sorption by specific interactions between the polar group of the agent and suitable reactive groups in the surface of the particle of ore, the hydrophobic group of the adsorbed amphipathic molecules being accordingly orientated outwards. The thermodynamics of this type of adsorption have been discussed in Chapter 3, p. 95, and an experimental study of a similar phenomenon with Prussian Blue and cetyltrimethylammonium bromide is described in Chapter 4, p. 175.

The best known collecting agents are undoubtedly the alkyl xanthates, and it seems to be generally agreed that they are chemi-sorbed by minerals such as lead sulphide (galena) by virtue of surface reactions such as

$$PbSO_4 + 2KSCSOC_2H_5 \rightarrow Pb(SCSOC_2H_5)_2 + K_2SO_4 \text{[1]}$$

The theory has however been advanced[2] that the alkyl xanthate ions react in the solution phase with dissolved ions of the mineral (in this case Pb^{++} ions) to form an insoluble compound which is then adsorbed. Although the practical consequences of either of these two possible pictures are much the same, it seems likely that a double decomposition in the interface itself is the more probable mechanism.

A considerable number of other collecting agents have also been described, including many which are familiar to users of surface-active agents in other fields. These include soaps, alkyl sulphates, and cationic agents such as long-chain pyridinium and quaternary ammonium compounds

[1] Adam, *Physics and Chemistry of Surfaces*, Oxford University Press, 3rd Edition, 1941, p. 196.

[2] Lipetz, *J. Phys. Chem. U.S.S.R.*, 1942, **16**, 59 (*Chem. Abs.*, 1943, **37**, 2225).

and long-chain amine salts.[1] The action of these agents seems in general to be in agreement with the surface reaction picture which we have sketched above : for example, sodium cetyl sulphate is effective for collecting cassiterite (tin oxide) particles if the pH of the medium is well on the acid side. In particular, Taggart and Arbiter[2] have studied the action of the alkylamine salts and have adduced further evidence in support of the theory of a double decomposition reaction on the surfaces of the particles.

A corollary of the action of collectors is that it is often desirable or necessary to treat a mineral chemically in such a way that it is "activated," after which a collector is more efficiently adsorbed. Sphalerite (zinc sulphide) can be activated, for example, by a treatment with soluble lead salts so as to form superficial layers of lead sulphide, on which (presumably after a certain amount of oxidation to the more reactive lead sulphate) collectors such as the alkyl xanthates are adsorbed.

The fact that a flotation agent may cover the surface of a particle substantially completely has been demonstrated by experiments by Wark and Cox,[3] who found that with a series of different minerals and different alkyl xanthates of varying chain length, the contact angle obtained was characteristic of the agent rather than of the substrate, increasing from 50° with methyl xanthate to 96° with cetyl xanthate.

As Pryor[4] has pointed out, the behaviour of a froth collector on a given mineral solid is not always reproducible, and is often considerably affected by the immediate pre-history of the mineral, particularly by the grinding or other comminution treatment. The lack of reproducibility is due to the difficulty of obtaining pure minerals, and to the possibility of contamination with air-borne sulphur compounds and other impurities. The influence of the comminution process can make itself felt in several ways : by the effect of particle size *per se* on flotability ; by the occurrence of a certain amount of rough separation of different mineral ingredients at the comminution stage; by the formation of freshly cleaved, highly adsorptive surfaces; by the formation of amorphous "Beilby layers" on the surface during grinding. All these factors can vary with different grinding conditions and can overlay the effect of the flotation agent itself.

The second possible rôle which surface-active agents may play in flotation processes, that of froth stabilisation, imposes special restrictions. If for example a frothing agent is added which decreases the contact angle by

---

[1] Dean and Ambrose, *U.S. Bureau of Mines Bull.* 449, 1944; Hergt, Rogers, and Sutherland, Tech. Publ. No. 2081 of the American Inst. of Mining and Metallurgical Engineers, 1947; Rogers and Sutherland, Tech. Publ. No. 2082, 1947, of the American Inst. of Mining and Metallurgical Engineers.

[2] Taggart and Arbiter, Tech. Publ. No. 1685 of the American Inst. of Mining and Metallurgical Engineers, 1944.

[3] See Adam, *loc. cit.*, p. 196.

[4] Pryor, *loc. cit.*

23

lowering the air-water and/or the solid-water interfacial tensions, it may have the effect of reducing or destroying the basic flotation mechanism.[1] It is perhaps for this reason that substances such as cresols or pine oil, for example, are widely used, since they have a foaming action without being powerful wetting-out agents. Foaming and wetting are of course quite distinct phenomena, foaming being favoured by the formation of stable films at the air-water interface, to the stability of which partly wetted particles may also contribute. These partly wetted particles may not only stabilise a foam once formed, but they may also have much the same effect during foam formation as a surface-active solute which reduces the surface tension, in that less work (though not in this case *reversible* work) is needed to create fresh interface between air and the suspension.

In conclusion reference should be made to the use of "suppressors" as a useful variable in flotation processes. These are usually substances such as the alkali cyanides, which will prevent certain sulphide ores (*e.g.*, iron and zinc sulphides) from reacting with xanthate flotation agents, while not interfering with the flotation of lead sulphide, for example. Surface-active agents such as wetting-out agents do not appear to have been used as suppressors, perhaps because their action in reducing the contact angles of water against different types of particles would be too drastic and too non-specific. Metal-sequestering agents have however been found to act as depressants, Gutzeit[2] having reported that ethylene diamine tetraacetic acid, for example, is effective. This and related compounds are believed to act by binding the metal cations of the mineral so that the reaction with the collector can no longer take place.

D. Emulsion polymerisation

An important special application of surface-active agents is in the preparation of synthetic polymers by emulsion polymerisation. Interest first arose in the emulsion polymerisation of olefines and diolefines as a method of manufacturing synthetic rubber, and this method was in fact first described about fifty years ago.[3] The emulsifying agents used at that time were colloids such as glue and other proteins, and according to Hohenstein and Mark,[4] the rate of polymerisation achieved was extremely low. It was not until the introduction of amphipathic substances such as soaps, salts of sulphonated fatty acids, salts of alkylated aromatic sulphonic acids, and the like, that emulsion polymerisation became technically important.[5] The development of this technique rendered Germany, and later the Allies,

---

[1] Adam, *loc. cit.*, p. 198.

[2] Gutzeit, Tech. Publ. No. 2077 of the American Inst. of Mining and Metallurgical Engineers, 1946.

[3] Bayer, D.R.P. 254,672 (1912).

[4] Hohenstein and Mark, *J. Polymer Sci.*, 1946, **1**, 127.

[5] I.G., B.P. 283,840, 16th January, 1928 (German Convention, 14th January, 1927).

to a large extent independent of supplies of natural rubber during the Second World War. One great advantage of this process is that it enables different types of synthetic rubber to be produced which have special properties and can therefore be used for purposes for which natural rubber is entirely unsuitable. Although a large proportion of commercial emulsion polymerisations is still devoted to the production of synthetic rubber, many other polymers are now also made by this technique.

In the emulsion polymerisation process, the actual polymerisation proceeds *via* a free-radical mechanism, and "catalysts" which produce free radicals are used to initiate the polymerisation. In practice these are usually soluble in the aqueous phase (*e.g.*, potassium persulphate, hydrogen peroxide, or cumene hydroperoxide) and almost insoluble in the monomer, but monomer-soluble catalysts such as benzoyl peroxide have also been used. In addition, "modifiers" (chain-transfer agents, inhibitors, and re-tarders) are also used to control the polymerisation. In many cases, the efficiency of these modifiers in the polymerisation reaction depends to some extent on whether they are soluble in the "true" aqueous phase, or in the micelles, as will be evident later. We are concerned here, however, with the role which the amphipathic solute plays in the polymerisation process.

Firstly, of course, the amphipathic substance is adsorbed at the interface between the monomer and the aqueous phase and so stabilises the emulsion droplets. Substances such as glue and proteins will also perform this function at least as efficiently. Williams and Walker[1] have shown that the polymerisation of chloroprene was accelerated when the monomer was emulsified with amphipathic electrolytes (sodium stearate or oleate or Turkey Red Oil) but not when the emulsifying agent was Irish Moss or acid or alkaline casein. They obtained similar results with oil-in-water and water-in-oil emulsions. With the latter type barium or magnesium oleates and zinc stearate produced only a slight acceleration, while rapid polymerisation resulted when sodium oleate was the emulsifying agent, provided that, in the latter case, sufficient water was present. It is well known[2, 3] that the presence of emulsion droplets is not necessary for polymerisation to take place in an aqueous medium. Thus, Hohenstein and Mark[3] showed by exposing an aqueous solution of potassium persulphate to the vapour of styrene, while avoiding contact between liquid styrene and the aqueous phase, that polystyrene appeared in the aqueous phase if a sufficiently long time was allowed to elapse. When the aqueous phase contained ammonium oleate in addition to the persulphate the rate of appearance of the polymer was much more rapid. It was thus evident that some property of the amphipathic substance in aqueous solution was responsible for the increased rate of polymerisation.

[1] Williams and Walker, *Ind. Eng. Chem.*, 1933, **25**, 199.
[2] Fryling and Harrington, *Ind. Eng. Chem.*, 1944, **36**, 114.
[3] Hohenstein and Mark, *J. Polymer Sci.*, 1946, **1**, 549.

We have seen that an amphipathic substance in aqueous solution exists as single molecules (or ions) and, above the critical concentration range, as aggregates or micelles. These micelles because of their essentially hydrocarbon interior are able to dissolve (solubilise) large quantities of hydrocarbons, so that the solubility of a hydrocarbon in a micelle-containing solution may be many times its solubility in water. For example, Frilette and Hohenstein[1] found the solubility of styrene at 25° c. to be 0·022% in water and about 0·65% in 2% potassium oleate, and Stearns, Oppenheimer, Simon, and Harkins[2] give solubilisation data for many hydrocarbons in aqueous solutions of amphipathic electrolytes. The amount solubilised will depend *inter alia* on the relative solubility of the hydrocarbon in water and in the micelle and on the capacity of the amphipathic electrolyte to form micelles. For instance, Fordyce and Chapin[3] showed that although acrylonitrile is much more soluble than styrene in water at 60·3° c., both solubilities are increased only slightly by adding to the water 4% of "Santomerse D" (an alkylaryl sodium sulphonate). When a monomer is emulsified in an aqueous solution of an amphipathic electrolyte, it is distributed in three loci, (1) in the emulsion droplets—this comprises by far the largest fraction of the total monomer, (2) in true solution in the aqueous medium, and (3) solubilised in the micelles. In the early stages of the reaction it is probable that polymerisation takes place in all three loci but, with water-soluble initiators, it is fairly generally agreed that the *principal* locus for the formation of polymer particles is the monomer solubilised in the micelles. Hohenstein and Mark[4] state that E. Valko put forward this view between 1935 and 1938, but a comprehensive picture of the course of the emulsion polymerisation reaction was not published until later, when W. D. Harkins[5] put forward a general theory based on the work done in the United States in previous years. Harkins pointed out that Fikentscher[6] in 1938 considered the aqueous phase to be the locus of the initial polymerisation but that he did not state whether or not he included the micelles in his term aqueous phase. Harkins considered that the formation of the primary polymer particles takes place almost wholly in the micelles where the solubilised monomer is converted to polymer. The aqueous phase surrounding the micelles and the emulsion droplets of monomer are relatively unimportant as sources of primary polymer particles when micelles are present. After polymerisation has taken place, the polymer particle is ejected from the micelle and exists in the aqueous phase as a discrete particle surrounded and stabilised by an adsorbed layer of the amphipathic emulsifying agent. The micelle may then solubilise a further

[1] Frilette and Hohenstein, *J. Polymer Sci.*, 1948, **3**, 22.
[2] Stearns, Oppenheimer, Simon, and Harkins, *J. Chem. Phys.*, 1947, **15**, 496.
[3] Fordyce and Chapin, *J. Amer. Chem. Soc.*, 1947, **69**, 581.
[4] Hohenstein and Mark, *J. Polymer Sci.*, 1946, **1**, 127.
[5] Harkins, *J. Amer. Chem. Soc.*, 1947, **69**, 1428.
[6] Fikentscher, *Angew. Chem.*, 1938, **51**, 433.

quantity of monomer which diffuses to it through the solution, and thus it may continue to produce polymer particles. This rôle of the emulsifying agent is convincingly demonstrated by the X-ray data of Hughes, Sawyer, and Vinograd[1] who found that the long X-ray spacing of potassium laurate solutions was increased when styrene was solubilised and reverted to almost its original value when the solubilised styrene was polymerised. The polymer particles ejected from the micelle are able to dissolve monomer, and the polymerisation reaction continues in this polymer-monomer particle while the monomer emulsion droplets gradually disappear. It is this locus (the polymer-monomer particle) which Harkins considered to be the principal one for the formation of polymer. Since the polymer particles when ejected from the micelle are surrounded by an adsorbed layer of the emulsifying agent and continue to adsorb emulsifying agent as they grow, the number of micelles rapidly decreases until with their disappearance the formation of primary polymer particles virtually ceases. The polymerisation reaction continues to completion in the polymer-monomer particle, but since the initiation of new polymer particles has stopped, it is evident that the amount of emulsifying agent is a factor in determining the molecular weight of the final polymer.

In a later paper, Harkins[2] examined further the initiation of polymerisation of solubilised monomer in the micelles. By adding enough styrene to undersaturate the micellar solution to different degrees, and by examining the molecular weight of the polymers formed in these experiments, he found that low molecular weight polymer is produced at low degrees of saturation. Harkins explained this on the grounds that in the absence of droplets of monomer, the larger part of the polystyrene molecule is formed from styrene which was not present in the micelle in which the free radical originally initiated growth. The monomer required to continue the growth of the particle is solubilised into the polymer from the aqueous phase, and monomer diffuses out of other micelles into the aqueous phase. The soap of the micelle in which polymerisation initially occurred becomes adsorbed soap, and with the growth of the polymer-monomer particle, more soap is adsorbed, and the micelles eventually disappear. The difference in molecular weight of the final product at different degrees of saturation of the micelles is explained, on this picture, by a lowering in the rate of diffusion of monomer from the micelles in which polymerisation has not been initiated. Several hundred micelles are present initially, leading to the formation of only one polymer particle, and it appears that the main function of this soap must be in the stabilisation of the resulting colloidal particles of polymer.

Several authors have made studies of the mechanism of emulsion polymerisation since Harkins first published the general theory. Smith and

---

[1] Hughes, Sawyer, and Vinograd, *J. Chem. Phys.*, 1945, **13**, 131.

[2] Harkins, *J. Polymer Sci.*, 1950, **5**, 217.

Ewart[1] have examined the kinetics of emulsion polymerisation. The free radicals which initiate polymerisation are assumed to be supplied from outside the reaction loci, which are isolated from each other. Three cases are examined, in which (a) the average number of free radicals per locus is small compared with unity, (b) the average number of half, and (c) the average number is large. The characteristic features of styrene emulsion polymerisation are explained by the second case, in which the number of free radicals for each locus is one-half. For this case the average rate of polymerisation per locus is constant, and Smith and Ewart show that the number of particles produced should increase with the soap concentration (three-fifths power) and with the rate of formation of free radicals (two-fifths power), but should decrease with increasing rate of growth of the free radicals (*minus* two-fifths power).

Van der Hoff[2] examined the mechanism of the emulsion polymerisation of styrene in order to test the Smith-Ewart theory for latices containing more than 10^{14} particles per c.c. of water. The polymerisation rate decreased at about 55% conversion, and this corresponded to the disappearance of monomer droplets as judged by the swelling ratios of the polymer particles, which were measured during polymerisation. Van der Hoff also interpreted the molecular weight data as showing that the emulsifier continues to play a part in the polymerisation process after the disappearance of the micelles. "Competitive growth" experiments carried out by Bradford, van der Hoff, and Alfrey[3] at particle concentrations of about 10^{13}/c.c. tend to confirm these findings. Kolthoff, Meehan, and Carr[4] obtained very different results in the emulsion polymerisation of styrene and of 3 : 1 butadiene-styrene co-polymer, under similar conditions, with the addition of emulsifier during the reaction. The kinetic results with styrene were in agreement with the theory of Smith and Ewart, while in the case of the co-polymer, increasing the amount of soap during the reaction increased the rate of polymerisation. This cannot be explained by emulsification or the production of an increased number of carboxylate free radicals from the interaction of non-micellar soap with persulphate. Kolthoff and his collaborators conclude that in diene polymerisation with persulphate as activator, the soap exerts a specific chemical effect that is absent or negligible in the polymerisation of styrene. The acceleration of butadiene-styrene polymerisation which is caused by the addition of non-micellar potassium caprate tends to support this view.

It has been mentioned previously that oil-soluble initiators can be used in emulsion polymerisations, but it has been found that in the absence of a reducing agent, no oil-soluble peroxide has proved to be of commercial

---

[1] Smith and Ewart, *J. Chem. Phys.*, 1948, **16**, 592.
[2] Van der Hoff, *J. Phys. Chem.*, 1956, **60**, 1250.
[3] Bradford, van der Hoff, and Alfrey, *J. Coll. Sci.*, 1956, **11**, 135.
[4] Kolthoff, Meehan, and Carr, *J. Polymer Sci.*, 1951, **7**, 577.

value as an initiator. This is possibly due to the oil-soluble peroxide giving rise to two free radicals at once in a given locus. In the very small loci which are most important in emulsion polymerisation, this will cause two growing chains to form, which will mutually terminate before growing to any extent. The main production of polymer will therefore probably take place in the larger emulsion droplets which will coalesce to form lumps, as has been demonstrated by Hauser and Perry[1] for the polymerisation of a styrene emulsion with benzoyl peroxide as initiator. This results in low molecular weights and low rates of conversion, although it has been suggested by Bovey, Kolthoff, Medalia, and Meehan[2] that additions of chain transfer agents which are able to diffuse through the water from one particle to another can overcome this problem. Other oil-soluble initiators have also been used, but the actual mechanisms involved have not been studied sufficiently to give any definite physical interpretations.

It is interesting that the presence of a surface-active agent increases the rate of polymerisation of a water-soluble monomer. Evans and his co-workers[3] showed that 1% of cetyltrimethylammonium bromide increased the rate of polymerisation of methyl methacrylate dissolved in water by more than ten times, and in addition allowed the polymerisation to go almost to completion. The effect of the surface-active agent in this case was to stabilise the "insoluble" polymer particles and, by preventing coagulation, to decrease the velocity of the chain termination.

The effect of various types of surface-active agents on the emulsion polymerisation of GR-S rubber has been examined by Helin, Gyenge, Beadell, Boyd, Mayhew, and Myatt[4] at 5° and 50° c., and they conclude that anionic agents (sulphates and sulphonates) give good conversion rates and adequate latex stability. They found with these types of surface-active agent that the pH of the solution did not affect the rate of polymerisation. The cationic surface-active materials were poor at 5° c., but gave higher rates at 50° c., although they failed to stabilise the latex adequately. Of the non-ionic agents tried, only the amide-ethylene oxide condensation products were approximately equal to the control (sodium soap) in rate of conversion and stability under certain pH conditions. Condensates of ethylene oxide with alcohols, esters, and amines gave only moderate rates of conversion and large variations in stability. Mixed emulsifiers sometimes gave improved rates of polymerisation and improved the stability of the latex, but these effects were unpredictable. Two interesting observations in this work were that the usable non-ionic agents were freer from objectionable foaming, and the latices were exceptionally stable, even to freezing

---

[1] Hauser and Perry, *J. Phys. Coll. Chem.*, 1948, **52**, 1175.

[2] Bovey, Kolthoff, Medalia, and Meehan, *Emulsion Polymerization*, Interscience, 1955, p. 65.

[3] Baxendale, Evans, and Kilhem, *Trans. Faraday Soc.*, 1946, **42**, 668; Baxendale and Evans, *ibid.*, 1947, **43**, 210.

[4] Helin, Gyenge, Beadell, Boyd, Mayhew, and Myatt, *Ind. Eng. Chem.*, 1953, **45**, 1330.

and thawing, so that special techniques were necessary for flocculating them.

Other emulsifying agents have been described for special applications and properties. Crouch and Cotton,[1] for example, describe the use of salts of organic bases, such as amine salts or quaternary ammonium salts, as emulsifying agents in strongly acidic media, while Park[2] describes the use as emulsifiers of primary alkyl amine salts such as octadecylamine acetate. He claims that the use of these agents enables the latex to be used without a flocculation and washing treatment, without adverse effects on moisture resistance or electrical properties. The use of the potassium soaps of petroleum naphthenic acids as emulsifiers for low temperature emulsion polymerisations below 0° c. has been patented by Sweely.[3] He claims that, using methanol to prevent freezing, the rate of polymerisation of butadiene and styrene is greater with the potassium salts than it is with previously known emulsifiers under similar conditions, and that the sodium salts are of no use under the same conditions. It is possible that, under the conditions specified, the micellar behaviour of the sodium and potassium salts is different, and that this accounts for this rather surprising effect.

E. Less common uses of modern surface-active agents

It will already have become apparent that modern synthetic surface-active agents find many different applications. These applications could be further enumerated and illustrated to an extent which would go beyond the compass of the present book. It may however be appropriate to conclude Part II with an account of a few of the less common uses which have been described for typical surface-active agents which are at present in commercial production, and which seem to us to illustrate the extraordinary versatility of such materials. It is not of course implied that other agents would not also have been effective for the purposes mentioned.

1. THE EFFECT OF SURFACE-ACTIVE AGENTS ON MASS-TRANSFER ACROSS INTERFACES

Considerable interest has been aroused in the past ten years in the use of surface films to retard the evaporation of water from reservoirs, especially in the dry regions of South Africa, Australia, and the United States. The action of these surface films appears to be largely mechanical—*i.e.*, an interference with the diffusion of water molecules—consequently water-soluble surface-active agents (which give surface films of the gaseous type) have not come into the picture. Gilby and Heymann[4] have in fact used

---

[1] Phillips Petroleum Co., Crouch, and Cotton, U.S.P. 2,645,631.
[2] Monsanto and Park, U.S.P. 2,580,315.
[3] Sun Oil Co. and Sweely, U.S.P. 2,664,415.
[4] Gilby and Heymann, *Australian Journal of Scientific Research*, 1948, **1A**, 197.

duplex films of paraffin oils containing 2% of amphipathic "spreaders" such as linseed oil, partially polymerised linseed oil, eucalyptus residues, or polymerised oleic acid. A duplex film, as its name implies, consists of a layer of amphipathic material (probably approximately monomolecular), on top of which is a very thin layer of oil in bulk. The requirements for such a film to be stable are that it should have a positive spreading pressure on water (*cf.* Chapter 4, p. 133), and that it should not break up into lenses of oil surrounded by a monomolecular layer of amphipathic molecules at the air-water interface. Mixtures of oils with simple amphipathic compounds tend to break up in this way, and this probably accounts for the superiority of mixed and/or macromolecular amphipathic ingredients for obtaining stable (perhaps metastable) duplex films. These films are at least to some extent self-healing when they are broken by the wind or other mechanical influences, and this fairly stable layer of oil retards evaporation, as shown by the results of Gilby and Heymann. (This technique is reminiscent of the use of spreading oils for smothering mosquito larvae, and is based on the same surface phenomenon.)

Fatty alcohols have also been found to be effective retarders of evaporation. A review of the position in Australia by Mansfield[1] has been usefully supplemented by several papers which were given to the Second Congress of Surface Activity.[2] Cetyl and octadecyl alcohols have been found to be the most efficient agents of this class, impure material being better than pure. It seems clear that monomolecular layers are formed and are responsible for retarding the evaporation, but that excess particles of fatty alcohol should also be present to provide material for repairing damage to the films.

Surface-active agents have also been found to have interesting effects on mass transfer in *extraction processes*. The agents are added to many such processes in order to increase the interfacial area under the conditions prevailing, for example, in air-purification sprays or liquid-liquid extractions, and also in order to wet out solid particles from the interface, or to ensure complete wetting of the plant or apparatus being used. It has frequently been observed, however, that the rate of transfer across unit interfacial area is considerably reduced by the surface-active agent. This appears to be due to one or both of two quite separate effects.

The first of these is illustrated by the work of Cullen and Davidson[3] on the absorption of carbon dioxide by water containing agents such as sulphated olefines, alkylphenol-ethylene oxide condensation products, or sodium dodecyl sulphate. The water ran in a thin film over spheres in a wetted-wall column. It was found that retardation of gas absorption, which could be as much as 25%, was due to the presence of impurities in the

---

[1] Mansfield, *Nature*, 1955, **175**, 247.

[2] La Mer, *Second Congress*, 1957, **I**, 259; McArthur and Durham, *ibid.*, 262; Grundy, *ibid.*, 270.

[3] Cullen and Davidson, *Chemical Engineering Science*, 1957, **6**, 49.

surface-active agents, such a dodecyl alcohol in the sodium dodecyl sulphate.
It seems fairly clear that in this case retardation is due to mechanical
interference with diffusion of gas, caused by a compact surface film—
quite possibly a complex layer of the two types of amphipathic molecules.

The other effect of surface-active agents on mass transfer is rather more
subtle, and has been fairly widely studied. A convenient summary is
provided by two papers which were given at the Second Congress of Surface
Activity.[1] When a liquid drop moves through a fluid medium which exerts a
viscous drag upon it, circulation occurs inside the drop, which is consequently able to move more quickly than would a rigid sphere of the same
size and density. This internal circulation also accelerates mass transfer
into (or out of) the drop, since it continually renews the liquid adjacent to
the interface. If a surface-active material is present, however, it will form
an interfacial film (usually of the gaseous type), and this film will be swept
along the drop. Since adsorption equilibrium is not instantaneously re-
established at the interface, the interfacial tension at the front of the drop
will be greater than at the rear, and a force will be set up which opposes
circulation. Equivalently, but perhaps more clearly expressed, the compressed interfacial film at the rear of the drop will set up a forward surface
pressure, which acts against circulation. This forward surface pressure
may also reduce turbulence on the external side of the interface as well.
The result of all these effects, which have nothing to do with interfacial
barriers to diffusion, is that the drop moves more slowly (more nearly as
if it were a solid particle), and that mass transfer is also slowed down.

2. SOME APPLICATIONS OF SURFACE-ACTIVE AGENTS IN METALLURGY

Colloidal materials such as glue, gums, and sulphite cellulose lye have
been used for some time in electroplating baths. Nearly all electro-deposits
are porous when they are thin, which is probably due to cracks or fissures,
or to included impurities such as particles of dirt. Cracks may be due to
hydrogen embrittlement, caused by adsorbed hydrogen atoms combining
together in intergranular spaces to form hydrogen gas, which then expands
violently when the pressure has built up sufficiently. Hydrogen bubbles
may also adhere to the surface and inhibit the deposition of further metal,
resulting in "pitting." Surface-active agents which lower the gas-liquid
interfacial tension sufficiently will reduce both effects by making it easier
for the gas to escape from the surface of the metal. Many surface-active
agents are capable of doing this, but it is important that the agent chosen
in a particular case should not have an adverse effect on the crystal habit
of the deposited metal.

Probably the most important function of surface-active agents in
electroplating baths is to act as "brighteners," *i.e.*, to produce a bright

---

[1] Linton and Sutherland, *Second Congress*, 1957, **I**, 494; Blokker, *ibid.*, 503.

deposit which requires little or no polishing. Brighteners (for example, sodium naphthalene-1 : 3 : 6-trisulphonate, sodium isopropylnaphthalene sulphonate, polyalkyleneamines, and benzylpyridinium derivatives) probably act by controlling the crystal size, smaller crystals giving a brighter deposit, and by controlling the orientation and rate of deposition.

The theory of electrolytic crystal growth has been studied by Vermilyea,[1] who considers the effect of the applied voltage on the current at surfaces which are perfectly smooth, atomically rough, or smooth except for the steps of screw dislocations (*cf.* Chapter 4, p. 187). When the voltage is sufficiently high, the rate-determining step is that of ionic discharge, but at low voltages and short times the surface structure plays an important part in determining the rate of deposition. The presence of adsorbed materials can therefore influence the rate of electrodeposition by affecting crystal shape, as well as by making it easier for any gas formed to escape.

It has also been reported that surface-active agents have other beneficial effects, such as giving harder deposits, improving the ductility, and "levelling" the plating deposits.[2] The last-named effect means that metal is deposited on areas which should theoretically receive less than other areas; it is, perhaps, due partly to "surface-poisoning" of the preferred areas, and to lowerings of the interfacial tensions, so that there is a diminution in the tendency for metal to be preferentially deposited in regions where deposition gives a smaller increment in interfacial free energy.

Surface-active agents are also of interest in metallurgy from the more negative aspect of their possible *corrosive action* in aqueous solutions. This question has been systematically investigated by Holness, Ross, and Langstaff.[3] Direct reference to this important series of papers is strongly to be recommended, but we can perhaps summarise their main findings as follows, it being noted that no simple generalisation can be made, the different combinations of metals and surface-active agents showing a high degree of specificity.

Copper was not affected by aqueous solutions of sodium dioctylsulphosuccinate, or by an alkylphenol-ethylene oxide condensation product, but an initial small gain in weight, followed by a loss, was observed with an alkylaryl sulphonate and a primary and a secondary aliphatic sulphate. Still more corrosion was caused by Turkey Red Oil (*cf.* Chapter 11, p. 427), by the triethanolamine salt of sulphated dodecyl alcohol, and by triethanolamine itself. Cetyltrimethylammonium bromide also caused some corrosion, but cetylpyridinium bromide formed a more protective, adhesive layer. On mild steel, corrosion (compared with tap water) was actually

[1] Vermilyea, *J. Chem. Phys.*, 1956, **25**, 1254.

[2] *Technical Proceedings of the American Electroplaters' Society*, 43rd Annual Convention, Washington, 1956. (Taken from *Chemical Abstracts*, 1957, **51**, 5593, 5594.)

[3] Holness and Ross, *J. Applied Chem.*, 1951, **1**, 158; Ross and Holness, *ibid.*, 1952, **2**, 520; Ross, *ibid.*, 1952, **2**, 526; Ross, *ibid.*, 1955, **5**, 10; Holness and Langstaff, *ibid.*, 1956, **6**, 115, 140.

diminished by Turkey Red Oil, a sodium *sec.* alkyl sulphate, a sodium alkylaryl sulphonate, sodium dioctylsulphosuccinate, and triethanolamine, while corrosion was increased by the primary alkyl sulphate, cetyltrimethylammonium bromide and cetylpyridinium bromide. All the synthetic surface-active agents except Turkey Red Oil caused more corrosion than did sodium oleate. All the agents examined caused some corrosion on aluminium, Turkey Red Oil and sodium dioctylsulphosuccinate causing the least, while on nickel only cetylpyridinium bromide caused some corrosion.

The corrosion of tin was studied in more detail. No attack was caused by Turkey Red Oil, triethanolamine, or the non-ionic agent, slight attack by the alkylaryl sulphonate, and some loss in weight by sodium dioctylsulphosuccinate and the alkyl sulphates. Cetyltrimethylammonium bromide and cetylpyridinium bromide also caused some corrosion, but the results were very similar to control experiments with sodium bromide. A series of specially prepared sodium alkyl sulphates (C_8 to C_{14}) was also examined. Corrosion was greater the longer the chain, and was greater with a 2-substituted sulphato group than with a 1-sulphato analogue; corrosion was less when the sulphato group was near the centre of the chain. These agents all tended to form protective layers on the metal surfaces, corrosion being to a large extent determined by whether or not the protective layers broke away.

3. SOME GEOPHYSICAL APPLICATIONS OF SURFACE-ACTIVE AGENTS

The water-proofing of soils with rosin derivatives, and the improvement of soil texture by the use of special polymers, fall outside the scope of this book. An application of more conventional surface-active agents which has also aroused considerable interest is in the displacement of petroleum from underground sand layers by means of aqueous solutions. A summary of this work, with a report on the performance of 150 different surface-active agents which are available in the United States, has been published by Johansen, Dunning, and Beaty.[1] Polyethenoxy agents seem to be the most effective, probably because of their relative insensitivity to electrolytes, and perhaps also because they do not tend to be adsorbed so readily as ionic agents. (Adsorption on sand, limestone, etc., will not only lead to depletion of the surface-active material, but if it occurs with reversed orientation could render the underground strata more oleophilic, and therefore act against the effect which it is desired to achieve.) It seems clear that the function of the surface-active agent in this process is to lower the advancing contact angle (measured inside the aqueous phase) at the solid-oil-water lines of contact. The process will be complicated geometrically,

---
[1] Johansen, Dunning, and Beaty, *Soap and Chemical Specialties*, 1955, **31**, No. 10, 41, 79, 81; No. 11, 53. See also Dunning, Gustafson, and Johansen, *Ind. Eng. Chem.*, 1954, **46**, 591.

but it appears to be essentially one of penetration into a system of interconnected capillaries, as discussed in Chapters 4, 5, and 8 (pp. 150, 221, and 294), and is analogous to the phase-displacement processes which we have discussed there.

It has also been proposed[1] to use a surface-active agent (a sodium alkylbenzene sulphonate) to increase the wettability of soils by rain. The patent specification in question recommends adding from fifteen to fifty pounds of the agent per acre, so that the surface tension of water is lowered to less than 45 dynes/cm. (If, for example, 50 lb. of agent are assumed to have been dissolved in the amount of water corresponding to one inch of rain on one acre of ground, a concentration of about 0·02% would result, which would certainly give a significant wetting-out effect, provided that the agent is not too strongly adsorbed by the soil.) As every gardener—amateur or professional—is aware, it is often very difficult to get water to wet the surface of the ground after a prolonged drought: this is presumably due to the formation of water-repellent, wax-like or greasy layers on the soil particles, greatly aggravated by the structure of the soil, which causes the surface to be highly "composite" (*cf.* Chapter 4, p. 140, and Chapter 5, p. 216)—*i.e.*, the apparent solid-liquid interface contains a great deal of air-liquid interface. The role of the wetting-out agent is such a case is clearly to decrease the advancing contact angle, and if the water is applied or falls rapidly, to reduce the surface tension so that the trapped air can escape from the soil. (This is the "total immersion" case which is discussed in Chapters 4 and 5.)

4. SOME APPLICATIONS OF SURFACE-ACTIVE AGENTS IN CONSTRUCTIONAL WORK

The use of surface-active agents in concrete mixes and in cement mortars, which has been reviewed by Wilson[2] and by Seddon and Hill,[3] is now well established. Three types of practical effects are achieved: (*i*) wetting-out and deflocculation of the solid particles in the concrete or mortar, (*ii*) entrainment of air, and (*iii*) actual foaming. Thorough wetting-out ensures that all the particles of Portland cement and of aggregate are in contact with water, so that hydration of the cement can occur, and the whole mass is properly knitted together. Deflocculation renders the mixture more fluid and "workable" at a given water content (*i.e.*, the sedimentation volume is decreased: *cf.* Chapter 4, p. 170), or alternatively, enables the water content to be reduced for a given consistency, which can lead to an improved compressive strength in the concrete after it has set.

"Air-entrainment" does not in any way imply incomplete wetting of the

[1] Atlantic Refining Company and Clarke, U.S.P. 2,689,173.
[2] Wilson, *First Congress*, 1954, 1196.
[3] Seddon and Hill, *ibid.*, 1204.

solid particles by the water in concrete or mortar, but rather that large numbers of small air bubbles are introduced into the mass when it is suitably worked mechanically. Surface-active agents do this by lowering the surface tension and by stabilising the air bubbles; the demands in the latter respect are not so great as in a fire-extinguishing foam, for example (see below). Air entrainment helps to "plasticise" cement mortars, but its main virtue is in improving the resistance to damage by freezing and thawing, the air cells taking up the pressure which is generated by growing ice crystals. In foamed concrete this inclusion of air is carried much further, up to 80% of the volume of a foamed mixture being air. (Complete wetting of the solid particles by the water is still essential.) When the foamed concrete is set, it has special uses by virtue of its low density, ease of handling cutting, etc., and good heat insulation properties.

Although many types of surface-active agents are added to concrete, the non-ionics are particularly useful because of their low sensitivity to electrolytes. For preparing foamed concrete, synthetic surface-active agents such as the alkylated naphthalene sulphonates are frequently mixed with specially liquefied proteins, which stabilise the foam, as in the product "Aphrosol FC."

Surface-active materials are also used in road-building, to increase the adhesion of bitumen to stone chippings in "tar-macadam" paving mixtures. The function of the agents here, which is reminiscent of the use of cationic surface-active agents for promoting the dispersion of pigments in oil media, is to lower the interfacial tension between stone and tar (*i.e.*, to lower the contact angle in the tar, or to increase the work of adhesion tar-stone, in competition with both air and water). It seems quite clear that such an effect is achieved even in the absence of special additions by chemisorption of various tar acids on to many types of stone, but special cationic agents appear to be considerably more efficient. Among the summaries of the use of cationic agents for this purpose are those of Snyder and Pavlish,[1] Hallberg,[2] and Nicholas and Matthews,[3] written from experience in the United States, Sweden, and the United Kingdom, respectively.

Amine salts, such as the hydrochlorides of octadecylamine, oleylamine, and tall oil amine are widely used, and are definitely preferred by Hallberg. Nicholas and Matthews's paper indicates that rather higher concentrations of octadecylamine hydrochloride are needed in this country than in Sweden; these authors also recommend cetylpyridinium bromide, and interpret the effect in terms of the high spreading pressure which the agent confers on the bitumen. This is, of course, an alternative way of expressing the effect to the one which we have used above; the essential requirements

---

[1] Snyder and Pavlish, *Ind. Eng. Chem.*, 1949, **41**, 2649.
[2] Hallberg, *First Congress*, 1954, 1208.
[3] Nicholas and Matthews, *ibid.*, 1213.

of the surface-active agent are that it should be strongly adsorbed by the stone, certainly at the stone-bitumen interface and preferably at the stone-water interface as well, *with reversed orientation*, and that it should not be salted out by electrolytes present, or hydrolysed by any alkali which may come from the stone or the water.

5. FOAMING AND ANTI-FOAMING AGENTS

A very full account of *fire-fighting foams* has been published by Bikerman.[1] Fire-extinguishing foams are of two kinds: air foams and so-called "chemical" foams, the former being generated mechanically by entraining or beating air into a solution of foaming agent, while the latter are formed by mixing a solution of acid and a solution containing sodium bicarbonate, with evolution of carbon dioxide. Synthetic surface-active agents, such as alkylated naphthalene sulphonates of various types[2] have been found to give voluminous foams, especially of air foams. The stability of such foams is, however, insufficient for many purposes, especially where the foam must persist for several hours. The foams must also usually be stable in contact with petrol, alcohol, or other solvents, and this condition is a severe one in practice. Practically all fire-fighting foams contain protein stabilisers, sometimes alone and sometimes mixed with synthetic agents, such as the alkylated naphthalene sulphonates just referred to.[3] The concentrated compositions frequently contain glue which has been specially liquefied to prevent gelling, while giving adequate stabilisation in the final foam. Treatments such as partial hydrolysis of the protein, treatment with nitric acid, or addition of urea of other protein "peptisers" have been described. A typical product containing a modified glue and a sodium alkyl-naphthalene sulphonate is "Aphrosol FC," the use of which for making foamed concrete has been referred to above.

Although it does not involve the use of synthetic surface-active agents, Sthamer's proposal[4] to use a mixture of hydrolysed protein with an oxidisable metal salt such as ferrous sulphate, is worth noting for its bearing on the mechanism of foam stabilisation. These preparations are only for use with air foams, the Fe^{++} ions being oxidised to Fe^{+++} ions at or near the interface. The protein material, which is not precipitated by ferrous ions, is insolubilised by ferric ions, so that completely insoluble films are formed *in situ* in the foam lamellae.

The different mechanisms by which anti-foaming agents work have been mentioned in Chapter 4 (p. 206). These agents are very widely used in

---

[1] Bikerman, *Foams, Theory and Industrial Applications*, Reinhold, 1953, pp. 189–242.

[2] See, for example, I.C.I. and Chapman, B.P. 289,630 and I.G., F.P. 665,017.

[3] See, for example, I.G., B.P. 460,596, and I.C.I., B.P. 323,720 = U.S.P. 1,873,580, B.P. 469,325.

[4] Sthamer, B.P. 476,552.

industry[1] and frequently involve more than one mechanism. It seems clear that the silicones and the other insoluble liquid agents act primarily as spreading liquids, which break the foam lamellae by displacing or mechanically rupturing the stabilising films. The silicones have the great virtue of insolubility in many liquids, including concentrated solutions of surface-active agents, and they have been proposed for use in the concentration by boiling of surface-active agents.[2]

Foaming in boilers has been reviewed by Denman.[3] He considers that the factors which affect foaming in a steam boiler are the presence of dissolved and suspended matter, organic matter, clays, oils, or soaps, as well as the design and variations in the steam demand. The efficiency of many anti-foaming agents is increased by the addition of deflocculating agents such as tannins, modified lignins, and agents such as the naphthalene sulphonic acid-formaldehyde condensation products. (The function of at least some of these agents is probably to keep finely-divided solids in a dispersed and completely wetted-out state, so that they do not stabilise foams, while at the same time the agents must not stabilise foam themselves.) Hawke and Alexander[4] suggest that an efficient anti-foaming agent should have a high insolubility in water at normal operating temperatures (over 100° c.), a moderate degree of surface activity at the steam-water interface, be able to form fluid films at the steam-water interface (with of course a high spreading pressure), be chemically stable in the boiler, and have a low tendency to be adsorbed on solid particles, the surface of the boiler, etc.

It seems likely that some of the ethylene oxide condensation products which are self-emulsifiable but not soluble in water, are particularly useful anti-foamers because they satisfy the dual function of forming a spreading layer on the surface, and also keep any suspended matter completely wetted-out and dispersed in the water.

---

[1] See the chapter by Currie in Bikerman's *Foams, Theory and Industrial Applications*, Reinhold, New York, 1953, pp. 297–329, which contains 258 references.

[2] Du Pont and Scott, U.S.P. 2,462,999.

[3] Denman, *Ind. Eng. Chem.*, 1954, **46**, 992.

[4] Hawke and Alexander, *J. Coll. Sci.*, 1956, **11**, 419.

PART III

THE CHEMICAL CONSTITUTION OF SYNTHETIC SURFACE-ACTIVE AGENTS

CHAPTER 10

ANIONIC SURFACE-ACTIVE AGENTS: SULPHONIC ACIDS AND THEIR SALTS

A. Historical introduction

THE history of synthetic surface-active agents began when the Industrial Revolution focused attention on the disadvantages of soap, which up to that time was the only readily available surface-active agent. The defects of soap—its instability in acid solution and the insolubility of its calcium and magnesium salts—are associated with the presence of the carboxylic acid group. By introducing into the fatty chain other hydrophilic groups, for example the sulphonic acid group, $- SO_3H$, in which the sulphur atom is attached directly to a carbon atom in the chain, and more especially the sulphate ester group, $- O \cdot SO_3H$, in which the sulphur atom is linked to the carbon chain through an oxygen atom, the first really competitive synthetic surface-active agents were produced. The first of these, Turkey Red Oil, took its name from its principal application, as an adjuvant to the dye-bath in the dyeing of fabrics with Turkey Red. It was prepared by the action of sulphuric acid on castor oil and was predominantly a mixture of sulphuric acid esters. It is interesting to note that, at least until fairly recently probably, over 90% of the total production of commercially important synthetic surface-active agents contained either a sulphonic acid or sulphuric ester group. Turkey Red Oil was followed by many other "soluble" or "sulphonated" oils prepared from a variety of natural fats, both vegetable and animal. All these "sulphonated oils," as we shall see in Chapter 11, contained only a small proportion of true sulphonic acids, their principal surface-active components being long-chain sulphate esters.

In the sulphuric acid refining of coal-tar and shale oil, and at a later date of petroleum, large quantities of acid sludge were produced. In this sludge were mixtures of sulphonic acids which, when isolated, have been termed "green" acids. Further quantities of sulphonic acids remain in the oil layer and are recovered from it. The latter, termed "mahogany" acids, are surface-active, and although they are not of great commercial importance, they have been used as a cheap source of emulsifying agents, chiefly for cutting oils, low-grade textile lubricants, and in agricultural winter washes. A refined product has however been claimed[1] as a detergent.

It was not until the end of the nineteenth century that a commercially important surface-active *sulphonic acid* was deliberately synthesised. This

---

[1] Petroff, D.R.P. 264,785, 2.4.12.

American discovery was the basis of the well-known Twitchell process[1] for the splitting of fats. The first of these sulphonic acid fat-splitting catalysts was prepared by reacting oleic acid with sulphuric acid at high temperature whereby a true sulphonic acid which Twitchell believed to be

$$C_{17}H_{34}(SO_3H)COOC_{17}H_{34}\cdot COOH$$

was produced. Twitchell considered[2] that the amphipathic character of this molecule was essential to its success in the fat-splitting process. The purely aliphatic Twitchell reagents were quickly replaced by the more readily prepared aliphatic-aromatic compounds,[3] the most effective product in this class being the product of the sulphonation of a mixture of naphthalene and oleic acid to which Twitchell assigned[4] the formula

$$HOOC\cdot C_{17}H_{34}\cdot C_{10}H_6SO_3H$$

The alkali metal salts of these reagents did not find any ready application as textile assistants, probably because of their rather poor wetting power and stability to hard water—it will be noted that the carboxylic acid group has not been eliminated although its defects are to some extent overcome by the sulphonic acid group. For aqueous systems, however, the hydrophobic portion of the molecule is too large for this to be an effective surface-active agent.

In 1913 Reychler published[5] the results of his work on aqueous solutions of hexadecane sulphonic acid and its salts. Since then many investigations into the properties of solutions of the alkane sulphonic acids, covering a wide range of chain lengths, have been described, which have shown that these compounds are surface-active, of fairly good stability to hard water, and very stable in mineral acid solution. Until fairly recently, however, they have not been developed commercially because the raw materials and the known methods for their manufacture were too costly. Again in 1913, the Badische Anilin- und Soda-Fabrik described[6] the preparation of water-soluble condensation products from formaldehyde and naphthalene sulphonic acids. The initial usefulness of these products lay in their ability to solubilise the water-insoluble portions of vegetable tanning agents and it was not until some years later that their outstanding efficiency as dispersing agents for solids in aqueous media was realised.

During the First World War, when Germany began to suffer from a shortage of fats, intensive attempts were made to produce an entirely synthetic detergent. This led to the production of a series of short-chain

[1] Twitchell, U.S.P. 601,603; D.R.P. 114,494.
[2] Twitchell, *Ind. Eng. Chem.*, 1917, **9**, 192.
[3] Twitchell, U.S.P. 628,503.
[4] Twitchell, *J. Amer. Chem. Soc.*, 1900, **22**, 22.
[5] Reychler, *Bull. soc. chim. Belg.*, 1913, **27**, 110, 113, 217.
[6] Badische, D.R.P. 292,531; B.P. 7137/13; U.S.P. 1,336,759.

alkyl naphthalene sulphonic acids by the Badische Anilin- und Soda-Fabrik.[1] The first of these was the sodium salt of diisopropylnaphthalene sulphonic acid, which was put on the market under the trade name "Nekal A." It was rather a poor detergent, but was a good wetting-out agent and was very stable in acid solutions. It was also an effective emulsifying agent for hydrocarbons and tar oils, especially in admixture with proteins.

The rapid expansion of the British organic chemical industry after the First World War, and the merger of several important German firms to form the I.G. Farbenindustrie, ushered in a decade of intensive research on synthetic surface-active agents, not only in those countries but on the Continent of Europe generally and somewhat later in the United States. In the present chapter many of the surface-active sulphonic acids which were synthesised during that period are described, and it will suffice here to mention only a few. The I.G. were the first in the field with two important sulphonates of fatty acid condensation products, "Igepon A" and "Igepon T." The former was the sodium salt of the condensation product of oleic acid chloride and hydroxyethane sulphonic acid,[2]

$$C_{17}H_{33} \cdot COOCH_2 \cdot CH_2SO_3^-, \; Na^+$$

and the latter was the sodium salt of the product obtained by condensing oleic acid chloride with N-methyltaurine,[3]

$$C_{17}H_{33} \cdot CON(CH_3)CH_2 \cdot CH_2SO_3^-, \; Na^+$$

An interesting paper by Kastens and Ayo[4] briefly outlines the history of detergents in the United States, and discusses in more detail the production of the "Igepons," and the properties of some of the many compounds of this type.

In Great Britain, Imperial Chemical Industries produced "Lissapol LS," the sodium salt of the condensation product of oleic acid chloride and *p*-anisidine sulphonic acid,

$$C_{17}H_{33} \cdot CONH - \langle \bigcirc \rangle - OCH_3$$
$$SO_3^-, \; Na^+$$

and in the United States the American Cyanamid and Chemical Corporation manufactured various esters of sulphosuccinic acid[5] which were sold

[1] Badishe, D.R.P. 336,558.
[2] I.G., D.R.P. 652,410; 657,357; B.P. 359,893; 366,916; F.P. 705,081.
[3] I.G., D.R.P. 584,730; 655,999; B.P. 341,053; F.P. 693,620; U.S.P. 1,932,180.
[4] Kastens and Ayo, *Ind. Eng. Chem.*, 1950, **42**, 1626.
[5] American Cyanamid and Jaeger, U.S.P. 2,028,091.

under the trade names "Aerosol" and "Vatsol." The product "Aerosol MA," for example, has the constitution

$$C_6H_{13}OOC \cdot \overset{|}{C}HSO_3{}^-, \; Na^+$$
$$C_6H_{13}OOC \cdot \overset{|}{C}H_2$$

During the Second World War no discovery of a new type of surface-active sulphonic acid has been reported. The Germans were very active in this field, but the products which found their way on to the market belonged to types which were already well known, though they were synthesised from new intermediates which had become available in Germany. The household detergent with the largest production in Germany at this time was an alkane sulphonate known as "Mersolat." This was produced by the well-known Reed reaction[1] from a hydrocarbon obtained by hydrogenerating "Kogasin," a product of the Fischer-Tropsch synthesis. The C_{14}—C_{16} hydrogenated "Kogasin" fraction, which was known as "Mepasin," was treated with sulphur dioxide and chlorine, in the presence of actinic light, to give a mixture of the mono- and di-sulphonyl chlorides ("Mersols"). The alkali metal salts of the corresponding sulphonic acids, which were the "Mersolats," were produced by caustic alkali hydrolysis of the sulphonyl chloride mixtures.

In the production of detergents the emphasis has been more recently on attempts to find continuous processes, and on better control of the sulphonation in order to obtain commercially more attractive products. Paulson[2] has reviewed the processes of sulphation and sulphonation as applied to the manufacture of detergents, and he discusses especially the newer methods used to obtain the required properties in the finished products. The demands for substantially complete sulphonation, and for light-coloured products with minimum odour, are to some extent incompatible. In general, the first of these requirements necessitates vigorous sulphonation, with an excess of sulphonating agent at high concentrations, while the preparation of a light-coloured product is more easily achieved under mild conditions of sulphonation. These demands, as Paulson points out, led to a careful study of batch-wise processes, with resulting improvements. With the advent of "builders" (see Chapter 8, p. 308), it became necessary to reduce the amount of sodium sulphate which was produced when the excess acid in the sulphonation mixture was neutralised. Improvements in the batch processes were achieved by diluting the reaction mixtures slightly, and utilising the difference in density to separate off some of the excess of sulphonating agent. More recently several patents have been published on the use of sulphur trioxide as the sulphonating agent, either in gaseous form

---

[1] Reed and Horn, U.S.P. 2,046,090; Reissue 20,968.
[2] Paulson, *J. Amer. Oil Chem. Soc.*, 1952, **29**, 556.

in an inert carrying gas, or dissolved in an inert liquid.[1] An inert carrying gas has the advantage that the heat evolved by the reaction is continually removed; in the inert solvents the reaction is usually carried out at fairly low temperatures, and cooling results from the evaporation of the solvent. The use of sulphur trioxide does not, as one might expect, lead to complete elimination of sodium sulphate from the product after neutralisation, but Seaton[2] has found that the addition of mercury (either as a salt or as the element) reduces the inorganic salt content. He suggests that the formation of inorganic salt at the neutralisation stage is due to the reaction

$$RH + 2SO_3 \rightarrow RSO_3 \cdot SO_3H$$

followed by neutralisation, the presence of mercury reducing the tendency for the reaction to occur. When a "keryl" benzene fraction (essentially dodecylbenzene) is sulphonated with sulphur trioxide in this way, the inorganic salt content (material insoluble in alcohol) is stated to be reduced from 4·3% to 1·7%.

Other continuous processes using chlorosulphonic acid as the sulphonating agent have also been described. These processes are based on re-cycling the reactants with the product, which is removed at a constant rate,[3] or on atomising the reactants in a common jet of inert gas.[4] Finally, it is interesting to note that gamma radiation has been used to catalyse the sulphonation of paraffins with oxygen and sulphur dioxide.[5]

An interesting collection and description of technical sulphonation processes has been given by Lindner.[6] It is especially useful in that there is ample use of diagrams to illustrate the chemical engineering processes involved.

B. Classification of sulphonic acids

In the search for industrially useful sulphonates (which are almost invariably used as their sodium salts) almost every conceivable material has been subjected to the action of sulphonating agents—these include vegetable and animal fats and waxes, crude and refined products from the petroleum industry, and many specially synthesised intermediates from the organic chemicals industry generally. Relatively few of this immense number of sulphonates have been carried further than the laboratory stage of preparation, but the literature on their preparation is very large, in particular the patent literature. It is impossible to mention in one chapter all the

[1] Universal Oil Products, B.P. 664,577; 666,642; 666,643; S.A. d'Innovations Chimiques, B.P. 799,199; Lever Brothers, B.P. 669,899.

[2] Monsanto and Seaton, U.S.P. 2,782,230.

[3] S.A. d'Innovations Chimiques, B.P. 799,199.

[4] S.A. d'Innovations Chimiques, B.P. 680,629.

[5] Black and Baxter, *Soap and Chemical Specialties*, 1958, **34**, No. 10, 43, 104.

[6] Lindner, *Textilhilfsmittel und Waschrohstoffe*, Wissenschaftliche Verlagsgesellschaft, Stuttgart, 1954, pp. 570–589.

substances which have been proposed for sulphonation in order to obtain surface-active agents, nor would it serve any useful purpose to do so. We have chosen instead to describe and illustrate some of the more important types of sulphonates, indicating briefly the methods of preparation, and referring whenever possible to their more important, novel, or scientifically interesting technological applications. The scheme of classification which we have adopted in attempting this is based on the chemical constitutions of several better-known types of surface-active sulphonates, with which we have grouped other examples which are less important, finally adding a section on some miscellaneous types.

It should be noted that in much of the literature the use of the expression "sulphonated" does not necessarily mean that a surface-active agent contains the group $-C-SO_2 \cdot O^-$, Na^+. The term is in fact still frequently used merely to mean that the product has been treated with a sulphonating agent, and frequently the surface-active material consists entirely or predominantly of *sulphate esters*, which are discussed in Chapter 11. For example, "Sulphonated Lorol" is predominantly sulphated dodecyl alcohol, $C_{12}H_{25}OSO_3^-$, Na^+, and "sulphonated castor oil" is used to describe the mixed sulphuric acid esters which are obtained when castor oil is treated with a sulphonating agent. All such products are excluded from the present chapter, which is confined to true sulphonic acids and their salts.

The classification of the true sulphonates which we have used is as follows, the first two sections dealing with agents in which the sulphonate group is attached directly to the hydrophobic portion of the surface-active molecule, while the others deal with products containing intermediate bridging groups:

(a) *Aliphatic sulphonates*, in which the hydrophobic portion of the amphipathic molecule consists essentially of an aliphatic hydrocarbon chain (straight or branched), a cycloaliphatic nucleus, or a combination of the two, this hydrophobic grouping being attached directly to the sulphonate group; the hydrophobic residue may however contain substituents such as halogen atoms, hydroxyl groups, etc.

(b) *Sulphonates of aliphatic-aromatic hydrocarbons*, comprising the sulphonates of alkylated benzene, naphthalene, or other aromatic nuclei, aromatic sulphonates in which the aromatic nuclei are linked by methylene bridges, and sulphonates of alkylated heterocyclic compounds.

(c) *Ester sulphonates*, which are based on esters of aliphatic or aromatic carboxylic acids, the sulphonate group being attached to either the ester or the acyl radical; the sulphonate group is therefore separated from the hydrophobic residue by a polar connecting grouping.

(d) *Amide sulphonates*, in which either a carboxyamide linkage $-CON\langle$ or a sulphonamide linkage $-SO_2N\langle$ is interposed between the sulphonate group and the hydrophobic residue, the sulphonate group being connected to either end of the amide linkage.

(e) *Miscellaneous sulphonates*, in which a variety of other non-ionising polar groups (*e.g.*, —O—, —NH—, or —SO$_2$—) are interposed between hydrophobic residues and ionising sulphonate groups.

C. Aliphatic sulphonates

The aliphatic sulphonates may be represented by the simple formula

$$R \cdot SO_2 \cdot O^-, \ Na^+$$

in which R may be a straight-chain or branched-chain, saturated or un-saturated paraffin chain, or a cyclo-aliphatic radical. Examples of this class are sodium tetradecane sulphonate,

$$C_{14}H_{29}SO_2O^-, \ Na^+$$

sodium octadec-9-ene sulphonate,

$$CH_3 \cdot [CH_2]_7 \cdot CH : CH \cdot [CH_2]_7 \cdot CH_2SO_2O^-, \ Na^+$$

and sodium ethylcyclohexane-*p*-sulphonate,

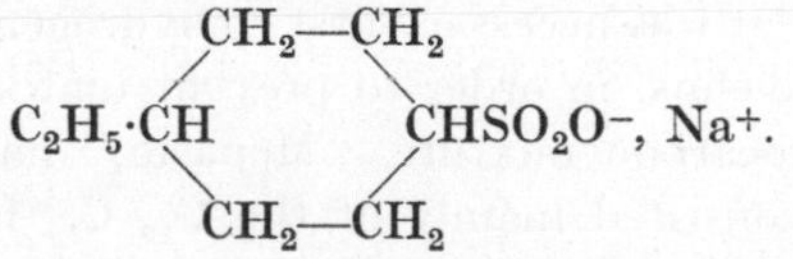

$$
\begin{array}{c}
CH_2 \!-\! CH_2 \\
C_2H_5 \cdot CH \qquad\quad CHSO_2O^-, \ Na^+. \\
CH_2 \!-\! CH_2
\end{array}
$$

Appreciable surface-activity in aqueous media is generally considered to begin in the straight-chain ω-sulphonic acid class with the C$_8$ compounds, while the C$_{18}$ compounds are not sufficiently soluble to be of much importance in aqueous media.

Reed and Tartar,[1] among others, have measured several of the properties of aqueous solutions of the purified sodium salts of the straight-chain alkane sulphonic acids and show them (*cf.* Chapter 2) to behave as typical amphipathic electrolytes. Since they are the salts of strong acids and strong bases, the data obtained on their aqueous solutions are not complicated by the presence of hydrolysis products such as those which are present in soap solutions. The calcium and magnesium salts, as Reed and Tartar show, have a low solubility in water, which accounts for their unpopularity as detergents and in the textile industry generally. They are, however, stable in hot acid media, a point which is in their favour in comparison with their near relatives, the aliphatic sulphates. It is probable, however, that had it not been for the necessity for conserving natural fats and the scarcity of

---

[1] Reed and Tartar, *J. Amer. Chem. Soc.*, 1936, **58**, 322. See also Lelong, Tartar, Lingafelter, O'Loane, and Cadle, *J. Amer. Chem. Soc.*, 1951, **73**, 5411.

alternative intermediates in Germany during the Second World War, the production of the alkane sulphonates would not have reached the high figures which were recorded during the war. Hoyt[1] quotes a figure of 75,000,000 lb. as the annual production of alkane sulphonates by the I.G. during the last war, and estimates it to be half the peak total German output of synthetic detergents. The alkyl chain in practically all the alkane sulphonates which were produced at that time was derived from the liquid hydrocarbon ("Kogasin") which was produced in the Fischer-Tropsch process. This large output was achieved by means of what is probably the most important industrial process for the production of alkane sulphonic acids, the Reed process. It was discovered in the United States in 1933 by C. F. Reed[2] and consists in reacting an aliphatic hydrocarbon with a halogen in the presence of the dioxide of sulphur, selenium, or tellurium. The reaction is activated by actinic light, and the main product is the sulphonyl (selenyl, etc.) halide. The sodium sulphonate is obtained by hydrolysis with caustic alkali. The reactions involved may be represented thus:

$$RH + SO_2 + Cl_2 \rightarrow RSO_2Cl + HCl$$

$$RSO_2Cl + 2NaOH \rightarrow RSO_2ONa + NaCl.$$

In the I.G. process,[3] it was necessary first to hydrogenate "Kogasin," since it contained some olefins, in order to prevent undesirable side reactions. The resulting hydrocarbon mixture, "Mepasin," had a boiling range of 220°–320° c., and consisted mainly of the C_{14}–C_{18} hydrocarbons. It was then treated with sulphur dioxide and chlorine under the influence of light to produce a mixture of mono- and di-sulphonyl chlorides and unreacted hydrocarbon. Three main types[4] of products were made—"Mersol D," "Mersol H," and "Mersol 30," in which the conversions to sulphonyl chlorides were 82%, 45%, and 30%, respectively. All these products contained small quantities of derivatives which were chlorinated in the paraffin chain. The sulphonyl chlorides were then hydrolysed to the sodium alkane sulphonates ("Mersolats D, H, and 30") with aqueous caustic soda. This last stage of the process for "Mersolat D" was usually carried out by soap-making firms while the manufacturer usually completed the process for "Mersolat H." The reduction in the degree of sulphochlorination in the series of "Mersols" resulted in a more than proportional decrease in the

---

[1] Hoyt, B.I.O.S. Miscellaneous Report No. 11, "Synthetic Detergents and Washing Agents."

[2] Reed and Horn, U.S.P. 2,046,090 (Reissue 20,968, 1939).

[3] Hoyt, *loc. cit.*; Baird, B.I.O.S. Final Report No. 478, "Textile Auxiliary Products: Development of Mersol and Hostapon Processes by I.G. Farbenindustrie, Höchst"; Brandner, Lockwood, Nagel, and Russell, F.I.A.T. Final Report No. 1141, "Synthetic Detergents and Related Surface-Active Agents in Germany."

[4] Vlugter, B.I.O.S. Final Report No. 1130, "Manufacture of Mersolat in Germany."

formation of disulphonyl chlorides, with a corresponding decrease in the amount of disulphonates in the final products. The presence of disulphonates was undesirable because of their poor detergent efficiency, and in this respect "Mersolat H" was much superior to "Mersolat D," the latter having too high a solubility in water for a favourable hydrophobe-hydrophile ratio. Brandner, Lockwood, Nagel, and Russell state that "Mersolat H" will wash cotton or wool as effectively as "Igepon T," but that three times the concentration is needed. The reduction in degree of sulphochlorination was also desirable from the point of view of the soap maker,[1] who could not readily handle the dilute solutions which were necessary for effective separation of the unreacted "Mepasin" from "Mersolat D." If these hydrocarbons were left in the products, they adversely affected the physical properties and detergent power of the "Mersolats." At a lower degree of sulphochlorination, the "Mepasin" could be separated from more concentrated solutions and returned for subsequent sulphochlorination. Henke and Lockwood[2] have described how the lower degree of sulphochlorination reduced the amount of polysulphonyl chlorides as well as improved the case of separation of the unreacted hydrocarbon. The I.G. also developed a process for purifying "Mersol H" by extracting the unreacted "Mepasin" with liquid sulphur dioxide.[3] This contrasts with the process proposed by Ross and Potter,[4] who extract with liquid sulphur dioxide and an organic solvent such as hexane or petroleum ether. The unreacted hydrocarbon in this case, together with chlorinated derivatives, goes into the organic solvent layer, and the sulphonyl chloride into the sulphur dioxide layer.

Schwartz, Perry, and Berch[5] state that in Germany the "Mersolats" appear to be losing ground to the alkylaryl sulphonates and, to a lesser extent, the "Teepol" type of detergents (*cf.* p. 417).

Since the Reed reaction gives random substitution of the —SO_2Cl group in the hydrocarbon chain the sulphonates manufactured by this process consist of mixtures of varying degrees of chain branching and positions of the sulphonate group.

The Reed reaction is not confined to hydrocarbons as starting materials, since sulphonates may be formed from carboxylic acids,[6] ethers, ketones, esters,[7] or alcohols.[8] According to Ross and Potter, the alcohols for this

---

[1] Hoyt, *loc. cit.*

[2] Du Pont, Henke, and Lockwood, B.P. 549,512.

[3] Hoyt, *loc. cit.*, p. 42.

[4] Colgate-Palmolive-Peet, Ross, and Potter, B.P. 538,374.

[5] Schwartz, Perry, and Berch, *Surface Active Agents and Detergents*, **II**, Interscience, 1958, p. 63.

[6] Du Pont, Downing, and Clarkson, U.S.P. 2,061,617.

[7] Henkel, F.P. 870,294.

[8] Colgate-Palmolive-Peet Company, Ross, and Potter, B.P. 538,407 and Henkel, F.P. 870,163.

process should contain not less than six carbon atoms, since otherwise alkyl sulphates are formed. Sulphuryl chloride may be used in place of sulphur dioxide and chlorine but it does not seem to be so reactive, and in some cases requires the addition of a catalyst, which is usually an organic base.[1]

A very simple new process for making alkane sulphonates, which were identical with those from the Reed reaction, was being developed in Germany towards the end of the War, but it had reached only the pilot plant stage. A full description of the chemistry and technology of the "Hostapon" process, as it was called, has been given by Baird,[2] and supplementary details have been reported by Caldwell and Smith.[3] The raw materials are simply the hydrocarbon ("Mepasin" was used at the I.G. factory at Höchst), sulphur dioxide, and oxygen. The reaction is catalysed by light or by acid anhydrides, acid chlorides, or ketones. The advantages of this process over the Reed process are that it avoids the production of the corrosive sulphonyl chlorides and requires only half the caustic alkali in order to obtain the finished product. The separation of the sodium salt from the unreacted hydrocarbon and the by-products of the reaction (sulphuric and acetic acids) is also more readily effected. The reaction is believed[4] to take place in the following two stages. The first is the production of an intermediate per-compound,

$$RH + SO_2 + O_2 + (CH_3 \cdot CO)_2O \rightarrow RSO_2O_2COCH_3 + CH_3 \cdot COOH$$

which then takes part in a further reaction to give the sulphonic acid

$$RSO_2O_2COCH_3 + 6RH + 6SO_2 + \tfrac{5}{2}O_2 + H_2O$$
$$\rightarrow 7RSO_3H + CH_3 \cdot COOH$$

Direct sulphonation of saturated paraffinic hydrocarbons to give alkane sulphonic acids is difficult to achieve, but Sveda[5] has stated that the lower hydrocarbons, propane, butane, etc., react in the vapour phase with sulphur trioxide to give sulphonic acids, the ammonium salts of which are claimed as tanning assistants. Sulphur trioxide and other energetic sulphonating agents such as chlorosulphonic acid or oleum react with a number of fatty derivatives to give true sulphonic acids. Thus the I.G. prepared sulphonic acids from

(a) high molecular weight non-aromatic carboxylic acids by reacting them above 35° c. with energetic sulphonating agents in inert diluents,[6]

---

[1] Du Pont, B.P. 545,521; Henkel, F.P. 870,294.

[2] Baird, B.I.O.S. Final Report No. 478, "Textile Auxiliary Products: Development of Mersol and Hostapon Processes by I.G. Farbenindustrie, Höchst."

[3] Caldwell and Smith, B.I.O.S. Final Report No. 1222, "Mersol and Hostapon Processes, I.G. Farbenindustrie, Höchst."

[4] Baird, *loc. cit.*, p. 20 ff.

[5] Du Pont and Sveda, U.S.P. 2,383,752.

[6] I.G., B.P. 288,612.

(b) higher unsaturated fatty acids by the action of fuming sulphuric acid in trichloroethylene,[1] and

(c) saturated or unsaturated fatty substances dissolved in liquid sulphur dioxide by treatment with a solution of sulphur trioxide in the same solvent.[2] In the case of the unsaturated fatty derivatives the products of sulphonation are usually hydroxy-sulphonic acids which are formed by addition at the double bond, followed by hydrolysis. The I.G.[3] stated, for example, that the reaction between oleic acid and the ethyl ester of chlorosulphonic acid takes place according to the following scheme

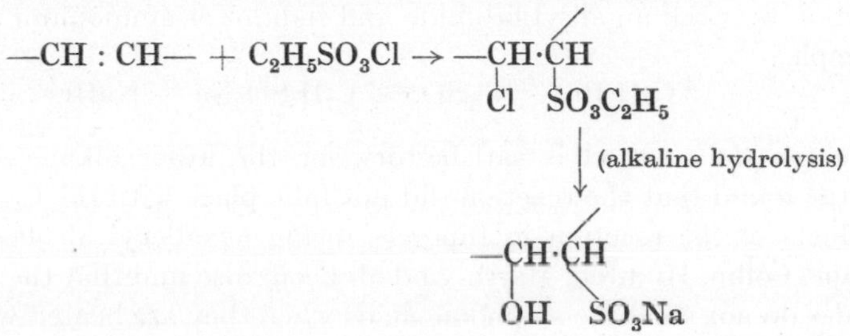

$$-CH : CH- + C_2H_5SO_3Cl \rightarrow -CH \cdot CH$$
$$\qquad\qquad\qquad\qquad\quad Cl \quad SO_3C_2H_5$$

(alkaline hydrolysis)

$$-CH \cdot CH$$
$$\;\; OH \quad SO_3Na$$

while in the reaction between oleic acid, ether, and chlorosulphonic acid, the first product formed is the oxonium salt, which reacts at the double bond, the sulphonic acid salt being formed finally by alkaline hydrolysis:

$$(C_2H_5)_2O + ClSO_3H \longrightarrow (C_2H_5)_2O \cdots\cdots \rightarrow H^+, ClSO_3^-$$

$$(C_2H_5)_2O \cdots\cdots \rightarrow H^+, ClSO_3^- + -CH : CH-$$

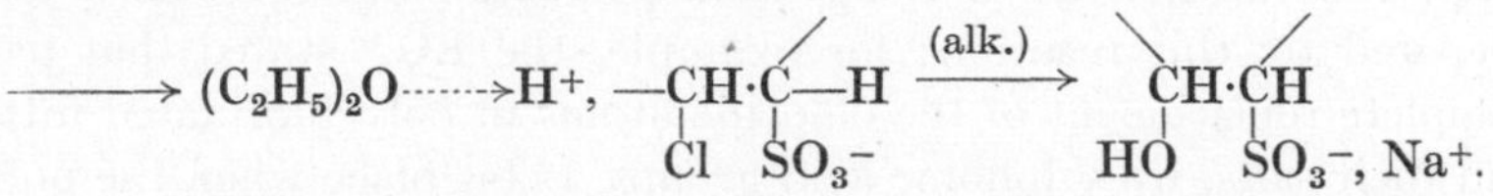

$$\longrightarrow (C_2H_5)_2O \cdots\cdots \rightarrow H^+, -CH \cdot C-H \xrightarrow{\text{(alk.)}} CH \cdot CH$$
$$\qquad\qquad\qquad\qquad\qquad\quad Cl \quad SO_3^- \qquad\qquad HO \quad SO_3^-, Na^+.$$

In a similar way, it is claimed that hydroxy sulphonic acids are obtained from higher aliphatic $\Delta 1 : 2$-olefins[4] (prepared by the dehydration of primary alcohols) by the action of energetic sulphonating agents or mixtures of mild sulphonating agents such as sulphuric acid and acid anhydrides such as acetic anhydride, phosphorus pentoxide, etc. It has not been ascertained whether or not the sulphonic acid group in these compounds is attached to the α or β carbon atom. The sulphonic acids produced by these processes are stated to have good emulsifying, wetting-out, and detergent properties, and are stable to hard water and acid solutions. They may also be used as solubilising agents,[5] and because of their solubilising and

---

[1] I.G., B.P. 296,999; U.S.P. 1,836,487.
[2] I.G., B.P. 346,945.
[3] I.G., B.P. 306,052; U.S.P. 1,931,491.
[4] I.G., B.P. 358,583; U.S.P. 2,094,451; D.R.P. 705,179.
[5] I.G., B.P. 273,757.

emulsifying power they are used in the production of synthetic rubber by emulsion polymerisation (*cf.* Chapter 9, p. 338).[1]

The action of energetic sulphonating agents on long-chain tertiary alcohols is also claimed to produce true sulphonic acids,[2] and even primary alcohols are stated to be converted to true sulphonic acids by the use of fuming sulphuric acid at elevated temperatures,[3] or in the presence of a dehydrating medium.

The introduction of a sulphonic acid group can often be effected by means of alkali metal sulphites or bisulphites. The classical method[4] is the reaction between an alkyl bromide and sodium or ammonium sulphite, for example,

$$C_2H_5Br + Na_2SO_3 \rightarrow C_2H_5SO_3Na + NaBr$$

Although the method is satisfactory for the lower alkane sulphonates, Norris[5] found that the reaction did not take place with the C_{16} radical, the products of the reaction in this case being hexadecyl alcohol and hexadecane. Collin, Hilditch, Marsh, and McLeod[6] also find that the higher alkyl iodides do not yield the sulphonic acids when they are heated with aqueous ammonium sulphite under pressure. The I.G.,[7] however, claimed to have made octadecane sulphonic acid by reacting the alkyl bromide with an aqueous solution of sodium sulphite at 130° to 160° c. for a long time, and also said that the higher alkyl sulphuric acid ester salts react with sodium sulphite at high temperatures to give the corresponding alkane sulphonic acid salts. Davidson[8] claims that improved yields result when a catalyst such as aniline or other aromatic base and a phosphate, or dianilido-phosphoric acid, is used. Long-chain polysulphonic acids have also been prepared by this reaction; for example, the I.G.[9] stated that partial or complete replacement of the chlorine atoms in polychlorinated fatty acids and their salts, by sulphonic acid groups, takes place when the polychloro compounds are reacted with aqueous sodium sulphite. The polychloro compounds preferably contain hydroxyl groups or unsaturated linkages as well. The products of this reaction are claimed to have particularly good resistance to lime salts and to be stable to hot concentrated mineral acid solutions. Böhme Fettchemie[10] treated high molecular weight Δ 1 : 2-olefins with hypochlorous acid and then with sulphites or bisulphites to produce the sulphonic acid, the reaction with cetene, for example, presumably being

[1] Standard Oil Development Co. and Serniuk, U.S.P. 2,384,969.
[2] Henkel, B.P. 424,891 and 429,036; Sw.P. 175,018.
[3] American Hyalsol Corp. and Bertsch, U.S.P. 1,986,794 and 1,968,796.
[4] Strecker, *Annalen*, 1868, **148**, 90; Haemilian, *Annalen*, 1873, **168**, 145.
[5] Norris, *J. Chem. Soc.*, 1922, **121**, 2161.
[6] Collin, Hilditch, Marsh, and McLeod, *J. Soc. Chem. Ind.*, 1933, **52**, 272T.
[7] I.G., B.P. 360,539.
[8] I.C.I. and Davidson, B.P. 433,312; U.S.P. 2,053,424.
[9] I.G., B.P. 342,761 and 343,071.
[10] Böhme, D.R.P. 687,462.

$$CH_3 \cdot [CH_2]_{13} \cdot CH : CH_2 \xrightarrow{\text{(HOCl)}} CH_3 \cdot [CH_2]_{13} \cdot \underset{OH}{CH} \cdot \underset{Cl}{CH_2}$$

$$\downarrow \text{(Na}_2\text{SO}_3)$$

$$CH_3 \cdot [CH_2]_{13} \cdot \underset{OH}{CH} \cdot CH_2 SO_3^-, \ Na^+$$

Böhme[1] also prepared α-sulpho-fatty carboxylic acids from the α-bromo acids in ammonia solution by the action of ammonium sulphite. Sargent[2] has prepared disulphonates from long-chain (C_{16}–C_{22}) olefins by halogenating them and reacting them with aqueous sodium sulphite solutions at temperatures between 130° and 200° c. Not unexpectedly, the solubility of these disulphonates is greater than that of the corresponding mono-sulphonates. It is also claimed that they have improved detergent power and are more stable to multivalent ions than are the mono-sulphonates.

The possible use of salts of α-sulphonated acids in detergent bars has been examined by Weil and his co-workers.[3] Promising results were obtained from mixed salts of α-sulphonated hydrogenated tallow acids, the best mixture consisting of 85% mono-ammonium salt and 15% of the ammonium monoethanolaminic salt. These authors found that mixed salts gave products with improved solubility, surface activity, and physical properties, compared with the single salts.

Although the oxidation of a mercaptan results in general in the formation of a disulphide

$$2 \text{ R.SH} \rightarrow \text{R.SS.R}$$

vigorous oxidation leads to the formation of true sulphonic acids. Reychler,[4] who was the first to prepare hexadecane sulphonic acid, oxidised hexadecyl mercaptan with aqueous permanganate. He prepared the mercaptan from hexadecyl iodide by reacting it with an alcoholic solution of sodium ethoxide saturated with hydrogen sulphide. Wagner and Reid, and Noller and Gordon[5] used nitric acid as oxidising agent while Collin, Hilditch, Marsh, and McLeod[6] prefer potassium permanganate or chromic acid in acetone or acetic acid. The secondary mercaptans can be oxidised with nitric acid or potassium permanganate or dichromate to give the branched-chain sulphonic acids, *e.g.*,

$$\begin{array}{c} C_7H_{15} \\ \diagdown \\ C_7H_{15} \diagup \end{array} CHSH \rightarrow \begin{array}{c} C_7H_{15} \\ \diagdown \\ C_7H_{15} \diagup \end{array} CHSO_3H$$

[1] Böhme, F.P. 694,692.
[2] California Research Corporation and Sargent, U.S.P. 2,787,639.
[3] Weil, Stirton, Maurer, Ault, and Palm, *J. Amer. Oil Chem. Soc.*, 1958, **35**, 461.
[4] Reychler, *Bull. Soc. chim. Belg.*, 1913, **27**, 110.
[5] Wagner and Reid, *J. Amer. Chem. Soc.*, 1931, **53**, 3407; Noller and Gordon, *J. Amer. Chem. Soc.*, 1933, **55**, 1090.
[6] Collin, Hilditch, Marsh, and McLeod, *J. Soc. Chem. Ind.*, 1933, **52**, 272T.

These branched-chain sulphonates are claimed[1] to be more soluble in water and organic solvents than the primary alkane sulphonates. Their wetting power is also claimed to be superior and in general the closer the sulphonate group is to the middle of the chain the more efficient is the product as a wetting-out agent. Another route to the secondary mercaptan has been described by du Pont,[2] who sulphurise an olefin to give a polysulphide of the general formula $C_nH_{2n}S_3$, which can be hydrogenated to the mercaptan by using cobalt polysulphide as catalyst. Oxidation with 70% nitric acid then gives the sulphonic acid.

It is apparent from the foregoing discussion that the aliphatic sulphonates can be prepared in a variety of ways, and that there has been a great deal of patenting activity in this field. Despite these facts, however, there are few representatives of this class on the market, and although the sulphonic acid group is more stable chemically than the sulphuric ester group, the alkyl sulphuric esters have been exploited commercially to a much greater extent. Among the chief reasons for this state of affairs was that the sulphation of the alcohols was a relatively cheap and simple process compared with the more complicated and expensive series of reactions which were required in manufacturing the true sulphonates—the cheap Reed reaction was not discovered until the sulphated alcohols were well established. In addition, the sulphonates are not so effective detergents as the corresponding alkyl sulphates.[3] The only long-chain sulphonate which achieved first-class importance in any market was "Mersolat," but it is doubtful, as we have already pointed out, whether this product would have been developed to any great extent if it had not been for the pre-war and war-time policy of autarky in Germany.

Perfluoroalkane sulphonates (in which the hydrogen atoms of the alkane group are replaced by fluorine) are relatively expensive, but they have been reported to have at least one commercial application, in the reduction of mist or spray from electrolysis baths. Electrolytic processes in which insoluble or highly polarisable anodes are used produce a fine mist or spray as the gas is evolved, and this can be objectionable because of the hazard to health, especially if the solutions being electrolysed are acidic. Surface-active agents which produce a foam at the surface of the solutions, and thus trap the mist droplets, are not technically attractive because of oxidation of the agents at the anode. It is claimed[4] that perfluoroalkane sulphonates, such as perfluorooctane sulphonic acid or its salts, are resistant to oxidation at the anode, are not precipitated by high concentrations of electrolytes, and form thin blankets of foam which trap any spray. It is stated that perfluorooctanoic acid and similar acids are

[1] Du Pont and Werntz, U.S.P. 2,142,162; 2,187,338; 2,187,339.
[2] Du Pont and Werntz, U.S.P. 2,338,830.
[3] Evans, *J. Soc. Dyers Colourists*, 1935, **51**, 233.
[4] Udylite Research Corporation and Brown, U.S.P. 2,913,377.

not effective because they form less stable foams, with different drainage characteristics.

D. Sulphonates of aliphatic-aromatic hydrocarbons

The common aromatic nuclei, benzene and naphthalene, are not sufficiently hydrophobic to produce a high degree of amphipathy when they are combined with a sulphonic acid group. When however the aromatic nucleus is substituted with one or more alkyl groups, which may be quite small, the amphipathic character of the molecule is greatly enhanced, and in this class we find many important surface-active agents.

Uses which are dependent on their feeble surface-activity have nevertheless been claimed for the non-alkylated aromatic sulphonic acids, and a few of these will be touched on briefly before considering the much more important aliphatic-aromatic class.* The sodium salt of trichloronaphthalene sulphonic acid has been used[1] in aqueous dyestuff pastes, in which its action appears to be two-fold. It is an effective deflocculating agent for the dispersed particles, and it also prevents sedimentation of the particles by itself forming a gel which however is readily made fluid by shaking.

It is well known that some surface-active agents in powder form do not wet-out readily in water but tend to form lumps of more or less dry powder surrounded by a jelly of the hydrated agent. This is a particularly bad feature if the agents are to be used in cold water, for example in agricultural sprays. Todd[2] has stated that this undesirable property can be overcome in the case of isopropylated petroleum sulphonates[3] and butylated naphthalene sulphonates[4] by adding, for example, solid sodium benzene disulphonate to these dry wetting-out agents. The action of the disulphonate is probably due to a combination of its feeble wetting-out action, its high speed of solution, and also in some measure to its hydrotropic action on the paraffin-chain surface-active molecules. Another non-alkylated aromatic sulphonate, which has been used as a wetting and dispersing agent, is sodium tetrahydronaphthalene sulphonate, marketed by du Pont as "Alkanol S,"[5] and by Deutsche Hydrierwerke under the name "Majamin."[5] It has been claimed[6] to be a valuable solubilising agent for fatty alcohols and ketones, as have also several non-alkylated aromatic sulphonic acids such as 1-chloronaphthalene-5-sulphonic acid and 1 : 3-dichlorobenzene sulphonic acid.[7]

---

* Concentrated solutions of aromatic sulphonates are used as special solvents, but these appear to us to fall outside the scope of this book.

[1] I.C.I., Gibson, Hailwood, Payman, and Shepherdson, B.P. 300,800.
[2] I.C.I. and Todd, B.P. 406,001.
[3] British Dyestuffs Corporation, Baddiley, and Chapman, B.P. 311,885.
[4] I.G., B.P. 246,817.
[5] Sisley, *Index des Huiles Sulphonées et Detergents Modernes*, Teintex, Paris, 1949.
[6] Schrauth, D.R.P. 371,293.
[7] I.G. and Schuster, D.R.P. 506,960.

1. ALKYLATED NAPHTHALENE SULPHONATES

As has been said, the scarcity of natural fats in Germany during the First World War led to the synthesis of the alkylnaphthalene sulphonates, "Nekals A" and "BX." Although these were produced and claimed[1] as soap substitutes, they are recognised to be rather poor detergents and have achieved importance because of their powerful wetting-out properties. The alkylbenzene sulphonates however are efficient detergents when the alkyl group contains 10 to 14 carbon atoms. It is to be expected that the short-chain alkyl compounds would be much less effective than the long-chain ones in reducing the oil-solution interfacial tension, which would be a contributory factor in their being inferior detergents (*cf.* Chapter 8).

In the preparation of alkyl aromatic sulphonates the alkylation is almost invariably carried out by means of the reaction between an olefin or aliphatic alcohol and an aromatic hydrocarbon or sulphonic acid, using catalysts such as hydrofluoric acid. The alkylation can of course be effected by other well-known methods such as the Friedel-Crafts reaction. An extensive tabular summary of the research which has been carried out on alkylation is given by Price,[2] while more detailed reviews are given by Calloway,[3] Nightingale,[4] and Price.[5] Sharrah and Feighner[6] have examined the preparation of dodecylbenzene from benzene and propylene tetramer, using different Friedel-Crafts catalysts. They conclude that the use of sulphuric acid as catalyst produces undesirable unsaturated products which are difficult to remove. The reaction can be carried out by a variety of alkylating agents such as olefins and alkyl halides, alcohols, ethers, and esters, and it can also be used for the introduction of aralkyl or cycloalkyl groups. The alkylation will also proceed when other substituents such as halogen, amino, hydroxyl, or sulphonic acid groups are present in the aromatic nucleus. Numerous catalysts are used; those mentioned by Price are aluminium chloride, ferric chloride, antimony pentachloride, boron trifluoride, zinc chloride, titanium tetrachloride, hydrofluoric acid, sulphuric acid, orthophosphoric acid, and phosphorus pentachloride.

The sulphonation of aromatic hydrocarbons is accomplished much more readily than that of aliphatic hydrocarbons. Benzene can be sulphonated in the cold with sulphuric acid of as low a concentration as 70% although the reaction is normally carried out with stronger acid and at a higher temperature.[7] With oleum, the di- and trisulphonic acids are produced.

---

[1] Badische, D.R.P. 336,558.

[2] Price, in Roger Adams's *Organic Reactions*, Wiley and Sons, New York, 1946, vol. III, Chapter 1.

[3] Calloway, *Chem. Rev.*, 1935, **17**, 327.

[4] Nightingale, *Chem. Rev.*, 1939, **25**, 329.

[5] Price, *Chem. Rev.*, 1941, **29**, 37.

[6] Sharrah and Feighner, *Ind. Eng. Chem.*, 1954, **46**, 248.

[7] See *e.g.*, Karrer, *Organic Chemistry*, Elsevier Pub. Co., New York, 1947, Chapter 27.

With cold concentrated sulphuric acid, naphthalene yields the α-mono-sulphonic acid, with only a small amount of the β-sulphonic acid while high temperatures favour the production of the β-isomer. With more energetic sulphonating agents such as oleum low temperature reactions yield the 1 : 5- and 1 : 6-disulphonic acids. Increasing the temperature favours the production of the 1 : 6-isomer while at still higher temperatures the 2 : 6- and 2 : 7-isomers are obtained and even appreciable quantities of the tri-sulphonic acids. The sulphonic acid group is however powerfully hydrophilic and the introduction of more than one usually has an adverse effect on the surface activity of the product.

As has been mentioned, the Badische Anilin- und Soda-Fabrik were the pioneers[1] of the alkylated aromatic sulphonic acids with the product "Nekal A," sodium diisopropylnaphthalene sulphonate[2] followed later[3] by "Nekal BX," sodium dibutylnaphthalene sulphonate. The early products contained only two alkyl groups but it was later found[4] that those with three alkyl groups had superior wetting-out properties and that no great improvement was achieved by introducing more than four groups. The length of the carbon chain was also important, those with three or four carbon atoms giving the optimum wetting-out power. An extensive patenting campaign by the I.G.[5] covered the alkylation of aromatic sulphonic acids which contained halogens, or nitro, amino, or hydroxyl groups in the nucleus and aryl, aralkyl, and cycloaliphatic substituents, but since none of these appeared on the market it is probably true to say that they showed no great advantage over the more simple propyl and butyl naphthalene sulphonates. Akin to the alkylnaphthalene sulphonates are the alkylated petroleum sulphonates described by Baddiley and Chapman,[6] the petroleum fraction being chiefly aromatic.

Mixed alkyl, alkyl-aryl, alkyl-aralkyl, and alkyl-alkoxy substituted naphthalene sulphonates have also been described, *e.g.*, isopropyl-butyl,[7] and butyl-phenyl and amyl-butyl-benzyl[8] all by the I.G. and butoxy-butyl[9] by I.C.I. The mixed alkyl type was sold during the Second World War as "Nekal A dry new type."[10] The higher alcohols have also been used as alkylating agents with naphthalene sulphonic acid, *e.g.*, the product with

---

[1] Badische, D.R.P. 336,558, 23.10.17.
[2] Brandner, Lockwood, Nagel, and Russell, F.I.A.T. Final Report No. 1141, "Synthetic Detergents and Related Surface Active Agents in Germany," p. 95.
[3] I.G., B.P. 246,817.
[4] I.G., B.P. 364,537; F.P. 718,809.
[5] See for example the British Specifications referred to in B.P. 364,537.
[6] British Dyestuffs Corporation, Baddiley, and Chapman, B.P. 274,611; U.S.P. 1,836,428.
[7] I.G. and Günther, U.S.P. 1,755,179.
[8] I.G., B.P. 247,588.
[9] I.C.I., F.P. 791,974.
[10] Brandner, Lockwood, Nagel, and Russell, *loc. cit.*

cetyl alcohol[1] is claimed as a dispersing agent for acetate silk dyes, while the compound substituted with an oleyl ($C_{18}H_{35}$) group is said to be an excellent detergent.[2]

The important naphthalene sulphonates rarely contain more than one sulphonate group, which is usually in the β-position, so that their surface-activity is controlled by the size and number of the alkyl groups. With the lower alkyl substituents containing three or four carbon atoms, we have products which are very soluble in water, stable in acid solution, and not precipitated by calcium or magnesium salts. They have been used most extensively in many textile processes such as the retting of flax, the wetting-out of fabrics before and during dyeing and stripping, in the oiling and sizing of textiles, and in tanning liquors. They are used in strongly acid solutions in the fulling of wool and in alkaline media in mercerising cotton, usually along with hydroxy bodies such as phenols or cresols.

The Grasselli Company advocate[3] the use of alkylnaphthalene sulphonates and particularly benzyl naphthalene sulphonate in electroplating baths in order to improve the hardness, brightness, and adherence of the electroplate to the metal (see p. 346) and the same firm also incorporate these agents in soldering fluxes[4] in order to give better penetration of the flux into the folded seams of cans, etc. The British Dyestuffs Corporation add these salts to inks in order to improve the free-flowing properties,[5] and to cotton wool, blotting paper, and kieselguhr in order to improve their absorptive powers.[6] An early use for these materials was as a solubilising agent for organic solvents in improved cleaning powders in admixture with soda ash or sodium sulphate.[7] The foaming properties of solutions of the alkylnaphthalene sulphonates have also been exploited by their use in fire-fighting solutions,[8] (see Chapter 9) and they have been used as flotation agents in the treatment of ores.[9]

The lower alkylnaphthalene sulphonates are useful emulsifying agents but they give emulsions of rather poor stability. The addition of protective colloids such as gelatin, glue (as in "Nekal AEM"[10]), and cellulose ethers[11] gives emulsions of greatly increased stability and these combined emulsifying agents have been extensively used for example with mineral oil for oiling textiles and with tar oils for agricultural winter washes. The wetting

[1] British Celanese, Stanley, Olpin, and Ellis, B.P. 365,170; Dreyfus, F.P. 706,131.
[2] S.C.I., Sw.P. 168,344.
[3] Grasselli, Lutz, and Westbrook, U.S.P. 1,818,229.
[4] Grasselli, U.S.P. 1,785,155.
[5] British Dyestuffs Corp., Hollins, and Chapman, B.P. 279,968.
[6] British Dyestuffs Corp., B.P. 278,485; 280,262; U.S.P. 1,777,459.
[7] Friesenhalm, B.P. 269,134. (Misprint for Friesenhahn?)
[8] I.G., B.P. 302,172; 319,083; F.P. 665,017.
[9] Grasselli, U.S.P., 1,768,308.
[10] Brandner, Lockwood, Nagel, and Russell, *loc. cit.*, p. 95.
[11] See *e.g.*, B.P. 258,551; 268,387; 323,720; U.S.P. 1,728,118.

action of these compounds is also applied in the breaking of emulsions[1] by enabling the aqueous phase to submerge any incompletely-wetted interfacial stabilising agents. They have been used in the preparation of dyestuff dispersions to facilitate the dispersion process during grinding or condensation.[2]

2. ALKYLATED BENZENE SULPHONATES

The general methods of preparation of the alkylbenzene sulphonates have already been dealt with in the previous section and, as in the naphthalene series, more than one sulphonate group in the benzene nucleus renders the compounds too hydrophilic to be generally useful as surface-active agents. It would appear that the introduction of a long alkyl chain leads to micelle formation much more readily when it is attached to the benzene nucleus than when it is attached to the larger naphthalene nucleus, and this may account for the success of the alkylated benzene sulphonates as detergents and the scarcity of compounds of this class as wetting-out agents, subject of course to special theories of these processes (see Chapters 5 and 8). Another factor besides the ready availability of intermediates from the petroleum industry, which has doubtless contributed to the widespread development of this type of surface-active agent is that the possibilities in this field do not seem to have been as completely dominated by early patents as they have been for other types of compounds.

A favourite source of the alkyl chain has been the aliphatic olefins[3, 4] which according to the I.G.[4] produce a product which can be represented thus:

$$R_1 \diagdown CH \diagup \langle \ \rangle SO_3^-, Na^+$$
$$R_2 \diagup$$

As has been already mentioned, however, the chief source of the fatty chain has been a petroleum fraction. This is usually chlorinated[4, 5, 6] and the chlorohydrocarbon is then condensed with benzene, using a Friedel-Crafts catalyst. Since chlorination takes place in a random manner along the hydrocarbon chain, the benzene nucleus is also attached to any carbon atom. The commercial products are accordingly mixtures, the composition and properties of which depend largely on the conditions under which they were made. The National Oil Products Company[7] have suggested

---

[1] I.G., U.S.P. 1,881,691; Empire Oil and Refining Co., U.S.P. 1,944,021.

[2] I.G., B.P. 264,860; D.R.P. 542,803.

[3] Chem. Fabrik Pott and Co., B.P. 263,873; U.S.P. 1,787,408.

[4] I.G., B.P. 416,379; D.R.P. 647,988; F.P. 766,903.

[5] Allied Chemical and Dye Corporation and Flett, U.S.P. 2,223,364 and 2,394,851.

[6] Allied Chemical and Dye Corporation and Toone, U.S.P. 2,314,255.

[7] National Oil Products Co., B.P. 559,265.

that optimum surface-activity is achieved by alkylating with primary C_{12} or C_{14} alcohols and introducing two alkyl chains into the aromatic nucleus. The Sharples Solvents Company,[1] however, prefer a longer alkyl chain (C_{18}) and two sulphonic acid groups when wetting-out properties are desired.

The alkylated benzene sulphonates have become increasingly important since the War because of their efficiency as detergents and the ready availability of the intermediates from the petroleum industry, although in recent years the production of sodium dodecylbenzene sulphonate types in the United States has tended to decrease somewhat from the very high proportions of the 1940's to an apparently fairly stable figure of 37%, which the United States Tariff Commission gives for 1957 and 1958. The total amount of anionics (sulphates and sulphonates) is about 73% of the total production. Comparable figures for the United Kingdom are more difficult to obtain, but it seems quite possible that a similar pattern will emerge. Thus Puplett's[2] estimates for the United Kingdom indicate that the production of alkylaryl sulphonates rose from a negligible amount in 1948 to 76% of the total manufacture of detergents in 1953. In view of the commercial and technical importance of this class of surface-active agents, it will perhaps be useful to consider their history briefly.

According to Richardson, Kern, Murray, and Sudhoff,[3] the alkylbenzene sulphonate type of detergent was discovered in 1932 by the I.G., who preferred to have an aliphatic chain of from 12 to 15 carbon atoms, although the Chemische Fabrik Pott and Co. patent on this subject was applied for in 1926. The first I.G. patent applications appear to have been made in 1932.[4] Two processes for sodium alkylbenzene sulphonate with a C_{12}–C_{14} chain were developed by the I.G. In one, benzene was alkylated with chlorinated "Mepasin," using $AlCl_3$ as catalyst and the resulting alkylbenzene was then sulphonated. The series of reactions was:

$$C_{14}H_{30} + Cl_2 \rightarrow C_{14}H_{29}Cl + HCl \xrightarrow{(C_6H_6)}$$

Manufacturing details of this process have been given by Baird,[5] the product being known as phenylmepasin sulphonate and marketed as

[1] Sharples Solvents Co. and Thomas, U.S.P. 2,210,962.

[2] Puplett, *Synthetic Detergents*, Sidgwick and Jackson, 1957.

[3] Richardson, Kern, Murray, and Sudhoff, C.I.O.S. No. XXVI–2, "Synthetic Emulsifying Agents, Wetting Agents, Detergents, and Soap Substitutes, I.G. Höchst."

[4] I.G., B.P. 416,379; D.R.P. 647,988.

[5] Baird, B.I.O.S. Final Report No. 421, "Textile Auxiliary Products: Manufacture by I.G. Farbenindustrie, Ludwigshafen."

"Igepal NA." In the other process[1] the alkylation was effected in the presence of anhydrous HF with a propylene polymerisate known as P-12, the production of which is described by Brandner, Lockwood, Nagel, and Russell.[1] Although the olefin process gave material, referred to as "Ho 1/181," of the same empirical formula as "Igepal NA" it was not considered to be as satisfactory, since the alkyl chain was more branched and a wide propylene polymer fraction was used. Aromatic hydrocarbons other than benzene were also used by the I.G.[1] When toluene was condensed with propylene polymer and then sulphonated, the product was found to be similar in detergent power to "Ho 1/181" and very much superior as an emulsifying agent; the potassium salt was marketed as such under the trade name "Emulphor STT." The introduction of another methyl group, as in "Emulphor STX" (potassium salt of sulphonated propylene polymer-xylene condensate) still further increased the emulsifying power. Another method of preparing alkylaromatic sulphonic acids disclosed by the I.G.[2] was to condense a fatty acid chloride with the aromatic hydrocarbon and then to reduce the resulting ketone before sulphonating. It is unlikely that this method could compete economically with the direct alkylation processes.

As has been mentioned, the optimum wetting-out power in the naphthalene monosulphonate series appears to be reached with two or three C_3 or C_4 alkyl substituents while optimum detergency in the benzene series is reached with one alkyl group of C_{10}–C_{14}. The commercial products are always a mixture not only of position isomers but also of products which differ in the configuration of the alkyl chain. An extensive literature exists on the effects of various catalysts, conditions, etc., on orientation in the alkylation reactions, which has been tabulated by Price,[3] and more recently Baumgartner[4] has published a systematic investigation of the influence of the structure of certain alkylbenzene sulphonates on detergency and other surface-active properties. As the solubility increases, the concentration at which detergent action begins also increases. The best detergent was the sodium sulphonate from 3-phenyldodecane, while optimum wetting-out power and maximum lowering of the surface tension seemed to lie with 5-phenyldodecane sulphonate. These results agree with the findings for the relation between structure and wetting-out behaviour of certain sulphates (see p. 411).

The Twitchell reagents which were mentioned in Section A of this chapter are structurally akin to the alkylated aromatic sulphonates which

[1] Brandner, Lockwood, Nagel, and Russell, *loc. cit.*, p. 75.

[2] I.G., B.P. 453,778; F.P. 801,499.

[3] Price, in Roger Adams's *Organic Reactions*, Wiley and Sons, New York, 1946, vol. III, Chapter 1.

[4] Baumgartner, *Ind. Eng. Chem.*, 1954, **46**, 1349. See also du Pont, U.S.P. 2,467,130–1–2; 2,467,170.

we have just been considering. British Celanese Ltd. have disclosed[1] the use of these reagents as dispersing or solubilising agents for dyestuffs. Their method of preparation is similar to that used by Twitchell: for example, sulphobenzenestearic acid is obtained by sulphonating and condensing benzene with oleic acid in 20% oleum at 40°–100° c. The condensation presumably takes place at the double bond so that the probable structure of the product is

$$CH_3 \cdot [CH_2]_x \cdot CH \cdot [CH_2]_y \cdot COOH$$

$$SO_3^-, Na^+$$

Stirton, Peterson, and Groggins[2] investigated the preparation and the wetting powers of a series of the sulphonated arylstearic acids. Although they found them not to be very much inferior, especially in acid solution, to some commercial wetting agents, they did not state the compositions of the compounds against which they were tested. A structure similar to that of the arylstearic acids was obtained by the S.C.I.[3] who condensed unsaturated alcohols with aromatic hydrocarbons and then sulphonated. The condensation probably took place at the double bond, a sulphonic acid group was introduced into the aromatic nucleus, and sulphation took place at the hydroxyl group; for example, the product from hexadecenyl alcohol and benzene has the structure of the above compound but with the carboxyl group replaced by a sulphuric acid ester group.

Surface-active sulphonates of alkylaromatic hydrocarbons have also been prepared in which the sulphonic acid group is attached to the alkyl chain and not to the benzene nucleus. In order to achieve this du Pont have used[4] the Reed reaction, already referred to, which appears to introduce the sulphonyl chloride group only on a paraffin carbon atom. The reaction takes place under the usual conditions for the Reed reaction and may be exemplified by:

$$C_6H_{13} + SO_2 + Cl_2 \rightarrow \quad C_6H_{12}SO_2Cl + HCl$$

$$(H_2O)$$

$$C_6H_{12}SO_3^-, H^+$$

[1] British Celanese and Ellis, B.P. 242,393; U.S.P. 1,694,413.
[2] Stirton, Peterson, and Groggins, *Ind. Eng. Chem.*, 1940, **32**, 1136.
[3] S.C.I., Sw.P. 166,498; 168,344; F.P. 763,990; U.S.P. 1,970,353.
[4] Du Pont, U.S.P. 2,321,022; 2,351,674.

The materials described by the Procter and Gamble Co. are similar to these but have the saturated carbon chain interrupted by a benzene nucleus. They sulphonate[1] a tertiary olefin with the SO_3-dioxane complex, which does not attack the double bond, and then react with an alkylaromatic hydrocarbon in a chlorinated solvent in the presence of a catalyst, preferably BF_3.[2] The probable course of the reaction is:

$$CH_3 \cdot \overset{\overset{CH_2}{\|}}{C} \cdot CH_3 + SO_3 \rightarrow CH_3 \cdot \overset{\overset{CH_2}{\|}}{C} \cdot CH_2SO_3H$$

An interesting alkylbenzene sulphonate has been described by the California Research Corporation.[3] The alkyl group is 4'-cyclohexylcyclohexyl, and this gives a greater structural rigidity to the molecule, *viz.*

Both *cis* and *trans* isomers are produced, but the *cis* configuration gives the better detergent. It is claimed to be superior to sodium dodecylbenzene sulphonate in hard water, when it is made into a detergent composition containing sodium sulphate, sodium tripolyphosphate, and isopropyllauramide.

3. ARALKYLAROMATIC SULPHONATES

Another very important type of surface-active aromatic sulphonate is obtained by linking sulphonated aromatic nuclei, by means of methylene groups. It seems likely that the commercial products of this type are "polymeric" in the sense of having a number of aromatic nuclei linked together, though their formula is usually given as the dimer

The aromatic nuclei may however contain alkyl substituents. The original members of this class were described by the Badische[4] for use as synthetic

[1] Procter and Gamble, and Suter, U.S.P. 2,365,783.
[2] Procter and Gamble, and Suter, U.S.P. 2,366,133.
[3] California Research Corporation and Lewis, U.S.P. 2,787,638.
[4] Badische, D.R.P. 292,531; B.P. 7137/1913.

tanning agents, the most effective compounds for this purpose containing hydroxyl groups in the aromatic nucleus. Later, the unhydroxylated compounds were found to be very effective deflocculating agents in aqueous media for a large variety of solids. The most popular product is obtained by condensing formaldehyde with naphthalene monosulphonic acid. This product is adsorbed to only a slight extent at an air-water interface: the surface tension of a 0·2% solution of a typical product of this class in water is about 55 dynes per cm. The small lowering of the surface tension of aqueous solutions is of great value in paste-milling with this product since the violent agitation in the mill does not lead to undesirable frothing (*cf.* Chapter 7). This may be partially due to the polymeric nature of these products. I.C.I. use this agent in dispersions of for example the fungicide, salicylanilide,[1] phthalocyanine pigments,[2] and the oestrogenic agent, triphenylchloroethylene,[3] while it is used by Dewey and Almy[4] in preparing carbon black dispersions and along with a hydrophilic colloid by Röhm and Haas[5] in preparing cuprous oxide dispersible powders. Another very valuable property of this agent is its ability to render fluid a stiff paste of solid and water, even when only a small amount is added. With the introduction of alkyl groups into the aromatic nucleus, the general amphipathy is increased, and although the compounds are still effective "dispersing agents," they are also good wetting-out agents. The condensation product of sodium diisopropylnaphthalene sulphonate and formaldehyde, to which the following formula (probably over-simplified) may be ascribed

has been described by the I.G.[6] Röhm and Haas claim[7] that when the alkyl group is branched at the carbon atom which is attached to the naphthalene ring the products are particularly surface-active at an oil-water interface. Many of the "Daxads" (Dewey and Almy Co.) belong to the alkylnaphthalene sulphonate-formaldehyde condensation product class.[8] Akin to these are the surface-active agents prepared by Geigy[9] by condensing alkylphenols and aromatic aldehyde sulphonic acids. The structure of the

---

[1] I.C.I., Hailwood, and Stewart, B.P. 350,642.
[2] I.C.I., Davies, Hailwood, and Todd, U.S.P. 2,213,693.
[3] I.C.I. and Collie, B.P. 543,897.
[4] Dewey and Almy Ltd., B.P. 414,932.
[5] Röhm and Haas, B.P. 542,575.
[6] I.G., Günther, and Cantzler, U.S.P. 1,696,199.
[7] Röhm and Haas, and Somerville, U.S.P. 1,722,904.
[8] McCutcheon, *Soap and Chem. Spec.*, 1958, **34**, Jan., 49.
[9] Geigy, D.R.P. 737,762; F.P. 816,959.

product from 4-butylphenol and benzaldehyde-2-sulphonic acid is presumably:

$$\text{(structure)}$$

Naphthalene sulphonates with aryl or aralkyl substituents have also been described as surface-active agents. For example, the I.G. found[1] that the sulphonic acid of benzylnaphthalene is soluble in oils so that it is specially useful in preparing "miscible" oils for oiling tanned hides.

4. MISCELLANEOUS ALKYLAROMATIC SULPHONATES

In the previous subsections some of the alkylated naphthalene and benzene sulphonates, as well as aralkylaromatic sulphonates, have been described, but the patent specifications which have been referred to are not, in general, limited to one aromatic nucleus nor to one type of substituent. In fact a phrase which is commonly used in patent specifications to describe the types of compounds we have been considering is "alkyl, aralkyl, or cycloalkyl aromatic sulphonates in which the aromatic nucleus may be halogenated or contain substituents such as hydroxyl, amino, etc., groups" in order to cover as broad a classification of compounds as possible. In order to illustrate the variety of aromatic compounds which have been used, a few of the products which have been cited will be described in this section.

Flett[2] condensed a chlorinated petroleum fraction (preferably in the C_{14} to C_{19} range) with phenol, and then sulphonated the resulting mixture of alkylphenols to obtain:

$$C_{14}H_{29}\text{—}\langle\quad\rangle\text{—}SO_3^-, Na^+$$

The Monsanto Co. have appeared to favour the diphenyl nucleus; their products are stated[3] to be sodium monobutylphenylphenol monosulphonate ("Areskap"), sodium monobutyldiphenyl disulphonate ("Aresket"), and disodium dibutylphenylphenol disulphonate ("Aresklene"). The Monsanto

---

[1] I.G., B.P. 247,588.
[2] Flett, Sw.P. 202,246.
[3] McCutcheon, *Chem. Ind.*, 1947, **61**, 811.

products are, as one might infer from the short chains which they contain, important principally as wetting-out agents.

The benziminazole nucleus forms the basis for the "Ultravons" of the S.C.I.[1] For example, o-phenylenediamine can be condensed with stearic acid to give 2-heptadecylbenziminazole, which is then sulphonated:

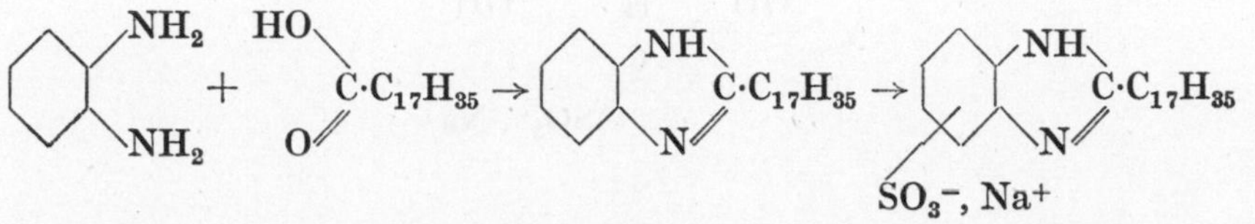

"Ultravon K" is the monosulphonate which, according to Chwala, is an excellent lime-soap-dispersing agent but is precipitated in acid solutions on account of the formation of the internal salt

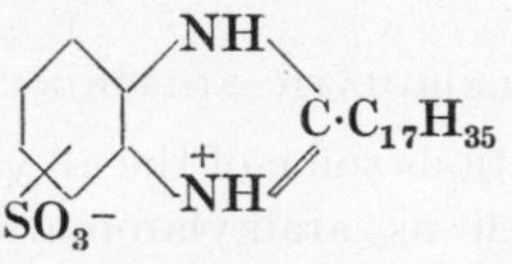

The disulphonate, "Ultravon W," is soluble in acid solution and is an effective detergent, especially for wool. The S.C.I.[2] claim that improved stability to acid media can be conferred on the monosulphonate by condensing it with an ester of chloroformic acid.

The salts of the long-chain alkyl indole sulphonic acids, in which the alkyl group may be attached to the nitrogen or to the α-carbon atom in the pyrrole ring, are also lime-soap-dispersing agents. The methods of preparation, which have been described by Geigy,[3] depend on whether the alkyl group is wanted in the 1- or in the 2-position. In the former case, the parent material is an N-alkyl toluidine, e.g., N-dodecyl-o-toluidine, which is formulated and then ring-closed by fusion with sodium methylate, the sequence of reactions being

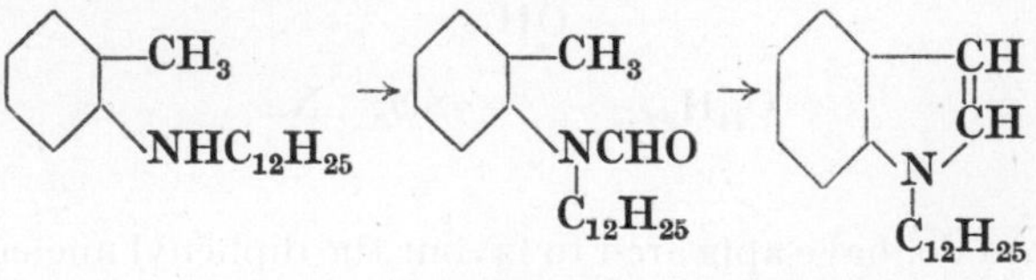

When the alkyl group is desired in the 2-position, i.e., on the α-carbon atom, the parent material is an acylated o-toluidine. Stearic acid and o-toluidine, for example, yield α-n-heptadecylindole:

---

[1] Chwala, *Textilhilfsmittel*, Springer, Vienna, 1939, p. 177.
[2] S.C.I., B.P. 555,443.
[3] Geigy, B.P. 466,635; Sw.P. 191,011; U.S.P. 2,204,544; F.P. 821,844.

$$\text{[structure]}\!-\!CH_3,\ NH_2 + C_{17}H_{35}COOH \rightarrow \text{[structure]}\!-\!CH_3,\ N(H)\!-\!COC_{17}H_{35} \rightarrow \text{[structure]}\!-\!CH,\ NH,\ C\cdot C_{17}H_{35}$$

The sulphonation of the substituted indoles is carried out in the cold with oleum or chlorosulphonic acid, the sulphonic acid group entering the benzene nucleus. The sulphonates of alkyl hydrogenated indoles have also been claimed by Geigy[1] to be effective detergents and lime-soap-dispersing agents.

E. Ester sulphonates

In the preceding sections we have dealt mainly with the synthetic surface-active sulphonates in which the sulphonate group was directly attached to the hydrophobic aliphatic chain or to an aromatic compound which contained an alkyl or aralkyl substituent. A large number of synthetic surface-active agents have been described in which the hydrophobic chain is separated from the hydrophilic sulphonate ionising group by linkages which have a relatively feeble hydrophilic character. Schwartz and Perry call these "intermediate linkages," while Chwala designates this class of agents by the generic term "fatty condensation products." Since many of the more recent surface-active agents have been modelled on two compounds which the I.G. found to be very effective, *viz.*, the fatty acid ester sulphonate "Igepon A" and the fatty acid amide sulphonate "Igepon T," we have preferred to base our treatment on these two important classes, and then to consider in a further section the many other "intermediate linkages" which have been interposed between the predominantly hydrophobic and hydrophilic parts of the molecule.

The ester sulphonates can be divided into two classes. In the first, the sulphonate group is attached to a carbon atom of the ester group, which usually (but not invariably) consists of a relatively small number of carbon atoms:

$$R\cdot\overset{\text{O}}{\overset{\|}{C}}\!-\!O\!-\![CH_2]_n SO_3{}^-,\ Na^+$$

$$R\cdot\overset{\text{O}}{\overset{\|}{C}}\!-\!O\!-\!Ar\!-\!SO_3{}^-,\ Na^+$$

in which Ar is an aromatic, aralkyl, or hydroaromatic group, and R is a hydrophobic hydrocarbon chain which usually contains between 10 and 20 carbon atoms.

---

[1] Geigy, B.P. 466,635; U.S.P. 2,180,801.

In the second class, the sulphonate is attached to a carbon atom of the acyl group:

$$R-O-\overset{\overset{\displaystyle O}{\|}}{C}-[CH_2]_nSO_3{}^-,\ Na^+$$

$$R_1-O-\overset{\overset{\displaystyle O}{\|}}{C}\cdot CH\cdot CH_2\cdot \overset{\overset{\displaystyle O}{\|}}{C}-O-R_2$$
$$\overset{|}{SO_3{}^-},\ Na^+$$

1. Sulphoester compounds

The first and most important of the ester sulphonates in which the sulphonate group is attached to the ester group is "Igepon A,"[1] the sulpho-ethyl ester of oleic acid,

$$CH_3\cdot[CH_2]_7\cdot CH : CH\cdot[CH_2]_7\cdot COO[CH_2]_2SO_3{}^-,\ Na^+$$

which is prepared by condensing oleic acid chloride with sodium hydroxy-ethane sulphonate. The I.G. process for this product has been described by Brown[2] and by Hoyt,[3] and a brief description is given here to illustrate the preparation of this type of ester sulphonate. Oleic acid was reacted with phosphorus trichloride at about 55° c., and the phosphorous acid was then separated from the acid chloride. The hydroxyethane sulphonate was made by reacting ethylene oxide with sodium bisulphite in aqueous solution at about 70° c., the water being subsequently evaporated off. The dry sulphonate and the acid chloride were then reacted at 110° c., the hydrochloric acid which is evolved being removed by an absorber, to give a solid concentrated "Igepon AP," which was diluted with water to give the paste brand "Igepon A." It appears that a greatly simplified process for "Igepon A" was being developed by the I.G. towards the end of the Second World War,[4] by the direct reaction of the fatty acid and the hydroxyethane sulphonate, the water which was split off being removed under reduced pressure.

Several other methods for preparing sulphoesters of fatty acids have been described. For example, the I.G.[5] reacted the sodium salt of a fatty acid with a chloroalkane sulphonate:

$$R\cdot COONa + Cl[CH_2]_2SO_3Na \rightarrow R\cdot COO[CH_2]_2SO_3{}^-,\ Na^+$$

---

[1] I.G., B.P. 359,893; 366,916; D.R.P. 652,410; 657,357; F.P. 705,081.

[2] Brown, B.I.O.S. Final Report 418, "Textile Auxiliary Products—Manufacture by I.G. Farbenindustrie, Hoechst," p. 3.

[3] Hoyt, B.I.O.S. Miscellaneous Report 11, "Synthetic Detergents and Washing Agents," p. 23.

[4] Hoyt, *loc. cit.*, p. 31.

[5] I.G., B.P. 366,916.

and also a fatty acid with carbyl sulphate or ethionic acid:

$$R \cdot COOH + \begin{matrix} H_2C - OSO_2 \\ | \\ H_2C - SO_2 \end{matrix} \!\!\! \Big\rangle O + H_2O \rightarrow R \cdot COO[CH_2]_2SO_3H + H_2SO_4$$

$$R \cdot COOH + HO_3SOCH_2 \cdot CH_2SO_3H \rightarrow R \cdot COO[CH_2]_2SO_3H + H_2SO_4$$

Henkel[1] described a method in which a halogenoalkyl ester of a fatty acid is treated with sodium sulphite:

$$R \cdot COOCH_2 \cdot CH_2Cl + Na_2SO_3 \rightarrow R \cdot COOCH_2 \cdot CH_2SO_3{}^-, Na^+ + NaCl$$

When the ester group is aromatic and the fatty acid is saturated, as in tolyl stearate, the sulphonic acid group can be introduced by the action of chlorosulphonic acid, as described by Lindner[2]

"Igepon A" was developed primarily as a detergent by the I.G., who found that optimum detergency was achieved if oleic acid was used as the fatty acid. This is also true of the amide sulphonates which are described in the next section. If a saturated acid such as stearic was used, the optimum hydrophobe-hydrophile balance was destroyed, and relatively poor detergents were obtained.[3] With fatty chains shorter than oleic, detergent power again diminished, but wetting-out and foaming properties were improved, and in view of the latter characteristics the products with shorter chains were preferred by the I.G. as household detergents. "Fex," a product of the Sunlicht A.G., was made from coconut or palm kernel oil fatty acids (mainly saturated C_{12} and C_{14} acids).

The ester sulphonates suffer from two disadvantages compared with the amide sulphonates, *viz.*, they are hydrolysed in hot acids and alkalis, and they do not appear to be so effective for removing solid dirt from fabrics. Both types of products are stable in hard water, and are in fact very efficient lime-soap-dispersing agents. For this reason they have often been used in admixture with soap.

Although oleic acid gives the most effective detergent of the sulpho-ethyl ester type, other fatty acids have also been described, and many were

---

[1] Henkel, B.P. 440,103.
[2] Lindner, F.P. 782,280.
[3] Brandner, Lockwood, Nagel, and Russell, F.I.A.T. Final Report 1141, "Synthetic Detergents and Related Surface-Active Agents in Germany."

used in Germany during the War. Brown[1] mentions, for example, the fatty acids which were reclaimed from waste fats, which were mainly oleic and stearic acids. The "Alipons," which were surface-active agents of the "Igepon A" type, were made from a number of fatty acids other than oleic; they are described in several reports by the Allied missions to Germany.[2, 3, 4, 5]

The sulphoethyl esters of abietic acid and hydrogenated abietic acid have been described by du Pont.[6]

Esters other than the sulphoethyl have also been used. A wide range have been described by the I.G.,[7] including

alkyl:

$$R \cdot COOCH_2SO_3^-, Na^+$$
$$R \cdot COOC_3H_7SO_3^-, Na^+$$

aryl:

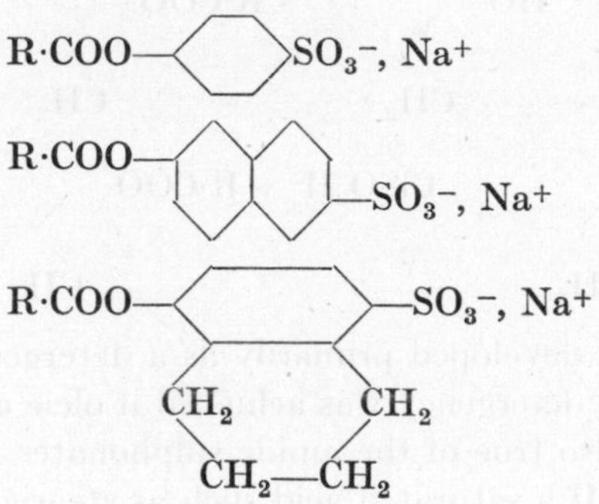

cycloalkyl:

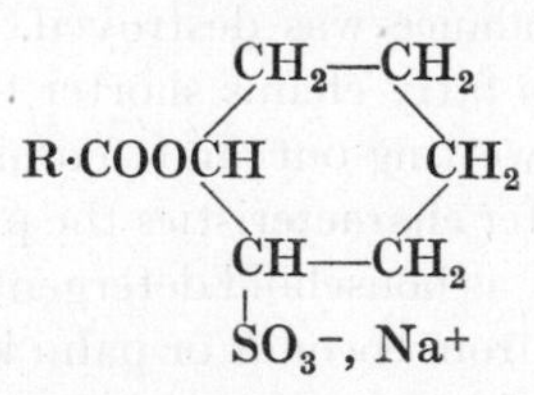

mixed aryl-alkyl:

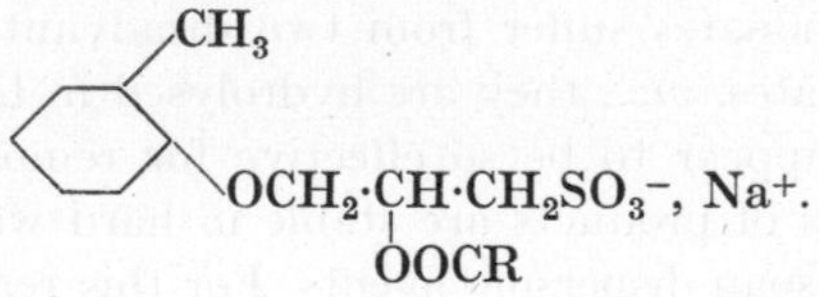

---

[1] Brown, *loc. cit.*, p. 4.

[2] Brown, *loc. cit.*, p. 10.

[3] Richardson, Kern, Murray, Sudhoff, C.I.O.S. XXVI–2, "Synthetic Emulsifying Agents, Wetting Agents, Detergents, and Soap Substitutes, I.G., Hoechst."

[4] Hoyt, *loc. cit.*

[5] Brandner, Lockwood, Nagel, and Russell, *loc. cit.*, p. 82.

[6] Du Pont, F.P. 755,769.

[7] I.G., B.P. 367,585; 372,005; D.R.P. 657,404; F.P. 39,893 (addition to F.P. 705,081); 720,590.

An interesting type of ester sulphonate in which the hydrophobic chain and the sulphonic group are part of the ester grouping is described in the report by Brandner, Lockwood, Nagel, and Russell.[1] This was made by the I.G. by condensing phenol with an olefin polymerisation product containing about 12 carbon atoms. The resulting alkyl phenol was further condensed with allyl chloride, and the ether so obtained was then heated, rearrangement occurring to the alkyl allyl phenol. Treatment with sulphuric acid and acetic anhydride gave a sulphonated product which was thought to be

$$CH_3 \cdot COO \quad \underset{C_{12}H_{25}}{\overset{}{\bigcirc}} -CH_2 \cdot \underset{\underset{SO_3^-, \ Na^+}{|}}{CH} \cdot CH_2 OOC \cdot CH_3$$

This product was an effective wetting-out agent, while the analogue containing a C_{16} to C_{18} alkyl group was a good detergent.

Monsanto[2] have also described the sodium salt of tridecyl-β-sulphopropionate, which they claim is especially useful as a dish-washing detergent. Tridecyl alcohol from the "Oxo" process is used to prepare tridecyl acrylate, which is treated with aqueous sodium sulphite to give the desired product:

$$ROOC \cdot CH:CH_2 + NaHSO_3 \rightarrow ROOC \cdot CH_2 \cdot CH_2 SO_3^-, \ Na^+$$

2. SULPHOACYL COMPOUNDS

The important surface-active esters of sulphomonocarboxylic acids appear to be largely confined to those of sulphoacetic acid. The I.G.[3] method of preparation was to esterify sulphoacetic acid or chloroacetic acid with a long-chain alcohol, in the case of the chloro compound subsequently treating with aqueous sodium sulphite:

$$ROH + HOOC \cdot CH_2 SO_3^-, \ Na^+ \rightarrow ROOC \cdot CH_2 SO_3^-, \ Na^+$$

or $\qquad ROH + HOOC \cdot CH_2 Cl \rightarrow ROOC \cdot CH_2 Cl$

$$\underset{(Na_2SO_3)}{\Big\downarrow}$$

$$ROOC \cdot CH_2 SO_3^-, \ Na^+$$

I.C.I.[4] and Geigy[5] condensed chloroacetyl chloride with the alcohol and then reacted the chloroacetic ester with aqueous sulphite. "Nacconol LAL" of the Allied Chemical and Dye Corporation is the alkyl sulphoacetate which is prepared from coconut oil alcohols. As an example of the esters of sulphoaromatic acids there may be cited the products described by Böhme[6] and

---

[1] Brandner, Lockwood, Nagel, and Russell, *loc. cit.*, p. 43.

[2] Monsanto and Kosmin, U.S.P. 2,818,426.

[3] I.G., B.P. 377,249; Sw.P. 154,507; 154,508; 158,117; 158,118; 158,430; 158,431; 158,432; F.P. 716,605.

[4] I.C.I., F.P. 735,211.

[5] Geigy, Sw.P. 157,337; 160,079; 160,080; 160,081; 163,000.

[6] Böhme, B.P. 350,595.

by Monsanto.[1] The latter firm advocated the use of these agents in tooth-
pastes, since they are tasteless and odourless; a preferred product is the
2-ethylhexyl ester of *o*-sulphobenzoic acid,

$$C_4H_9 \cdot CH \cdot CH_2OOC - \underset{\underset{SO_3^-, \; Na^+}{}}{\bigcirc}$$
$$\underset{C_2H_5}{|}$$

Similar compounds obtained by reacting the alcohol fraction from the
"Oxo" process, utilising triisobutylene and tetrapropylene, with sulpho-
benzoic acid, have been described by Monsanto.[2] The alkylolamine salts of
these compounds are the subject of a subsequent patent.[3] Monsanto claim
that the alkylolamine salts are useful in the preparation of mayonnaise
emulsions and in instant coffee preparations. Sulphophthalate esters from
the reaction of 4-sulphophthalic anhydride with 2-methylpentanol and
2-methylhexanol have been described as useful wetting-out agents.[4]

Probably the most important of the sulphoacyl surface-active agents
are the salts of sulphosuccinic diesters. These have been very energetically
developed by the American Cyanamid Company,[5] who market them under
the trade name "Aerosol." (It should be noted, however, that the trade
name "Aerosol" is not confined to the sulphosuccinic esters and that the
sulphosuccinates are also available under other trade names.) Many different
esters are available commercially, and the properties and methods of preparation of a number of them have been described by Caryl.[6] The general
method is to esterify maleic anhydride with the appropriate alcohol or
mixture of alcohols, and then to treat with sodium bisulphite, which adds
across the double bond:

$$\begin{matrix} CH \cdot C \diagup^{O} \\ \| \qquad \diagdown O \\ CH \cdot C \diagdown_{O} \end{matrix} + 2C_8H_{17}OH \rightarrow \begin{matrix} CH \cdot COOC_8H_{17} \\ \| \\ CH \cdot COOC_8H_{17} \end{matrix}$$
$$\downarrow (NaHSO_3)$$
$$\begin{matrix} Na^+, \; {}^-O_3S\overset{}{C}H \cdot COOC_8H_{17} \\ CH_2 \cdot COOC_8H_{17}. \end{matrix}$$

The preparation of branched-chain alkyl sulphosuccinates has been
described by American Cyanamid.[7] The bis-decyl and bis-tridecyl esters
obtained from "Oxo" alcohols are said to have better solubility in water,

[1] Monsanto, Gluesenkamp, and Kosmin, U.S.P. 2,359,291.
[2] Monsanto and Kosmin, U.S.P. 2,676,979.
[3] Monsanto and Kosmin, U.S.P. 2,683,736.
[4] Monsanto, Doerr, and Miller, U.S.P. 2,828,326.
[5] American Cyanamid and Jaeger, U.S.P. 2,028,091; 2,181,087.
[6] Caryl, *Ind. Eng. Chem.*, 1941, **33**, 731.
[7] American Cyanamid, B.P. 760,121.

and to be better wetting-out agents, than the straight-chain analogues. American Cyanamid[1] also record the preparation and use of salts of sulphosuccinate esters of 4-alkylphenoxy ethanols:

$$R—C(CH_3)_2—\langle \rangle—OC_2H_4OOC·CH—SO_3^-,\ Na^+$$

$$R—C(CH_3)_2—\langle \rangle—OC_2H_4OOC·CH_2.$$

When R is a short chain containing between one and four carbon atoms, the compounds are stated to be useful anti-misting agents (*cf.* p. 217), while, with a longer carbon chain, the solubility in oil is increased, and the products can be used as detergents and as suspending agents in hydro-carbon lubricating oils.

In the process for the I.G. product "Dismulgan VII," sodium diethyl-hexyl sulphosuccinate, which has been described by Richardson, Kern, Murray, and Sudhoff,[2] the ester was prepared from maleic acid, using *p*-toluene sulphonic acid as catalyst, while the addition of sodium bisulphite was effected in aqueous ethanol. The disodium monocetyl monosulphosuc-cinate,

$$C_{16}H_{33}OOC·CH_2·CH·COO^-,\ Na^+,$$
$$SO_3^-,\ Na^+$$

has been described by the Allied Chemical and Dye Corporation.[3]

Esters of sulphopolycarboxylic acids have also been prepared. The National Oil Products Company,[4] for example, sulphonate aconitic acid by adding sodium bisulphite to the double bond and then esterify, or alterna-tively the esterification may be carried out before the sulphonation. The U.S. Rubber Company[5] also record the preparation of polymeric esters by heating the half ester of 2-ethyl-1 : 3-hexanediol with maleic acid. The product is then reacted with sodium bisulphite to give polymeric esters of sulphosuccinic acid. These agents are claimed to be especially useful in emulsion polymerisation processes. They are said to be non-foaming, and to be less prone than the naphthalene sulphonic acid/formaldehyde conden-sates to cause discolouration when the emulsion polymers containing them are used to stiffen white fabrics. The S.C.I.[6] have been very active in the field of aromatic dicarboxylic acids. The acid used is generally 4-sulpho-phthalic acid, and this is esterified with short-chain alcohols such as amyl

---

[1] American Cyanamid and Lynch, U.S.P. 2,507,030.

[2] Richardson, Kern, Murray, and Sudhoff, C.I.O.S. XXVI–2, "Synthetic Emulsifying Agents, Wetting Agents, Detergents, and Soap Substitutes."

[3] Allied Chemical and Dye Corporation and Flett, U.S.P. 2,316,234.

[4] National Oil Products Company, B.P. 551,246.

[5] U.S. Rubber Co., Wilson, and Davison, U.S.P. 2,489,943.

[6] S.C.I., B.P. 370,845; 371,144; 573,014; Sw.P. 153,479; 183,449;. FP. 713,082.

or butyl alcohol, or with phenols such as cresols, to give agents which are characterised chiefly by good wetting-out properties. Detergents are obtained if the esterifying alcohols are cetyl, octadecyl, or oleyl.

F. Amide sulphonates

The carboxy amide sulphonates, like the ester sulphonates, can be conveniently treated in two broad classes. In the first, which we have called the "sulphoamide" compounds, the sulphonic acid group is part of the grouping which is attached to the carboxyamide nitrogen atom, so that the representative formula is

$$R \cdot CON \diagdown \begin{array}{l} R_1 \\ R_2 SO_3^-,\ Na^+ \end{array}$$

The compounds in which the sulpho group is directly attached to the nitrogen atom, *i.e.*, the acyl sulphamic acids, will also be discussed along with the sulphoamide compounds. In the second class, that of the "sulphoacyl amide" compounds, the sulphonic acid group is attached to a carbon atom of the acyl residue:

$$\begin{array}{c} R_1 \diagdown \\ R_2 \diagup \end{array} N\overset{\overset{\textstyle O}{\|}}{C} \cdot RSO_3^-,\ Na^+$$

The third class consists of the sulphonamide sulphonates.

1. Sulphoamide compounds

The prototype of all the amide sulphonates was the I.G. product "Igepon T," which is the sodium salt of oleyl-N-methyltaurine,*

$$CH_3 \cdot [CH_2]_7 \cdot CH : CH \cdot [CH_2]_7 \cdot CON(CH_3)CH_2 \cdot CH_2 SO_3^-,\ Na^+$$

A process for this product is described by Hoyt,[1] by Richardson, Kern, Murray, and Sudhoff,[2] and by Brown,[3] and consists in reacting sodium methyltaurine and oleic acid chloride in caustic soda solution. The method used for preparing oleic acid chloride has already been described. Sodium

---

* According to Chwala (*Textilhilfsmittel*, p. 65), the N-methyl group is present in order to eliminate the possibility of a tautomeric equilibrium between the amide group as written above and its enol form:

$$R \cdot CONHCH_2 \cdot CH_2 SO_3^-,\ Na^+ \rightleftarrows R \cdot \underset{\underset{\textstyle OH}{|}}{C} = NCH_2 \cdot CH_2 SO_3^-,\ Na^+$$

Chwala suggests that the optimum hydrophobe-hydrophile balance is destroyed in the enol form, in which the amide group is more hydrophilic.

[1] Hoyt, *loc. cit.*, p. 21.
[2] Richardson, Kern, Murray, and Sudhoff, *loc. cit.*, p. 8.
[3] Brown, B.I.O.S. Final Report 418, "Textile Auxiliary Products," p. 7.

methyltaurine is made by the reaction between sodium hydroxyethane sulphonate and an excess of methylamine:

$$HOCH_2 \cdot CH_2SO_3Na + CH_3NH_2 \rightarrow CH_3NHCH_2 \cdot CH_2SO_3Na + H_2O$$

The reaction is carried out in aqueous caustic soda solution in a continuous flow tube at 280° c., under a pressure of 200 atmospheres; the excess amine is distilled off and recovered. The condensation of the acid chloride with the methyltaurine,

$$C_{17}H_{33} \cdot COCl + \begin{array}{c} H \\ \diagup \\ CH_3 \end{array} \!\!\! NCH_2 \cdot CH_2SO_3Na$$

$$\downarrow$$

$$C_{17}H_{33} \cdot CON(CH_3)CH_2 \cdot CH_2SO_3{}^-, Na^+ + HCl$$

is also carried out in aqueous caustic soda solution, at a temperature of 24–50° c., and the resulting solution is then neutralised with hydrochloric acid and dried. The I.G. product "Igepon T" was standardised to constant strength with salt. As was the case with "Igepon A," fatty acids other than oleic were also used during the War, for example the fatty acids from coconut and palm kernel oils ("Igepon 702K" or "Alipon CT") and synthetic fatty acids ("Alipon OT"); both these products had fatty chains which were predominantly C_{12}–C_{14}. The I.G. also used taurine (made from ammonia and hydroxyethane sulphonic acid) in place of methyltaurine, and the resulting product,

$$C_{17}H_{33} \cdot CONHCH_2 \cdot CH_2SO_3{}^-, Na^+$$

was called "Igepon KT." In order to avoid the use of ethylene oxide, which is a raw material for hydroxyethane sulphonic acid, the I.G. developed the product "Oda Igepon" or "Ho 1/81,"

$$C_{17}H_{33} \cdot CONHCH_2SO_3{}^-, Na^+$$

This was prepared[1] by simply mixing the sodium bisulphite-formaldehyde addition product, oleic acid amide, anhydrous sodium sulphate and a small amount of piperidine together for about one hour at 210° c., in the dry state; the piperidine acts as a catalyst. "Luwipal R" was a product of the same type, but the fatty acids were obtained from waste fats. The I.G. were reported to consider this product to be somewhat inferior to "Igepon T" as a detergent, and it was not stable in acid solutions. A similar product has been described by the General Aniline and Film Corporation.[2]

In the patent specifications which deal with the preparation of "Igepon T" and related compounds, the I.G.[3] described many other types of sulphoamides. Thus for example the amino sulphonic acid may be aromatic, as in

[1] I.G., F.P. 853,845; *cf.* Brandner, Lockwood, Nagel, and Russell, *loc. cit.*, p. 21.

[2] General Aniline, Yamasita, and Yosizaki, U.S.P. 2,313,695.

[3] I.G., B.P. 341,053; 343,524; 343,899; D.R.P. 584,703; 655,999; 663,845; U.S.P. 1,932,180; Dutch P. 30,150.

the case of sodium oleyl-N-ethylanilide sulphonate, or cycloaliphatic, or mixed aromatic-aliphatic. The nitrogen atom may also be substituted by other groups, as in the compound

$$C_{17}H_{33}\cdot CON \diagdown \begin{array}{c} \bigcirc \\ CH_2\cdot CH_2SO_3^-,\ Na^+ \end{array}$$

or form part of a heterocyclic ring, as in

$$C_{17}H_{33}\cdot CON \diagdown \begin{array}{c} CH_2\!-\!CH_2 \\[-2pt] \diagup \qquad \diagdown CH_2 \\[-2pt] CH_2\!-\!CH \diagup \\[2pt] \underset{SO_3^-,\ Na^+}{|} \end{array}$$

The introduction of halogen atoms, usually between two and four per molecule, into the hydrophobic chain was claimed[1] to give enhanced wetting-out and detergent power. An interesting type of amide had the long chain attached directly to the nitrogen atom: chloroethane sulphonate was condensed with cetylamine to give cetyltaurine, which was then further condensed with acetic anhydride to give the sodium salt of acetyl-N-cetyltaurine,

$$CH_3\cdot CON \diagdown \begin{array}{c} C_{16}H_{33} \\ CH_2\cdot CH_2SO_3^-,\ Na^+. \end{array}$$

Geigy[2] have described the preparation of N-benzoyl-α-undecylbenzyl-amine sulphonate, in which the hydrophobic chain is still further removed from the carbonyl group:

$$\bigcirc\!-\!CONHCH\!\!-\!\!\underset{C_{11}H_{23}}{|}\bigcirc\!\!\diagdown SO_3^-,\ Na^+$$

Next to the "Igepon T" type, the class of sulphoamides which has aroused the most interest is probably that prepared by the condensation of fatty acid chlorides with sulphonated aromatic amines. Representatives of this class were early recognised by the I.G.[3] as dispersing agents, for example,

$$C_{17}H_{35}\cdot CONH\!-\!\bigcirc\!\!\diagdown SO_3^-,\ Na^+$$

I.C.I.[4] claim that the introduction of an alkoxy group into the aromatic

---

[1] I.G., B.P. 389,543; 390,840.
[2] Geigy, Sw.P. 210,340.
[3] I.G., B.P. 264,860.
[4] I.C.I. and Baldwin, B.P. 452,139; F.P. 797,631; U.S.P. 2,115,758.

nucleus yields purer products which are better detergents. "Lissapol LS" is a product of this type, being sodium oleyl-*p*-anisidide sulphonate,

$$C_{17}H_{33}\cdot CONH-\!\!\!\left\langle\;\right\rangle\!\!\!-OCH_3$$
$$SO_3{}^-,\ Na^+$$

which can be prepared by condensing oleic acid chloride with *p*-anisidine sulphonic acid. One of the chief virtues of this product is its great stability to hard water, and it is in fact an effective lime-soap-dispersing agent. Venkataraman and co-workers[1] have studied a variety of fatty acid aryl-amide sulphonates, in which they varied the length of the chain in the acyl group, introduced methyl groups on the nitrogen atom, and substituted methyl groups or chlorine atoms in the aromatic ring. Comparative figures for a number of the products which they made are given for the Herbig (immersion wetting-out) test, sinking time test, interfacial tension against kerosene, and calcium soap dispersing power.

Many commercial products are described as the sulphonated condensation products of aromatic amines and fatty acid chlorides. If however the fatty acid is unsaturated, and the sulphonation is carried out after the condensation, then the product will usually consist of a mixture of the aromatic sulphonate (I) and the sulphation (II) and sulphonation (III products of reaction at the double bond:

$$CH_3\cdot[CH_2]_7\cdot CH:CH\cdot[CH_2]_7\cdot CONH-\!\!\!\left\langle\;\right\rangle\!\!\!-SO_3{}^-,\ Na^+ \qquad (I)$$

$$CH_3\cdot[CH_2]_7\cdot CH\cdot CH_2\cdot[CH_2]_7\cdot CONH-\!\!\!\left\langle\;\right\rangle \qquad\qquad (II)$$
$$OSO_3{}^-,\ Na^+$$

$$CH_3\cdot[CH_2]_7\cdot CH\cdot CH(OH)\cdot[CH_2]_7\cdot CONH-\!\!\!\left\langle\;\right\rangle \qquad\quad (III)$$
$$SO_3{}^-,\ Na^+$$

and may also contain compounds in which both the aromatic nucleus and the double bond have been attacked. Condensation of the amino aromatic sulphonic acid with the fatty acid chloride avoids what may be an undesirable mixture of types.

The salts of sulphoamides in which the sulphur atom is linked directly to the nitrogen atom (acyl sulphamic acids) have also been claimed as surface-active agents. The I.G.,[2] for example, prepared palmityl sulphamic acid by sulphonating palmitic acid amide with chlorosulphonic acid:

$$C_{15}H_{31}\cdot CONH_2 + ClSO_3H \rightarrow C_{15}H_{31}\cdot CONHSO_3{}^-,\ H^+ + HCl$$

or by reacting sulphamic acid with palmitic acid chloride:

$$C_{15}H_{31}\cdot COCl + H_2NSO_3H \rightarrow C_{15}H_{31}\cdot CONHSO_3{}^-,\ H^+ + HCl$$

---

[1] Uppal and Venkataraman, *J. Soc. Dyers Colourists*, 1939, **55**, 125; Shirolkar and Venkataraman, *J. Soc. Dyers Colourists*, 1941, **57**, 41.
[2] I.G., B.P. 372,389; D.R.P. 572,283; F.P. 715,205.

2. Sulphoacyl amide compounds

None of the amide sulphonates in which the sulphonate group is attached to the acyl radical are comparable in importance with the corresponding agents in the ester sulphonate class, *i.e.*, the sulphosuccinic esters, but several have been described and appear to be worth mentioning briefly. The general formula of the sulphoacyl amide compounds can be written

$$\begin{matrix} R_1 \\ \\ R_2 \end{matrix}\!\!\!\!\Big\rangle NOC \cdot RSO_3^-, Na^+$$

in which the hydrophobic portion of the molecule resides predominantly either in R or in R_1 or R_2. The I.G. exemplified both these types. They condensed dodecylamine with chloroacetyl chloride, for example, and then treated the resulting amide with sodium sulphite,[1] obtaining

$$C_{12}H_{25}NHOC \cdot CH_2SO_3^-, Na^+$$

or they reacted heptadecylamine with the sodium salt of ethyl sulphoacetate[2] to give

$$C_{17}H_{35}NHOC \cdot CH_2SO_3^-, Na^+$$

or they treated the ethylanilide of α-bromolauric acid with sodium sulphite[1] in order to obtain

Similar products have been described by Deutsche Hydrierwerke[3] as being particularly effective emulsifying agents for waxes, while Henkel[4] described products in which the hydrophobic chain consists of an alkylhydroaromatic residue, as in

An interesting product of the sulphoacyl type, but which contains both the ester and amide linkages in a single molecule, has been claimed by the S.C.I.[5] They start with 4-sulphophthalic anhydride, which they condense

---

[1] I.G., B.P. 382,718.
[2] I.G., Hentrich, and Keppler, U.S.P. 1,931,540.
[3] Deutsche Hydrierwerke, B.P. 406,862; F.P. 750,647.
[4] Henkel, B.P. 484,910; F.P. 823,380.
[5] S.C.I., F.P. 822,058; Sw.P. 193,075.

with N-ethylcyclohexylamine and then esterify with cetyl alcohol to obtain

$$C_{16}H_{31}OOC \underset{\overset{\displaystyle}{\begin{array}{c}\\ \\ \end{array}}}{\bigcirc} \quad CON(C_2H_5)\overset{\displaystyle CH_2-CH_2}{\underset{\displaystyle CH_2-CH_2}{CH}} CH_2$$

$$SO_3^-, \; Na^+$$

Other products which contain both ester and amide linkages in a single molecule have been claimed by Lever Brothers and Unilever.[1] These are the alkali metal or amine salts of a higher fatty acid ester of a lower sulphocarboxylic acid amide, such as

$$C_{11}H_{23}COOCH_2 \cdot CH_2NHCO \cdot CH_2SO_3^-, \; Na^+$$

and $\quad C_{11}H_{23}COOCH_2 \cdot CH_2NHCO \cdot CH_2SO_3^-, \; ^+NH(C_2H_4OH)_3.$

These compounds are stated to be very efficient lime soap dispersing agents, and can be used in combination with a water-soluble soap in toilet preparations.

3. SULPHONAMIDE SULPHONATES

The amides of long-chain sulphonic acids have also served as intermediates for the preparation of surface-active sulphonates. The I.G.[2] have described the preparation of products of this type by condensing fatty sulphonylchlorides with aliphatic or aromatic aminosulphonates, the aliphatic sulphonylchlorides being obtained from the hydrocarbons by the Reed reaction, which we have already discussed. Typical reactions are:

$$C_{12}H_{25}SO_2Cl + HN(CH_3)CH_2 \cdot CH_2SO_3Na$$
$$\downarrow$$
$$C_{12}H_{25}SO_2N(CH_3)CH_2 \cdot CH_2SO_3^-, \; Na^+ + HCl$$

$$C_{14}H_{29}SO_2Cl + H_2N\!-\!\!\bigcirc\!\!-SO_3Na$$
$$\downarrow$$
$$C_{14}H_{29}SO_2NH\!-\!\!\bigcirc\!\!-SO_3^-, \; Na^+ + HCl$$

Brandner, Lockwood, Nagel, and Russell[3] describe "Emulphor ELO" and "Emulphor STU," which were based on sodium mepasin sulphonamidomethane sulphonate. In this process, "Mepasin" was converted to the sulphonylchloride with sulphur dioxide and chlorine, and then to the

---

[1] Lever Brothers and Unilever, B.P. 631,421.
[2] I.G., B.P. 413,457; U.S.P. 2,242,086.
[3] Brandner, Lockwood, Nagel, and Russell, *loc. cit.*, p. 46.

sulphonamide by treatment with ammonia. The amide was then reacted in aqueous alkaline solution with formaldehyde and sulphur dioxide:

$$C_{12}H_{25}SO_2Cl + NH_3 \rightarrow C_{12}H_{25}SO_2NH_2$$

$$C_{12}H_{25}SO_2NH_2 + HCHO + SO_2 + NaOH$$

$$\downarrow$$

$$C_{12}H_{25}SO_2NHCH_2SO_3{}^-, Na^+ + H_2O$$

"Emulphor STU," which contained some free sulphonamide, was claimed to be an excellent emulsifying agent for mineral and vegetable oils and fatty acids, while "Emulphor ELO" was used mainly for the preparation of oleic acid emulsions for textile processing.

General Aniline[1] have prepared N-alkylbenzenesulphonyl-N-alkyl-taurine salts, for example

$$\begin{matrix} C_8H_{17} \\ \\ CH_3 \end{matrix} \diagup\!\!\!\diagdown \hspace{-1em} \bigcirc \hspace{-0.5em} SO_2N(CH_3)CH_2\!\cdot\!CH_2SO_3{}^-, Na^+$$

which they claim are excellent wetting-out agents and stable to the action of hot acids and alkalies.

Sulphonated sulphonamides in which the fatty chain is attached to the nitrogen atom have been patented by Henkel.[2] They prepared the sodium salt of ethane-1-(N-dodecylsulphonamide)-2-sulphonic acid by the following series of reactions:

$$ClCH_2\!\cdot\!CH_2SO_2Cl + C_{12}H_{25}NH_2 \rightarrow ClCH_2\!\cdot\!CH_2SO_2NHC_{12}H_{25} + HCl$$

$$ClCH_2\!\cdot\!CH_2SO_2NHC_{12}H_{25} + Na_2SO_3$$

$$\downarrow$$

$$C_{12}H_{25}HN\!\cdot\!O_2SCH_2\!\cdot\!CH_2SO_3{}^-, Na^+ + NaCl$$

G. Miscellaneous sulphonates

1. ETHER SULPHONATES

Although amphipathic sulphonates in which an ether link is interposed between the ionising group and the hydrophobic part of the molecule are frequently described in the patent literature they have not achieved great economic importance. Many methods for their preparation have been described, for example the I.G.[3] condensed octadecyl chloride with sodium hydroxyethane sulphonate

$$C_{18}H_{37}Cl + HOC_2H_4SO_3Na \rightarrow C_{18}H_{37}OC_2H_4SO_3{}^-, Na^+$$

[1] General Aniline, Cross, and Chiddix, U.S.P. 2,694,727.
[2] Henkel, B.P. 436,862; U.S.P. 2,120,512; 2,139,037.
[3] I.G., B.P. 377,258; Sw.P. 154,170; F.P. 715,585.

while I.C.I.[1] achieved the same object by using an alkali alkoxide and β-halogenoethane sulphonic acid

$$C_{18}H_{35}ONa + BrC_2H_4SO_3Na \rightarrow C_{18}H_{35}OC_2H_4SO_3^-, Na^+$$

The same structure is obtained by treating a fatty alcohol with ethylene oxide, converting the terminal hydroxyl group to chloride, and then treating with sodium sulphite, as illustrated by Deutsche Hydrierwerke[2]

$$C_{12}H_{25}OH \xrightarrow{(C_2H_4O)} C_{12}H_{25}OC_2H_4OH \xrightarrow{(HCl)}$$
$$C_{12}H_{25}OC_2H_4Cl \xrightarrow{(Na_2SO_3)} C_{12}H_{25}OC_2H_4SO_3^-, Na^+$$

Orthner and Langbein[3] carried this process a step further, introducing a second ether oxygen, by using the chloromethylether of dodecyl alcohol as the starting material. The series of reactions is:

$$C_{12}H_{25}OCH_2Cl \xrightarrow{(C_2H_4O)} C_{12}H_{25}OCH_2OCH_2 \cdot CH_2Cl$$
$$\downarrow (NaHSO_3)$$
$$C_{12}H_{25}OCH_2OCH_2 \cdot CH_2SO_3^-, Na^+.$$

Rohm and Haas[4] claim that the use of caustic soda as a catalyst in the reaction of an alcohol with the alkali metal hydroxyethane sulphonate gives purer products, and that the chemicals are easier to handle and are less corrosive. The water produced in the reaction is continually distilled off, the reaction temperature being kept between 180° and 250° c. The reaction can be represented as follows:

$$C_{12}H_{25}OH + HOC_2H_4SO_3Na \xrightarrow{(NaOH)} C_{12}H_{25}OC_2H_4SO_3Na + H_2O.$$

Henkel described the preparation of long-chain ether sulphonates as well as the related thioethers[5] and compounds in which the oxygen atoms form part of a heterocyclic ring[6] such as, for example:

$$C_{12}H_{25}OCH_2 \cdot CH\!-\!O \diagdown \qquad \diagup SO_3^-, Na^+$$
$$CH_2\!-\!O \diagup CH \cdot CH \diagdown SO_3^-, Na^+$$

which is obtained by reacting the sodium salt of acetaldehyde disulphonic acid and the monododecyl ether of glycerol.

Mixed aromatic-aliphatic and hydroaromatic-aliphatic ethers have also been prepared. When aromatic radicals are present the sulphonation, which takes place in the aromatic nucleus, may be carried out after the formation

[1] I.C.I., Baldwin, and Hailwood, B.P. 378,867; U.S.P. 2,062,957; 2,062,958.
[2] Deutsche Hydrierwerke, F.P. 752,756.
[3] Orthner and Langbein, U.S.P. 2,316,538.
[4] Rohm and Haas, Hollander, and Bock, U.S.P. 2,535,677.
[5] Henkel, F.P. 748,460; D.R.P. 666,388.
[6] Henkel, F.P. 791,246.

of the ether as illustrated by I.C.I.[1] who sulphonated alkylbenzyl ethers with monohydrate thus:

$$C_{16}H_{33}OH + ClCH_2\langle\bigcirc\rangle \rightarrow C_{16}H_{33}OCH_2\langle\bigcirc\rangle \xrightarrow{(H_2SO_4)}$$

$$C_{16}H_{33}OCH_2\langle\bigcirc\rangle SO_3^-, Na^+$$

and by the I.G.[2] who sulphonated, for example, cyclohexylphenyl-isodo-decyl ether; the product being presumed to be:

$$\begin{array}{c}CH_2-CH_2\\CH_2 \qquad CH\langle\bigcirc\rangle OC_{12}H_{25}\\CH_2-CH_2 \qquad SO_3^-, Na^+\end{array}$$

The structure of this product is similar to that of the branched chain type which Hartley showed (see Chapter 2) had a pronounced effect on its amphipathic properties. Hartley's work[3] on this type was indeed first illustrated with the ethers of dihydroxy aromatic sulphonates which he prepared[4] by sulphonating, *e.g.*, the mixed decyl and hexyl ether of resorcinol to give,

$$C_{10}H_{21}O-\langle\bigcirc\rangle-SO_3^-, K^+$$
$$OC_6H_{13}$$

Dow[5] have claimed a method of preparing alkyldiphenyl ether sulphonates, which consists in carrying out a Friedel-Crafts reaction, using aluminium chloride as catalyst, on diphenyl ether and polypropylenes (mainly $C_{12}H_{24}$), and sulphonating the product in methylene chloride with sulphur trioxide. The product is then neutralised and drum-dried. It has two sulphonic acid groups on each diphenyl ether nucleus, and has pronounced surface activity in concentrated electrolyte solutions, such as 10% caustic soda.

Branched-chain aliphatic ethers have been prepared by the I.G.[6] who reacted glycerol β-chlorhydrin with octyl alcohol and then replaced the halogen by the use of sodium sulphite, for example the product:

$$C_8H_{17}OCH_2 \cdot CH \cdot CH_2OC_8H_{17}$$
$$SO_3^-, Na^+$$

[1] I.C.I., Hailwood, and Baldwin, B.P. 378,454.
[2] I.G., B.P. 495,414.
[3] Hartley, *Trans. Faraday Soc.*, 1941, **37**, 130.
[4] Hartley, *J. Chem. Soc.*, 1939, 1828.
[5] Dow Chemical Co. and Steinhauer, U.S.P. 2,854,477.
[6] I.G., B.P. 500,032.

An almost wholly aromatic ether sulphonate has been described by the S.C.I.[1] who condensed 2-chloromethyltetrahydronaphthalene and 2-naphthol-6-sulphonate to give:

which was claimed to be a particularly effective detergent for wool.

It is also common practice to use an ether link along with another hydrophilic group between the ionising group and the hydrophobic part of the molecule. The commonest groups so used appear to be the ester and the amide links. Geigy[2] condensed the sodium alkoxide of a mixture of coconut and palm kernel oil alcohols with glycerol chlorhydrin

$$RONa + ClCH_2 \cdot CH(OH) \cdot CH_2OH \rightarrow ROCH_2 \cdot CH(OH) \cdot CH_2OH$$

and then reacted with chloracetyl chloride to give the ester of chloracetic acid

$$ROCH_2 \cdot CH(OH) \cdot CH_2OH + ClCH_2 \cdot COCl \rightarrow ROCH_2 \cdot CH(OH)CH_2O\overset{O}{\overset{\|}{C}} \cdot CH_2Cl$$

Reaction with sulphite then gave the sulphonate;

$$ROCH_2 \cdot CH(OH)CH_2O\underset{O}{\overset{\|}{C}} \cdot CH_2SO_3^-,\ Na^+$$

The sulphonate group may also be on the ester radical and aromatic radicals may be introduced into the molecule as in the product

which has been described by the I.G.[3] An interesting variation of this mixed type in which the ether and ester links are in separate branches of the molecule is also described by the I.G.[4] who claimed that the sodium salt of γ-cresoxy-β-oleyl-β-hydroxypropane sulphonic acid is an effective wetting and foaming agent.

[1] S.C.I., U.S.P. 2,399,434.
[2] Geigy, Sw.P. 162,732.
[3] I.G., B.P. 479,122.
[4] I.G., Sw.P. 155,309.

The ether-amide combination may be exemplified by the product prepared by Waldmann and Chwala[1] by the following route:

$$ClC_2H_4OC_2H_4Cl \xrightarrow{(Na_2SO_3)} ClC_2H_4OC_2H_4SO_3Na \xrightarrow{(CH_3NH_2)}$$

$$CH_3NHC_2H_4OC_2H_4SO_3Na \xrightarrow{(C_{17}H_{33}COCl)}$$

$$\overset{O}{\overset{\|}{C_{17}H_{33}\cdot CN}}(CH_3)C_2H_4OC_2H_4SO_3{}^-, \ Na^+$$

and by the condensation product[2] of *p*-isooctylphenoxyacetic acid chloride with the sodium salt of methyltaurine.

$$C_8H_{17}\!\!\left\langle\!\!\bigcirc\!\!\right\rangle\!\!OC_2H_4\cdot\!\underset{O}{\overset{\|}{C}}N(CH_3)C_2H_4SO_3{}^-, \ Na^+$$

2. Sulphonates containing amino linkages

Substituted amino groups provide another type of linkage which has been used for synthesising surface-active sulphonates. Probably the most important compounds of this type are the so-called "solution salts," such as "Solution Salt AO" (I.C.I.), in which the active agent is sodium monobenzyl sulphanilate

$$\left\langle\!\!\bigcirc\!\!\right\rangle\!\!CH_2NH\!\!\left\langle\!\!\bigcirc\!\!\right\rangle\!\!SO_3{}^-, \ Na^+$$

and "Solution Salt SV" (I.C.I.), which is the dibenzyl analogue. These agents are mainly used as adjuvants in dyebaths, but they have also been used to solubilise cyclohexanol and other sparingly-soluble alcohols.[3] Other N-substituted aminoaromatic sulphonates which have been proposed include salts of N : N-diethylmetanilic acid and sulphonated N : N-diamyl-α-naphthylamine,[4]

$$(C_2H_5)_2N\!\!-\!\!\left\langle\!\!\bigcirc\!\!\right\rangle\!\!\underset{SO_3{}^-, \ Na^+}{} \quad \text{and} \quad (C_5H_{11})_2N\!\!-\!\!\left\langle\!\!\bigcirc\!\!\bigcirc\!\!\right\rangle\!\!\underset{SO_3{}^-, \ Na^+}{}$$

which were claimed to be emulsifying agents and agents for preparing dispersible powders of insoluble dyestuffs; sodium N : N-di(naphthylmethyl) sulphanilate,[5]

---

[1] Waldmann and Chwala, B.P. 434,358; F.P. 779,503; Sw.P. 180,400.
[2] I.G., B.P. 501,004.
[3] Kallé and Spröngerts, D.R.P. 433,732.
[4] I.G., B.P. 252,392; *cf.* U.S.P. 1,853,414; 1,853,415.
[5] Kallé, Schmidt, and Voss, D.R.P. 721,719.

$$CH_2 \diagup \atop CH_2 \diagdown N - \hexagon - SO_3^-,\ Na^+$$

which was described as a detergent; sodium 1-cetylaminobenzene-2 : 4-disulphonate[1]

$$C_{16}H_{33}NH - \hexagon - SO_3^-,\ Na^+ \atop SO_3^-,\ Na^+$$

and analogues containing shorter aliphatic chains, for which a variety of uses were claimed; and a series of N-substituted aromatic aminosulphonates which are of general formula

$$R_1 \diagdown \atop R_2 \diagup N - Ar - SO_3^-,\ Na^+$$

in which R_1 and R_2 comprise at least one aliphatic or cycloaliphatic residue containing not less than 8 carbon atoms, and Ar is an aromatic nucleus.[2] The N-substituents have also been interrupted with ester groups, as in the structure[3]

$$ROOC \cdot CH_2NH - \hexagon - SO_3^-,\ Na^+$$

in which R represents the mixture of alkyl radicals in the fatty alcohols from coconut and palm kernel oil.

Aminoalkyl sulphonic acids, substituted at the nitrogen atom with hydrophobic groupings, have also been proposed as surface-active agents, as in the structures

$$C_{17}H_{35}NHCH_2CH_2SO_3^-,\ Na^+ \quad [4]$$

$$sec.\ C_8H_{17} - \hexagon - OSO_2 - \hexagon \atop CH_3 \qquad NHCH_2CH_2SO_3^-,\ Na^+ \quad [5]$$

$$C_8H_{17}OOC \cdot CH_2 \atop and \qquad C_8H_{17}OOC \cdot CHNHCH_2 \cdot CH_2SO_3^-,\ Na^+ \quad [6]$$

[1] Deutsche Hydrierwerke, F.P. 753,753.
[2] " Unichem " Chemikalien Handels and Schirm, U.S.P. 2,067,463.
[3] Geigy, Sw.P. 163,002.
[4] I.G., B.P. 356,218.
[5] Deutsche Hydrierwerke, B.P. 517,339.
[6] American Cyanamid, B.P. 575,608.

Although they are not actually substituted amines, the alkyl-substituted sulphamic acids are most conveniently considered under the present heading. These agents, which appear to be of particular interest as mercerising wetting-out agents, are illustrated by the product "Leophen KN" (I.G.), which contained sodium dibutylsulphamate[1]

$$\begin{array}{c} C_4H_9 \\ \diagdown \\ C_4H_9 \diagup \end{array} NSO_3{}^-,\ Na^+$$

Further examples of this structure will be found in the relevant I.G. patents.[2]

3. SULPHONATES CONTAINING KETONE GROUPS

Surface-active agents of the general formula

$$R \cdot CO \text{—} \langle \ \rangle \text{—} SO_3{}^-,\ Na^+$$

in which R·CO— represents a fatty acyl group such as palmityl, stearyl, or oleyl, and the benzene nucleus may be substituted with groups such as methyl or ethyl, have been described by Milch[3] and by Oranienburger.[4]

More complicated structures have been described by Geigy[5] who sulphonated ketones of the general formula

$$Ar \cdot CH(X) \cdot CO \cdot Ar$$

in which Ar is a phenyl or diphenyl group, and X is a substituent such as an alkyl or cycloalkyl group containing more than 5 carbon atoms, exemplified by

$$\left[\langle \ \rangle \text{—} \langle \ \rangle \text{—} CO \cdot \underset{\underset{C_{17}H_{35}}{|}}{CH} \text{—} \langle \ \rangle \right] \text{—} SO_3{}^-,\ Na^+$$

The I.G. also claimed to have made textile assistants by chlorinating aliphatic ketones (*e.g.*, diheptyl ketone), and then replacing the chlorine atom(s) with sulphonate groups by treatment with sodium thiosulphate or thiosulphite.[6]

A number of compounds obtained by condensing aromatic sulphonic acids with benzoin (or with mixtures of benzoin and alcohols such as isopropyl alcohol) have been described by the S.C.I. in a series of patents.[7]

---

[1] Baird, B.I.O.S. Final Report No. 239, "Textile Auxiliary Products Manufactured by I.G. Farbenindustrie, Mainkur Works," p. 8.
[2] I.G., B.P. 455,893; U.S.P. 2,116,583; F.P. 803,896.
[3] Chem. Fabrik Milch, B.P. 269,917.
[4] Oranienburger Chem. Fabrik, B.P. 313,453.
[5] Geigy, Engel, and Pfaehler, U.S.P. 2,199,789.
[6] I.G., F.P. 850,753.
[7] S.C.I., Sw.P. 130,420; 133,377; 138,489; 138,490–1; 160,439; 162,902–3–4–5–6; 163,770; U.S.P. 1,833,245.

The sodium salt of the condensation product of naphthalene-2-sulphonic acid with one molecule of benzoin can be represented as

$$CO \cdot CH \qquad SO_3^-, Na^+$$

The S.C.I. product "Albatex WS" was stated by Sisley[1] to be of this type. The similarity of these agents to the alkylated aromatic sulphonates, with which they could equally well be classified, is at once apparent; we have included them in the present section in order to emphasise the fact that the hydrophobic residue is interrupted by a keto group.

4. SULPHONATED SULPHONES

The use of sulphone linkages in sulphonated surface-active agents is illustrated by the proposal of the S.C.I.[2] to sulphonate compounds such as

$$RSO_2 \qquad CH_3$$

in which R represents the fatty alkyl radical from coconut oil, and an I.G. patent[3] which describes the reaction between sulphones such as dodecylvinyl sulphone and octadecylvinyl sulphone and sodium bisulphite, yielding products to which are assigned formulae such as

$$C_{12}H_{25}SO_2CH_2 \cdot CH_2SO_3^-, Na^+$$

5. SULPHONATES CONTAINING OTHER SULPHUR LINKAGES

Monsanto[4] have described alkylmercaptoalkane sulphonates, which can be prepared from the reaction of alkane sultones and alkane thiols in an alkaline medium. The compounds are said to be good wetting-out agents and to have improved lathering properties. Monsanto[5] have also recorded the preparation of sulphonium sulphonates:

$$R_1-S^+(R_2)[CHR_3]_n SO_3^-,$$

where R_1 and R_2 contain a total of up to 18 carbon atoms, R_3 is H or CH_3, and n lies between one and four.

This zwitterion can be made by condensing a mercaptoalkane sulphonate with an alkyl sulphate, or an alkyl thioether with an alkane sultone. The products are described as biological toxicants and week-killers.

[1] Sisley, *Index des Huiles Sulfonées et Détergents Modernes*, Teintex, Paris, 1949, p. 249.
[2] S.C.I., F.P. 758,078.
[3] I.G., B.P. 446,992.
[4] Monsanto and Gaertner, U.S.P. 2,799,702.
[5] Monsanto and Gaertner, U.S.P. 2,813,898.

CHAPTER 11

ANIONIC SURFACE-ACTIVE AGENTS: THE ALIPHATIC SULPHATES

A. Introduction

THE aliphatic sulphates are, as their name implies, characterised by containing solubilising sulphuric ester groups, which have usually been converted to the sodium salts.* The generic formula of their surface-active constituents can be written as

$$R(OSO_3^-, Na^+)_n$$

in which R contains one or more hydrophobic groups, which are sufficiently large in the aggregate to make the molecule appreciably amphipathic in the particular media involved. In the simplest representatives of this type of surface-active molecule, n is unity, and R is a saturated or unsaturated aliphatic group, branched or with a straight chain, which usually contains at least 12 carbon atoms, though shorter chains may be present in agents which are intended for special uses. Typical examples are:

$C_{12}H_{25}OSO_3^-$, Na^+ (sodium dodecyl sulphate),
$C_{16}H_{33}OSO_3^-$, Na^+ (sodium cetyl sulphate), and

$$\underset{CH_3 \cdot CH_2 \cdot \overset{\overset{\textstyle C_2H_5}{|}}{CH} \cdot [CH_2]_2 \cdot \overset{\overset{\textstyle OSO_3^-,\ Na^+}{|}}{CH} \cdot CH_3}{} \text{ (sodium 4-ethylheptyl-2-sulphate).}$$

Frequently, however, R will be more complex. It may for example represent a fatty acid or fatty ester grouping, as in the structures

$$CH_3 \cdot [CH_2]_7 \cdot \overset{\overset{\textstyle OSO_3^-,\ Na^+}{|}}{CH} \cdot CH_2 \cdot [CH_2]_7 \cdot COO^-,\ Na^+$$

$$CH_3 \cdot [CH_2]_5 \cdot \overset{\overset{\textstyle OSO_3^-,\ Na^+}{|}}{CH} \cdot CH_2 \cdot CH : CH \cdot [CH_2]_7 \cdot COO^-,\ Na^+$$

$$CH_3 \cdot [CH_2]_7 \cdot \overset{\overset{\textstyle OSO_3^-,\ Na^+}{|}}{CH} \cdot CH_2 [CH_2]_7 \cdot COOCH_3$$

which are possible constituents of sulphated oleic acid, sulphated ricinoleic acid, and sulphated methyl oleate, respectively. Alternatively, R may be the residue of a fatty glyceride such as olein or castor oil, which has been sulphated at the double bond and/or at the hydroxyl groups, or it may even

---

* The expression "aliphatic sulphates" is accordingly used here to denote only ionisable compounds, and excludes alkyl sulphates such as dimethyl sulphate or its higher homologues.

represent a polymerised structure of a very complex nature. The fatty glycerides themselves will contain mixtures of fatty acids. In these cases it becomes increasingly difficult to specify the exact chemical nature of the effective surface-active molecules, and the technical surface-active agents —which even in the simplest cases are not usually entirely homogeneous— become extremely heterogeneous mixtures.

The aliphatic sulphates owe their great technical importance, especially as auxiliary products for the textile industry, to the following facts:

(a) They combine a high degree of surface-activity in many processes (for example wetting-out, scouring, and emulsification) with good solubility and adequate chemical stability. It is worth noting that they are, on the whole, more soluble in water than are the corresponding true sulphonates, but that they are less stable chemically; in particular, they hydrolyse relatively easily in hot aqueous acids to give the free aliphatic alcohols.

(b) The synthesis of the aliphatic sulphates is usually not difficult, given the right starting material.

(c) Many suitable raw materials for the manufacture of the aliphatic sulphates are readily available in nature (*e.g.*, castor oil, olein, and other unsaturated glycerides), or are easily derived from such materials (*e.g.*, by the saponification of sperm oil to give technical oleyl alcohol, or by the alcoholysis of coconut oil with glycerol to the monoglycerides of lauric and other fatty acids).

(d) The synthesis of the aliphatic sulphates has derived a great impetus from the development of the synthetic routes to the fatty alcohols, from the availability of a large number of olefinic hydrocarbons from the cracking of petroleum wax, and more recently from the development of the Fischer-Tropsch and "Oxo" processes.

The synthesis of the aliphatic sulphates is based essentially on one, and occasionally on both, of two reactions which we propose to describe as "sulphations," reserving the term "sulphonation" for methods of preparing true sulphonic acids and sulphonates (*cf.* Chapter 10).* The first of these is the esterification of an aliphatic OH group, exemplified by the reaction

$$C_{16}H_{33}OH + H_2SO_4 \rightarrow C_{16}H_{33}OSO_3H + H_2O$$

while the second is the addition of sulphuric acid to a double bond, as in the reaction

$$C_nH_{2n+1} \cdot CH : CH_2 + H_2SO_4 \rightarrow C_nH_{2n+1} \cdot CH \begin{cases} CH_3 \\ OSO_3H \end{cases}$$
(petroleum olefin)

When the substance undergoing sulphation contains both OH and

---

* In so doing we shall be following a usage which is over a hundred years old: see Mercer and Greenwood, B.P. 11252/1846, as summarised in *Abridgements of Specifications relating to Bleaching, Dyeing, and Printing, Etc.*, Eyre and Spottiswoode, London, 1859, p. 270.

·CH : CH· groups, the latter are not attacked until the OH groups have been eliminated by esterification or polymerisation.[1]

The chemistry of sulphation processes is the subject of a considerable literature, convenient summaries of which have been given by Burton and Robertshaw,[1] Suter,[2] and Ralston.[3] The actual sulphation reactions are usually accompanied by side reactions, which may affect the efficiency of sulphation, or even lead to the formation of quite different products, which may be more or less surface-active, or even surface-inactive. Some of the possible reactions, which are particularly important in considering the so-called "sulphonated oils," are considered in Section D below. It should however be emphasised here that, except in a relatively few cases such as that of the sulphated fatty alcohols, it is unlikely that technical surface-active agents of the aliphatic sulphate class are ever chemically pure substances. This is of course quite apart from the fact that such products usually contain inorganic electrolytes such as sodium sulphate, or that they may be buffered to reduce the risk of an autocatalytic hydrolysis during storage. The degree of chemical heterogeneity may not be great: thus technical sodium oleyl sulphates will usually contain only small amounts of the products resulting from sulphation of the double bond, though the hydrocarbon part of the agent may represent a mixture of radicals. As we pass to the sulphation products of the unsaturated or hydroxy fatty acids and of their esters and glycerides, however, it becomes increasingly important to bear in mind that we are dealing with complicated mixtures. It may still be possible to characterise their general chemical nature, but it is out of the question to attempt an exact physico-chemical interpretation of their properties, such as their states of solution, or their adsorption behaviour as deduced from the Gibbs equation.

In the preceding sections we have used sulphuric acid to typify sulphating agents. As will become apparent later, other sulphating agents, especially chlorosulphonic acid and sulphur trioxide, are widely used under appropriate conditions.

B. Sulphated fatty alcohols

1. STRAIGHT-CHAIN SULPHATED ALCOHOLS

The straight-chain sulphated alcohols, such as sodium dodecyl, tetra-decyl, cetyl, and oleyl* sulphates, constitute one of the most important

---

* Although, strictly speaking, "oleyl" refers to the unsaturated *acyl* radical ($C_{17}H_{33}·CO—$) from oleic acid, rather than to the corresponding alkylene radical ($C_{18}H_{35}—$), it has seemed preferable in the present context to conform to a convenient and wide-spread usage and use "oleyl" to describe the *cis* form of the Δ9-octadecenyl radical.

[1] Burton and Robertshaw, *Sulphated Oils and Allied Products*, Harvey, 1939, pp. 21–35.
[2] Suter, *The Organic Chemistry of Sulfur*, Wiley and Chapman and Hall, 1944, pp. 1–93.
[3] Ralston, *Fatty Acids and Their Derivatives*, Wiley and Chapman and Hall, 1948, pp. 459–465, 752–754.

classes of textile and household wetting-out agents and detergents. They are prepared by the action of sulphuric acid, chlorosulphonic acid, or sulphur trioxide, for example, on alcohols which are derived from two general types of starting materials:

(a) naturally occurring esters of fatty alcohols with fatty acids (*e.g.*, oleyl oleate, cetyl palmitate), which are found for example in sperm oil and spermaceti; the alcohols are obtained by a simple saponification;

(b) fatty acids, fatty acid esters, and fatty acid glycerides, which are reduced to the corresponding alcohols.

Although the technical products usually contain inorganic electrolytes, buffers, and organic by-products, the straight-chain aliphatic sulphates are usually fairly homogeneous chemically, and can also be purified more easily than most other surface-active agents; it is also possible to purify the starting materials in many cases. It is partly for these reasons that there is perhaps more exact information about their properties than about any other class of synthetic anionic surface-active agent.

The fatty alcohol-fatty acid esters in spermaceti and sperm oil are substantial sources of raw materials for this type of agent,* but supplies of them are limited, and the importance of the sulphated alcohols was enormously increased by the appearance of the various catalytic routes to the fatty alcohols. The history of the development of these catalytic processes, from the fatty acids, their mono-esters, and the glycerides, as it affected the manufacture of the sulphated alcohols, has been discussed in a number of pre-war articles.[1] Among the best and most objective of these earlier reviews are those by Lederer[2] and by Chwala,[3] who attribute the development of the hydrogenation processes to the independent work of four groups of people: Schmidt and co-workers of the I.G.,[4] Adkins and Folkers at the University of Wisconsin,[5] Schrauth and colleagues of the Deutsche Hydrierwerke,[6] and Normann and co-workers of the Böhme concern.[7] Both Chwala and Lederer also give useful summaries of the earlier publications on the preparation and properties of the sulphated alcohols themselves.

The preparation of fatty alcohols by the reduction of fatty glycerides by metallic sodium, an alternative method which has also become

---

* Thus B.I.O.S. Final Report 1151, by W. Baird, makes it clear that sperm oil was an important source of technical oleyl alcohol even in those German concerns in which the catalytic routes to the fatty alcohols had been highly developed.

[1] See for example Kling, *Textilber.*, 1931, **12**, 111; Hueter, *ibid.*, 1932, **13**, 152; Briscoe, *Dyer*, 1932, **67**, 68, 83, 679; Killefer, *Ind. Eng. Chem.*, 1933, **25**, 138; Lindner, *Seifensieder Ztg.*, 1934, **61**, 470, 490.

[2] Lederer, *Seifensieder Ztg.*, 1932, **59**, 13.

[3] Chwala, *Textilhilfsmittel*, Springer, 1939, pp. 160 ff.

[4] Schmidt, *Ber.*, 1931, **64**, 2051; and F.P. 689,713.

[5] Adkins and Folkers, *J. Amer. Chem. Soc.*, 1931, **53**, 1095.

[6] Schrauth, Schenck, and Stickdorn, *Ber.*, 1931, **64**, 1314.

[7] Normann, *Z. angew. Chem.*, 1931, **44**, 714; and F.P. 708,286.

technically important, has been described in a paper by Kastens and Peddicord.[1]

The patent literature on the sulphation of the fatty alcohols, especially of those from the catalytic hydrogenation processes, is very extensive, and it is only possible to give selected references here, with particular attention to British and United States specifications. Deutsche Hydrierwerke[2] were early in the field, describing the preparation of "moistening, emulsifying, and cleansing media" by the action of strong sulphuric acid on an aliphatic alcohol containing more than eight carbon atoms, and no free or combined carboxylic acid group, in the presence of anhydrides (*e.g.*, acetic anhydride) which were capable of reacting with the water formed during the sulphation. Cetyl alcohol is given in the example, while the alcohols from wool fat, beeswax, and sperm oil are also mentioned. At almost the same time, Böhme were granted a British Patent,[3] in which was described the sulphation of oleyl alcohol with concentrated sulphuric acid or oleum at about 0° c., in order to obtain "wetting, cleaning, foaming, and dispersing agents." This specification, which stresses the importance of eliminating all carboxylic acid groups in order to prevent precipitation by hard water, also mentions octadecyl alcohol.* Böhme followed this patent by specifications in which were described various technological applications of the sulphated fatty alcohols (see Section E of the present chapter), and other methods of preparation.[4] Böhme also suggested that the sulphation products of dodecyl and tetradecyl alcohols were superior in wetting-out, dispersing, foaming, and other properties, to the alkyl sulphates of greater or shorter chain length.[5]

The I.G. have described the use of alkyl sulphates containing only four to eight carbon atoms as wetting-out agents in the strong caustic soda solutions (*e.g.*, 29° Be., or 23% NaOH) which are used for mercerising cotton.[6] Among the examples given are the sulphation products of normal butyl, amyl, and hexyl alcohols, or of mixtures of hexyl and heptyl alcohols. The sulphates may be used alone or in admixture with surface-active agents such as Turkey Red Oil, or with solvents such as the monoethyl ether of 1 : 3-butylene glycol. This patent, which presumably relates to the product "Leophen M," is of particular interest as an example of the fact that the

---

* The amended specification, which was published on May 31st, 1932, contains no reference to sodium octadecyl sulphate, and includes an acknowledgment of B.P. 307,709. The possible legal significance of these changes is outside the scope of the present book, in which we are treating these specifications only as literature.

[1] Kastens and Peddicord, *Ind. Eng. Chem.*, 1949, **41**, 438.

[2] Deutsche Hydrierwerke, B.P. 307,709, accepted June 11th, 1930, claiming a Convention Date (Germany) of March 9th, 1928.

[3] Böhme, B.P. 308,824, accepted May 27th, 1930, German Convention Date March 30th, 1928. *Cf.* U.S.P. 1,968,793 and 1,968,797.

[4] Böhme, B.P. 317,039 and Sw.P. 145,980.

[5] Böhme, B.P. 350,432.

[6] I.G., B.P. 354,946.

optimum ratio of hydrophobic to hydrophilic groups is not necessarily the same in different media. It seems reasonable to assume that a smaller hydrophobic group is required in a mercerising liquor than in water, because the high concentration of sodium hydroxide in the former will reduce the degree of solvation of the sulphate group, by suppressing the degree of ionisation and by competing with it for the available water dipoles.

The I.G. also described the sulphation of fatty alcohols other than those already mentioned. Thus according to one specification[1] they treated the mixture of alcohols which is obtained from the oxidation of paraffin, with sulphating agents such as 33% oleum. In a British specification[2] of earlier publication, but later filing date, they described the sulphation of the alcohols which are obtained by hydrogenating the oxidation products of soft paraffin wax and other petroleum fractions. Another interesting proposal from the same patentees[3] is the sulphation of the synthetic isomer of oleyl alcohol:

$$CH_3 \cdot [CH_2]_4 \cdot CH : CH \cdot [CH_2]_{10} \cdot CH_2OH$$

which is obtained by splitting off one molecule of water from 1 : 12-octadecylene glycol. They have also suggested sulphating the reduction or hydrogenation products of wool fat.[4]

A considerable number of procedures have been described in the patent literature for improving sulphation processes,[5] or for improving the physical form of the sulphated fatty alcohols obtained.[6]

In recent years a considerable amount of work has been done on continuous sulphation processes, and many patents have been taken out in this field. The difficulties in the sulphation process are that (a) the reactions are reversible, which means that it is preferable to use concentrated sulphating agents; (b) the agents used react very vigorously, so that undesirable side reactions occur, while the high local temperatures cause darkening of the product, due to destruction of organic compounds; (c) hydrolysis and excessive increases in temperature can occur during neutralisation. These problems have been overcome by the use of better chemical engineering principles, involving heat transfer and/or agitation studies. Whyte[7] has examined the continuous sulphation of fatty alcohols with concentrated sulphuric acid. The effect of the time of reaction before neutralisation, of the concentration, and of the excess of acid over the theoretical amount,

[1] I.G. and Martin Luther, U.S.P. 1,908,376; see also B.P. 373,642.
[2] I.G., B.P. 352,537.
[3] I.G., B.P. 388,485 and F.P. 735,235.
[4] I.G., F.P. 809,405.
[5] See for example Sandoz, B.P. 442,198; I.G., B.P. 382,942; Richards Chemical Works, U.S.P. 2,042,952; Procter and Gamble, U.S.P.'s 2,049,670; 2,075,914; 2,075,915; 2,098,114; 2,099,214; Mauersberger, F.P. 753,080; Flesch, F.P. 763,426; Böhme, F.P. 763,691.
[6] Böhme, B.P. 365,938.
[7] Whyte, *J. Amer. Oil Chem. Soc.*, 1955, **32**, 313.

were all examined with respect to the yield of sulphated product. Temperature control is very important, and conditions were standardised at 99% sulphuric acid, with a reaction time of 10 seconds, which gave a temperature of about 66° c. By using efficient mixing and adequate heat removal at the neutralisation stage, difficulties due to hydrolysis were overcome. The use of sulphuric acid in the continuous sulphation of long-chain ethanolamides has been described by Paquot,[1] whose method also relied on more efficient mixing and removal of heat. He also reported high yields, of 85% or better. Monsanto[2] claim that an improvement in sulphation can be obtained by using sulphur trioxide in liquid sulphur dioxide as sulphating agent. In this process a stream of sulphur trioxide in liquid dioxide is mixed with the aliphatic alcohol in sulphur dioxide and sprayed into a chamber at atmospheric pressure. The pressure drop across the nozzle is 40 to 100 lb./square inch, and the heat of sulphation causes some of the liquid sulphur dioxide to evaporate. The evaporation removes a large amount of heat, and the temperature at the sulphation stage is controlled in the range 20°–70° c. by using an appropriate amount of sulphur dioxide. The sulphation takes place almost instantaneously, and the unreacted alcohol is re-cycled, while the vaporised sulphur dioxide and the sulphated product are separated in any convenient manner.

A number of proposals have been made for chemically modifying the simpler, straight-chain aliphatic sulphates. Thus the I.G.[3] suggested halogenating alkyl or cycloalkyl sulphates (*e.g.*, sodium octadecyl sulphate), while Deutsche Hydrierwerke[4] proposed halogenating a sulphated unsaturated alcohol, such as sodium oleyl sulphate, at the double bond. Mauersberger,[5] on the other hand, suggested sulphation after halogenation; he claimed that replacement by halogen of one or two of the terminal hydrogens in cetyl alcohol, for example, and then sulphating above 50° c. with fuming sulphuric acid, gives products of improved wetting, scouring, and foaming properties, and of improved stability to salts, alkalis, and acids. Air-blowing of unsaturated fatty alcohols such as oleyl alcohol, before sulphation, has been claimed by the National Oil Products Company[6] to give surface-active materials which are less prone to become rancid.

An interesting method of sulphation, which recalls the Reed process for preparing alkane sulphonates (*vide* Chapter 10), has been proposed by Henkel,[7] who prepared the chlorosulphonic acid esters of fatty alcohols by reacting them with sulphur dioxide and chlorine in ultraviolet light, and then hydrolysing to the sulphates in aqueous alkali solutions.

[1] Paquot, *Bull. soc. chim.*, 1955, 220.
[2] Monsanto, B.P. 676,690.
[3] I.G., B.P. 394,043.
[4] Deutsche Hydrierwerke, B.P. 400,986 and F.P. 736,771.
[5] Mauersberger, B.P. 462,202 and F.P. 801,106.
[6] National Oil Products Company, B.P. 541,481.
[7] Henkel, F.P. 870,163.

A large part of the patent and technical literature which we have just outlined comes from German sources; it is therefore of considerable interest to compare it with the information given in the F.I.A.T. and B.I.O.S. reports, though the general picture is not radically altered. Two such reports seem to us to be worth special study in the present connection. Brandner, Lockwood, Nagel, and Russell[1] report that sodium oleyl sulphate was considered to be the most suitable detergent of this class in Germany for commercial laundry and textile use, both for cotton and wool, while the sulphates from dodecyl and tetradecyl alcohols were stated to be better for household use because of their greater foaming power, and their more suitable physical condition in the dry state. At the time of the report, the principal fatty alcohol available in Germany was octadecyl alcohol, obtained by the catalytic hydrogenation of rape seed oil; chlorination, either before or after sulphation, had been found to improve the solubility and foaming properties, the introduction of two chlorine atoms into the molecule giving a sulphate which was practically equal in solubility to sodium oleyl sulphate. The methods used by the Böhme concern for sulphating "laurol" (technical dodecyl alcohol) and technical oleyl alcohol are discussed by Baird,[2] who also outlines the I.G. methods, and the latter's process for the preparation of oleyl alcohol by the saponification of sperm oil. It is interesting to note that Baird reports (p. 5) that the Böhme chemists whom he interviewed considered that, if the sulphation of oleyl alcohol was carried out with chlorosulphonic acid in pyridine, in order to minimise attack on the double bond, a product was obtained which was less substantive to textiles than the oleyl sulphates in which the double bond had been appreciably attacked.

The ready availability of tallow alcohols has led to investigations of the possible use of their derivatives as detergents and wetting-out agents. The sulphated hydrogenated tallow alcohols are good detergents and surface-active agents generally, but they have only a limited solubility in water at room temperatures. Sulphated tallow alcohols (consisting mainly of sodium tetradecyl, hexadecyl, octadecyl, and oleyl sulphates) are good detergents and are adequately soluble in cold water, presumably because of the solubilisation of the saturated paraffin chain salts by the formation of mixed micelles with the oleyl compound. The presence of unsaturated sulphates (of a given chain length) improves the solubility, but restricts the choice of sulphating agents and conditions. This difficulty has been overcome by Weil, Stirton, and Maurer,[3] who chlorinated the tallow alcohols and then carried out the sulphation with chlorosulphonic acid. The presence of the

---

[1] Brandner, Lockwood, Nagel, and Russell, F.I.A.T. Final Report No. 1141, "Synthetic Detergents and Related Surface-Active Agents in Germany."

[2] Baird, B.I.O.S. Final Report No. 1151, "Miscellaneous Surface-Active Agents and Related Intermediates."

[3] Weil, Stirton, and Maurer, *J. Amer. Oil Chem. Soc.*, 1955, **32,** 148.

sodium 9 : 10-dichlorooctadecyl sulphate makes the mixed tallow alcohol sulphates soluble in cold water. In a further paper on the possibility of obtaining synthetic detergents from animal fats (tallow alcohols), Bistline, Stirton, Weil, and Maurer[1] investigated the effect on the solubility of tallow alcohol sulphates of condensing the fatty alcohols with ethylene oxide before sulphating. They examined the properties of the sulphated ethenoxylated hexadecyl and octadecyl alcohols of average compositions corresponding to the formulae:

$$C_{16}H_{33}[OC_2H_4]_2OSO_3^-, \; Na^+$$
$$C_{18}H_{37}[OC_2H_4]_2OSO_3^-, \; Na^+$$
$$C_{18}H_{37}[OC_2H_4]_{10}OSO_3^-, \; Na^+,$$

The inclusion of two ethenoxy groups improved the solubility without loss in detergency. When the number of ethenoxy groups was increased to ten, the products were inferior detergents. The product from octadecyl alcohol containing two ethenoxy groups was the best emulsifying agent, and all three products had a high stability to metal ions and were good lime soap dispersing agents.

2. Sulphated secondary, tertiary, and branched-chain fatty alcohols

The aliphatic sulphates which we have been considering are characterised by the fact that the polar group is present at the end of an unbranched aliphatic chain. Owing to the possibility of free rotation around most or all of the linkages in this chain, and to the fact that the hydrocarbon grouping will strive to expose a minimum surface to the water molecules, these amphipathic anions will adopt a spheroidal shape in aqueous solutions, and this shape will probably persist in those ions which are present in adsorbed gaseous monomolecular layers. The fact that the chains are straight, however, and that the polar groups are in the terminal positions, means that interactions of various sorts are possible between the chains, either saturated or unsaturated, leading to phenomena such as

(a) formation of micelles (either spherical or crystalline) in aqueous solutions;

(b) formation of condensed unilayers (solid or liquid) at many interfaces;

(c) the formation of well-defined crystals when the surface-active agent is isolated from solution.

This tendency for hydrocarbon chains to gather together into random or organised micelles, condensed unilayers, or macroscopic crystals, will obviously be diminished if the polar group is moved to a secondary or

---

[1] Bistline, Stirton, Weil, and Maurer, *ibid.*, 1957, **34**, 516.

tertiary position, and/or the hydrocarbon chain is branched. These possibilities can be illustrated by means of the following generic formulae:

$$R—CH\begin{smallmatrix}R'\\ \\OSO_3Na\end{smallmatrix}$$ secondary aliphatic sulphate, in which R is a long aliphatic chain, usually containing not less than eight carbon atoms, and R' is a methyl group or larger;

$$R—\overset{R'}{\underset{R''}{C}}—OSO_3Na$$ tertiary aliphatic sulphate, in which R, R', and R" are all methyl or larger aliphatic groups, the total number of carbon atoms usually being at least twelve;

$$R—\overset{R'}{\underset{R''}{C}}—CH_2OSO_3Na$$ branched-chain primary aliphatic sulphate, normally saturated, in which R, R', and R" may themselves be branched.

The present theoretical picture and experimental evidence all go to suggest that any of these three structural modifications markedly diminishes micelle formation in aqueous solutions, which means that a higher concentration of molecularly disperse solute can be reached than is possible with the straight-chain sulphates.[1] Alternatively expressed, the activity coefficient of a branched-chain, secondary, or tertiary sulphate will generally be higher, at a given concentration, than that of a straight-chain sulphate of similar surface-activity. This picture is in good agreement with the fact that the secondary alkyl sulphates are exceptionally good wetting-out agents and reduce the surface tension of water very markedly, as reported by Wilkes and Wickert,[2] and by Dreger, Keim, Miles, Shedlovsky, and Ross,[3] since both wetting-out (an immersional wetting test was used) and lowering of the surface tension will be favoured if a solute is *per se* highly surface-active and is also present at an exceptionally high thermodynamical activity.

The results obtained from all three types of structural modifications also appear to increase solubility in water, presumably because the tendency for a new phase to crystallise out of solution (or perhaps in some cases to separate as an amorphous phase) has been reduced on account of the interference by the side groupings with the alignment of the paraffin chains in the crystals. In other respects, however, the effects of the modifications are quite different. Thus Wilkes and Wickert[2] refer to the fact that the secondary sulphates are inferior to the primary sulphates as detergents and emulsifying agents; this is probably attributable to their inability to

[1] Hartley, *Trans. Faraday Soc.*, 1941, **37**, 130.
[2] Wilkes and Wickert, *Ind. Eng. Chem.*, 1937, **29**, 1234.
[3] Dreger, Keim, Miles, Shedlovsky, and Ross, *Ind. Eng. Chem.*, 1944. **36**, 610.

form stabilising, condensed unilayers at oil-water interfaces. It seems clear on the other hand that the sulphates obtained from the branched-chain primary alcohols of the "Oxo" process are comparable to the straight-chain primary aliphatic sulphates in detergent power.

The preferred wetting-out agents and detergents of the secondary, tertiary, and branched-chain aliphatic sulphate types appear to have larger hydrocarbon groups, on the whole, than do the straight-chain primary sulphates. This suggests that the hydrophobic effect of the hydrocarbon groups in the former types is less, for a given total size, than in the straight-chain primary sulphates. A very elegant demonstration of this fact is afforded by the work of Padgett and Degering,[1] who prepared the sulphates from the series 2-, 3-, 4-, 5-, and 6-dodecanol, and compared them with sodium dodecyl sulphate as regards foaming power and effect on the interfacial tension water-benzene. Both foaming power and extent of lowering of the interfacial tension decreased progressively as the sulphato group was moved nearer to the centre of the molecule.

A very considerable number of secondary, tertiary, and branched-chain primary aliphatic sulphates have been described or proposed in the technical and patent literature. Thus Wickert[2] described the preparation of a di(ethylheptyl)carbinol, the sulphato derivative of which was stated to have good wetting-out properties and to lower the surface tension of water very considerably. Other proposals which have been made by the same group of patentees in an extensive patenting campaign, which presumably related to the "Tergitol" products, include the sulphates of the following alcohols:

$$CH_3 \cdot CH_2 \cdot \underset{\underset{C_2H_5}{|}}{CH} \cdot [CH_2]_2 \cdot \underset{\underset{OH}{|}}{CH} \cdot CH_3 \quad \text{(3-ethyl-heptanol-6)}\,[3]$$

$$CH_3 \cdot CH_2 \cdot \underset{\underset{C_2H_5}{|}}{CH} \cdot [CH_2]_2 \cdot \underset{\underset{OH}{|}}{CH} \cdot [CH_2]_2 \cdot \underset{\underset{C_2H_5}{|}}{CH} \cdot CH_2 \cdot CH_3 \quad \text{(3 : 9-diethylundecanol-6)}\,[3]$$

$$CH_3 \cdot CH_2 \cdot \underset{\underset{C_2H_5}{|}}{CH} \cdot [CH_2]_2 \cdot \underset{\underset{OH}{|}}{CH} \cdot [CH_2]_4 \cdot CH_3 \quad \text{(3-ethylundecanol-6)}\,[3]$$

$$CH_3 \cdot \underset{\underset{CH_3}{|}}{CH} \cdot CH_2 \cdot \underset{\underset{OH}{|}}{CH} \cdot [CH_2]_2 \cdot \underset{\underset{C_2H_5}{|}}{CH} \cdot [CH_2]_3 \cdot CH_3 \quad \text{(2-methyl-7-ethylundecanol-4)}\,[4]$$

$$CH_3 \cdot [CH_2]_3 \cdot \underset{\underset{C_2H_5}{|}}{CH} \cdot [CH_2]_2 \cdot \underset{\underset{OH}{|}}{CH} \cdot [CH_2]_2 \cdot \underset{\underset{C_2H_5}{|}}{CH} \cdot [CH_2]_3 \cdot CH_3 \quad \underset{\text{decanol-8)}\,[5]}{\text{(5 : 11-diethylpenta-}}$$

[1] Padgett and Degering, *Ind. Eng. Chem.*, 1940, **32**, 204.
[2] Carbide and Carbon and Wickert, B.P. 440,539; F.P. 789,406; U.S.P. 2,088,016.
[3] Carbide and Carbon, Wickert, and Carter, B.P. 446,084; F.P. 798,967.
[4] Union Carbide and Wickert, U.S.P. 2,088,019.
[5] Union Carbide and Wickert, U.S.P. 2,088,020.

The sulphation of alcohols of these types is stated by Law and McNamee[1] to proceed more efficiently, with a smaller formation of the corresponding olefins, if the alcohol and sulphating agent are allowed to react as solutions in mutual solvents. Among the alcohols which were sulphated by these authors may be mentioned

$$\langle\hexagon\rangle CH_2 \cdot CH_2 \cdot \underset{\underset{OH}{|}}{CH} \cdot C_4H_9 \quad (\beta\text{-phenylethylisobutylcarbinol})$$

and its analogue in which the phenyl group is replaced by a cyclohexyl group.

Two patent specifications of the I.G. reveal a number of interesting proposals for sulphating secondary alcohols. The first[2] mentions the penta-triacontanol obtained by the reduction of stearone, which is the di-*n*-heptadecylcarbinol:

$$CH_3 \cdot [CH_2]_{16} \cdot \underset{\underset{OH}{|}}{CH} \cdot [CH_2]_{16} \cdot CH_3$$

This is stated to give a sulphate which is a good emulsifying agent. The second specification[3] describes the sulphation of a number of secondary alcohols of increasing complexity, perhaps the most interesting structure being the 2 : 4 : 6 : 9 : 10 : 12 : 14-heptamethylpentadecanol-7.

The sulphato derivatives of secondary aliphatic alcohols containing two hydroxyl groups, which are claimed to be detergents, wetting-out agents, and emulsifying agents, have been suggested by du Pont.[4] Two examples of this type of alcohol are:

$$CH_3 \cdot [CH_2]_{10} \cdot \underset{\underset{OH}{|}}{CH} \cdot \underset{\underset{OH}{|}}{CH} \cdot [CH_2]_{10} \cdot CH_3 \quad (1 : 2\text{-diundecylethylene glycol})$$

$$CH_3 \cdot [CH_2]_{8} \cdot \underset{\underset{OH}{|}}{CH} \cdot \underset{\underset{OH}{|}}{CH} \cdot [CH_2]_{8} \cdot CH_3 \quad (1 : 2\text{-dinonylethylene glycol})$$

Finally, it is worth noting that the sulphuric acid esters of unsaturated secondary alcohols (*e.g.*, methylheptadecenylcarbinol[5] and dimethyloleyl-carbinol[6]) have been described.

The sulphation products of the so-called "Oxo" synthetic higher alcohols, which were developed in Germany during the Second World War, are mixtures in which the major constituents are branched-chain primary sulphates. These products, which have aroused a considerable amount of

[1] Carbide and Carbon, Law, and McNamee, B.P. 456,214; U.S.P. 2,088,027.
[2] I.G., B.P. 343,872.
[3] I.G., B.P. 471,483.
[4] Du Pont and Benner, U.S.P. 2,091,956.
[5] General Aniline, Haussmann, Nüsslein, Schütte, and Schöller, U.S.P. 2,229,649.
[6] Henkel, B.P. 424,891.

interest, are discussed in several reports by the F.I.A.T. and B.I.O.S. missions. The "Oxo" process itself is described in the first monograph of the present series,[1] and in publications by Holm, Nagel, Reichl, and Vaughan,[2] by Hall and Craxford,[3] and by Baird.[4] It consists essentially in the catalytic addition of hydrogen and carbon monoxide to olefins:

$$R \cdot CH : CH \cdot R' + CO + 2H_2 \rightarrow \underset{\underset{CH_2OH}{|}}{R \cdot CH \cdot CH_2 \cdot R'} \text{ and } \underset{\underset{CH_2OH}{|}}{R \cdot CH_2 \cdot CH \cdot R'}$$

in which R' is preferably hydrogen, *i.e.*, the double bond is preferably in the terminal position. The total process may be interrupted at the aldehyde stage. The olefins used by the Germans were obtained from several sources, among them being the thermal or catalytic cracking of hydrocarbon waxes and the Fischer-Tropsch process.

The mechanism of the "Oxo" reaction is discussed by Holm, Nagel, Reichl, and Vaughan,[5] who also summarise the information obtained by them on the structure of those "Oxo" alcohols which were converted to surface-active agents by sulphation (pp. 36–37). These authors report that it was preferred to avoid branching of the paraffin chains as much as possible, since it led to a poorer detergent power, a noticeable odour, and dry preparations which were "plastic" in consistency. When α-olefins were used, such as those from cracked Fischer-Tropsch wax, the degree of branching was stated to be slight, the only substituents being methyl and ethyl groups. The adverse effect of chain branching on detergent power could apparently be compensated for, however, by using a larger molecular weight: thus the branched-chain C_{18} sulphates were as good detergents as the C_{16-17} straight-chain sulphates. This information is usefully supplemented in the report by Brandner, Lockwood, Nagel, and Russell.[6] They were informed that a sulphato group which was near the centre of a highly branched alkyl chain gave a better wetting-out agent, but a poorer detergent, than a sulphato group nearer the end of the chain. (The latter were stated to give sulphates with similar detergent properties to those from straight-chain alcohols.) These authors report that a contributory cause to the high degree of branching in the "Oxo" alcohols is the tendency for the double bonds in the olefins to migrate during the synthesis of the alcohols, when a cobalt catalyst was used.

---

[1] Goldstein, *The Petroleum Chemicals Industry*, Spon, 2nd Edition 1958, pp. 183–186.

[2] Holm, Nagel, Reichl, and Vaughan: F.I.A.T. Final Report No. 1000, "The Oxo Process."

[3] Hall and Craxford, B.I.O.S. Final Report No. 1722, "Additional Information concerning the Fischer-Tropsch Process and Its Products."

[4] Baird, B.I.O.S. Final Report No. 1151, "Miscellaneous Surface-Active Agents and Related Intermediates."

[5] Holm, Nagel, Reichl, and Vaughan, *loc. cit.*, pp. 26 ff.

[6] Brandner, Lockwood, Nagel, and Russell, F.I.A.T. Final Report No. 1141, "Synthetic Detergents and Related Surface-Active Agents in Germany," pp. 23–26.

The "Oxo" reaction continues to be a useful source of wetting-out agents, and du Pont[1] claim the production of an improved agent, which is also soluble in organic solvents, from the reaction of tetraisobutylene, carbon dioxide, and hydrogen, using a cobalt naphthenate catalyst and sulphating the reaction products with chlorosulphonic acid. Branched-chain alcohols from the "Oxo" process have been reacted with ethylene oxide before sulphation.[2] It is claimed that this improves the solubility and gives products with better lathering power, both of which are desirable if the products are to be used in liquid detergents or shampoos.

Monsanto[3] also propose reacting 2-butyl-1-octanol with ethylene oxide, sulphating, and forming the alkylolamine salt, for example, the ethanolamine salt of the sulphated triethylene glycol ether of 2-butyl-1-octanol. They claim that concentrated aqueous solutions of this compound give a liquid detergent with very good lathering properties.

A second synthetic route to the higher aliphatic alcohols studied by the Germans was the so-called "Synol" process, a modification of the Fischer-Tropsch synthesis in which hydrogen and carbon monoxide are reacted catalytically.[4] This process appears to have been less important for the production of surface-active agents, the alcohols produced being mainly in the C_5–C_{10} range, with only a relatively small proportion of higher alcohols.

Finally, mention should be made of the alcohols which are produced on a small scale in the United States by the catalytic air-oxidation of petroleum hydrocarbons, especially the "Alox" products.[5]

3. SULPHATED OLEFINS

Although it is not strictly correct to refer to them as sulphated "alcohols," the sulphuric acid esters obtained by adding a molecule of sulphuric acid to a double bond in an unsaturated hydrocarbon (*cf.* Section A of the present chapter) are chemically identical with the products obtained by sulphating the equivalent alcohols (which would be secondary alcohols). The two processes can in fact sometimes be considered to be alternative routes to the same product.[6] It is therefore permissible, and certainly very convenient, to consider the sulphated olefins in the present section.

Perhaps the most practicable way of dealing with the extensive patent literature on the sulphated olefins is to classify the specifications according to whether they describe (a) the sulphation of specific olefinic hydrocarbons,

[1] Du Pont and Bruner, U.S.P. 2,633,473.

[2] Monsanto and Kosmin, B.P. 757,937; Atlas Powder Co., B.P. 766,706.

[3] Monsanto and Kosmin, U.S.P. 2,644,833.

[4] Baird, B.I.O.S. Final Report No. 1151, "Miscellaneous Surface-Active Agents and Related Intermediates," pp. 1–2.

[5] Goldstein, *The Petroleum Chemicals Industry*, 2nd edition, Spon, 1958, p. 61.

[6] Brandner, Lockwood, Nagel, and Russell, *loc. cit.*, p. 25.

or of the products of special synthetic routes to the olefins, (b) the sulphation of more heterogeneous mixtures, often by-products, which have
become available through the development of the petroleum industry or of
special techniques such as the Fischer-Tropsch process, or (c) improvements in methods or processes for sulphating various unsaturated
hydrocarbons.

A number of patent specifications are worth special mention under the
first of these headings. Thus the I.G.[1] have described the sulphation products of tetradecylene, octadecylene, octadecadiene, and other olefins, each
of which is stated to contain at least one terminal double bond. Pott and
Company[2] proposed "polymerising" alcohols such as butanol in a strongly
dehydrating medium, for example concentrated sulphuric acid, and then
sulphating the resulting oil. The I.G.[3] in a slightly later patent described the
sulphation of dodecylene and hexadecylene, as well as tetradecylene and
octadecylene; the hexadecylene, for example, was obtained by the distillation of spermaceti wax under conditions which caused dehydration. Similarly, olefins were obtained by splitting off water from the aliphatic
alcohols obtained by the oxidation of liquid or solid naphthenic hydrocarbons. The sulphates from dodecylene were stated to be exceptionally
good wetting agents, while those from the higher olefins were claimed to be
good detergents as well. The I.G. later extended this principle to include
sulphation of the olefins which are derived from the oxidation products of
hard paraffin wax by splitting off water or carbon dioxide by destructive
distillation.[4] The same principle was further explored by Böhme,[5] who
described the sulphation of hexadecylene (again from the distillation of
spermaceti) and of decylene, which was made by the dry distillation of the
barium salt of undecylenic acid in the presence of sodium ethoxide. Downing and Clarkson[6] proposed dehydrating primary fatty alcohols and then
sulphating the resulting olefins, which contain terminal double bonds. It is
interesting to note that they proposed to start with primary alcohols, such
as those obtained by the hydrogenation of coconut oil, which are usually
sulphated directly to the primary alkyl sulphates; presumably the object of
the extra process was to obtain a secondary rather than a primary sulphate.
An alternative to dehydration as a method for obtaining olefins is to treat
halogenated higher paraffinic hydrocarbons, containing more than eight
carbon atoms and at least two halogen atoms in the molecule, with an acid-
binder such as an aqueous or alcoholic alkali or carbonate.[7]

---

[1] I.G., F.P. 716,178 and Sw.P. 148,754.
[2] Chemische Fabrik Pott, B.P. 329,622 and U.S.P. 1,950,287.
[3] I.G., B.P. 343,872.
[4] I.G., B.P. 364,669 and U.S.P. 1,914,321.
[5] Böhme, B.P. 360,602 and U.S.P. 2,027,896.
[6] Du Pont, Downing, and Clarkson, U.S.P. 2,061,617 and 2,061,618.
[7] I.G., B.P. 344,829.

One of the most highly unsaturated hydrocarbons which has been proposed for sulphation is squalene:

$$CH_2 \cdot CH : \overset{\overset{\textstyle CH_3}{|}}{C} \cdot [CH_2]_2 \cdot CH : \overset{\overset{\textstyle CH_3}{|}}{C} \cdot [CH_2]_2 \cdot CH : C(CH_3)_2$$
$$CH_2 \cdot CH : \underset{\underset{\textstyle CH_3}{|}}{C} \cdot [CH_2]_2 \cdot CH : \underset{\underset{\textstyle CH_3}{|}}{C} \cdot [CH_2]_2 \cdot CH : C(CH_3)_2$$

This hydrocarbon, which occurs in shark liver and other fish oils, is the major constituent (up to 70%) in materials which have been sulphated by I.C.I.[1] to give emulsifying agents.

Substituted olefins have also been proposed for sulphation: for example, Böhme[2] described the sulphation of higher aliphatic unsaturated amines such as oleylamine ($C_{18}H_{35}NH_2$). (This patent also refers to the sulphation of saturated primary hydroxyamines such as octadecanolamine.)

The sulphated derivatives of the olefins obtained from the petroleum and related industries are technically the most important of this type of surface-active agent. They are represented in Great Britain, for example, by the "Teepol" products of the Shell organisation. The methods which have been proposed for preparing olefins by cracking hydrocarbons, and for subsequently sulphating them, are illustrated by two United States specifications. McLaren[3] cracks petroleum at 450–482° c., and then sulphates the fraction which boils above 232° c., with oleum or chlorosulphonic acid. The products are described as wetting-out agents, textile oils, and fat-splitting agents. The Bataafsche Company[4] crack cake paraffin wax in the vapour phase, and then sulphate the 160–220° c. fraction with 90% sulphuric acid at 5–10° c.

An interesting paper on the manufacture of "Teepol" by Inskeep and Mussard[5] gives the following information. The olefins are obtained from cracked petroleum stocks, and the product for sulphation preferably contains 60–75% of olefins in the range C_8–C_{18}. It is preferable that the addition of the sulphate group should occur on the second carbon atom, but since foaming power is improved when the sulphate group is near the middle of the chain, this condition is not rigorous. (Since these products are popular in Europe as liquid household detergents, good foaming and lathering power are useful commercial properties.) Inskeep and Mussard consider the various reactions which can take place with sulphuric acid: dialkyl sulphates, sulphonic acids, sulphones, sulphur dioxide, and polymeric

---

[1] I.C.I., Bunbury, Sexton, and Stewart, B.P. 354,417 and U.S.P. 1,961,683.
[2] Böhme, B.P. 353,232 and U.S.P. 1,951,469.
[3] Standard Oil Co. and McLaren, U.S.P. 1,999,128.
[4] Bataafsche Petroleum, U.S.P. 2,152,292 and Sw.P. 185,143.
[5] Inskeep and Mussard, *Ind. Eng. Chem.*, 1955, **47**, 2.

materials can be produced, in addition to the secondary alkyl sulphates. The formation of the less desirable materials is limited by controlling the acid concentration and reducing the time of reaction.

One of the chief problems in making the sulphated olefins—quite apart from finding the most suitable sulphation conditions—appears to be to ensure a good separation of the aliphatic sulphates from the unsulphated materials which are present. Methods for improving the separation are therefore prominent in the patent literature on this phase of the subject: these include the use of organic solvents[1] and separation by centrifuging.[2]

Sulphated olefins containing halogen atoms have been described by the I.G. and by Standard Oil Development Company. The former[3] sulphated aliphatic hydrocarbons containing at least fifteen carbon atoms, a halogen, and at least one double bond near the middle of the chain, *e.g.*,

$$ClCH_2 \cdot [CH_2]_7 \cdot CH : CH \cdot [CH_2]_7 \cdot CH_3 \quad \text{(1-chloro–9 : 10-octadecylene)}.$$

Buc[4] proceeds in a more indirect way, first converting the olefins (*e.g.*, hexadecylene) to the chlorhydrins, and then sulphating.

Surface-active agents, which were prepared by sulphating telomers of polymerisable monoolefin hydrocarbons with allyl or methallyl alcohols, have been described by du Pont.[5] Allyl or methallyl alcohol, and a catalyst which yields free radicals under the appropriate reaction conditions, are charged to a pressure reaction vessel under nitrogen. A monoolefin such as ethylene is then charged to the reactor, after which the pressure is increased and heating and agitation begun. The reaction product is discharged and fractionated, and the fraction which boils between 60° and 250° c. at 2 mm. pressure is then sulphated.

The above selection of patent proposals on the preparation of sulphated olefins can be usefully supplemented by reference to several of the B.I.O.S. and F.I.A.T. reports. Special attention should be drawn to that by Hall and Craxford,[6] in which is described the sulphation of the C_{12}–C_{18} olefins from the Fischer-Tropsch process, which are stated to contain a high proportion of α-olefins. The products would therefore presumably contain a high proportion of secondary sulphates, with the sulphato groups on the penultimate carbon atoms. It is also interesting to note that Brandner, Lockwood,

[1] Bataafsche Petroleum, U.S.P. 2,078,516 and 2,139,393; F.P. 791,964–5–6; Standard Oil Development and Sweeney, U.S.P. 2,153,286; Shell Development and Tulleners, U.S.P. 2,155,027.
[2] Shell Development and Tulleners, U.S.P. 2,339,038.
[3] I.G., B.P. 498,008.
[4] Standard Oil Development and Buc, U.S.P. 2,139,669.
[5] Du Pont and Lindsey, U.S.P. 2,733,255.
[6] Hall and Craxford, *loc. cit.*

Nagel, and Russell[1] report that the I.G. technologists preferred to convert the Fischer-Tropsch olefins directly into sulphates, rather than to proceed to the sulphates *via* the "Oxo" alcohols. Although this might be interpreted as an argument that the secondary sulphates are superior surface-active agents to the primary sulphates, it seems more likely that the preference for the olefins was due to economic reasons and therefore has no bearing on the question of the relative efficiencies of the two types.

The preparation and sulphation of the higher olefins is also discussed in Goldstein's book in the present series.[2] It contains in particular summaries of the Fischer-Tropsch process for the catalytic condensation of carbon monoxide with hydrogen (pp. 47–53), which yields mixtures of paraffins and olefins, and of other special routes to the higher olefins (pp. 122–125), including synthesis by controlled polymerisation of the lower olefins.

4. MISCELLANEOUS SULPHATED ALCOHOLS

A number of proposals have been made in the patent literature for preparing sulphated alcohols which differ significantly from the types already discussed. Although, as far as we are aware, none of these miscellaneous sulphates is comparable in technical importance with the ordinary paraffin-chain sulphates, several of the proposals are worth special mention, if only because of the interesting molecular types which they display. Thus Howard and Sons have patented the sulphation of cyclohexylcyclohexanol and its homologues such as methylcyclohexylmethylcyclohexanol.[3] This proposal yields an amphipathic molecule with a saturated paraffinic group of considerable size ($C_{14}H_{25}$), which however differs from a straight-chain paraffin chain in at least two respects: it will be more compact and it will be less flexible (*i.e.*, it will be unable to assume a spheroidal shape in aqueous solution).

Other substances which have been proposed for sulphation include terpineol,[4] the alcohols from naphthenic acids,[5] substituted benzyl alcohols such as butyl-, octyl-, and dodecylbenzyl alcohol,[6] the oxidation products (presumably sulphoxides or sulphones) of thioethers containing hydroxy groups or double bonds, such as dihydroxypropyl cetyl sulphide or ethyl oleyl sulphide,[7] and the products obtained by the reduction or catalytic hydrogenation of wool fat.[8] The last-named material would presumably give a complicated mixture, containing both straight-chain sulphates and

[1] Brandner, Lockwood, Nagel, and Russell, *loc. cit.*, pp. 6, 25–26.
[2] Goldstein, *The Petroleum Chemicals Industry*, 2nd edition, Spon, 1958.
[3] Howard and Sons, Ltd., Blagden, and Clark, B.P. 425,239.
[4] S.C.I., B.P. 398,086 and F.P. 749,013.
[5] "Unichem" Chemikalien Handels A.G. and Schrauth, U.S.P. 2,000,994.
[6] Henkel, F.P. 796,980.
[7] Henkel, F.P. 762,405.
[8] I.G., F.P. 809,405.

sulphated sterols. Abietyl and hydroabietyl alcohols, the former having the structure

$$(CH_3)_2CH \qquad CH_3$$

$$CH_3 \quad CH_2OH$$

have also been suggested as starting materials for sulphation.[1]

Finally, it is worth noting that the introduction of two sulphato groups into an amphipathic molecule, by sulphating compounds such as octadecylene glycol, has been proposed.[2]

C. Sulphated fatty condensation products

We have seen in Chapter 10 that the *sulphonated* fatty condensation products, in which a long aliphatic chain is connected to a sulphonate group by an intermediate, relatively polar structure, constitute an important class of surface-active agents. An analogous class of *sulphated* fatty condensation products also exists, and has attained a considerable commercial significance,[3] though perhaps for rather different reasons from those which apply to the sulphonated products. In the first place, the sulphation of the fatty alcohols and olefins has always been relatively easily accomplished, so that special condensation reactions did not offer an easier synthetic route, as they did in the case of "Igepon T" *vis-à-vis* the long-chain alkane sulphonates, for example. Secondly, the straight-chain aliphatic sulphates, unlike the corresponding alkane sulphonates, were sufficiently water-soluble for most technical purposes, so that the improvements in physical properties obtained by introducing further polar groups between the ionising group and the hydrocarbon residue were less marked. The development of sulphated fatty condensation products such as the sulphated fatty monoglycerides appears to have been due rather to the fact that they offered a synthetic route from a very plentiful and economical starting material. It is interesting to note in this connection that the sulphated monoglycerides, although falling structurally within our definition of "condensation" products, are in fact prepared by partial saponification of an ester, or by alcoholysis of an ester with glycerol, rather than by condensing glycerol with a fatty acid—again for obvious economic reasons.

The sulphated fatty condensation products are the subject of a considerable patent literature, from which a number of interesting examples

---

[1] Du Pont, U.S.P. 2,021,100.

[2] Böhme, B.P. 358,535 and D.R.P. 736,400.

[3] See for example the description of the Colgate-Palmolive-Peet products in Schwartz and Perry's *Surface Active Agents*, Interscience, 1949, pp. 69 ff.

of amphipathic molecules can be selected. The examples which we give below fall naturally into four types, according to whether the intermediate group is based on an amide, an ether (or polyether), an ester, or an amine linkage.

Sulphated fatty condensation products containing amide linkages are illustrated by several I.G. proposals which at once recall the structure of "Igepon T," *viz.*,

$C_{17}H_{35} \cdot CONHCH_2 \cdot CH_2OSO_3Na$, and the analogous compound from oleic acid [1]

$C_{17}H_{31}(Cl_4)CONHCH_2 \cdot CH_2OSO_3Na$ [2]

$C_{17}H_{34}(Cl)CON(C_6H_5)CH_2 \cdot CH_2OSO_3Na$ [3]

These products were claimed to be good wetting-out, emulsifying, and scouring agents. Compounds of this type continue to be the subject of patent applications, for example

$$R \cdot CH \cdot CONHR',$$
$$\overset{|}{O}SO_3^-, \ M^+$$

where R is C_6–C_{10}, R' is C_8–C_{15}, and M is a metal ion.[4] Piggott[5] proposed the preparation of textile assistants which contain two sulphato groups in a molecule containing an amide linking group

$$\overset{\text{CH}_2\text{OSO}_3\text{Na}}{\underset{\text{CH}_2\text{OSO}_3\text{Na}}{C_{17}H_{35} \cdot CONH\overset{|}{C} \cdot CH_2OH}}$$

A variation on the above type of amide linkage occurs in two I.G. patents,[6] which proposed a number of urethane structures, such as

$$\overset{\text{OSO}_3\text{Na}}{C_{12}H_{25}OCONHCH_2 \cdot CH_2 \cdot \overset{|}{CH} \cdot CH_3}$$

Proposals for making sulphated fatty condensation products which are based on ether linkages of various types are more numerous. Thus the sulphation of the condensation products of aliphatic alcohols with ethylene oxide, to give products of the general formula $R[OC_2H_4]_nOSO_3Na$, in which n may vary considerably from unity upwards, has been described by the I.G.[7] If n is limited to unity, and R is a fairly short chain such as n-butyl, this type of molecule was claimed to be effective as a wetting-out agent for use in mercerising baths.[8]

---

[1] I.G., B.P. 386,966 and D.R.P. 633,334.

[2] I.G., B.P. 389,543.

[3] I.G., B.P. 390,840.

[4] Rohm and Haas, and de Benneville, U.S.P. 2,632,766.

[5] I.C.I., and Piggott, B.P. 414,403.

[6] I.G., D.R.P. 552,758 and F.P. 728,415.

[7] I G., B.P.'s 443,559; 443,631; 463,624; F.P. 714,029; D.R.P. 705,357.

[8] I.G., B.P. 377,678 and U.S.P. 1,897,741.

The sulphation of monoalkyl ethers of glycerol yields surface-active agents in which at least a portion of the molecules probably contain two sulphato groups. Thus Baldwin and Bunbury[1] prepared detergents by sulphating batyl, chimyl, and selachyl alcohols; the first of these has the formula

$$CH_3 \cdot [CH_2]_{17} OCH_2 \cdot \underset{\underset{OH}{|}}{CH} \cdot CH_2OH$$

A more recent proposal by Price and Dombrow[2] yields a similar structure, but one which contains only one sulphato group: thus in one example methallyl dodecyl ether was sulphated, presumably yielding the product

$$C_{12}H_{25} \cdot O \cdot CH_2 \cdot \underset{\underset{OSO_3H}{|}}{CH} \cdot CH_3$$

The same or a similar product was probably obtained by Hentrich, Kirstahler, and Schlegel,[3] who sulphated the secondary alcohols which were obtained by condensing fatty alcohols (*e.g.*, dodecyl alcohol) with halogeno-ketones (*e.g.* chloroacetone) and then reducing the keto group. An interesting variant on this type of structure, containing an alkylated aromatic hydrophobic group, has been proposed by the I.G.,[4] *viz.*,

Reference should also be made to a specification by Böhme,[5] in which the sulphation of glucosides such as lauryl glucoside was described, and to a proposal by the I.G.[6] to sulphate the condensation products from long-chain aliphatic aldehydes and glycerol, in order to obtain products such as

which was described as a wetting-out agent and detergent.

Long-chain aliphatic sulphates containing intermediate ester linkages are illustrated by the following proposed structures:

$$C_{15}H_{31} \cdot COOCH_2 \cdot CH_2OSO_3Na$$

[1] I.C.I., Baldwin, and Bunbury, B.P. 398,818.

[2] National Oil Products, Price, and Dombrow, B.P. 545,416.

[3] "Unichem" Chemikalien Handels, Hentrich, Kirstahler, and Schlegel, U.S.P. 2,320,181.

[4] I.G., U.S.P. 2,167,326. See also C. B. Brown, B.I.O.S. Final Report 418, "Textile Auxiliary Products—Manufacture I.G. Farbenindustrie, Hoechst," p. 23.

[5] Böhme, B.P. 405,195.

[6] I.G., B.P. 414,772 and F.P. 755,143.

and the sulphation products from glycerol monooleate, ethylene glycol monoricinoleate, and 1 : 3-butylene glycol palmitate;[1] this product recalls the structure of the sulphonated fatty condensation product "Igepon A." Other proposals include:

$$C_{17}H_{33} \cdot COOCH_2 \cdot CH_2OCH_2 \cdot CH_2OCH_2 \cdot CH_2OSO_3Na;\ [2]$$

and
$$C_{11}H_{25} \cdot COOCH_2 \cdot \underset{\underset{OSO_3Na}{|}}{CH} \cdot CH_3.\ [3]$$

The history of this type of surface-active agent, and the development of improved processes for preparing them, is discussed in Schwartz and Perry's book.[4]

It is worth noting that the use of amine linkages has been proposed in synthesising sulphated fatty condensation products, giving such structures as

$$CH_3 \cdot [CH_2]_3 \cdot \underset{\underset{C_2H_5}{|}}{CH} \cdot CH_2NHCH_2 \cdot CH_2OSO_3Na\ [5]$$

$$C_8H_{17} - \underset{\underset{CH_2 \cdot CH_2OSO_3Na.}{|}}{N} - C_8H_{17}\ [6]$$

It has been suggested by Colgate *et al.*[7] that surface-active agents can now be made efficiently by the reaction of sulphamic acid with hydroxyl-containing alkyl ethers, carboxylic acid esters, and alcohols, using amides as catalysts. In the absence of catalysts, the reaction is very slow; among suitable catalysts are stated to be urea, acetamide, dicyandiamide, and thiourea. The reaction is carried out by heating at 90°–150° c., with stirring, and is completed in ten minutes to two and a half hours. In a subsequent patent,[8] it is stated that excess sulphamic acid can be removed by adding compounds such as acetamide, which react with sulphamic acid but not with the sulphated products. Any acidic matter, which might cause trouble in subsequent applications, is thus eliminated.

Finally, mention should be made of an interesting reaction which has been used by Bert and Procofieff[9] for preparing alkyl sulphates. When an alkyl formate is reacted with chlorosulphonic acid in a neutral solvent, the product obtained is the corresponding alkyl sulphate. The reaction is believed to take place *via* the formation of the sulphated alkyl formate,

[1] I.G., B.P. 364,107.
[2] Procter and Gamble, B.P. 494,870.
[3] National Oil Products, B.P. 545,415.
[4] Schwartz and Perry, *loc. cit.*, pp. 69–72.
[5] I.G., B.P. 377,695 and F.P. 715,756.
[6] I.G., B.P. 512,022.
[7] Colgate–Palmolive–Peet, Malkenus, Ross, and Potter, U.S.P. 2,452,943.
[8] Colgate–Palmolive–Peet, Clark, and Malkenus, U.S.P. 2,493,444.
[9] S.A. d'Innovation Chimique, Bert, and Procofieff, U.S.P. 2,441,865.

which is unstable and rearranges to give the alkyl sulphate and carbon monoxide:

$$HCOOR + HOSO_2Cl \rightarrow HOSO_2COOR + HCl$$
$$\downarrow$$
$$HO_3SOR + CO$$

Heating during a sulphation generally has a deleterious effect, but in this case the reaction is carried out in an inert solvent such as carbon tetrachloride, under reflux, and high yields are reported. When the evolution of gas ceases, the solvent is distilled off, and the residue from the distillation is the acid alkyl sulphate; this is converted to the sodium or ammonium salt, for example, for use as a surface-active agent.

D. Sulphated fatty glycerides, acids, and esters: "Sulphonated oils"

The so-called "sulphonated oils" are predominantly sulphuric acid esters which are obtained by treating olive oil, castor oil, and a considerable number of other fatty glycerides with sulphating agents such as sulphuric or chlorosulphonic acids. Although they represent the oldest class of synthetic surface-active agent, we have not discussed them earlier in the present chapter because of the fact that most of them are very complex mixtures, the composition of which is not known with any certainty. The early history of these products has been fully dealt with by a number of authors[1] and need not concern us here.

The possible side reactions which may take place during the preparation of "sulphonated oils" have been summarised by Burton and Robertshaw. Although not all of these reactions will be involved in every case, it is worth noting them as a general background to the processes and patent proposals which are about to be described.

1. HYDROLYSIS OF A SULPHURIC ESTER TO A HYDROXY-FATTY ACID

A sulphuric ester which is formed by the addition of sulphuric acid to an unsaturated fatty acid

$$R_1{\cdot}CH : CH{\cdot}R_2{\cdot}COOH + H_2SO_4 \rightarrow R_1{\cdot}CH{\cdot}CH_2{\cdot}R_2{\cdot}COOH$$
$$OSO_3H$$

$$(I) \qquad\qquad\qquad (II)$$

may hydrolyse to the corresponding saturated hydroxy fatty acid:

$$R_1{\cdot}CH{\cdot}CH_2{\cdot}R_2{\cdot}COOH + H_2O \rightarrow R_1{\cdot}CH{\cdot}CH_2{\cdot}R_2{\cdot}COOH + H_2SO_4$$
$$OSO_3H \qquad\qquad\qquad\qquad OH$$

$$(II) \qquad\qquad\qquad\qquad (III)$$

---

[1] See for example Burton and Robertshaw, *Sulphated Oils and Allied Products*, Harvey, 1939, pp. 1–7.

The hydroxy fatty acid (III) may partially re-combine with sulphuric acid to give the sulphuric ester (II) if conditions alter suitably, or it may partially condense with the sulphuric ester to give a complex sulphuric ester (IV),

$$R_1 \cdot \underset{\underset{OSO_3H}{|}}{CH} \cdot CH_2 \cdot R_2 \cdot COO \cdot \underset{\underset{R_1}{|}}{CH} \cdot CH_2 \cdot R_2 \cdot COOH \quad (IV)$$

the sulphuric ester group of which may become hydrolysed:

$$R_1 \cdot \underset{\underset{OH}{|}}{CH} \cdot CH_2 \cdot R_2 \cdot COOCH \cdot CH_2 \cdot R_2 \cdot COOH \quad (V)$$
$$\underset{R_1}{}$$

The hydroxy fatty acid (III) may also react partially with the original unsaturated fatty acid (I):

$$R_1 \cdot CH : CH \cdot R_2 \cdot COOCH \cdot CH_2 \cdot R_2 \cdot COOH \quad (VI)$$
$$\underset{\underset{R_1}{|}}{}$$

Finally, still more complicated sulphuric esters may be formed, for example by the reactions between the hydroxy fatty acid (III) and the complex sulphuric ester (IV), to give a product

$$R_1 \cdot \underset{\underset{OSO_3H}{|}}{CH} \cdot CH_2 \cdot R_2 \cdot COOCH \cdot CH_2 \cdot R_2 \cdot COOCH \cdot CH_2 \cdot R_2 \cdot COOH \quad (VII)$$
$$\qquad\qquad\qquad R_1 \qquad\qquad\qquad R_1$$

Apart from our "effective agent" (II), the above scheme shows that at least five by-products may be formed by various side reactions. Three of these, (III), (V), and (VI), are not aliphatic sulphates at all, and will almost certainly be insoluble in hard water and acid media. The other two, (IV) and (VII), have a higher molecular weight than (II) and a different balance between hydrophobic and hydrophilic groups, though it is not possible to say *a priori* whether this is advantageous or disadvantageous for a particular application.

2. HYDROLYSIS OF A FATTY GLYCERIDE DURING SULPHATION

The sulphation of a fatty triglyceride such as castor oil may take place before, during, or after hydrolysis of the glyceride ester groups, depending upon the sulphation conditions. This means that, at least in theory, a considerable number of sulphuric esters are possible, ranging in molecular size from the sulphated triglyceride itself,

$$CH_2OCO[CH_2]_7 \cdot CH : CH \cdot CH_2 \cdot CH \underset{\diagdown OSO_3Na}{\overset{\diagup [CH_2]_5 \cdot CH_3}{}}$$

$$CHOCO[CH_2]_7 \cdot CH : CH \cdot CH_2 \cdot CH \underset{\diagdown OSO_3Na}{\overset{\diagup [CH_2]_5 \cdot CH_3}{}} \quad \begin{array}{c} (VIII) \\ \text{(theoretical fully sul-} \\ \text{phated, unhydrolysed} \\ \text{castor oil)} \end{array}$$

$$CH_2OCO[CH_2]_7 \cdot CH : CH \cdot CH_2 \cdot CH \underset{\diagdown OSO_3Na}{\overset{\diagup [CH_2]_5 \cdot CH_3}{}}$$

through sulphated mono- and di-glycerides, to the sulphated ricinoleic acids. These sulphuric esters would of course vary considerably in their ratios of hydrophilic to hydrophobic groups, and in their molecular weights; consequently their surface-active properties would be expected to vary.

3. FORMATION OF LACTONES, LACTIDES, AND ESTOLIDES

Single molecules of certain aliphatic hydroxy acids, in which the hydroxy and carboxy groups are suitably situated, may lose a molecule of water to give lactones:

$$R \cdot \underset{\underset{OH}{|}}{CH} \cdot CH_2 \cdot COOH \rightarrow R \cdot \underset{\underset{O \underline{\quad} CO}{| \quad \ |}}{CH \underline{\quad} CH_2} + H_2O$$

$$(IX)$$

or two molecules of a hydroxy acid may condense, with the loss of two molecules of water, to give a lactide

$$\begin{array}{c} R_1 \underline{\quad} CH \underline{\quad} CH_2 \underline{\quad} R_2 \underline{\quad} CO \\ O{\Large\diagup}{\Large\diagdown}O \quad (X) \\ OC \underline{\quad} R_2 \underline{\quad} CH_2 \underline{\quad} CH \underline{\quad} R_1 \end{array}$$

If two molecules of the same, or of two different hydroxy acids, condense with the loss of only one molecule of water, an estolide results:

$$R_1 \cdot \underset{\underset{OH}{|}}{CH} \cdot CH_2 \cdot R_2 \cdot COO \underset{\underset{R_3}{|}}{CH} \cdot CH_2 \cdot R_4 \cdot COOH \quad (XI)$$

or

$$R_3 \cdot \underset{\underset{OH}{|}}{CH} \cdot CH_2 \cdot R_4 \cdot COO \underset{\underset{R_1}{|}}{CH} \cdot CH_2 \cdot R_2 \cdot COOH \quad (XII)$$

and the possibility also exists that more complex estolides may be formed by the further elimination of water between carboxy and hydroxy groups in compounds such as (XI), and (XII), and the original aliphatic hydroxy acid.

It will be at once apparent that compounds such as (IX), (X), (XI), and (XII) will have very different properties from the sulphated product which we are nominally synthesising:

$$R_1 \cdot \underset{\underset{OSO_3Na}{|}}{CH} \cdot CH_2 \cdot R_2 \cdot COONa \quad (II)$$

Thus (IX) and (X) will not be water-soluble, though they may dissolve hydrotropically in an excess of (II) to give clear solutions. Although one would expect such hydrotropic mixtures to be less effective in general than the pure surface-active compound (II), it is probably unwise to assume that this will hold true in all cases. Thus we have seen in Chapter 3 (p. 82) that the presence of a small amount of dodecyl alcohol in sodium dodecyl sulphate, for example, gives a lower attainable surface tension than does the pure sulphated alcohol. There are moreover practical examples of the superiority of hydrotropic mixtures, for special purposes, to pure paraffin-chain salts (see Chapter 15). Surface-active species such as (XI) and (XII), as well as the still more complex estolides, will presumably form water-soluble salts, but these salts will almost certainly be unstable to hard water and acid solutions, and will have different amphipathic properties from the sulphate such as (II).

4. HIGHLY OXIDISED, POLYMERISED, OR CONDENSED PRODUCTS OF UN-KNOWN CONSTITUTION

These substances, which are probably macromolecular, are formed by reactions which are analogous to those taking place in the oxidation or "bodying" of unsaturated oils. They are probably often produced in sulphation processes, but it is not possible to estimate the extent or nature of the reactions involved, nor to predict with any certainty what effect their presence will have on the surface-active properties of the products. They are frequently removed, at least partly, during "working-up" operations after sulphation.

5. FORMATION OF TRUE SULPHONATES

Burton and Robertshaw list two possible reactions which may lead to the formation of true sulphonic acids:

$$R_1 \cdot CH : CH \cdot R_2 + H_2SO_4 \rightarrow R_1 \cdot \underset{OH}{CH} \cdot \underset{SO_3H}{CH} \cdot R_2$$

and

$$R_1 \cdot CH_2 \cdot CH : CH \cdot R_2 + H_2SO_4 \rightarrow R_1 \cdot \underset{SO_3H}{CH} \cdot CH : CH \cdot R_2 + H_2O$$

It is to be anticipated that the surface-active properties of an aliphatic sulphate would be much less affected by the presence of small amounts of the products of these two reactions than by the types of by-products listed in the preceding paragraphs.

It will be apparent from the above discussion that a number of reactions are possible when a fatty glyceride is treated with sulphuric acid or other sulphating agent. Thus sulphates will be formed by esterification of the hydroxyl groups in the triglyceride of ricinoleic acid, by addition to the double bond in unsaturated fatty glycerides, and by the esterification of partially saponified triglycerides, whether saturated or unsaturated. Water-insoluble or sparingly soluble by-products may also be formed, as well as simple soaps and carboxylic acids of high molecular weight. The net result is that only part of the material in the classical "sulphonated oils" such as Turkey Red Oil was genuinely sulphated or sulphonated, so that their surface-activity was not very great on modern standards, and they suffered from specific defects such as instability to hard water and dilute acids. It was these defects, which had been only partly overcome over a period of nearly ninety years, which led to the considerable amount of activity on the "highly sulphonated oils" between about 1923 and 1935. The result is that the modern descendants of the classical "sulphonated oils," such as "Prestabit Oil V" (Stockhausen) and "Calsolene Oil HS" (Imperial Chemical Industries) to name only two examples, are fundamentally different in their properties from the earlier products.

A useful account of the preparation of the sulphated vegetable and animal oils, with a historical introduction, typical recipes, descriptions of suitable apparatus, and a summary of the more important applications, is given by Lindner.[1] A good summary of the principal starting materials will also be found in Burton and Robertshaw's monograph.[2] More recently, Burton and Byrne have published a series of papers on the constitution of the sulphated oils. The composition of commercial ricinoleic acid, and the possible presence of lactones, lactides, estolides, and more highly condensed products, are discussed with reference to the reaction with sulphuric acid.[3] Under the conditions investigated, reaction occurs at the double bond as well as at the hydroxyl group. Considerable amounts of sulphonates are formed by reaction at the double bond, and this increases if the acid strength is increased from 25% to 40% by weight of concentrated sulphuric acid, and the temperature is increased from 30° to 50° c. Further papers on the sulphation of castor oil,[4] oleic acid,[5] and fish oils,[6] using the analytical techniques described in the earlier papers of the series, reveal the complications which can arise. These authors conclude that a considerable amount of hydrolysis occurs when the sulphation products of castor oil are washed. There is practically no formation of sulphonate if the castor oil is first acetylated and then treated with oleum, or if glacial acetic acid is used to dilute the castor oil before it is treated with chlorosulphonic acid. It appears to be fairly generally true that increasing the amount of sulphuric acid increases the amount of sulphonate formed in all these products, while in the case of the fish oils the degree of hydrolysis of the glycerides also increases markedly with increasing content of sulphuric acid.

The defects of the classical "sulphonated oils" were due to two main causes: a relatively low degree of sulphation, and the presence, even in the sulphated molecules themselves, of free carboxylic acid (or free neutralised carboxylate) groups. The low degree of sulphation is illustrated by the fact

---

[1] Lindner, *Textilhilfsmittel und Waschrohstoffe*, Wissenschaftliche Verlagsgesellschaft, Stuttgart, 1954, pp. 338–353.

[2] Burton and Robertshaw, *loc. cit.*, pp. 9–20.

[3] Burton and Byrne, *J. Soc. Leather Trades' Chem.*, 1952, **36**, 309.

[4] Burton and Byrne, *ibid.*, 1953, **37**, 243.

[5] Burton and Byrne, *ibid.*, 1953, **37**, 321.

[6] Burton and Byrne, *ibid.*, 1954, **38**, 10.

that the effective agent in a typical Turkey Red Oil, for example, will contain only three or four per cent of combined SO_3, whereas it is theoretically possible to sulphate castor oil to a much higher degree, as illustrated by the following examples:

(*i*) complete sulphation of the hydroxyl groups in the triglyceride, without hydrolysis, gives 19.4% SO_3 in the trisodium salt;

(*ii*) complete sulphation of the hydroxyl groups in ricinoleic acid, with complete elimination of all glycerol by hydrolysis, gives 19% SO_3 in the disodium salt;

(*iii*) complete sulphation of both the hydroxyl group and the double bond in ricinoleic acid, with elimination of all glycerol by hydrolysis, gives 29.5% SO_3 in the trisodium salt.

The low degrees of sulphation in the final products appear to be due both to a low efficiency of the initial sulphation, and to the occurrence of at least some of the side-reactions which we have already discussed.

The modern sulphated oils, on the other hand, are in general substantially more highly sulphated, and as a result they have in general a higher surface-activity (as regards wetting-out, emulsifying, and deflocculating power, for example). This higher degree of sulphation, and in certain cases the fact that the carboxylate group is blocked by esterification, means that in general they are also more stable to hard water and to dilute acids. The methods used to achieve these results are illustrated by the following selections from the extensive patent literature on the subject.

The addition of acid anhydrides or chlorides to sulphating agents, in order to obtain more highly sulphated hydroxy fatty acids, is the theme of a number of patents. In two early specifications, Böhme[1] claimed the use of organic acid anhydrides and chlorides, explaining that these function by taking up the water which is formed as the result of the sulphation reaction, which is stated to be reversible. In the example given, castor oil (100 kg.) is mixed with acetic anhydride (30 kg.), and then treated in the cold with 100 kg. of concentrated sulphuric acid "in the usual manner." The unused sulphuric and acetic acids can be removed by washing with water, after which the resulting "oil" may be neutralised. The patentees claimed, incidentally, that true sulphonation of methylene groups in the hydrocarbon chain also occurs to some extent as a result of the more vigorous sulphation conditions. In a later patent, Böhme[2] used a very similar recipe in which oleic acid takes the place of castor oil; they also claimed that the method can be applied to non-hydroxy unsaturated fatty acids in general, or to their esters with lower monohydric alcohols. Although the specification speaks throughout of "fatty sulphonic acids," it seems likely that the products are, in fact, chiefly sulphato compounds.

---

[1] Böhme, B.P. 261,385 and B.P. 263,117.
[2] Böhme, B.P. 298,559; see also U.S.P. 1,923,608.

The same general principle of removing the water formed during sulphation probably underlies a number of other proposals. Thus Rozenbroek[1] used oxides, chlorides, or oxychlorides of phosphorus in the "sulphonation" of castor oil with sulphuric acid, oleum, or chlorosulphonic acid, while St. Denis[2] used both acetic anhydride and aluminium chloride in oleum. Rülke[3] proposed acetonitrile as a water-removing agent. An interesting variation on this theme was the I.G. proposal to use acetyl sulphuric acid as a sulphating agent, for example with castor oil.[4] Presumably the liberation of water is avoided, or at any rate substantially diminished, as the result of using the sulphation reaction

$$ROH + CH_3COOSO_3H \rightarrow ROSO_3H + CH_3COOH$$

More specific catalysts for promoting sulphation have also been described in the patent literature. Erba[5] described the use for this purpose of compounds which "are capable of giving off active oxygen in acid solution," such as hydrogen peroxide, alkali and alkaline earth peroxides, alkali persulphates, percarbonates, benzoyl peroxide, *etc.* In the example a mixture of 3 kg. of 30% hydrogen peroxide, stabilised with phosphoric acid, and 100 kg. of castor oil are "sulphonated" with 25 kg. of 96–98% sulphuric acid for four hours at 70–80° c. The S.C.I.[6] claimed that a wide variety of substances containing hydroxyl groups (*e.g.*, shellac, colophony, and other natural resins, phenolformaldehyde condensation resins, castor oil, ricinoleic acid) can be more readily sulphated by the use of addition products of sulphur trioxide and organic bases such as pyridine or dimethylamine. Unlike so many of the patent specifications in this field, which confine themselves to qualitative observations on the improved properties of the products, this patent gives a definite figure for the degree of sulphation achieved in one example: it claims (Example 4) that the degree of sulphation of castor oil, using the addition products of pyridine and sulphur trioxide, is 85% of theory, compared with 25% for a typical Turkey Red Oil.

The use of a substantial excess of sulphuric acid as a means of increasing the degree of sulphation figures in a number of patents. Thus Böhme[7] diluted 100 kg. ricinoleic acid with 50 kg. benzene, cooled to −10° c., and then treated with 100 kg. sulphuric acid. Similarly, Stockhausen[8] recommended the use of a large excess of sulphuric acid at 10°–15° c. or lower, and

[1] Chemisch Fabriek "Servo," and Rozenbroek, B.P. 293,690.

[2] Société pour l'Industrie Chimique à St. Denis, F.P. 690,022 (*Chem. Zentr.*, 1931, vol. I, 710).

[3] Rülke, D.R.P. 548,189 (*Chem. Zentr.*, 1932, vol. II, 3514).

[4] I.G., B.P. 288,127; *cf.* F.P. 465,221 and D.R.P. 606,776.

[5] Erba, B.P. 292,574; *cf.* U.S.P. 1,804,183.

[6] S.C.I., B.P. 365,468.

[7] Böhme, B.P. 284,280; *cf.* U.S.P. 1,816,071.

[8] Chem. Fabrik Stockhausen, B.P. 293,717; *cf.* U.S.P. 1,849,209, F.P. 632,738, and D.R.P. 561,715.

suggested that the sulphation and isolation should both be carried out as quickly as possible, presumably in order to avoid hydrolysis of the sulphato groups and other side reactions. This principle is carried to the limit in Böhme's proposal to run the oil which is to be sulphated into an excess of sulphation medium: for example 100 kg. castor oil are added to 300 kg. concentrated sulphuric acid, the temperature being maintained throughout the process at 0° c. or lower.[1]

The possibility of obtaining more highly sulphated oils by mechanically removing unsulphated material has not been overlooked. Stockhausen[2] described the sulphation of castor oil in the presence of trichloroethylene, followed by a further addition of trichloroethylene after sulphation. It was claimed that an appreciable amount of unsulphated material is removed in the layer of trichloroethylene which separates after the product is washed. Alternatively, the addition of trichloroethylene may be postponed until after sulphation is complete. This idea is carried a step farther by Seltzer,[3] who proposed the use of a further quantity of sulphatable oil (preferably the oil which is itself being sulphated) as a solvent for the unsulphated material. The oily layer which is thus separated from the product is subsequently returned to the sulphation process and used again.

It is worth noting that the I.G.[4] claimed that true sulphonic acids are obtained if a solution of castor oil in trichloroethylene is treated with fuming sulphuric acid or chlorosulphonic acid.

Reference has already been made to the fact that the presence of a free carboxylic group in a product such as sodium ricinosulphate,

$$CH_3 \cdot [CH_2]_5 \cdot \underset{\underset{OSO_3Na}{|}}{CH} \cdot CH_2 \cdot CH : CH \cdot [CH_2]_7 \cdot COONa$$

has an adverse effect on the solubility of the product in hard water or in dilute acids. Esterification of this group with monohydric alcohols such as methanol, butanol, *etc.*, is therefore very commonly practised, and is described in a number of patent specifications. Böhme[5] claimed that improvements in wetting-out power are also obtained by esterifying either this group, or the sulphato group, or both, giving for example:

$$CH_3 \cdot [CH_2]_5 \cdot \underset{\underset{OSO_3Na}{|}}{CH} \cdot CH_2 \cdot CH : CH \cdot [CH_2]_7 \cdot COOR \qquad (I)$$

$$CH_3 \cdot [CH_2]_5 \cdot \underset{\underset{OSO_3R}{|}}{CH} \cdot CH_2 \cdot CH : CH \cdot [CH_2]_7 \cdot COONa \qquad (II)$$

or $\qquad CH_3 \cdot [CH_2]_5 \cdot \underset{\underset{OSO_3R}{|}}{CH} \cdot CH_2 \cdot CH : CH \cdot [CH_2]_7 \cdot COOR \qquad (III)$

[1] Böhme, D.R.P. 597,957 (*Chem. Zentr.*, 1934, vol. II, 1224).
[2] Chem. Fabrik Stockhausen, B.P. 293,480.
[3] Seltzer, B.P. 370,022.
[4] I.G., B.P. 296,999.
[5] Böhme, B.P. 313,160.

respectively, where R represents an alkyl group of unspecified size. The first of these three types of compounds would be expected to have better stability to hard water than sodium ricinosulphate itself, and both (I) and (II) might be superior wetting-out agents if the blocking of one ionising group gave a more favourable hydrophobe-hydrophile ratio. We find it hard to believe, however, that type (III) could be either water-soluble or strongly surface-active. The type of compound represented by (I) is further illustrated in two later Böhme patents,[1] which describe the sulphation, under a variety of conditions, of esters such as *n*-butyl ricinoleate, methyl-cyclohexyl ricinoleate, benzyl oleate, *n*-butyl 12-hydroxystearate, and isopropyl oleate. Esterification either before or after sulphation is exemplified. Advantages are claimed in the ease of sulphation, and the products are stated to be good wetting-out, emulsifying, and solubilising agents.

It is interesting to check the general picture provided by the two Böhme patents just mentioned against the recipe for sulphated butyl ricinoleate ("Avirol AH extra") in one of the B.I.O.S. reports.[2] According to this recipe, the butylation was done before sulphation, which was effected by slowly adding sulphuric acid to an equal weight of butyl ricinoleate at − 2° to 0° c.

The I.G. have also described a number of sulphated esters of hydroxy or unsaturated fatty acids, including for example the sulphato derivatives of ethyl oleate, methyl ricinoleate, and benzyl oleate, all of which were esterified after sulphation in order to avoid hydrolysis of the ester group,[3] and of butyl ricinoleate and isopropyl ricinoleate.[4] The good wetting-out properties of the products are again stressed.

A rather different proposal has been made by Hailwood and McGlynn,[5] who acetylated or benzoylated castor oil or ricinoleic acid and then treated with 20% oleum. Although it seems possible that the resulting neutralised products might have the type of structure represented by

$$CH_3 \cdot [CH_2]_5 \cdot \underset{\underset{OCOCH_3}{|}}{CH} \cdot CH_2 \cdot CH_2 \cdot \underset{\underset{OSO_3^-,\ Na^+}{|}}{CH} \cdot [CH_2]_7 \cdot COONa$$

the work of Grün[6] suggests that a sulphato group displaces the acetyl radical, rather than being formed by addition to the double bond.

The β-ethoxyethyl radical has been suggested by Böhme[7] for blocking the carboxy group by esterification: for example ricinoleic acid may be sulphated and then condensed with ethylene glycol monoethyl ether, or

    [1] Böhme, B.P. 315,832 and B.P. 350,425.
    [2] Baird, B.I.O.S. Final Report 1151, "Miscellaneous Surface-Active Agents and Related Intermediates," p. 6.
    [3] I.G., B.P. 343,989.
    [4] I.G., B.P. 344,828.
    [5] I.C.I., Hailwood, and McGlynn, B.P. 357,670.
    [6] Grün, *Ber.*, 1906, **39**, 4400.
    [7] Böhme, F.P. 705,710 (*Chem. Zentr.*, 1931, vol. II, 1355).

12-hydroxy stearic acid may be sulphated in the presence of the same alcohol, the former reaction presumably yielding

$$CH_3 \cdot [CH_2]_5 \cdot CH \cdot CH_2 \cdot CH : CH \cdot [CH_2]_7 \cdot COOCH_2 \cdot CH_2OCH_2 \cdot CH_3$$
$$\underset{\displaystyle OSO_3Na}{|}$$

Reference should also be made to a proposal by Böhme[1] to sulphate esters of dibasic fatty acids, for example the dibutyl ester of the dibasic hydroxy acid which is obtained by adding hydrocyanic acid to the double bond in ricinoleic acid and then saponifying the nitrile; the formula of the product is presumably

$$CH_3 \cdot [CH_2]_5 \cdot CH \cdot CH_2 \cdot CH_2 \cdot CH \cdot [CH_2]_7 \cdot COOC_4H_9$$
$$\underset{\displaystyle OSO_3^-, \ Na^+}{|} \qquad \underset{\displaystyle COOC_4H_9}{|}$$

The position of the hydrogen and of the —$COOC_4H_9$ group on the two possible carbon atoms is not certain, though this point is probably not of great importance.

Blocking of the carboxyl group by amidation has also been proposed, as in the I.G. product "Humectol CX," a sulphated mixture of oleic acid and oleyldiisobutylamide,

$$C_{17}H_{33}CON(C_4H_9)_2 \ ^2$$

One of the earliest and best known of the methods for improving the classical "sulphonated oils," especially as regards stability to hard water, was Stockhausen's proposal[3] to boil Turkey Red Oil with caustic solutions containing not less than 6% of sodium hydroxide. The resulting gelatinous products, which were developed as the "Monopol" soaps and oils, are distinguished from ordinary Turkey Red Oils by the fact that hydrolysis of the original triglyceride is complete, and that polymerisation also probably occurs. This type of product, which is discussed by Lindner,[4] has been the subject of a considerable amount of work. A further example of the same general idea is furnished by Schlotterbeck's proposal[5] to hydrolyse those sulphato groups in Turkey Red Oil, for example, which have been formed by addition to the double bonds, and then to "polymerise" the resulting product. (See in this connection the reactions arising from the hydrolysis of the sulphato group which have already been discussed.) It is interesting to note that the products obtained were claimed to be especially effective as hydrotropic agents.

---

[1] Böhme, B.P. 362,195.

[2] Baird, B.I.O.S. Final Report 239, "Textile Auxiliary Products, Manufactured by I.G. Farbenindustrie, Mainkur Works," p. 4.

[3] Chem. Fabrik Stockhausen, D.R.P. 113,433 (*Chem. Zentr.*, 1900, vol. II, 1220).

[4] Lindner, *loc. cit.*, pp. 346 ff.

[5] Schlotterbeck, D.R.P. 454,458 (*Chem. Zentr.*, 1928, vol. I, 2677).

E. Technical applications of the aliphatic sulphates

Many of the technical applications of the aliphatic sulphates have already been indicated in the present chapter. Thus the sulphated fatty alcohols, olefins, and fatty condensation products are practically without exception either detergents, or wetting-out agents, or both, the detergents being characterised on the whole by larger hydrocarbon residues than are the wetting-out agents. For the relatively dilute aqueous media involved in most of the relevant technological processes, wetting-out power first becomes really pronounced at about ten to twelve carbon atoms, but we have seen that much smaller hydrocarbon groups are preferable in concentrated electrolyte solutions such as mercerising baths. The good wetting-out and scouring properties of the higher aliphatic sulphates follow in part from their ability to reduce the surface tension of water, and the interfacial tensions between oils and aqueous solutions. These and other relevant physico-chemical properties are summarised or discussed elsewhere.[1]

Most of the newer "sulphonated oils" are also good wetting-out agents, but they are only of minor importance as detergents. They are however valuable emulsifying agents—usually for specific purposes, such as the preparation of emulsions of olein and other "textile oils,"[2] rather than for general use—and it will be recalled that their use in dyeing processes was the starting point of the original sulphated castor oils, for example.

In addition to these well-known applications, however, many other uses have been proposed for the aliphatic sulphates, and a few of these special applications merit a brief discussion. The deflocculating power of the alkyl sulphates for dispersed solid particles, especially in aqueous media, is the basis for several patent specifications. Thus Clapham and Hailwood[3] ground inorganic and organic pigments (*e.g.*, insoluble azo compounds, Prussian Blue, indigo) with sodium dodecyl, cetyl, oleyl, and octadecyl sulphates, claiming superior tinctorial power and improved dispersibility in aqueous and oil media and in rubber. Clarke and Bunbury[4] dispersed rubber and rubber-like substances by milling with aqueous solutions of the higher alkyl sulphates, while Geigy[5] dyed cellulose acetate in acidic aqueous dispersions of insoluble dyestuffs, stabilised with higher alkyl sulphates. Another example of the deflocculating power of the sulphated alcohols is furnished by Böhme's[6] proposal to improve the lustre of viscose fibres by adding an alkyl sulphate (in this case chosen from the range from hexyl to dodecyl) to the acid baths into which the cellulose xanthate is

[1] See for example the summary by Lederer, *Koll. Z.*, 1936, **75**, 236, and the paper by Robinson in *Wetting and Detergency*, Harvey, London, p. 137.

[2] Chwala, *Textilhilfsmittel*, Springer, Vienna, 1939, p. 207.

[3] I.C.I., Clapham, and Hailwood, B.P. 399,497.

[4] I.C.I., Clarke, and Bunbury, U.S.P. 2,033,276.

[5] Geigy, F.P. 748,439.

[6] Böhme, B.P. 449,792.

spun: the surface-active agent deflocculates the elementary sulphur which is formed in the bath and prevents it from being deposited on the fibre.

The highly sulphated oils also have marked deflocculating properties. In the well-known "pigment padding" process for applying vat dyestuffs to heavy fabrics and linen piece goods,[1] a very fine dispersion of the vat dyestuff in the insoluble (oxidised) form is applied to the cloth in such a way as to ensure a high degree of penetration; the dyestuff is subsequently "fixed" by reduction and re-oxidation. The success of the "padding" operation depends on having the dyestuff present in a very finely divided form, and on the presence of a highly sulphated oil which acts as a wetting-out agent (in what is a capillary penetration process), and as a powerful deflocculating agent which prevents coagulation of the suspension and adhesion of the dyestuff particles to the pores through which they enter the textile fabric.

Although the aliphatic sulphates are not precipitated by dilute acids, they are adsorbed by protein fibres, especially from acid media. This phenomenon is usually unfavourable to detergent action under these conditions, but it has been usefully exploited for at least two purposes. Thus the I.G.[2] used a highly sulphated castor oil, prepared according to the first example of their B.P. 288,127 (*q.v.*), to prevent the adsorption of acid wool dyestuffs by the silk in wool-silk combinations, the surface-active agent presumably competing with the dyestuff for the available sites in the silk. In another patent, Böhme[3] suggested carrying out the acid-felting of wool in the presence of a sulphated fatty alcohol such as sodium octadecyl sulphate. Although the specification does not elucidate the action of the sulphate, it seems likely that the octadecyl sulphate ions are adsorbed by virtue of salt linkages between their sulphato groups and the $-NH_3^+$ groups in the wool: the adsorbed ions are therefore orientated with their paraffin chains turned away from the fibre and towards the solution. The general effect of the adsorption is therefore probably to encourage adhesion between wool fibres rather than between fibre and water, while at the same time coating the fibres with a tenaciously adherent lubricating layer.

The addition of sulphated fatty alcohols to ordinary soaps, or to Turkey Red Oils, has been suggested or described in a number of patents.[4] The aim of the addition is usually to improve the stability of the soaps to hard water, sea water, or acid media. (It will be recalled that the alkyl sulphates themselves are not stable to prolonged treatment with hot acid solutions.) The improvement of the aliphatic sulphates themselves by means of suitable additions has also been proposed. Thus soluble cellulose derivatives

---

[1] Horsfall and Lawrie, *The Dyeing of Textile Fabrics*, 2nd, revised edition, Chapman and Hall, London, 1946, pp. 91, 405.

[2] I.G., B.P. 297,124.

[3] Böhme, B.P. 354,851.

[4] See, for example, Böhme, B.P. 361,565; F.P. 725,111; B.P. 379,534; Yamel, Ltd., B.P. 436,866.

have been added for improving their detergent power.[1] The addition of unsulphated saturated higher alcohols, normal or secondary, to higher normal alkyl sulphates has also been used as a method for improving the lathering and detergent power of the latter.

Reference has already been made to the use of the lower alkyl sulphates as wetting-out agents in mercerising baths. The highly sulphated oils have also been suggested for this purpose, usually in admixture with other substances, such as the higher alcohols,[2] phenols,[3] and mixtures of phenols with alkylated naphthalene sulphonates.[3] A number of commercial products appear to be based on this principle of mixing a sulphated oil with a phenolic body or an alcohol which is not highly water-soluble: it seems likely that some of the special additions render the sulphated oil more soluble by forming mixed micelles in the resulting solution. (See in this connection Chapter 15, pp. 493–494.)

Although they are perhaps not strictly surface-active agents, it is interesting to note the materials which have been made in attempts to prepare a synthetic anti-coagulant for blood, superior to the natural product heparin. Carbohydrates and carbohydrate derivatives have been sulphated in these attempts, but in general their toxicity is too high and their anti-coagulating effect is insufficient. Details of this work will be found in the yearly unit process reviews on sulphation and sulphonation by Gilbert and Jones.[4]

Finally, it is worth noting that the alkyl sulphates (*e.g.*, sodium dodecyl sulphate) have been used as surface-active agents in emulsion polymerisation processes.[5]

---

[1] Linhart, B.P. 488,291; *cf.* Brandner, Lockwood, Nagel, and Russell, F.I.A.T. Final Report No. 1141, "Synthetic Detergents and Related Surface Active Agents in Germany," p. 18.

[2] Böhme, B.P. 292,919.

[3] Böhme, B.P. 297,383.

[4] Gilbert and Jones, *Ind. Eng. Chem.*, Chemical Engineering Reviews, Unit Processes, 1951–1959.

[5] See, for example, Wingfoot Corporation, U.S.P. 2,386,661.

CHAPTER 12

OTHER ANIONIC SURFACE-ACTIVE AGENTS

ALTHOUGH the sulphonates and sulphuric acid esters are by far the most important synthetic anionic surface-active agents, it is necessary to discuss several other anionic types briefly, the most important being those in which a carboxylate group replaces the sulphato or sulphonate solubilising group. A detailed consideration of the ordinary soaps such as sodium stearate and sodium oleate is outside the scope of the present book, but no account of synthetic surface-active agents would be complete which omitted the carboxylic acids which have been specially synthesised, as well as a few other miscellaneous types. The most noteworthy property of these special carboxylic acids is the stability of their alkali-metal salts to hard water.

The most important of the synthetic surface-active carboxylates are the "Medialans" and "Lamepons." The former, the structures of which recall "Igepon T," are sarcosine derivatives of general formula

$$R \cdot CON(CH_3)CH_2 \cdot COO^-, M^+$$

in which M^+ is a simple ion such as Na^+, and $R \cdot CO$ is a group such as stearyl or oleyl. Their use as textile-treating agents generally (detergents, dyeing assistants, mercerising wetting-out agents, and sizing agents) was patented by the I.G. in 1931.[1] According to the information in one of the F.I.A.T. reports,[2] "Medialan A" was the sodium salt of oleyl sarcoside. It was described as a good detergent, of fairly good stability to hard water (up to 15° hardness on the German scale, which is equivalent to 270 parts per million of calcium carbonate), and it was claimed to be specially suitable for personal use because of its mild "feel" and of the fact that it did not remove fat from the skin to an excessive extent.

In the related "Lamepon" products, sarcosine is replaced by polypeptides which are obtained by degrading glue. According to Brandner, Lockwood, Nagel and Russell (loc. cit., p. 69), the polypeptide averages between three and six amino-acid groups in the molecule, and is acylated with the chloride of stearic or palm kernel fatty acids, for example. Owing to the facts that the polypeptides (and to a less extent the fatty acids) are mixtures, that considerable amounts of soaps are formed as by-products, and that an excess of polypeptide must be present in the reaction, the products are very complex mixtures, though they can be purified to some

---

[1] I.G., B.P. 360,982; cf. F.P. 720,278.

[2] Brandner, Lockwood, Nagel and Russell, F.I.A.T. Final Report 1141, "Synthetic Detergents and Related Surface-Active Agents in Germany."

extent by repeated fractional precipitation with mineral acids. The "Lamepons" are stated to be resistant to hard water, and to be lime-soap-dispersing agents, though they are precipitated by acids. The preparation of these fatty-acylated protein degradation products is the subject of a number of patent specifications.[1]

The earlier patents on the "Medialan" type of surface-active agents were followed by a series of specifications in which this and other methods of linking hydrophobic groups with carboxylic solubilising groups were explored. The following examples are selected from among the wide claims and disclosures of these patents, some of the structures being admittedly only probable ones:

$$H_2C \underset{CH_2-CH_2}{\overset{CH_2-CH_2}{\diagup}} CH \cdot CH_2 \cdot CH \underset{CH_2-CH_2}{\overset{CH_2-CH_2}{\diagup}} CH \cdot CH_2 \cdot COO^-, \; Na^+ \; [2]$$

$$C_4H_9 - \underset{}{\bigcirc} - [CH_2]_3 \cdot COO^-, \; Na^+ \; [3]$$

$$H_2C \underset{CH_2-CH_2}{\overset{CH_2-CH_2}{\diagup}} CH \cdot CH \underset{CH_2-CH_2}{\overset{CH_2-CH_2}{\diagup}} CH \cdot [CH_2]_3 \cdot COO^-, \; Na^+ \; [3]$$

$$(isobutyl)_3 \underset{}{\diagdown} \underset{}{\bigcirc} CH_2 \cdot CH_2 N(CH_3) CH_2 \cdot COO^-, \; Na^+ \; [4]$$

$$C_{10}H_{21} \cdot CH \underset{HNCH_2 \cdot CH_2 \cdot COO^-, \; Na^+ \; [5]}{\overset{COOCH_3}{\diagup}}$$

$$R \underset{}{\diagdown} \underset{}{\bigcirc} - CH_2 \cdot COO^-, \; Na^+$$

(where R represents a mixture of aliphatic groups[6]),

$$R - \underset{}{\bigcirc} - COO^-, \; Na^+$$

(in which R is dodecyl, etc.[7]),

---

[1] See for example I.G., B.P. 435,481 and 450,467; U.S.P. 2,041,265; Chem. Fabrik Grünau Landshoff and Meyer, B.P. 413,016.

[2] Henkel, B.P. 446,498 and F.P. 794,439.

[3] I.G., B.P. 449,865.

[4] I.G., B.P. 455,379.

[5] I.G., B.P. 456,142 and 461,328; cf. U.S.P. 2,108,725.

[6] I.G., B.P. 493,109; F.P. 835,554.

[7] I.G., B.P. 497,353; U.S.P. 2,195,198.

$$C_{14}H_{29}\!-\!\big\langle\ \big\rangle\!-\!OCH_2 \cdot CON(CH_3)CH_2 \cdot COO^-,\ Na^{+\,1}$$

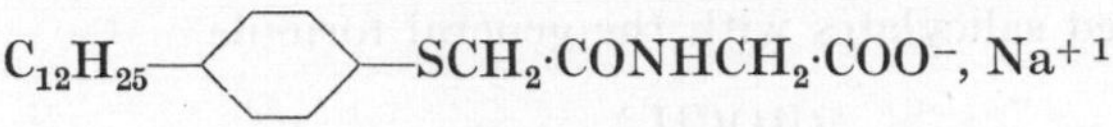

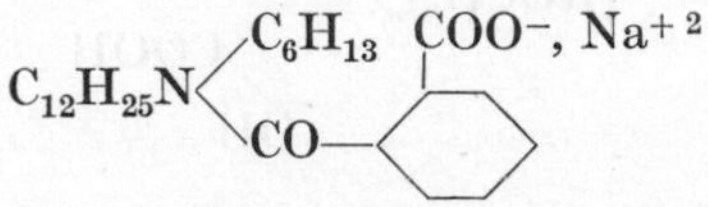

$$C_{12}H_{25}\!-\!\big\langle\ \big\rangle\!-\!SCH_2 \cdot CONHCH_2 \cdot COO^-,\ Na^{+\,1}$$

$$C_{12}H_{25}N\!\!\begin{array}{c} C_6H_{13} \quad COO^-,\ Na^{+\,2} \\[2pt] \big| \\[-2pt] CO\!-\!\big\langle\ \big\rangle \end{array}$$

$$CH_3 \cdot [CH_2]_3 \cdot \overset{C_2H_5}{\underset{\big|}{CH}} \cdot CH_2NCH_2 \cdot \overset{C_2H_5}{\underset{\big|}{CH}} \cdot [CH_2]_3 \cdot CH_3{}^2$$
$$COCH_2 \cdot CH_2 \cdot COO^-,\ K^+.$$

Substituted succinic acid structures have been described in a number of patent specifications. Examples are

$$C_{12}H_{25}O\overset{\big|}{CH} \cdot COOH{}^3$$
$$CH_2 \cdot COOH$$

and

$$R' \!-\! \overset{\big|}{CH} \cdot COOH$$
$$CH_2 \cdot COOH$$

in which R′ is an alkylene group such as hexadecylene.[4] A similar type of structure, but containing an amide linkage between the succinic acid residue and the hydrophobic grouping, was prepared by the I.G.[5] by the reaction between asparaginic acid and oleyl chloride, yielding

$$C_{17}H_{33} \cdot CON\overset{\big|}{H}CH \cdot COOH$$
$$CH_2 \cdot COOH$$

The same specification also describes the condensation product of imino-diacetic acid and oleyl chloride,

$$C_{17}H_{33} \cdot CON\!\!\begin{array}{c} CH_2 \cdot COOH \\ CH_2 \cdot COOH. \end{array}$$

Sandoz[6] have proposed a number of surface-active agents which combine the use of polyether and carboxylate solubilising groups, *e.g.*,

$$ROCH_2 \cdot CH_2OCH_2 \cdot COO^-,\ Na^+$$

and

$$ROCH_2 \cdot CH_2OCH_2 \cdot CH_2OCH_2 \cdot COO^-,\ Na^+$$

in which R may be butyl, isoamyl, or isooctyl, for example, as wetting-out agents in mercerising baths. The obvious conclusion is that solubility in

---

[1] I.G., B.P. 498,136; U.S.P. 2,215,365.
[2] I.G., B.P. 510,308.
[3] Monsanto and Kyrides, U.S.P. 2,377,246.
[4] Monsanto and Kyrides, U.S.P. 2,360,426.
[5] I.G., Hentrich, Keppler, and Hintzmann, D.R.P. 546,942.
[6] Sandoz, B.P. 523,549.

the strong caustic soda solutions involved is improved by the combination of both types of solubilising groups.

Substituted salicylates with the general formula

$$(ROCH_2)_n \underset{OH}{\overset{}{\bigcirc}} COOH$$

in which R is a hydrophobic group such as octadecyl, and n is one or two, have been patented by Geigy[1] as textile softening agents.

An interesting type of surface-active agent (exemplified by the products "Emulphor STH" and "Emulgator 2") was prepared by the I.G. by the reaction between paraffin-chain sulphonyl amides, which were obtainable from the sulphonyl chlorides of the Reed reaction (see Chapter 10, p. 362), and sodium chloroacetate. The principal ingredients present in these products would appear to have the general formulae

$$RSO_2NHCH_2 \cdot COO^-, \; Na^+$$

and
$$RSO_2N \begin{cases} CH_2 \cdot COO^-, \; Na^+ \\ CH_2 \cdot COO^-, \; Na^+ \end{cases}$$

in which R is the hydrophobic residue derived, according to Brandner, Lockwood, Nagel, and Russell (*loc. cit.*, pp. 35–36) from hydrogenated gas oils or Fischer-Tropsch oils, with smaller quantities of such compounds as

$$(RSO_2)_2NCH_2 \cdot COO^-, \; Na^+.$$

An interesting class of carboxylic acids, which are anionic analogues of the water-proofing agents such as "Velan" (*cf.* Chapter 13), has been prepared by Engelmann and Pikl of the du Pont Company.[2] These are illustrated by the condensation product of methylolstearamide and glycollic acid,

$$C_{17}H_{35} \cdot CONHCH_2OCH_2 \cdot COOH.$$

Among the special surface-active carboxylates which have been proposed are the following types:

$$R_1 \cdot CONH - \underset{\underset{SCH_2 \cdot COOH}{|}}{\overset{\overset{CH : CH \cdot CH_3}{|}}{CH}}$$

in which R_1 is a long paraffin chain, or a mixture of chain lengths such as that in technical stearic acid;[3] and the agents prepared by the reaction (in

---

[1] Geigy, B.P. 526,550 and U.S.P. 2,312,864.
[2] Du Pont, Engelmann, and Pikl, U.S.P. 2,313,741; B.P. 583,031.
[3] CIBA and Sallmann, U.S.P. 2,494,966.

the presence of a catalyst, such as benzoyl peroxide, which yields free radicals)

$$n\text{CH}_2 : \text{CH}_2 + \text{HR}_1\text{R}_2\text{C·COOH} \rightarrow \text{H}[\text{CH}_2\text{·CH}_2]_n\overset{\text{R}_1}{\underset{\text{R}_2}{\text{C·COOH}}}.$$

The reactant $\text{HR}_1\text{R}_2\text{C·COOH}$ may be an acid such as acetic, propionic, etc., up to the higher alkanoic acids such as myristic, or it may be a branched-chain alkanoic acid or a polybasic acid such as succinic, adipic, or sebacic.[1] Finally, mention may be made of the poly-condensed citrates, prepared by condensing three to thirty moles of citric acid,

$$\text{HOOC·CH}_2\text{·C(OH)(COOH)·CH}_2\text{·COOH},$$

with one mole of an aliphatic alcohol such as dodecyl alcohol.[2] These last-named agents are fairly clearly mixtures of different molecular weights, probably solubilised by the numerous ester as well as the free carboxylic acid groups.

A number of other types of anionic surface-active agents have also been proposed. The most important are probably the xanthates of general formula ROCSSH, the use of which as flotation agents is discussed in Chapter 9. The hydrophobic group in such agents is usually fairly small, but longer chains (*e.g.*, dodecyl) have been stated by Deutsche Hydrierwerke[3] to give compounds which are good wetting-out agents for textiles.

Other anionic groups containing sulphur atoms which have been proposed for solubilising surface-active agents include thiosulphuric acid esters, as in the compounds

$$\text{C}_{12}\text{H}_{25}\text{OCH}_2\text{SSO}_3{}^-, \text{Na}^+\ [4]$$

and $$\text{C}_{12}\text{H}_{25}\text{SCH}_2\text{·CH}_2\text{·SSO}_3{}^-, \text{Na}^+\ [5]$$

and persulphonates and persulphuric esters to which the following formulae have been assigned by their inventors:

$$\text{R·SO}_2\text{OO}^-, \text{Na}^+$$

in which R is octadecyl or amylnaphthyl, for example,[6] and

$$\text{C}_{16}\text{H}_{33}\text{O·SO}_2\text{·OO·SO}_2\text{O}^-, \text{Na}^+\ [7]$$

---

[1] Du Pont, B.P. 605,848.
[2] Du Pont and Werntz, U.S.P. 2,473,460.
[3] Deutsche Hydrierwerke, B.P. 369,978.
[4] Deutsche Hydrierwerke, B.P. 390,416; *cf.* U.S.P. 2,012,073 and F.P. 742,897.
[5] Henkel, B.P. 417,930.
[6] Farb- und Gerbstoffwerke Carl Flesch, D.R.P. 561,521 and F.P. 726,140.
[7] Du Pont and Fox, U.S.P. 2,315,514.

These "per" salts are stated to have bleaching and disinfecting properties as well as being wetting-out, emulsifying, and scouring agents.

Sulphinates of general formula RSO_2Na, in which R represents an aliphatic group present in the Reed reaction products, have been made by Fox[1] by reducing the corresponding sulphonyl chlorides.

Salts of phosphoric acid esters have also been patented as surface-active agents. Thus Böhme[2] described the phosphation of ricinoleic and oleic acids by analogy with the sulphation process, though without attempting to give any exact formulae. The I.G.[3] have described similar phosphated oils, and also compounds such as mono- and di-cetyl phosphates:

$$C_{16}H_{33}OPO(OH)_2^{--}, 2Na^+$$

and

$$\begin{array}{c} C_{16}H_{33}O \\ C_{16}H_{33}O \end{array} \!\! \overset{-}{P} \!\! \begin{array}{c} O \\ OH, Na^+ \end{array}$$

I.C.I.[4] have patented similar compounds derived from *p-tert*. octylphenol, such as

$$C_8H_{17}-\!\!\!\bigcirc\!\!\!-O \underset{C_2H_5\cdot O}{\overset{}{\searrow}} P \underset{O^-, Na^+}{\overset{O}{\diagup}}$$

These alkylphenyl phosphates are stated to be good oil-soluble emulsifying agents and (like the alkyl phosphates in general) to be effective anti-corrosive agents, especially in the presence of oils. (This last effect is probably due to the fact that many alkyl phosphates increase the work of adhesion of oils to metals.)

The use of esters (*e.g.*, octadecenyl) of polymerised metaphosphoric acids of general formula $(HPO_3)n$, in which n lies between three and twelve, has been claimed by Benckiser.[5] Finally, mention should be made of the agents prepared by Standard Oil Development Company,[6] such as sodium di(tertiaryamylphenyl)phosphate and other phosphates from alkylated phenols.

A type of surface-active agent which has aroused considerable interest in recent years is based on *perfluoro* hydrophobic groups, in which the hydrogen atoms in an aliphatic hydrocarbon radical are replaced by fluorine atoms. As Scholberg, Guenthner, and Coon[7] have pointed out, the parent perfluoro hydrocarbons themselves are characterised by having very low surface free energies, so that the radicals derived from them, when combined with suitable solubilising groups, give powerfully surface-active

[1] Du Pont and Fox, U.S.P. 2,315,514.
[2] Böhme, B.P. 281,232; *cf.* U.S.P. 1,900,973.
[3] I.G., B.P. 354,300 and B.P. 388,485; *cf.* U.S.P. 1,914,331.
[4] I.C.I., Zenftman, and Whitworth, B.P. 699,080 and B.P. 709,628.
[5] Chem. Fabrik J.A. Benckiser, B.P. 492,350; *cf.* F.P. 819,918.
[6] Standard Oil Development, B.P. 533,327.
[7] Scholberg, Guenthner, and Coon, *J. Phys. Chem.*, 1953, **57**, 923.

compounds. The more strongly hydrophobic properties of the perfluoro radicals is illustrated by the fact that considerably shorter chains (C_5–C_9) are equivalent in effect to C_{12} to C_{18} hydrocarbon chains. These authors, and Klevens and Raison,[1] have found that the C_5–C_9 perfluoroalkanoic acids give the usual shape of curve for surface tension of aqueous solutions against the logarithm of the concentration, with a break at the critical micelle concentration. The critical micelle concentrations for this series range from 0·1 to 0·001 molar. Scholberg, Guenthner and Coon conclude that the films formed are of the gaseous type, which explains why these particular agents are good wetting-out agents but poor emulsifiers.

The preparation of perfluorocarboxylic acids has been described by Kauck and Diesslin.[2] Perfluorosulphonic acids, *e.g.*, perfluoro-*n*-hexane sulphonic acid, have also been described,[3] as well as incompletely fluorinated alkanoic acids such as $CF_3 \cdot [CH_2]_{16} \cdot COOH$. [4]

Hydrophobic radicals of low surface free energy have also been derived from silicon (*cf.* Chapter 5, p. 244), such as

$$(CH_3)_3 \, Si—O—\underset{\underset{CH_3}{|}}{\overset{\overset{CH_3}{|}}{Si}}—CH_2—S—CH_2 \cdot COOH$$

and $(C_2H_5)_3 \, Si \, [CH_2]_n COOH$, where *n* lies between 6 and 10.[5]

In conclusion, reference should be made to the synthetic water-softening ("calcium-sequestering") agents, even though they are perhaps not, strictly speaking, surface-active agents. Their chemistry and applications have been reviewed in articles by Bird[6] and by Summersgill,[7] and more recently in the monographs by Smith[8] and by Chaberek and Martell.[9]

Sequestering agents are used for a wide, and increasing, variety of purposes in which it is desired to suppress the activity of metal ions such as Ca^{++}, Mg^{++}, Cu^{++}, or Fe^{+++}, in aqueous solutions, without forming a precipitate. The best-known of these products, and the most interesting from our point of view, is the sodium salt of ethylenediamine-tetracetic acid

$$\begin{matrix} HOOC \cdot CH_2 \diagdown & & \diagup CH_2 \cdot COOH \\ & NCH_2 \cdot CH_2 N & \\ HOOC \cdot CH_2 \diagup & & \diagdown CH_2 \cdot COOH \end{matrix}$$

[1] Klevens and Raison, *J. chim. phys.*, 1954, **51**, 1.

[2] Kauck and Diesslin, *Ind. Eng. Chem.*, 1951, **43**, 2332.

[3] Minnesota Mining and Manufacturing Co., Brice, and Trott, U.S.P. 2,732,398.

[4] Gavlin and Maguire, U.S.P. 2,827,471.

[5] Schwarz, Perry, and Berch, *Surface Active Agents and Detergents*, **II**, Interscience, 1958, p. 148.

[6] Bird, *J. Soc. Dyers Colourists*, 1940, **56**, 473.

[7] Summersgill, *ibid.*, 1954, **70**, 28.

[8] Smith, *The Sequestration of Metals*, Chapman and Hall, 1959.

[9] Chaberek and Martell, *Organic Sequestering Agents*, Wiley, 1959.

This agent is used in scouring or dyeing baths, for example, to sequester calcium, barium, magnesium, ferric, and other metal ions, which it can do not only from their water-soluble salts, but also by a reversible double decomposition with insoluble or sparingly soluble metal soaps and other salts:

$$Ca(RCOO)_2 + Na_4X \rightleftharpoons 2RCOONa + Na_2CaX,$$

where R is an alkyl group such as $C_{15}H_{31}$, and X is the ethylenediamine-tetraacetate radical. Although the complex ion CaX^{--} has a much lower dissociation constant than $Ca(RCOO)_2$, it is soluble in water, so that in effect the "lime soap" spontaneously dissolves (if given time) in the solution of sequestering agent. This action is therefore different from that of the "lime soap dispersing agents" such as "Igepon T" and "Lissapol LS," which act as peptising agents and protective colloids, and is due to the formation of a metal chelate, such as

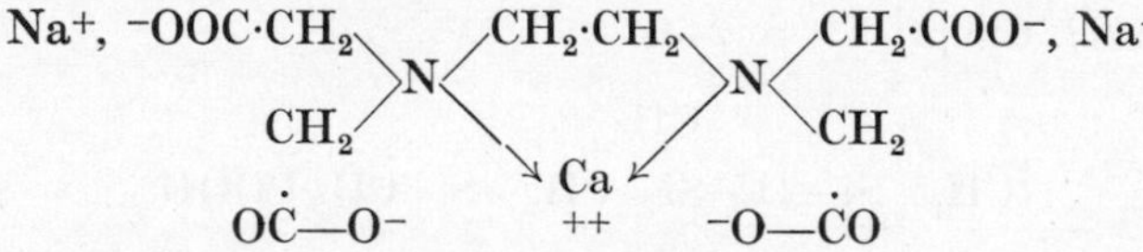

in which the metal ion is held by co-ordinate bonds to the nitrogen atom as well as by salt linkages with the carboxylic groups.

Although the ethylenediamine-tetraacetates are the most widely used of these sequestering agents, the simpler nitrilotriacetic acid ("Trilon A")

$$N[CH_2{\cdot}COOH]_3$$

and its sodium salts have also been made, and other, more complicated proposals in the patent literature include[1]

$$Na^+, {}^-OOC{\cdot}[CH_2]_{10}{-}\underset{\displaystyle CH_2{\cdot}COO^-, Na^+}{N}{-}[CH_2]_2{-}\underset{\displaystyle CH_2{\cdot}COO^-, Na^+}{N}{-}[CH_2]_{10}{\cdot}COO^-, Na^+$$

and the compound[2]

$$\left[\begin{matrix} Na^+, {}^-OOC{\cdot}CH_2 \\ Na^+, {}^-OOC{\cdot}CH_2 \end{matrix}\Big\rangle N{-}CH_2{\cdot}CH_2{-}\right]_3 N$$

[1] Bersworth, U.S.P. 2,530,147.

[2] Monsanto and Worrall, U.S.P. 2,683,740.

CHAPTER 13

CATIONIC SURFACE-ACTIVE AGENTS

A. Introduction

CATIONIC surface-active agents, like the anionic types which have been discussed in the preceding chapters, contain hydrophilic groups which are capable of ionisation in aqueous media. The two classes differ in that, when ionisation occurs, the amphipathic properties of a cationic surface-active compound reside in the cation, as in the classical example of cetyltriethylammonium iodide,[1]

$$C_{16}H_{33}(C_2H_5)_3NI \rightleftarrows C_{16}H_{33}(C_2H_5)_3N^+ + I^-$$

Cationic agents cover a wide variety of structures, but they can be quite simply classified according to the nature of the ionising group. Compounds such as cetyltriethylammonium iodide, cetylpyridinium bromide, or stearamidomethylpyridinium chloride, for example, are all salts of strong quaternary bases, the ionogenic group having the general electronic configuration

$$\begin{bmatrix} & R_2 & \\ & \ddot{} & \\ R_1 : & N : & R_3 \\ & \ddot{} & \\ & R_4 & \end{bmatrix}^+$$

in which each of the four linkages $N—R_1$, $N—R_2$, etc., represents a covalent nitrogen-carbon bond; *i.e.*, none of the groups $R_1 \ldots R_4$ is a hydrogen atom. The pyridinium, quinolinium, piperidinium, and other quaternary salts derived from heterocyclic bases represent a special case of this grouping, in which three of the N—R bonds are shared between the two carbon atoms in the ring system, or between these two carbon atoms and a group outside the ring. Although many of these quaternary ammonium compounds are decomposed by heat treatment or by treatment with hot alkaline solutions, they can nevertheless exist in alkaline media, a point which is of considerable practical importance. The same is true of the ternary sulphonium and quaternary phosphonium groups,

$$\begin{bmatrix} & R_2 & \\ & \ddot{} & \\ R_1 : & S : & R_3 \\ & \ddot{} & \end{bmatrix}^+ \quad \text{and} \quad \begin{bmatrix} & R_2 & \\ & \ddot{} & \\ R_1 : & P : & R_3 \\ & \ddot{} & \\ & R_4 & \end{bmatrix}^+$$

---

[1] Reychler, *Bull. Soc. Chim. Belgique*, 1913, **27**, 217.

respectively, but not of the amine salts, such as the acetates or hydro-chlorides of octadecylamine or N-oleyl-N':N'-diethylethylenediamine,

$$C_{17}H_{33}CONHCH_2 \cdot CH_2N(C_2H_5)_2$$

The cationic properties of these amine salts is due to the grouping

$$R_1 : \overset{\overset{R_2}{\cdot\cdot}}{\underset{\underset{R_3}{\cdot\cdot}}{N}} : H^+$$

in which up to two of the R groups may be hydrogen atoms, while the proton is held by a co-ordinate bond. Although the basicity of such a group may be increased by suitable substitution at R_1, R_2, or R_3, it will not be so strongly basic as the corresponding quaternary ammonium group, for example.[1] In alkaline solutions, the amine salt group will lose its proton and hence its cationic properties, reverting to the unionised form

$$R_1 : \overset{\overset{R_2}{\cdot\cdot}}{\underset{\underset{R_3}{\cdot\cdot}}{N}} :$$

It is probably true to say that for many years the cationic surface-active agents were regarded as scientific curiosities, though Reychler (*loc. cit.*) had drawn attention to their similarity to the soaps, and to their detergent power, in 1913. Their wide-spread industrial use probably dates from the discovery of their property of fixing substantive dyestuffs (*cf.* Chapter 9) and of softening textile fabrics ("Sapamines," "Fixanol," etc.). The expectations that they would prove to be useful as detergents and wetting-out agents does not seem to have been fulfilled, except in special cases. This failure is often attributed to an antagonism between the negative electrokinetic potentials which textile fibres and most other solids tend to acquire in contact with aqueous media, and the positive electrokinetic potentials which cationic surface-active agents usually impart to such interfaces. It would perhaps be more correct to say that cationic surface-active agents tend to be adsorbed more strongly, especially by solids, than are anionic and non-ionic agents, and that this adsorption often occurs with reversed orientation, *i.e.*, with the hydrophobic groupings orientated towards the aqueous medium. This phenomenon, which renders the surface of a solid more hydrophobic, will generally be antagonistic to wetting-out and detergent processes, but it is favourable to and appears to play an important part in such applications of cationic surface-active agents as water-proofing, flotation, rendering the surfaces of pigment particles

---

[1] *Cf.* Sidgwick, *The Organic Chemistry of Nitrogen*, Oxford University Press, 1937–1942, p. 27 ff.

hydrophobic, or in bactericidal action. Other more specialised applications of the cationic agents are given at the end of the present chapter.

The states of solution of several of the simpler cationic surface-active agents such as cetylpyridinium bromide, cetyltrimethylammonium bromide, and the salts of the long-chain alkyl amines, have been extensively studied (*cf.* Chapter 2). In these properties, and in their non-specific adsorption at air-water interfaces, for example, they are typical amphipathic compounds and are not markedly different from the analogous anionic surface-active agents.

B. Amine salts

Salts of long-chain primary alkyl amines, such as the hydrochlorides or acetates of octadecylamine, dodecylamine, etc., are markedly surface-active, and can be used as emulsifying, deflocculating, wetting-out, and scouring agents in acid media, as flotation agents (*cf.* Chapter 9), and for making the surfaces of pigment particles hydrophobic.[1] In general, however, they are less useful technically than either the secondary or tertiary amines or the quaternary ammonium salts.

Among the first of the commercially developed cationic agents were the "Sapamines" of the Society of Chemical Industry in Basle, illustrated by the acetate and the hydrochloride of N-oleyl-N′ : N′-diethylethylene-diamine. The parent specification[2] also describes other agents derived from fatty acids and ethylene diamine, such as salts of the primary amine *as.*-distearylethylenediamine,

$$\begin{array}{c} C_{17}H_{35}\cdot CO \\ \diagdown \\ C_{17}H_{35}\cdot CO \diagup \end{array} NCH_2\cdot CH_2NH_2$$

The use of this type of agent for fixing direct cotton colours,[3] and as assistants in dyeing with the sulphuric acid esters of leuco vat dyestuffs[4] were described in later patent specifications, and a general account of their behaviour as cationic surface-active agents was published by Hartmann and Kägi[5] in 1928.

Another class of surface-active amine salts which were developed relatively early and are still technically important are the fatty *esters* of primary, secondary, and tertiary hydroxyalkyl amines. The I.G.,[6] for example, claimed the esterification of alkyl amines containing not less than two hydroxyl groups (*e.g.*, triethanolamine or the condensation products of

---

[1] See for example du Pont, B.P. 499,334.
[2] S.C.I., B.P. 219,304.
[3] S.C.I., B.P. 366,918.
[4] Durand and Huguenin, B.P. 334,508.
[5] Hartmann and Kägi, *Z. angew. Chem.*, 1928, **41**, 127.
[6] I.G., B.P. 306,116; *cf.* F.P. 669,517.

ethylenediamine with ethylene oxide) with fatty acids such as stearic or oleic acids, by heating the materials together at 150° c. or above.* The structures which can result from this proposal are illustrated by the following:

$$C_{17}H_{35}\cdot COOCH_2\cdot CH_2N(CH_2\cdot CH_2OH)_2$$
$$(C_{17}H_{35}\cdot COOCH_2\cdot CH_2)_3N$$

the salts of which are used as wetting-out agents in acid baths for dyeing and treating textiles. "Emulphor FM," the monooleate of triethanolamine,[1] belongs to this type of agent. A later patent[2] also deals with this type of structure, describing fatty acid esters of monohydroxyalkyl amines, derived for example from stearic acid and monoethanolamine, and from oleic acid and 2-hydroxyethyldimethylamine:

$$C_{17}H_{35}\cdot COOCH_2\cdot CH_2NH_2$$
$$C_{17}H_{33}\cdot COOCH_2\cdot CH_2N(CH_3)_2$$

The S.C.I. have pointed out[3] that the reaction between monoethanolamine and stearic acid, for example, normally gives the amide, but that the latter can be converted to the salt of the ester amine by treatment with an aqueous solution of an acid, *e.g.*,

$$C_{17}H_{35}\cdot CONHCH_2\cdot CH_2OH + HCOOH$$
$$\rightarrow C_{17}H_{35}\cdot COOCH_2\cdot CH_2\overset{+}{N}H_3,\ HCOO^-$$

An interesting proposal for joining alkyl chains to amine groups by means of ester linkages comes from the American Cyanamid Company,[4] who claim that the hydrochloride of diamyl-N-(2-hydroxyethyl) aspartate

$$CH_3$$
$$CH_3\cdot CH_2\cdot \overset{|}{C}H\cdot CH_2OOC\cdot \overset{|}{C}HNHCH_2\cdot CH_2OH$$
$$CH_3\cdot CH_2\cdot \overset{|}{C}H\cdot CH_2OOC\cdot \overset{|}{C}H_2$$
$$\overset{|}{C}H_3$$

is a good wetting-out agent.

Long-chain aliphatic amine derivatives have also been described in

---

* An earlier British patent of the du Pont Company (B.P. 295,024) describes the mixing of fatty acids with hydroxyamines. It is not stated clearly, however, that the mixture is heated to a temperature at which esterification occurs, and our own interpretation of this specification is that it refers to hydroxyalkyl amine *salts* of fatty acids, such as triethanolamine stearate,

$$C_{17}H_{35}\cdot COO^-,\ H^+N(CH_2\cdot CH_2OH)_3$$

[1] Brandner, Lockwood, Nagel, and Russell, F.I.A.T. Final Report No. 1141, "Synthetic Detergents and Related Surface-Active Agents in Germany."

[2] I.G., B.P. 337,737.

[3] S.C.I., B.P. 581,325. See also Phillips and Baltzly, *J. Amer. Chem. Soc.*, 1947, **69**, 200.

[4] American Cyanamid, B.P. 553,166.

which the ester linkage has been avoided. The I.G.,[1] for example, have described the acetates of N-octadecyl-N-hydroxyethylamine

$$C_{18}H_{37}NHCH_2 \cdot CH_2OH$$

which was stated to be a good softening agent for viscose rayon, and of the mixed tertiary amines of general formula

$$CH_2 \Big\langle {{CH_2 - CH_2} \atop {CH_2 - CH_2}} \Big\rangle CHN \Big\langle {R \atop C_3H_6OH}$$

in which R represents the mixture of alkyl radicals derived from coconut oil, which was claimed to be a good wetting-out agent. I.C.I., Piggott, and Statham[2] describe the salts of the addition products of fatty amides with ethylene imine, *e.g.*, stearylethylenediamine

$$C_{17}H_{35} \cdot CONHCH_2 \cdot CH_2NH_2$$

while American Cyanamid[3] have claimed the fatty amides of polyethylene polyamines, such as

$$R \cdot CONH[CH_2 \cdot CH_2NH]_n CH_2 \cdot CH_2NHOC \cdot CH_3$$

in which R is the mixed alkyl radicals from palm oil or cottonseed oil, and the polyethylene polyamine is a mixture of approximately 50% diethylene-triamine, 25% triethylenetetramine, and 25% tetraethylenepentamine.

A number of amine salts containing cyclic structures have been proposed as surface-active agents. The S.C.I., for example, have described two types containing the benziminazole structure, exemplified by mono-methylated μ-heptadecylbenziminazole[4] (hydrochloride),

$$C_{17}H_{35} \cdot C \Big\langle {{N} \atop {N}} \Big\rangle {\underset{CH_3}{|}}$$

and N-substituted benziminazoles[5] such as the hydrochlorides of

$$\Big\langle {{N} \atop {N}} \Big\rangle C \cdot CH_3 \atop C_{12}H_{25} \quad \text{and} \quad \Big\langle {{N} \atop {N}} \Big\rangle {{C \cdot CH_3} \atop {CH_2 \cdot CON(CH_3)C_{12}H_{25}}}$$

[1] I.G., B.P. 372,325.
[2] I.C.I., Piggott, and Statham, B.P. 475,095; *cf.* U.S.P. 2,163,807 and F.P. 821,604.
[3] American Cyanamid, B.P. 571,591.
[4] S.C.I., B.P. 419,010.
[5] S.C.I., B.P. 439,261; *cf.* U.S.P. 2,053,822 and 2,056,449.

The use of the products of B.P. 439,261 as dyeing assistants is described in another patent of the S.C.I.[1] Waldmann and Chwala[2] have described the C-substituted iminazolines, such as the hydrochloride of

$$C_{11}H_{23}{\cdot}C \underset{\diagdown N-\!\!-\!\!-CH_2}{\overset{\diagup NH-\!\!-\!\!CH_2}{<}}$$

Mention should also be made of the di-substituted analogues, such as

$$\begin{array}{c} C_{17}H_{33}{\cdot}C{\diagup}{\overset{N}{}}{\diagdown}CH_2 \\ H_2NCH_2{\cdot}CH_2N\!\!-\!\!-\!\!-\!\!-CH_2 \end{array}$$

which have been patented by Carbide and Carbon Chemicals Corporation, Wilson, and Wilkes.[3] This compound, which is derived from oleic acid and diethylenetriamine, is dissolved in mineral oils in order to prepare self-emulsifiable oils (*cf.* Chapter 6, p. 251).

A class of amine salts which have been patented as durable water-proofing agents (*cf.* Chapter 5, p. 241, and also Section C—2 of the present chapter) is derived from the isothiourea structure

$$-S-C \underset{\diagdown NH_2}{\overset{\diagup NH}{<}}$$

by substitution of the reactive hydrogen which is attached to the sulphur atom. Thus the I.G.[4] reacted thiourea with methylolstearamide in hydrochloric acid, to obtain what are presumably salts of the base

$$C_{17}H_{35}{\cdot}CONHCH_2SC \underset{\diagdown NH_2}{\overset{\diagup NH}{<}}$$

The S.C.I. have extended this principle in a series of patents[5] which describe a number of compounds which are used as durable water-proofing agents, such as the example just mentioned, and salts of other types such as

$$C_{17}H_{35}{\cdot}COOCH_2SC \underset{\diagdown NH_2}{\overset{\diagup NH}{<}}$$

$$C_{11}H_{23}SCH_2SC \underset{\diagdown NH_2}{\overset{\diagup NH}{<}}$$

---

[1] S.C.I., B.P. 439,890.
[2] Waldmann and Chwala, B.P. 479,491.
[3] Carbide and Carbon, Wilson, and Wilkes, B.P. 524,847.
[4] I.G., B.P. 511,144.
[5] See for example S.C.I., B.P. 527,008 and 527,012; U.S.P. 2,302,762; 2,331,387; 2,345,109.

Like the other durable water-proofing agents, these compounds are all decomposed by heat on the fabric, though the chemistry of the decomposition processes has not been studied to the same extent as that of the processes for water-proofing with "Velan," which are described in Chapter 5.

A series of compounds based on isothiourea and isourea, which are probably to be regarded more as dyestuff-fixing agents, wetting-out agents, etc., than as water-proofing agents, were described by Hunsdiecker and Vogt in an earlier series of patent specifications.[1] These included for example S-dodecylthiourea and O-dodecylurea hydrochlorides

$$C_{12}H_{25}SC\overset{NH}{\underset{NH_2}{\Big\langle}} \cdot HCl \quad \text{and} \quad C_{12}H_{25}OC\overset{NH}{\underset{NH_2}{\Big\langle}} \cdot HCl$$

dodecyloxyethylthiourea acetate

$$C_{12}H_{25}OCH_2 \cdot CH_2SC\overset{NH}{\underset{NH_2}{\Big\langle}} \cdot HOOC \cdot CH_3$$

and the lauric acid ester of S-hydroxyethylthiourea acetate

$$C_{11}H_{23} \cdot COOCH_2 \cdot CH_2SC\overset{NH}{\underset{NH_2}{\Big\langle}} \cdot HOOC \cdot CH_3$$

C. Quaternary ammonium compounds

The literature of the quaternary ammonium surface-active agents, which is chiefly in the form of patent specifications, is very extensive, and it is possible to give only typical examples of the chemical structures which have been used or suggested. We propose for the sake of convenience to classify these examples into three general groups: (*i*) tetrasubstituted ammonium compounds in which four separate groups are attached by C–N bonds to the nitrogen atom, (*ii*) pyridinium salts, and (*iii*) other compounds in which the quaternary nitrogen atom is part of a ring system. The border-lines between these classes is not very sharp, because in many cases a publication will describe several types of groups, usually as alternative methods of quaternising some starting material. We propose in such cases to classify a patent according to the type which appears to be of greater importance technically, but to refer to the alternative method of quaternisation.

1. TETRA-SUBSTITUTED QUATERNARY AMMONIUM COMPOUNDS

Reference has already been made to Reychler's synthesis in 1913 of cetyltriethylammonium iodide, which he made by heating equimolecular amounts of triethylamine and cetyl iodide at 130° c. The first quaternary

---

[1] Hunsdiecker and Vogt, B.P. 425,188; 428,987; 428,153; 428,988; U.S.P. 2,051,947.

ammonium surface-active compounds which were made commercially appear to have been the quaternised members of the "Sapamine" range of fixing agents of the S.C.I., for example oleylamidoethyldiethylbenzyl-ammonium chloride[1]

$$C_{17}H_{33} \cdot CONHCH_2 \cdot CH_2 \overset{+}{N} (C_2H_5)_2 CH_2 — \bigcirc, \ Cl^-$$

and oleylamidoethylmethyldiethylammonium iodide[2]

$$C_{17}H_{33} \cdot CONHCH_2 \cdot CH_2 \overset{+}{N} (C_2H_5)_2 CH_3, \ I^-$$

The use of these compounds as stripping agents is described in a separate specification.[3] Similar agents containing aromatic "bridges" between the amide and quaternary ammonium groups were also patented by the S.C.I.; for example they claimed the use as a fixing agent for direct dyestuffs of *p*-stearamidophenyltrimethylammonium methosulphate[4]

$$C_{17}H_{35} \cdot CONH — \bigcirc — \overset{+}{N} (CH_3)_3, \ SO_4CH_3^-$$

A considerable impetus was given to the commercial development of the simpler tetraalkylammonium salts, of the type described by Reychler, by Evans's and Lawrie's discovery[5] that these agents were useful for stripping insoluble azoic dyeings from textile fabrics (*cf.* Chapter 9, p. 323). Among the compounds listed by them as being suitable were cetyltrimethyl-ammonium bromide ("Lissolamine A"), cetyltriethylammonium bromide, and also "Sapamines" of the quaternised type such as those just described. The good stability of these agents in the stripping baths, which are hot, alkaline solutions of reducing agents, is of course an important property. For stripping vat dyestuffs, cetyltrimethylammonium bromide, for example, is mixed with fatty materials (as in the product "Lissolamine V"); it has also been proposed to add anthraquinone to cetyltrimethyl-ammonium bromide in the stripping of azoic dyeings.[6] A similar type of quaternary ammonium compound is represented by octadecyl-β-hydroxy-ethyldimethylammonium hydroxide

$$C_{18}H_{37} \overset{+}{N} (CH_3)_2, \ OH^-$$
$$\underset{|}{CH_2 \cdot CH_2OH}$$

which is prepared according to the I.G.[7] by treating octadecyldimethyl-amine with ethylene oxide in the presence of water. It is claimed to be

[1] S.C.I., B.P. 358,202.
[2] S.C.I., B.P. 294,582; *cf.* U.S.P. 1,737,458 and D.R.P. 559,500.
[3] S.C.I., B.P. 398,150.
[4] S.C.I., B.P. 366,918.
[5] I.C.I., Evans, and Lawrie, B.P. 400,239; U.S.P. 2,003,928.
[6] I.C.I., Dunbar, Evans, and Lawrie, B.P. 436,076; *cf.* U.S.P. 2,052,612.
[7] I.G., B.P. 459,309.

effective as a detergent, stripping agent, fixing agent, and wetting-out agent.[1] A broadly similar structure, in which the octadecyl group is replaced by a dehydroabietinyl radical, and two polyethenoxy chains are introduced, has been patented by General Aniline :[2]

$$\text{(Dehydroabietinyl)} - \overset{+}{N} \begin{cases} [CH_2 \cdot CH_2O]_m CH_2 \cdot CH_2OH \\ \\ [CH_2 \cdot CH_2O]_n CH_2 \cdot CH_2OH \end{cases} , \ CH_3SO_4{}^-$$

with CH_3 on the nitrogen.

A still more complicated structure, which also contains non-ionic solubilising groups, has been proposed more recently :[3]

$$C_{12}H_{25} - \overset{+}{N} - CH_2 \cdot CH \cdot CH_2 - O - CH_2 \cdot [CHOH]_4 \cdot CH_2OH, \ Cl^-$$

with CH_3 and CH_3 OH substituents.

The usefulness of benzyl chloride as an alkylating agent[4] is illustrated by the well-known Bayer and Röhm and Haas antiseptics of the general formula

$$R\overset{+}{N}(CH_3)_2, \ Cl^-$$

with CH_2— attached to a benzene ring

in which R represents dodecyl, octadecyl, or the mixed fatty radicals derived from coconut oil (*cf.* Chapter 9, p. 326).

A number of other structures have been proposed in which the nitrogen atom of a tetra-substituted quaternary ammonium salt is not joined directly to the hydrophobic group. Deutsche Hydrierwerke,[5] for example, patented compounds of the type represented by octadecyloxymethyltriethylammonium chloride

$$C_{18}H_{37}OCH_2\overset{+}{N}(C_2H_5)_3, \ Cl^-$$

as dyestuff-fixing agents; they claimed that these agents are more stable than the pyridine analogues described in B.P. 390,553 (*vide infra*). I.C.I. and Piggott[6] described compounds with keto connecting groups, such as *p*-stearylphenyltrimethylammonium methosulphate

$$C_{17}H_{35} \cdot CO - \underset{\text{(benzene ring)}}{\bigcirc} - \overset{+}{N}(CH_3)_3, \ SO_4CH_3{}^-$$

The I.G. used amide linkages—though as "mirror images" of those in the quaternised "Sapamines"—in preparing fixing agents and dyeing assistants

[1] I.G., B.P. 372,325.
[2] General Aniline and Sanders, U.S.P. 2,623,870.
[3] Atlas Powder Co. and Zech, U.S.P. 2,775,604.
[4] *Cf.* S.C.I., B.P. 358,202.
[5] Deutsche Hydrierwerke, B.P. 434,911 and F.P. 782,802.
[6] I.C.I. and Piggott, U.S.P. 2,097,640.

for increasing the affinity of direct dyestuffs for viscose, which are exemplified by the compounds

$$C_{18}H_{37}N(CH_3)OC \cdot CH_2\overset{+}{N}(CH_3)_3, \; Cl^- \; [1]$$

$$C_{18}H_{37}NHOC \cdot CH_2\overset{+}{N}(CH_3)_2, \; Cl^- \; [2]$$
$$CH_2 \cdot COOCH_3$$

Another proposal from the S.C.I.[3] employs two amide groups in a surface-active molecule which is obtained by condensing chloroacetmethylolamide with stearanilide, and then reacting with trimethylamine:

$$C_{17}H_{35} \cdot CONH \underset{}{-\!\!\left\langle\right\rangle\!\!-} OCH_2NHOC \cdot CH_2\overset{+}{N}(CH_3)_3, \; Cl^-$$

A still more recent example of the use of an amide bridging group is illustrated by

$$C_{17}H_{35}CONHCH_2 \cdot CH_2 \cdot CH_2 \!-\!\!\overset{+}{\underset{CH_3}{N}}\!\!-\!\!\overset{CH_2-\left\langle\right\rangle}{\underset{CH_3}{}}, \; Cl^-$$

which is claimed as a germicide, textile softening agent, and wetting-out agent.[4]

Ester linkages are present in the large number of surface-active agents, described by Harris,[5] which are based on an esterified betaine structure

$$ROCO \cdot CH_2\overset{+}{N}\!\!\!<$$

in which R contains the hydrophobic group, and the nitrogen atom may be either tri-substituted or included in a pyridinium or other heterocyclic ring. A typical example is the cetyl ester of betaine chloride

$$C_{16}H_{33}OOC \cdot CH_2\overset{+}{N}(CH_3)_3, \; Cl^-$$

Two proposals by Geigy are worth special mention. In the first,[6] substituted amidines such as dimethylphenylbenzamidine are quaternised to give compounds such as

$$C_{12}H_{25}\overset{+}{N}(CH_3)_2, \; Br^-$$
$$\left\langle\right\rangle\!\!-\!\!\left\langle\right\rangle\!\!-\!\!\underset{}{C} = N\!-\!\!\left\langle\right\rangle$$

[1] I.G., B.P. 466,099.
[2] I.G., B.P. 466,772.
[3] S.C.I., B.P. 549,172; *cf.* U.S.P. 2,312,896.
[4] American Cyanamid, Cook, and Moss, U.S.P. 2,459,062.
[5] Harris, U.S.P. 2,023,075.
[6] Geigy, B.P. 498,090; *cf.* U.S.P. 2,211,280 and F.P. 840,429.

which are claimed as dyeing assistants. The second[1] reveals the use of compounds such as α-undecylbenzyltrimethylammonium methosulphate

$$C_{11}H_{23}\cdot\overset{+}{C}HN(CH_3)_3, \; SO_4CH_3{}^-$$

as fixing agents, disinfectants, etc.

Alkylated aromatic groups are used in place of long-chain alkyl groups in tetra-substituted quaternary ammonium compounds, as in the disinfectant "Phemeride"

$$R-\!\!\underset{}{\bigcirc}\!\!-OCH_2\cdot CH_2OCH_2\cdot CH_2\overset{+}{N}(CH_3)_2, \; Cl^-$$
$$CH_2-\!\!\underset{}{\bigcirc}$$

in which R is a tertiary octyl group, and in the isopropylated naphthyl-trimethylammonium hydroxide which has been described by Pott and Müller.[2]

Structures containing thioether connecting groups, such as dodecylthio-methyltrimethylammonium chloride

$$C_{12}H_{25}SCH_2\overset{+}{N}(CH_3)_3, \; Cl^-$$

have been described by the I.G.[3]

In conclusion, it is worth noting two proposals for making polymeric cationic agents of this class. The I.G.[4] have described fixing agents for direct cotton dyeings which contain no long-chain alkyl or other hydrophobic groups; these are made by the "far-reaching" alkylation (*e.g.*, with dimethylsulphate) of polyethylene polyamines of the general formulae

$$H_2N[CH_2\cdot CH_2NH]_nCH_2\cdot CH_2NH_2$$
$$(CH_2\cdot CH_2NH)_n$$

in which *n* is greater than two, and Rohm and Haas[5] have described as textile softening agents and dyestuff fixing agents the polymeric quaternary ammonium salts obtained by condensing secondary amines with epihalo-hydrins, *e.g.*,

$$\begin{array}{c}CH_3 \\ | \\ N\!\!-\!\!CH_2\cdot CH\cdot CH_2- \\ | \qquad\quad | \\ C_{18}H_{37} \quad OH \end{array} \left[\begin{array}{c} CH_3 \\ \overset{+}{N}\!\!\diagdown\!\!-\!\!CH_2\cdot CH\cdot CH_2 \\ | \qquad\qquad | \\ C_{18}H_{37} \quad OH \end{array} \right]_n n \; Cl^-$$

[1] Geigy, B.P. 536,881; *cf.* U.S.P. 2,276,587.
[2] Pott and Müller, U.S.P. 1,902,515.
[3] I.G., B.P. 436,725.
[4] I.G., B.P. 435,388.
[5] Rohm and Haas, Bock, and Houk, U.S.P. 2,454,547.

2. SURFACE-ACTIVE PYRIDINIUM COMPOUNDS

The preparation of the simpler long-chain alkyl pyridinium salts such as the dodecyl, cetyl, and octadecylpyridinium bromides, by the reaction between pyridine and a long-chain alkyl bromide or iodide, is described in patents issued to I.C.I., Baldwin, and Hailwood.[1] Alternatively, Hunsdiecker and Vogt[2] stated that agents of this type can be made by the reaction between a fatty alcohol, pyridine, and hydrobromic acid; they also made the general statement that other heterocyclic bases such as quinoline or isoquinoline can be used in place of pyridine. The products are described in these specifications as detergents, wetting-out agents, "dispersing agents," etc.; their important application as fixing agents for direct dyestuffs on cellulosic fibres (*cf.* Chapter 9, p. 322) was claimed later by I.C.I., Barlow, and Lawrie.[3]

Pyridinium salts containing intermediate connecting groups between the quaternary nitrogen atom and a hydrophobic residue have also been proposed. The S.C.I.,[4] for example, esterified hydroxyalkylpyridinium chlorides and bromides with fatty acid chlorides to obtain compounds such as oleyloxyethylpyridinium chloride,

$$C_{17}H_{33}{\cdot}COOCH_2{\cdot}CH_2\overset{+}{N}\langle\quad\rangle,\ Cl^-$$

The I.G.[5] have proposed compounds containing both ether and ester linkages, such as oleyloxyethyloxyethylpyridinium chloride,

$$C_{17}H_{33}{\cdot}COOCH_2{\cdot}CH_2OCH_2{\cdot}CH_2\overset{+}{N}\langle\quad\rangle,\ Cl^-$$

and others containing recurrent ether groups, such as octadecenoxyethyloxyethylpyridinium chloride,

$$C_{18}H_{35}OCH_2{\cdot}CH_2OCH_2{\cdot}CH_2\overset{+}{N}\langle\quad\rangle,\ Cl^-$$

A simpler type of structure, such as

$$\langle\quad\rangle{-}CH_2{-}\overset{+}{N}\langle\quad\rangle,\ Cl^-$$
$$\diagdown OC_{12}H_{25}$$

has been proposed for use as cationic bactericides.[6]

The heat-decomposable pyridinium salts containing long-chain aliphatic

[1] I.C.I., Baldwin, and Hailwood, B.P. 379,396 and F.P. 738,028.
[2] Hunsdiecker and Vogt, B.P. 392,763 and F.P. 743,973.
[3] I.C.I., Barlow, and Lawrie, B.P. 398,175.
[4] S.C.I, B.P. 388,840.
[5] I.G., F.P. 819,000 and U.S.P. 2,214,352.
[6] Alles and Wisegarver, U.S.P. 2,477,850.

substituents, which are used as durable water-proofing agents for textiles (*cf.* Chapter 5, p. 241), have been the subject of intense patenting activity. I.C.I., Reynolds, Walker, and Woolvin,[1] described the treatment of cellulosic materials with compounds of the general formula

$$ROCH_2\overset{+}{N}(R_1)(R_2)(R_3),\ X^-$$

in which R is a long-chain aliphatic group, R_1, R_2, and R_3 are substituent radicals or represent the three bonds attached to the nitrogen in a pyridinium or similar heterocyclic ring, and X^- is a halide ion, for example octadecyloxymethylpyridinium chloride

$$C_{18}H_{37}OCH_2\overset{+}{N}\langle\rangle,\ Cl^-$$

This specification, which claims water-proofing as distinct from dye-fixing treatments, contains several references to earlier proposals for making these and similar compounds. In the second of the series of I.C.I. patents,[2] the quaternary salt is formed *in situ* on the fibre by a reaction such as that between chloromethyloctadecylether and pyridine or diethylaniline.

The preparation of the first of the commercial durable water-proofing agents, stearamidomethylpyridinium chloride ("Velan PF")

$$C_{17}H_{35}\cdot CONHCH_2\overset{+}{N}\langle\rangle,\ Cl^-$$

was described by I.C.I., Baldwin, and Walker,[3] who condensed stearamide with formaldehyde and pyridine hydrochloride. What is presumably an alternative method of preparing this compound, the reaction between N-chloromethyl stearamide and pyridine, has been disclosed by Farberei A.G.[4] The water-proofing of cellulosic materials by these and similar compounds was claimed by I.C.I., Baldwin, Evans, and Salkeld.[5] They give a list of suitable compounds, which includes the interesting example N-carbomethoxyheptadecylaminomethylpyridinium chloride

$$C_{17}H_{35}\underset{\underset{COOCH_3}{|}}{N}CH_2\overset{+}{N}\langle\rangle,\ Cl^-$$

The water-proofing of silk and wool by compounds such as stearamidomethylpyridinium chloride (a considerable number of examples are given) is claimed by I.C.I., Evans, and Salkeld.[6]

[1] I.C.I., Reynolds, Walker, and Woolvin, B.P. 466,817.
[2] I.C.I., Baldwin, Reynolds, Walker, and Woolvin, B.P. 469,476.
[3] I.C.I., Baldwin, and Walker, B.P. 475,170.
[4] Farberei, B.P. 492,699.
[5] I.C.I., Baldwin, Evans, and Salkeld, B.P. 477,991.
[6] I.C.I., Evans, and Salkeld, B.P. 493,920.

Other chemical types which are proposed in subsequent I.C.I. patents are illustrated by the following examples:

$$C_{17}H_{35}\cdot CONHCONHCH_2\overset{+}{N}\langle\underset{}{\bigcirc}\rangle, \; Cl^-$$

(by the reaction between pyridine, hydrochloric acid, paraformaldehyde, and octadecylurea[1]);

$$C_{17}H_{35}NHCONHCH_2\overset{+}{N}\langle\underset{}{\bigcirc}\rangle, \; Cl^-$$

(by the reaction between pyridine, hydrochloric acid, paraformaldehyde, and N-heptadecylurea[1]);

$$C_{16}H_{33}(CH_3)NCONHCH_2\overset{+}{N}\langle\underset{}{\bigcirc}\rangle, \; Cl^-$$

(as in the previous reaction, using N-methyl-N-cetylurea[1]);

$$C_{18}H_{37}OCONHCH_2\overset{+}{N}\langle\underset{}{\bigcirc}\rangle, \; Cl^-$$

(as before, using octadecyl carbamate[2]);

$$C_{17}H_{35}\cdot CONCH_2\overset{+}{N}\langle\underset{}{\bigcirc}\rangle, \; Cl^-$$
$$\underset{C_{17}H_{35}\cdot CONCH_2\overset{+}{N}\langle\underset{}{\bigcirc}\rangle, \; Cl^-}{\overset{\mid}{CH_2}}$$

(by the reaction between distearyldiaminomethane, paraformaldehyde, and hydrochloric acid, followed by quaternisation with pyridine[3]);

$$C_{18}H_{37}OOCN\!\!-\!\!\langle\underset{}{\bigcirc}\rangle\!\!-\!\!NCOOC_{18}H_{37}$$
$$Cl^-, \; \langle\overset{+}{\underset{}{\bigcirc}}\rangle\overset{\mid}{N}CH_2 \qquad CH_2\overset{+}{N}\langle\underset{}{\bigcirc}\rangle, \; Cl^-$$

(by condensing dioctadecyl-*p*-phenylenedicarbamate with paraformaldehyde and then quaternising with pyridine[4]). Products for combined water-proofing and crease-resistant treatments have also been described; these are obtained for example by condensing methylolstearamide with the dimethyl ether of dimethylolurea, or methylolstearamide with methoxymethyl melamine, and then reacting the product with a mixture of pyridine, pyridine hydrochloride, and paraformaldehyde.[5] The exact chemical constitution of these products is of course not certain; their chief interest in

---

[1] I.C.I., Cusa, Salkeld, and Walker, B.P. 497,856.
[2] I.C.I., Cusa, Salkeld, and Walker, B.P. 498,287.
[3] I.C.I. and Rogers, B.P. 517,475.
[4] I.C.I. and Rogers, B.P. 517,631.
[5] I.C.I. and Lane, B.P. 596,153 and 596,154.

the present connection is that they represent amphipathic substances containing substituent groups which can "resinify" by the well-known polycondensation reactions such as those between urea and formaldehyde or between melamine and formaldehyde.

Sulphonamide groups have been proposed by the I.G.[1] in place of the carboxyamide groups in the "Velan" type of compound, as in the surface-active agent of presumed formula

$$C_{18}H_{37}SO_2NHCH_2\overset{+}{N}\langle\ \rangle, \ Cl^-$$

(This specification also describes analogues solubilised by a thiouronium group.)

Compounds of the type represented by stearoxymethylpyridinium chloride

$$C_{17}H_{35}\cdot COOCH_2\overset{+}{N}\langle\ \rangle, \ Cl^-$$

have been patented by the Ellis-Foster Company and Rust[2] and by the Warwick Chemical Company.[3] Stearoxymethylpyridinium chloride has been stated to be the basis of the durable water-proofing agent "Norane" of the Warwick Chemical Company.[4]

Products which are illustrated by the presumed structure

$$C_{11}H_{23}\cdot CONHCH_2NHCO\cdot CH_2\overset{+}{N}\langle\ \rangle, \ Cl^-$$

have been patented by the S.C.I.[5] The example given is made by condensing methylollauramide with chloroacetamide, and then treating with pyridine in the presence of hydrochloric acid. It is not clear from the patent specification whether or not these compounds are intended primarily as water-proofing agents. Similarly, the S.C.I.[6] have described water-proofing agents which are prepared for example by condensing μ-heptadecylbenziminazole with methylolchloroacetamide in sulphuric acid, and then quaternising with pyridine, presumably giving the product

---

[1] I.G., B.P. 508,801; *cf.* U.S.P. 2,344,321.
[2] Ellis-Foster Company and Rust, U.S.P. 2,261,097.
[3] Warwick Chemical Company, B.P. 560,448.
[4] Schwartz and Perry, *Surface-Active Agents*, Interscience, New York, 1949, p. 179.
[5] S.C.I., B.P. 533,220.
[6] S.C.I., B.P. 533,155.

Du Pont, Coffman, and Sauer[1] have prepared further examples of what we might term "di-functional" water-proofing agents such as ethane-1 : 2-bis(N-octadecylsulphonamidomethylpyridinium chloride)

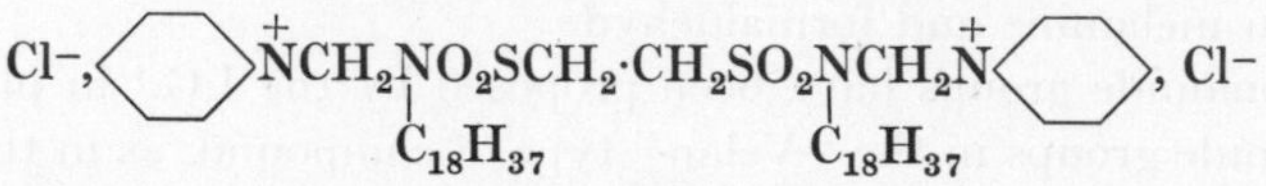

$$Cl^-, \overset{+}{N}CH_2NO_2SCH_2 \cdot CH_2SO_2\overset{+}{N}CH_2\overset{+}{N}, Cl^-$$
$$C_{18}H_{37} \qquad C_{18}H_{37}$$

Two interesting proposals for making complex, polyfunctional pyridinium salts are represented by the structures

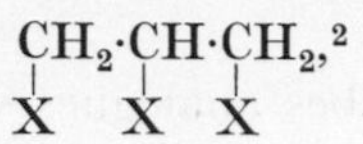

$$CH_2 \cdot CH \cdot CH_2,[2]$$
$$X \quad X \quad X$$

where X denotes the grouping

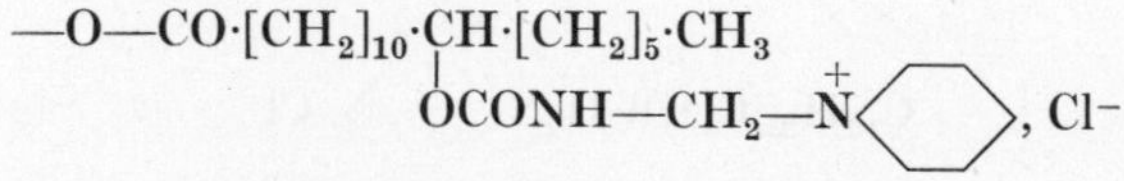

$$-O-CO\cdot[CH_2]_{10}\cdot CH\cdot[CH_2]_5\cdot CH_3$$
$$OCONH-CH_2-\overset{+}{N}, Cl^-$$

and

$$\left[-CH_2\cdot CH- \atop \overset{+}{N}-CH_2\cdot CH_3 \right]_n, n\ Br^-\ [3]$$

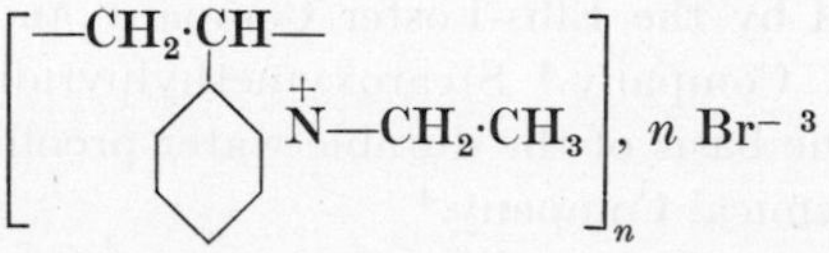

The first of these types is claimed to give water-proofing and anti-shrink agents for textiles, and the second to give fungicides, insecticides, and general surface activity.

3. OTHER QUATERNARY AMMONIUM COMPOUNDS

The use of other heterocyclic bases as alternatives to pyridine in the preparation of surface-active quaternary ammonium compounds is mentioned or described in a number of the patent specifications discussed in the preceding section. These include for example quinoline, isoquinoline, picoline, and nicotine. According to I.C.I. and Oakeshott,[4] the reaction products of nicotine and alkyl halides combine surface-active and insecticidal properties in a single agent. They state that either or both of the two nitrogen atoms in nicotine

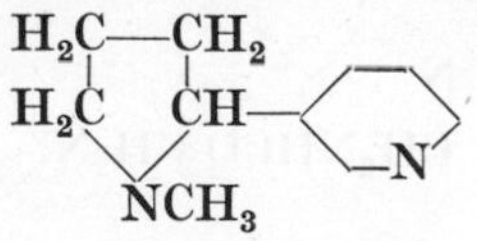

$$H_2C-CH_2$$
$$H_2C \quad CH-$$
$$NCH_3 \qquad N$$

may be quaternised.

[1] Du Pont, Coffman, and Sauer, U.S.P., 2,362,886.
[2] I.C.I., Baird, Barr, and Lowe, B.P. 615,838 and U.S.P. 2,518,266.
[3] Du Pont and Richards, U.S.P. 2,487,829.
[4] I.C.I. and Oakeshott, B.P. 401,707.

Piperidine has been used in preparing what are perhaps, strictly speaking, tetra-substituted quaternary ammonium compounds. A typical agent of this type is cetylmethylpiperidinium methosulphate[1]

$$C_{16}H_{33}\overset{+}{N}\underset{CH_3}{\overset{CH_2-CH_2}{\diagdown}}\underset{CH_2-CH_2}{\diagup}CH_2, SO_4CH_3^-$$

More complicated compounds, the exact structure of which seems to us to be a matter of conjecture, are obtained according to Hunsdiecker and Vogt[2] by quaternising hexamethylenetetramine

$$\begin{array}{c} N\text{————}CH_2 \\ H_2C \underset{N}{\overset{CH_2}{\diagup}} \overset{CH_2}{\underset{CH_2}{\diagdown}} N-CH_2-N \\ N\text{————}CH_2 \end{array}$$

to obtain compounds to which were assigned general formulae such as

$$[(CH_2)_6N_4CH_2\cdot COOC_{12}H_{25}]^+, CH_3\cdot COO^-$$

$$[(CH_2)_6N_4CH_2\cdot CH_2OC_{10}H_{21}]^+, CH_3\cdot COO^-$$

Surface-active agents which contain quaternary nitrogen atoms in benziminazole rings have been proposed by the S.C.I. These fall into two general classes, illustrated by the compounds

$$C_{17}H_{35}\cdot C, \ Cl^{-}{}^{[3]}$$

$$CH_3\cdot C, \ Cl^{-}{}^{[4]}$$

$$C_2H_5 \qquad C_{16}H_{33}$$

---

[1] Deutsche Hydrierwerke, B.P. 433,356; *cf.* also Chapter 9, p. 328.
[2] Hunsdiecker and Vogt, B.P. 424,717.
[3] S.C.I., B.P. 419,010.
[4] S.C.I., B.P. 439,261; *cf.* U.S.P. 2,053,822 and 2,056,449.

Morpholinium groups have also been proposed, for example in structures such as dodecylhydroxyethylmorpholinium bromide[1]

$$C_{12}H_{25}\overset{+}{N}\underset{CH_2{-}CH_2}{\overset{CH_2{-}CH_2}{<}}>O,\ Br^-$$
$$CH_2{\cdot}CH_2OH$$

4-stearylamido-3-methylphenylmethylmorpholinium methosulphate[2]

$$C_{17}H_{35}{\cdot}CONH{-}\underset{CH_3}{\bigcirc}{-}\overset{+}{N}\underset{CH_3}{\overset{CH_2{-}CH_2}{<}}>O,\ SO_4CH_3^-$$

and didodecyl (or dioctadecyl) morpholinium chloride.[3]

Finally, long chain pyrrolidinium salts, such as hexadecylmethylpyrrolidinium bromide

$$C_{16}H_{33}{-}\overset{+}{N}{-}CH_3,\ Br^-$$
$$H_2C\qquad CH_2$$
$$H_2C{-}{-}{-}CH_2$$

have been claimed as bactericides.[4]

D. Other quaternary and ternary cationic surface-active agents

A number of proposals have been made in the patent literature for synthesising and using surface-active quaternary phosphonium, arsonium, and stibonium, and ternary sulphonium salts, though to the best of our knowledge none of these agents has become technically important. Examples of such compounds, which have been described as dyestuff fixing agents, dyeing assistants, etc.,[5] are cetyldimethylsulphonium methosulphate

$$C_{16}H_{33}\overset{+}{S}(CH_3)_2,\ SO_4CH_3^-$$

dodecyltriethylphosphonium bromide*

---

* A quaternary phosphonium salt, which has achieved technical importance, though it is not perhaps strictly a surface-active agent, is the moth-proofing agent "Eulan NK"

$$\underset{Cl}{\bigcirc}CH_2\overset{+}{P}\left({-}\bigcirc\right)_3,\ Cl^-$$

(*cf.* B.I.O.S. Final Report 259).
  [1] I.G., B.P. 436,942.
  [2] Geigy, B.P. 518,989.
  [3] Erickson and Keps, U.S.P. 2,694,707.
  [4] Onyx Oil and Chemical Co., Tesoro, and Wakeman, U.S.P. 2,819,285.
  [5] See for example I.G., B.P. 435,443; 435,444; 438,508; 439,675; U.S.P. 2,228,369; I.C.I., B.P. 436,592; 437,273; U.S.P. 2,121,823; Shell Development, U.S.P. 2,204,976.

$$C_{12}H_{25}\overset{+}{P}(C_2H_5)_3, \ Br^-$$

dodecyltrimethylarsonium hydroxide

$$C_{12}H_{25}\overset{+}{As}(CH_3)_3, \ OH^-$$

and undecyltrimethylstibonium chloride

$$C_{11}H_{23}\overset{+}{Sb}(CH_3)_3, \ Cl^-.$$

Methods of preparation are described in the patent specifications cited.

E. Some special uses of cationic surface-active agents

In addition to the applications of the cationic surface-active agents which have already been mentioned, it seems worth while to draw attention to a few of the special uses which have been found for these agents. Ternary sulphonium salts, for example, have been proposed as additions to viscose spinning baths in order to prevent blocking of the spinnerettes.[1] This use depends upon their deflocculating action in strongly acid media; the opposite principle appears to underlie the use of cetylpyridinium chloride, for example, in coagulating baths into which sodium alginate solutions are injected in the spinning of alginate fibres.[2]

Durable water-proofing agents of the "Velan" type have been applied to synthetic fibres by addition before spinning: thus I.C.I., Evans, and Shepherdson[3] suggested adding compounds such as stearamidomethyl-pyridinium chloride to cellulose acetate spinning "dopes" before extrusion, and du Pont and Waltmann[4] added octadecylthiomethylpyridinium chloride to the cellulose xanthate solutions which are extruded in the spinning of viscose rayon.

The tendency for cationic surface-active agents to cause disperse particles to adhere to the surfaces of solids, which militates against their general use as detergents, has been turned to good account in a number of uses. These can be illustrated by the process patented by Wilsdon and Blow[5] for promoting the adhesion of rubber latex particles (both natural and synthetic) to wool fabrics, by impregnating the fabric with a cationic surface-active agent such as cetyltrimethylammonium bromide, and then immersing it in the latex. Alternatively, a positively charged latex may be prepared, into which the fabric is then immersed, thus obtaining the same result by a one-bath treatment. A further illustration is afforded by the

---

[1] Vereinigte Glanzstoff, B.P. 521,727.
[2] Courtaulds and Tallis, B.P. 568,177.
[3] I.C.I., Evans, and Shepherdson, B.P. 493,111.
[4] Du Pont and Waltmann, U.S.P. 2,335,980.
[5] Rubber Producers Research Association, Wool Industries Research Association, Wilsdon, and Blow, B.P. 483,496 and 497,793.

use of cationic agents to promote the adhesion of tars and bitumen to the surfaces of solids such as stones, in road-making, which we discuss on p. 350.

The use of cationic surface-active agents for promoting the transfer of pigments from aqueous to oil media, or for rendering the surfaces of pigment particles more easily wetted by oils, has been referred to in Chapter 7, p. 284. The suggestion that these agents are surface-active in non-aqueous media receives further support from Dunbar's proposal,[1] for example, to add cetylpyridinium bromide to dry-cleaning solvents in order to improve their efficiency.

---

[1] I.C.I. and Dunbar, B.P. 453,523.

CHAPTER 14

NON-IONIC SURFACE-ACTIVE AGENTS

THE effective ingredients in all the surface-active agents which have been discussed in the preceding chapters are electrolytes in aqueous solutions, the amphipathic molecular unit being either an anion or a cation. Although this may be a necessary characteristic for specific purposes—agents for fixing direct cotton dyestuffs, for example, are cationic—it is not a general prerequisite for surface-activity. The only general requirements in a surface-active molecular unit are that (a) it shall contain one or more groups which tend to be expelled by an aqueous phase or which have an affinity for an external phase, and (b) it shall contain solubilising groups which are hydrated by the water molecules. Although ionogenic polar groups (e.g., $-SO_3^-$, $-OSO_3^-$, $-N(CH_3)_3^+$) will be individually more highly hydrated than non-ionised polar groups (e.g., $-O-$, $-OH$, $-CONH-$, $-COO-$), an adequate total degree of hydration can be achieved in a surface-active molecule if a sufficient number of non-ionising polar groups are present. This is the principle on which the water-soluble non-ionic surface-active agents are based, and it is worth noting that it has several inherent advantages which are often valuable. The most important of these advantages are that

(i) non-ionic surface-active molecules, being independent of the degree of ionisation of a polar group for attaining a suitable balance between hydrophilic and hydrophobic groups, are relatively less affected by high concentrations of electrolytes, and

(ii) the degree of solubilisation conferred by the polar groups can be varied in smaller steps than is possible with ionising surface-active molecules, since the solubilising effect of each non-ionising polar group is much smaller.*

The increasing importance of the polyethenoxy and other non-ionic surface-active agents is largely due to these advantages and to their main corollary, viz., that they make possible the use of a considerable number of cheap and available raw materials as starting materials for synthesising surface-active agents.

---

* The German workers quoted by Brandner, Lockwood, Nagel, and Russell in F.I.A.T. Final Report No. 1141, "Synthetic Detergents and Related Surface-Active Agents in Germany," suggested that one sulphato group is approximately equal in solubilising effect to four polyether groups of the type $-(OCH_2CH_2)-$, which are perhaps the most important of the non-ionising solubilising polar groups.

465

A. Polyethenoxy agents (ethylene glycol polyethers)

These agents* have the general formula $R([CH_2 \cdot CH_2O]_mH)_n$, in which m and n are each unity or greater, the product mn usually being at least two, and R is an organic residue of varying complexity which usually, but not always, contains a hydrophobic group such as a long paraffin chain, an aromatic residue, or an alkylated aromatic group. They are usually made either by condensing an insoluble compound containing one or more reactive hydrogen atoms (*e.g.*, an alcohol, carboxylic acid, amine, amide, or mercaptan) with an alkylene oxide such as ethylene oxide, according to the general reaction

$$RH_n + mn\underset{O}{CH_2 \cdot CH_2} \rightarrow R([CH_2 \cdot CH_2O]_mH)_n$$

which is the most important route to these products,† or by reacting the insoluble compound with a polyglycol:

$$RH_n + nHO(CH_2 \cdot CH_2O)_mH \rightarrow R([CH_2 \cdot CH_2O]_mH)_n$$

An alternative route is the use of ethylene chlorhydrin instead of ethylene oxide,

$$RH_n + mn \underset{OH \ Cl}{CH_2 \cdot CH_2} \rightarrow R([CH_2 \cdot CH_2O]_mH)_n + mn \ HCl$$

but this method appears to be of no technical importance.

Owing to the fact that the addition of ethylene oxide to the available reactive hydrogen atoms occurs in a largely random manner, the poly-ethenoxy surface-active agents which are obtained in practice are not chemical entities, but mixtures of compounds containing different numbers of polyether groups. If for example ethylene oxide is reacted with cetyl-amine, the first increment of ethylene oxide to react will give the compound $C_{16}H_{33}NHCH_2 \cdot CH_2OH$ (I). The next increments of ethylene oxide can react with cetylamine to give more of compound (I), or with (I) to give either

$$C_{16}H_{33}N\begin{cases} CH_2 \cdot CH_2OH \\ CH_2 \cdot CH_2OH \end{cases} \quad \text{(II)}, \quad \text{or} \quad C_{16}H_{33}NHCH_2 \cdot CH_2OCH_2 \cdot CH_2OH \quad \text{(III)}.$$

Subsequent increments can react with any of these four compounds, and thereafter there is a steadily increasing number of compounds containing reactive hydrogen atoms with which the ethylene oxide can condense. The relative amounts of the different compounds which are eventually formed

---

* A comprehensive review of polyethenoxy surface-active agents has recently been published by Schönfeldt, *Oberflächenaktive Anlagerungsprodukte des Äthylenoxyds*, Wissenschaftlicher Verlag, Stuttgart, 1959.

† The origin of this process in the prohibition of thiodiglycol in Germany after the First World War is discussed by Baird, B.I.O.S. Final Report 421, "Textile Auxiliary Products," p. 4.

in appreciable quantity will of course depend on the velocity constants of the different possible reactions at the temperature prevailing, on the relative concentrations of the different possible reactants, and on the mechanical treatment of the reaction mixture and the manner in which the ethylene oxide is introduced into it. It is therefore important to bear in mind that, in general, a definite chemical formula such as

$$C_{16}H_{33}N \Big\langle \begin{matrix} [CH_2 \cdot CH_2O]_4 CH_2 \cdot CH_2OH \\ [CH_2 \cdot CH_2O]_4 CH_2 \cdot CH_2OH \end{matrix}$$

cannot be correctly assigned to the condensation product of cetylamine with ten molecular proportions of ethylene oxide, for example, since this condensate is a mixture of what is at present an unknown distribution of molecular weights. We propose instead to use the shorthand notation "cetylamine-10EtO," or "cetylamine-10PrO" or "cetyl alcohol-10BuO" in cases in which a higher alkylene oxide such as propylene or butylene oxide is used.

Several authors have considered possible distributions of molecular weight in polyethenoxy condensates, beginning with Flory's[1] study of the addition of ethylene oxide to water and to ethylene glycol, in which it was assumed that all the hydroxyl groups present were equally reactive, so that a "Poisson" distribution of molecular weights would result. This assumption was found to hold good for the phenol-ethylene oxide condensates which were prepared and fractionally distilled by Miller, Bann, and Thrower,[2] after the initial reaction

$$PhOH + C_2H_4O \rightarrow PhOC_2H_4OH,$$

which went to completion before the secondary reactions

$$Ph[OC_2H_4]_nOH + C_2H_4O \rightarrow Ph[OC_2H_4]_{n+1}OH$$

began. The Flory treatment was also found to be in reasonably good agreement with the distribution of molecular weights which was found by molecular distillation of the nonylphenol-6EtO and nonylphenol-9·5EtO condensates studied by Mayhew and Hyatt,[3] and in the dodecyl alcohol-6·88 and dodecyl alcohol-9·90EtO condensates investigated by Karabinos and Quinn.[4] This latter paper also gives some interesting results on the variation of detergent action (in a "built" mixture—*cf.* p. 308) as a function of the molecular weight of the different fractions. Dirt-removing power fell steeply at first with increasing molecular weight, then rose steeply, and finally became constant, the optimum being at 6–7EtO for the

[1] Flory, *J. Amer. Chem. Soc.*, 1940, **62**, 1561.
[2] Miller, Bann, and Thrower, *J. Chem. Soc.*, 1950, 3623.
[3] Mayhew and Hyatt, *J. Amer. Oil Chem. Soc.*, 1952, **29**, 357.
[4] Karabinos and Quinn, *J. Amer. Oil Chem. Soc.*, 1956, **33**, 223.

6·88EtO condensate, but at 7–8EtO for the 9·90EtO condensate. (This difference, which reveals differences between fractions of the same empirical formula from two different starting condensates, underlines the chemical heterogeneity of these products.) The "whiteness-retention" (*i.e.*, dirt-suspending power), on the other hand, at first rose sharply, passed through a maximum at about 3–4EtO in both cases, and then decreased. Apart from their interest in the present connection, these results provide a good example of the complexity of detergent processes which we have discussed more fully in Chapter 8.

The polyethenoxy agents are closely related to the polymerisation products of ethylene oxide itself, which are water-soluble waxes of high molecular weight in which R of our general formula is probably hydroxyl, *n* is probably unity, and *m* is very large, sometimes in the hundreds. Although these polymers do not contain large hydrophobic groups, it was soon observed that they had valuable surface-active properties. They have for example been patented as dispersing or emulsifying agents for pigments, dyestuff lakes, waxes, nitrocellulose, and other insoluble substances,[1] and also as restraining and stripping agents in dyeing with vat dyestuffs and sulphur colours.[2] These substances cannot be highly amphipathic, and it appears likely that they function as protective colloids in much the same way as do glue, soluble gums, polyvinyl alcohol, etc., introducing steric factors, and/or forming hydrated sheaths around the particles, which prevent flocculation (*cf.* Chapter 4, p. 169). It seems possible that adsorption of a polyethylene glycol by the micelles of a leuco vat dyestuff, for example, may also occur as the result of interactions between the recurring ether oxygen atoms in the surface-active agent and specific groups in the dyestuff molecule.

The preparation of the monostearic acid ester of triethylene glycol,

$$C_{17}H_{35} \cdot CO[OCH_2 \cdot CH_2]_3OH$$

was described in a French Patent issued in 1929,[3] but the systematic preparation of a range of amphipathic polyethenoxy compounds was first published in an important series of patents by the I.G. and associated companies. In the first specification,[4] thirty-three examples were given of the preparation and technical application of products obtained by " esterifying or etherifying a water-insoluble organic compound other than a water-insoluble carbohydrate but containing at least one hydroxyl or carboxylic acid group, or a group reacting like a carboxylic acid group

---

[1] I.G., B.P. 353,926; *cf.* U.S.P. 1,930,853.

[2] I.G., B.P. 367,420.

[3] Goldschmidt, F.P. 664,261 (application date 5th November, 1928, published 31st August, 1929).

[4] I.G., B.P. 380,431 (application date, 10th October, 1931; accepted 12th September, 1932).

under the conditions of working, with polyethylene glycols containing a chain of at least four ethenoxy groups, or with mono-ethers or -esters of such polyethylene glycols," or by the modified process in which the poly-ethylene glycols or their mono-ethers are replaced by "a corresponding quantity of ethylene oxide or ethylene halogenhydrin, at least $3n + 1$ molecular proportions of the said ethylene oxide or ethylene halogenhydrin being employed, n being the number of the hydroxy and/or carboxy groups present in the molecule of the water-insoluble compound." Among the water-insoluble compounds which were mentioned in the examples were fatty alcohols such as octadecyl alcohol or the mixed alcohols which are obtained by the hydrogenation of fatty glycerides, fatty acids, hydroxy-fatty acids such as ricinoleic acid, dihydroxy-alcohols such as 1 : 12-octade-canediol, castor oil, and hydroxy-amines such as N-hydroxyethyloctade-cylamine. A large number of other types of water-insoluble compounds were also mentioned as being suitable in the general descriptive matter in this specification; these included mono- and di-glycerides, substituted phenols, and even fatty amides. The terminal hydroxyl groups of the polyethenoxy chains may be etherified with lower alkyl groups, or even sulphated with chlorosulphonic acid (*cf.* Chapter 11, p. 415). A typical preparation was described in Example 1 of the complete specification, in which 200 parts of a technical mixture of C_8–C_{18} saturated aliphatic alcohols, which is obtained by the hydrogenation of a glyceride (coconut oil?) and contains approxi-mately 50% of dodecyl alcohol, are heated to 180° c. and then treated by gradually passing in 400 parts of ethylene oxide. The time during which the ethylene oxide is passed in, the method of distribution and agitation, and the yield were not specified.

A great variety of uses were claimed for the products of B.P. 380,431. They were stated, for example, to be good wetting-out agents, detergents, dyeing assistants, "dispersing agents" in both aqueous and non-aqueous media, and emulsifying agents. It is interesting to note that the claims of this patent were not restricted to water-soluble condensates, but also included those which only disperse in water.

The reference in B.P. 380,431 to the fatty amides as starting materials for the preparation of polyethenoxy condensates was amplified in another British Specification of the same application and publication dates.[1] This described the addition of polyethenoxy chains, which as in the other specification could be done either step-wise with ethylene oxide or by reaction with a polyethylene glycol, to fatty amines such as octadecylamine, amides such as stearamide and oleylamide, and sulphonamides such as dodecane sulphonamide. It will be noticed that these products, unlike those of B.P. 380,431, probably contain compounds in which two poly-ethenoxy chains are attached to each hydrocarbon residue. The technical

---

[1] I.G., B.P. 380,851.

properties claimed for the products are however similar. A third specification which belongs to this early group[1] appears to have been a selection from the broad claims and disclosures of B.P. 380,431, limiting itself to those condensation products of the monohydric aliphatic alcohols (octyl alcohol and higher in the series) which contain two or three molecular proportions of ethylene oxide, or alternatively to the condensation products of these alcohols with di- or tri-ethylene glycols. Emphasis is placed in this patent on the use of these products as emulsifying agents, and on mixtures of them with organic solvents and with other surface-active agents such as soaps, Turkey Red Oils, alkyl sulphates, and amphipathic sulphonates. It is interesting to observe that the condensates described in this patent, many of which are oil-soluble, were stated to be suitable for making self-emulsifiable oils (*cf.* Chapter 6, p. 251).

It is worth noting that the basic character of the nitrogen atom in a long-chain alkyl amine such as octadecylamine, for example, is not destroyed by condensation with ethylene oxide. Consequently, these condensates may act as both non-ionic and cationic surface-active agents in acid media, in the sense that the hydrophilic portion of the molecule consists of an ionising $-NH^+\!\!<$ group as well as a polyether chain.

A large number of other "solubilisable" substances have been proposed for condensation with ethylene oxide in the patent literature, as will be seen from the following examples:

(a) Compounds of the general formula $R \cdot CONR_1R_2$, in which R is a hydrophobic group, R_1 is a hydroxyalkyl group, and R_2 is hydrogen, alkyl, aryl, or a hydroxyalkyl group, have been condensed with up to three molecular proportions of alkylene oxide for each reactive hydrogen atom in R_1 and R_2.[2] Examples are the N-β-hydroxyethylamide of lauric acid and of other fatty acids, condensed with 1·5 to 4 molecular proportions of ethylene oxide.

(b) Long-chain alkyl mercaptans have been condensed with ethylene oxide to give products with the generic formula

$$RSCH_2 \cdot CH_2[OCH_2 \cdot CH_2]_n OH.[3]$$

Examples are dodecyl mercaptan-4EtO, oleyl (*i.e.*, octadecenyl) mercaptan-9EtO, and cetyl mercaptan-20EtO. The products were stated to be readily soluble in organic solvents. Ethylene oxide condensates of branched-chain mercaptans, obtained from polymeric olefines, have been developed on a commercial scale in the United States.[4] They are cheaper than the straight-chain analogues which were originally patented by the I.G., and they are

[1] I.G., B.P. 404,931 (published 9th January, 1934; *cf.* F.P.748,091).
[2] I.G., B.P. 420,545.
[3] I.G., B.P. 437,590; *cf.* F.P. 794,830 and U.S.P. 2,129,709.
[4] Eaton and Kayser, *Soap and Chemical Specialties*, 1957, **33**, No. 10, 48, 115.

stated to be superior to the ethylene oxide condensates of fatty alcohols and alkylphenols (which we discuss below) for emulsifying grease in dishwashing and dairy-cleaning operations. Mercaptobenzothiazole has also been condensed with (for example) 8 moles of ethylene oxide, the products being claimed as detergents and corrosion inhibitors.[1]

(c) Nuclear-substituted phenols and substituted hydrogenated phenols, covering a wide variety of chemical types, have been condensed with alkylene oxides, alkylene chlorohydrins, or pre-formed polyethylene glycols.[2] The substituent group or groups were described as hydrocarbon or acyl radicals containing a total of at least four carbon atoms. Examples of the agents prepared were *p*-isooctylphenol-10EtO (a water-soluble oil, which was stated to be a good detergent for wool), *p*-isooctylphenol-6EtO (an oil which is not completely water-soluble, but which was stated to be a good detergent), isododecylphenol-12-15EtO (a butter-like, soluble substance, claimed as a detergent for cotton), isohexylphenol-7EtO (a water-soluble oil, detergent for wool), *p*-oleylphenol (*i.e.*, phenol substituted in the *p*-position with the acyl radical of oleic acid)-25EtO, which was described as a water-soluble "fatty mass," isobutylphenol-3EtO (an oily product which, when mixed with nineteen times its own weight of xylenol, was stated to be a good wetting-out agent for mercerising baths), and isooctylphenol-20EtO. A number of chemically less well-defined substituted phenols were also mentioned as starting materials for condensation with ethylene oxide. Examples of these are

(*i*) an isononylphenol which is obtained by condensing phenol with a mixture of olefins, chiefly isononylenes, from the polymerisation of propylene,

(*ii*) an alkylated phenol obtained by condensing phenol with an "equimolar" proportion of an olefin of average molecular weight 194 (boiling range 180–220° c.), which is the polymerisation product of C_6–C_7 olefins which are derived from alcohols from the catalytic reduction of carbon monoxide,

(*iii*) impure isododecylphenols made by condensing phenol with mono-chlorinated natural or synthetic oils which are chiefly C_{12} hydrocarbons,

(*iv*) an alkylated cresol prepared by the reaction of crude cresol with the mono-chlorination product of a "middle oil" fraction of boiling range 160°–220° c., in the presence of aluminium chloride or zinc chloride.

The alkylphenol-ethylene oxide condensates are at present the most widely used non-ionic detergents.

Combination of the terminal hydroxyl group with an organic acid was described as a method of increasing the water-solubility of several of the polyethenoxy agents in B.P. 470,181. The triisobutylphenol-5EtO condensate, for example, was described as being only emulsifiable in water,

[1] Monsanto, B.P. 692,414.
[2] I.G., B.P. 470,181; *cf.* F.P. 823,454 and U.S.P. 2,213,477.

but it was stated to be rendered water-soluble by reaction with diglycollic
acid anhydride to give a detergent of the general type

$$(C_4H_9)_3 \text{---} \langle \bigcirc \rangle \text{---} [OCH_2 \cdot CH_2]_n OCO \cdot CH_2 OCH_2 \cdot COONa$$

while the *p*-cyclohexylcyclohexanol-3PrO condensate was solubilised by
condensation with sodium chloroacetate to what was described as the
sodium salt of cyclohexylcyclohexyltripropylene glycol (hydr)oxyacetic
acid,

$$CH_2 \bigg\langle {{CH_2 \cdot CH_2} \atop {CH_2 \cdot CH_2}} \bigg\rangle CH \cdot CH \bigg\langle {{CH_2 \cdot CH_2} \atop {CH_2 \cdot CH_2}} \bigg\rangle CH[OCH_2 \cdot CH(CH_3)]_3 OCH_2 \cdot COONa$$

(d) Secondary aliphatic alcohols, such as the mixture of secondary
C_{11}–C_{17} aliphatic alcohols which are obtained *via* ketonisation from a
technical mixture of caproic, oenanthic, caprylic, and pelargonic acids,
or the highly branched 7-ethyl-2-methyl-4-undecanol[1] have also been
condensed with ethylene oxide.[2]

(e) Long-chain alkyl aldehydes[3] and ketones[4] have been condensed with
ethylene oxide to give detergents, wetting-out agents, etc. The general
formula

$$C_{11}H_{23} \cdot CO[CH_2 \cdot CH_2 O]_n CH_2 \cdot CH_2 OH$$

can be assigned to the products from lauryl aldehyde, where *n* is zero or
greater, while those from dioctyl ketone are presumably

$$C_8H_{17} \cdot CO \cdot CH \cdot C_7H_{15}$$
$$[CH_2 \cdot CH_2 O]_n H$$

or, if the condensation takes place with the ketone in the enol form

$$C_8H_{17} \cdot C = CH \cdot C_7H_{15}$$
$$[OCH_2 \cdot CH_2]_n OH$$

(f) Urea,[5] and dimethylolurea[6] have been condensed with ethylene
oxide and the condensates then esterified with fatty acid chlorides to give
complex condensates. Substituted biguanides[7] have also been condensed
with ethylene oxide, a typical product being octadecylbiguanide-9EtO,
which is used as its salicylate or other organic acid salt for softening
textiles. Substituted guanidines have been condensed with ethylene oxide,
to give products such as octadecylguanidine-6EtO,[8] which is both non-
ionic and (at a low enough pH value) cationic.

---

[1] Monsanto and Kosmin, U.S.P. 2,617,830.
[2] Procter and Gamble and Schlegel, U.S.P. 2,355,823.
[3] I.G., Hopff, and Schmidt, U.S.P. 2,095,814.
[4] I.G., B.P. 500,615.
[5] I.C.I. and Piggott, B.P. 420,137.
[6] I.C.I. and Piggott, B.P. 432,356.
[7] I.G., B.P. 511,441.
[8] American Cyanamid, B.P. 650,820.

(*g*) Fatty acid esters (usually, but not always, mono-esters) of anhydro-sorbitols ("sorbitans"), such as

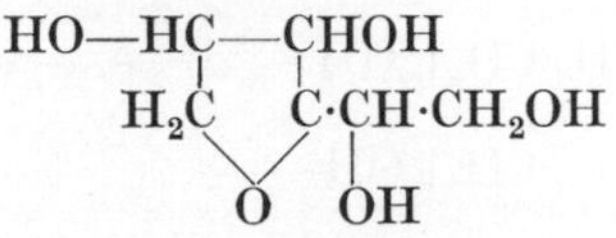

$$HO—HC—CHOH$$
$$H_2C \quad C·CH·CH_2OH$$
$$O \quad OH$$

1:4-anhydrosorbitol

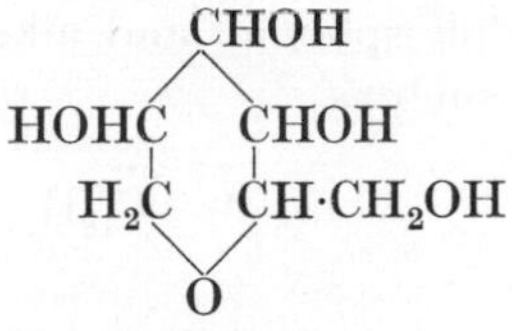

$$CHOH$$
$$HOHC \quad CHOH$$
$$H_2C \quad CH·CH_2OH$$
$$O$$

1:5-anhydrosorbitol

$$O$$
$$HO—HC—CH \quad CH_2$$
$$H_2C \quad CH—CHOH$$
$$O$$

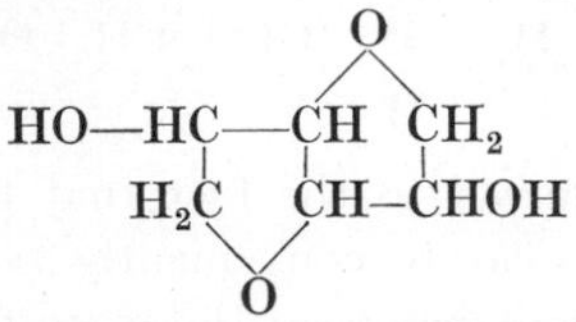

1:4:3:6-dianhydrosorbitol

have been condensed with ethylene oxide.[1] The sorbitan esters themselves (laurates, oleates, and stearates), which are oil soluble, are well known as the "Span" range of products, while their ethylene oxide condensates, which are water-soluble, are the "Tween" emulsifying agents.

(h) Among the other substances which have been proposed for conden-sation with ethylene oxide and other alkylene oxides are soya bean lecithin,[2] "sod oil" and other oils recovered in the manufacture of chamois leather,[3] aliphatic and aromatic sulphinic acids,[4] which would be expected to give condensates of the type illustrated by

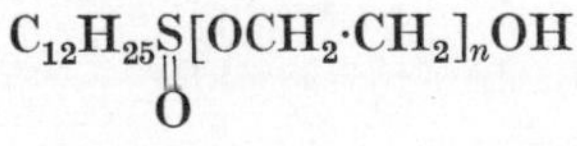

$$C_{12}H_{25}S[OCH_2·CH_2]_nOH$$
$$O$$

cyclic amidines such as undecyliminazoline,[5] yielding for example

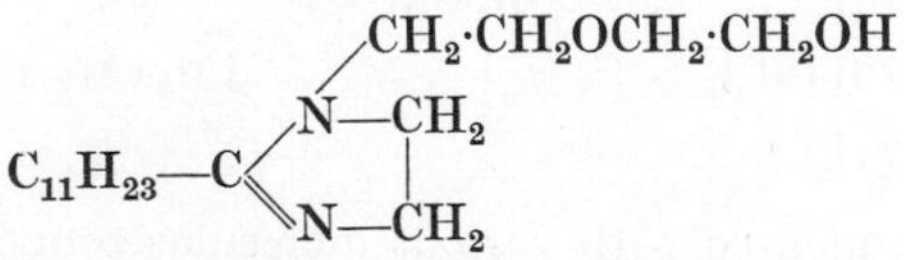

$$CH_2·CH_2OCH_2·CH_2OH$$
$$N—CH_2$$
$$C_{11}H_{23}—C$$
$$N—CH_2$$

alkylaminotriazoles[6] such as

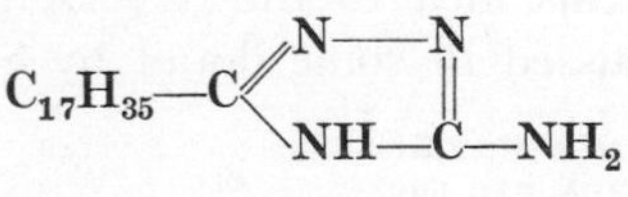

$$N——N$$
$$C_{17}H_{35}—C$$
$$NH—C—NH_2$$

[1] I.G., Schmidt and Meyer, U.S.P. 1,959,930; Atlas Powder Co. and Brown, U.S.P. 2,322,820–1; Atlas Powder Co. and Griffin, U.S.P. 2,380,166.
[2] Petrolite Corporation, de Groote, and Keiser, U.S.P. 2,310,679.
[3] I.C.I., Piggott, and White, B.P. 434,424; *cf.* F.P. 785,800.
[4] Hentrich and Gündel, U.S.P. 2,378,551.
[5] I.G. and Chwala, B.P. 512,846.
[6] I.G., B.P. 520,394.

abietic acid,[1] N-monoethanolamides of abietic acid,[2] dehydroabietinyl *prim.* amine,[3] and alkylbenzene sulphonamides.[4] Polyethenoxy derivatives of alkylphosphonic[5] and alkenyl phosphonous[6] acids have also been described, such as

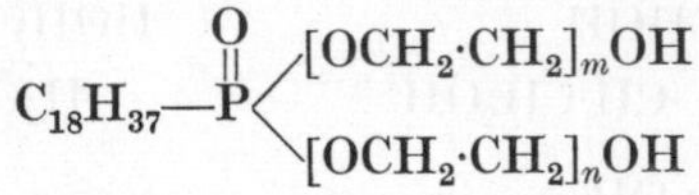

$$C_{18}H_{37}-\overset{\overset{\textstyle O}{\|}}{P}\Big\langle\begin{array}{l}[OCH_2{\cdot}CH_2]_mOH\\[OCH_2{\cdot}CH_2]_nOH\end{array}$$

and

$$C_{12}H_{23}-\overset{\overset{\textstyle O}{\|}}{\underset{\textstyle H}{P}}-[OCH_2{\cdot}CH_2]_nOH.$$

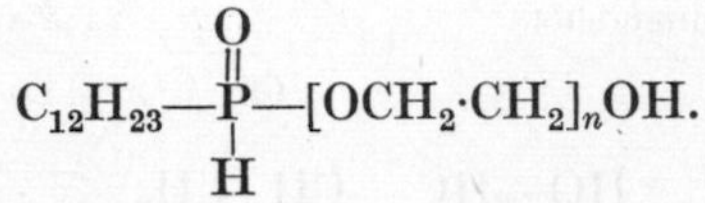

We have already referred to the fact that the hydrophilic group in polyethenoxy compounds can be conveniently varied in small increments. An interesting development has been the more recent discovery that the *hydrophobic* portion of the molecule can also be varied in small steps. This is due to the fact that polymers of propylene and butylene oxides,

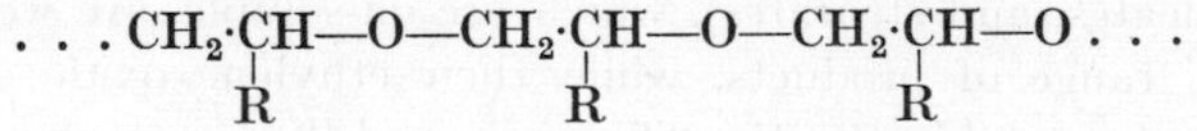

$$\ldots CH_2{\cdot}\underset{\textstyle R}{CH}-O-CH_2{\cdot}\underset{\textstyle R}{CH}-O-CH_2{\cdot}\underset{\textstyle R}{CH}-O\ldots$$

where R is CH_3 or C_2H_5, are essentially hydrophobic.[7] Structures such as

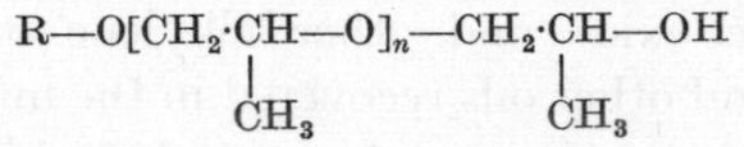

$$R-O[CH_2{\cdot}\underset{\textstyle CH_3}{CH}-O]_n-CH_2{\cdot}\underset{\textstyle CH_3}{CH}-OH \tag{I}$$

(where R may vary from methyl to hexadecyl),

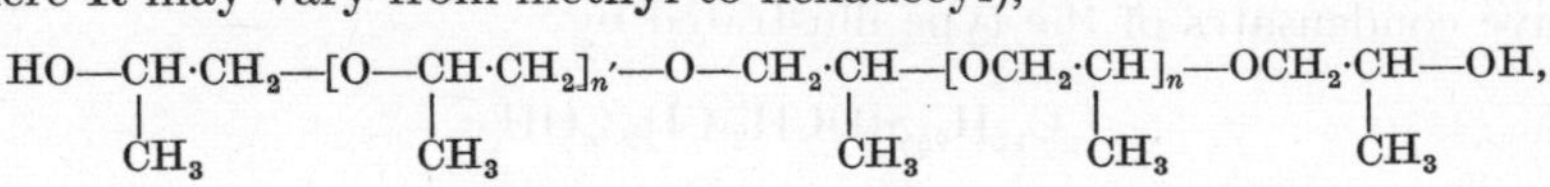

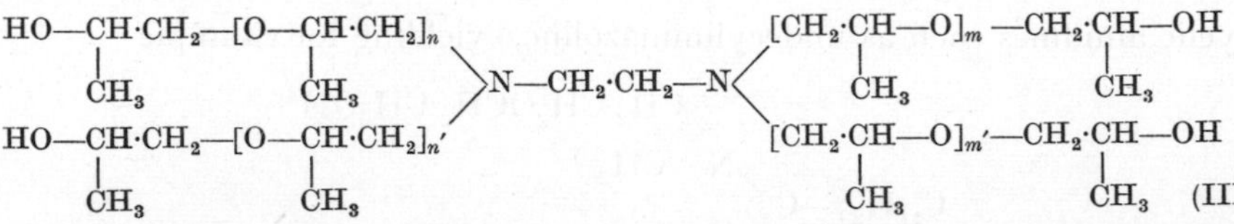

$$HO-\underset{\textstyle CH_3}{CH{\cdot}}CH_2-[O-\underset{\textstyle CH_3}{CH{\cdot}}CH_2]_{n'}-O-CH_2{\cdot}\underset{\textstyle CH_3}{CH}-[O\underset{\textstyle CH_3}{CH_2{\cdot}CH}]_n-O\underset{\textstyle CH_3}{CH_2{\cdot}CH}-OH, \tag{II}$$

and

which are then condensed with various molecular proportions of ethylene oxide, have been proposed.

The application of this idea to the development of the "Pluronic" products has been discussed in some detail by Stanton.[8] He points out

[1] Monsanto and Morrill, U.S.P. 2,519,780.

[2] American Cyanamid, B.P. 716,128.

[3] General Aniline and Sanders, U.S.P. 2,703,797.

[4] Henkel, B.P. 678,004.

[5] California Research Corp., Lewis, and Stayner, U.S.P. 2,670,367.

[6] California Research Corp. and Stayner, U.S.P. 2,686,803.

[7] Wyandotte and Lunsted, B.P. 722,746 and U.S.P. 2,674,619; Wyandotte, Lunsted, and Langdon, B.P. 776,661; Wyandotte, Jackson, and Lunsted, U.S.P. 2,677,700. See also Dow Chemical Co. and Spriggs, U.S.P. 2,828,345.

[8] Stanton, *Soap and Chemical Specialties*, 1957, **33**, No. 6, 47.

that a "block" polymer of propylene glycol is made (usually with a molecular weight between 800 and 2,500), the size of this "block" enabling the hydrophobic part of the final surface-active molecule to be controlled. The block polymer is mono-functional or di-functional towards ethylene oxide, depending on whether a monohydric or dihydric alcohol is used as the starting material, as in (I) or (II) respectively. In the "Tetronic" products, ethylene diamine is used as the starting material for the block polymer, which can therefore form *four* polyethenoxy chains (III)*. The products are named and numbered systematically with reference to the molecular weight of the block, and to the amount of ethylene oxide with which it is condensed, and performance is correlated with a "screen" plot, in which the molecular weight of the block polymer is given vertically, and the percentage of condensed ethylene oxide is given horizontally. The products, which cover the range of molecular weight between 1,000 and 27,000, are stated to be useful as relatively non-foaming detergents and dispersing agents, and to have good solubility in water, including hot water.

It has also been proposed to convert polypropylene glycol condensates into anionic/non-ionic surface-active agents such as

$$C_8H_{17}\text{---}[OCH_2\cdot CH]_n\text{---}OCH_2\cdot COO^-, \ Na^+$$
$$\underset{\displaystyle CH_3}{|}$$

where n averages between 5 and 6.[1]

The uses and properties which have been claimed for the polyethenoxy agents probably cover a wider range than for any other class of surface-active agent. A perusal of the patents to which reference has already been made shows that they have been claimed to be wetting-out, emulsifying, and "dispersing" agents, detergents, textile softening agents, finishing agents, deflocculating agents in non-aqueous media, and dyeing assistants. Although the general claims in any given patent specification are usually so broadly drawn that every claim cannot be expected to apply to every possible product coming within the scope of the patent, there is no doubt of the great versatility of the polyethenoxy agents considered as a class. This versatility is to a large extent due to the compatibility of these agents with concentrated solutions of electrolytes, to their solubility in non-aqueous

---

* Dr. W. Baird has pointed out to us that (I), (II), and (III) are probably simplified formulae, since the condensation of an alcohol, for example, with propylene oxide can give both primary and secondary alcohols,

$$ROCH(CH_3)\cdot CH_2OH \text{ and } ROCH_2\cdot CH(OH)\cdot CH_3,$$

depending on the catalyst, etc. (*cf.* Chitwood and Freure, *J. Amer. Chem. Soc.*, 1946, **68**, 680). In formula (III) there is the further complication that the hydroxyl group which is formed by the addition of the first propylene oxide to an amine group is likely to be more reactive in the subsequent condensation than the three remaining hydrogens which are attached to nitrogen, which may also vary in this respect. The four integers n, n', m, and m' may therefore differ considerably; *i.e.*, the structure (III) may be highly unsymmetrical.

[1] Dow Chemical Co., Britton, and Petrie, U.S.P. 2,745,857.

media, to the fact that the hydrophilic nature of the polar group can be increased in small increments, and to the large number of starting materials which can be used. These properties lie behind many of the uses indicated above, or described in Chapters 5–9, and are the basis of the specialised applications described in the patent literature, a few of which are worth a brief mention here.

Polyethenoxy surface-active agents have been claimed to be effective for preventing the fouling of the fine spinning jets which are used for spinning cellulose xanthate solutions into acid coagulating baths in the manufacture of viscose rayon.[1] Their use has also been described in latex-dipping processes,[2] in the dyeing of wool with metal complexes of acid dyestuffs,[3] for preparing emulsified intaglio printing inks,[4] and as surface-active agents in the emulsion-polymerisation of butadiene.[5] They have even been incorporated in blasting compositions (such as mixtures of ammonium and sodium nitrates, woodmeal, cellulose nitrate, and nitroglycerine) in order to improve their plasticity.[6] Finally, it is interesting to note the claim[7] that the technical properties of certain polyethenoxy agents can be improved by the addition of water-insoluble amphipathic substances: the addition of one part of dodecylethanolamine to two parts of oleyl alcohol-20EtO, for example, is stated to convert the latter into a good detergent for wool.

A good illustration of the unusual applications of polyethenoxy agents, many of which are due to their good solubility in electrolyte solutions, is the use of "Lissapol N" (an alkylphenol-EtO condensate) for washing fuel oil tanks in ships at sea. The procedure followed is illustrated by the following quotation from the manufacturers' files:[8]

"The technique was then tried out on a large scale in ships on the run from Singapore to Sydney, several tanks being treated with Lissapol N. The treatment consisted of flushing the tanks with sea water so as to remove as much oil as possible; they were then two-thirds filled with sea-water and Lissapol N added from time to time during filling, so that the final concentration was $\frac{1}{2}$ oz. Lissapol N per gallon of sea-water.* The solution was left in the tanks for about 48 hours, agitation being obtained by the movement of the ship. In most cases the treatment was carried out without heating but on one vessel the solution in the tanks was heated to about 40° c. After treatment the detergent solution was pumped overboard and

---

* This corresponds to a concentration of about 0·3%.
[1] American Viscose and Collins, U.S.P. 2,359,749–50; 2,519,227.
[2] U.S. Rubber and Ogilby, U.S.P. 2,215,562.
[3] I.G., B.P. 411,474; cf. U.S.P. 2,040,796 and F.P. 747,043.
[4] I.G., B.P. 414,801.
[5] I.G., D.R.P. 711,840.
[6] I.C.I., Fordham, and Moilliet, B.P. 586,224.
[7] I.G., B.P. 425,680.
[8] Private communication from Dr. S. H. Oakeshott, Polymer and Chemicals Service Department, Imperial Chemical Industries Limited, Dyestuffs Division.

the tanks flushed with plain sea-water. No further cleaning was done, and when the tanks were opened, the interiors were clean enough for Lloyds' surveyor to carry out an examination of the ship's plates. Previously cleaning had to be done by hand."

The information given in the I.G. patents which have been discussed above can be usefully checked and amplified by reference to the reports by Brandner, Lockwood, Nagel, and Russell (*loc. cit.*), by Baird,[1] and by Brown.[2] These reports, which are still of considerable use, give a number of recipes, such as that for the preparation of "Emulphor O" by condensing sperm oil alcohols with ethylene oxide at 150°–160° c. in the presence of sodium hydroxide as a catalyst. The first report also gives a useful index of German surface-active agents of all types, reference to which shows that the starting materials which were condensed with ethylene oxide included fatty alcohols from the catalytic reduction of glycerides such as coconut oil, synthetic alcohols (*cf.* Chapter 11, pp. 412 ff), oleyl alcohol, alkylated phenols of various degrees of purity, dioctadecyldiethanolamine, oleic and stearic acids, castor oil, dihydroabietyl alcohol, alkylated β-naphthols, oleylamine ($C_{18}H_{35}NH_2$), diethanolamine stearate, and stearoethanolamide. In a few cases the polyethenoxy agents were further solubilised by sulphation of the terminal hydroxyl group, yielding for example iso-octylphenol-3EtO-sulphate ("Igepal B. conc.") and hexyl/heptyl-β-naphthol-4EtO-sulphate ("Leonil LS"). The applications disclosed for these products are similar to those which we have already enumerated, and they are as varied.

One of the most interesting properties of the polyethenoxy surface-active agents is their negative temperature coefficient of solubility. It was suggested by Chwala and Martina[3] that water molecules are bound to the ether oxygen atoms in the polyethenoxy chains by hydrogen bonds:

$$ROCH_2 \cdot CH_2OCH_2 \cdot CH_2 \ldots OH,$$
$$\downarrow$$
$$HOH$$

and that this is the solubilising mechanism. This picture of the formation of weak oxonium bases is in agreement with the fact that polyethenoxy agents tend to be feebly cationic in acid media, and that they form insoluble precipitates with phosphomolybdic acid, a reaction which can be used to determine them analytically.[4] It seems to be generally agreed that an increasing proportion of the relatively weak hydrogen bonds break down as the temperature rises, and that the destruction of this particular solubilising mechanism (even though it may not be the only one) is responsible for the negative temperature coefficient of solubility.

---

[1] Baird, B.I.O.S. Final Report 421, "Textile Auxiliary Products."

[2] Brown, B.I.O.S. Final Report 418, "Textile Auxiliary Products."

[3] Chwala and Martina, *Textilber.*, 1937, **18**, 992. See also Chwala, *Textilhilfsmittel*, Springer, Vienna, 1939.

[4] Oliver and Preston, *Nature*, 1949, **164**, 242.

An interesting qualitative summary of the physical and technical properties of a series of dodecyl alcohol-EtO condensates, which was obtained from the I.G. chemists, has been published by Brandner, Lockwood, Nagel, and Russell in diagrammatic form.[1] Although a considerable amount of further information has been published in the past ten years, much of it quantitative, this summary is still worth reproducing here. The German workers had compared the properties of the technical products, as functions of the average number of ether groups in the molecule, with those of analogues which were stated to be "pure" (*i.e.*, chemically homogeneous), which were prepared from dodecyl alcohol and polyethylene glycols, the results being summarised in the following table:

Table 8
Dodecyl alcohol-ethylene oxide condensates—Effect of number of polyether groups on physical and technical properties

Property	Effect of Increasing Number of Polyether Groups between 3 and 16 on	
	(I) Technical (mixed) Product	(II) "Pure" (chemically homogeneous) Preparation
Solubility	Increases regularly	Increases regularly, remaining below (I)
Surface Tension	Decreases regularly	Decreases regularly, remaining below (I)
Interfacial Tension against Paraffin Oil	Rises to 5EtO, then decreases regularly	Decreases regularly from 5EtO to 9EtO, remaining below (I)
Interfacial Tension against Olive Oil	Rises from 4EtO to 5EtO, then decreases regularly to 16EtO	Decreases regularly from 5EtO to 9EtO, crossing (I) at 6EtO
Foaming Power	Increases regularly from 3EtO to 6EtO, then remains constant to 16EtO	Increases regularly to 5EtO, above (I), then remains constant to 6EtO
Wetting Power, immersion test	Increases regularly to 16EtO	Increases regularly to 16EtO, remaining above (I)
Wetting Power, sinking test ("laying on")	Increases regularly to 5EtO, then decreases regularly to 9EtO	Parallel to (I), but remains higher
Detergent Power, olive oil on wool, neutral	Increases from 3EtO to 4EtO, then decreases regularly to 16EtO	Increases regularly to 5EtO, crossing (I) at 4EtO, decreases to 9EtO
Detergent Power, olive oil on wool, alkaline	Similar to detergent power in neutral solution	Increases regularly to 6EtO, then falls to 9EtO
Lime soap-dispersing power	Increases regularly from 3EtO to 16EtO	Increases regularly from 3EtO to 9EtO, remaining above (I)
Levelling action (wool dyestuffs)	Increases regularly from 3EtO to 16EtO	Increases regularly from 3EtO to 6EtO, remaining above (I)

[1] Brandner, Lockwood, Nagel, and Russell, *loc. cit.*, p. 11. This diagram is also given in a captured internal I.G. report by Günther and Valko, dated 30.9.35, reference PB 70344 (86–153).

The physico-chemical, technological, and biological properties of the polyethenoxy surface-active agents have been comprehensively summarised by Schönfeldt,[1] who gives over 400 references, and a particularly useful summary (pp. 181–195) of the published information on the effect of the number of EtO-groups on the different properties, some of which can be briefly noted here:

(*i*) The "cloud-point," *i.e.*, the temperature at which one or more of the components in a dissolved polyethenoxy agent begin to come out of aqueous solution, increases approximately linearly with increasing number of EtO-groups. The cloud-point of a given agent is also higher the higher its concentration, and is higher for a straight-chain aliphatic hydrophobic residue than for an octylcresol. (These last two results suggest that solubility is to a considerable extent determined by the formation of micelles, *cf.* Chapter 2, p. 26.)

(*ii*) Although the critical micelle concentration decreases, as would be expected, with increasing length of a simple straight-chain hydrophobic group, it does not appear to be greatly influenced by the number of EtO-groups in the polyethenoxy chain. With nonylphenol-EtO condensation products, the effect of the number of EtO groups appears to be greater, the 25EtO and 30EtO products having higher critical micelle concentrations, by about a power of ten, than the 6EtO and 10EtO condensates.

(*iii*) The wetting-out power of the nonylphenol-EtO condensates goes through an optimum at about 9–12EtO. The structure of the alkylphenyl residue is important, with optimum wetting-out power at C_7–C_{10} for a monoalkylated phenol, and at C_4–C_7 for each alkyl group in a dialkylated phenol.

(*iv*) The emulsifying power of a series of tallow fatty alcohol-EtO condensates was at a maximum at about 8EtO.

(*v*) The foam-stabilising effect of nonylphenol-EtO condensates was at a maximum at about 18EtO, while that of a series of tallow fatty alcohol-EtO condensates went through a maximum at about 10EtO.

(*vi*) A number of investigations agree in general with the observation in Table 8 that there is an optimum number of EtO for detergent power. This is perhaps most clearly shown by the results of Kehren and Rösch,[2] on the scouring of wool with condensates of *normal* decyl, dodecyl, tetradecyl, hexadecyl, and octadecyl alcohols, in neutral, alkaline, and acid solutions. The optimum number of moles of ethylene oxide under each set of pH conditions increased regularly with increasing chain length of the parent fatty alcohol. With each fatty alcohol, the optimum number of moles of ethylene oxide increased regularly as the scouring conditions were altered in the direction of decreasing pH. We have already referred above to

---

[1] Schönfeldt, *loc. cit.*, Chapter III, pp. 81–195.
[2] Kehren and Rösch, *Textilber.*, 1956, **37**, 1194, 1308, 1421.

the experiments of Karabinos and Quinn on fractionated dodecyl alcohol-EtO condensates, which showed that the optimum number of EtO for dirt-removal and for dirt-suspension, respectively, are not identical.

Finally, a paper which seems to us to merit special study is that of Wrigley, Smith, and Stirton,[1] who made a systematic comparison of a range of fatty acids and fatty alcohols which had been condensed with 10, 15, 20, 30, and 40 moles of ethylene oxide. They found that the fatty alcohol derivatives were more soluble and were better textile wetting-out agents and foam stabilisers, while the fatty acid derivatives gave greater lowerings of the surface tensions of aqueous solutions and of interfacial tensions against oil. Both types were good emulsifying agents and good detergents in the presence of "builders" (*cf.* p. 308).

B. Surface-active derivatives of polyglycerols

The surface-active derivatives of the glycerol polyethers are similar to the polyethenoxy agents in that they are based on non-ionic solubilising groups which contain recurring ether oxygen atoms, as expressed in the simplest possible general formula:

$$R[OC_3H_5OH]_nOH$$

in which R is (or contains) a hydrophobic group. They differ in being probably even more complicated mixtures: not only do they tend to be mixtures of individual compounds characterised by different values of n in the above formula, but even the compounds which have the same value of n may be mixtures of isomers, characterised by different structures of the grouping $—[OC_3H_5OH]_nOH$. This possible existence of large numbers of isomers is of course due to the fact that glycerol, which is a trihydric alcohol, may condense to form branched as well as linear "polymers."

The complexity of the polyglycerol derivatives can be seen by considering the polyglycerols themselves. There are for example three possible diglycerols:

$$\underset{\underset{\displaystyle OH}{|}}{HOCH_2 \cdot CH} \cdot CH_2OCH_2 \cdot \underset{\underset{\displaystyle OH}{|}}{CH} \cdot CH_2OH \qquad (I)$$

$$\begin{array}{c} HOCH_2 \cdot \underset{\underset{\displaystyle OCH_2 \cdot \underset{\underset{\displaystyle OH}{|}}{CH} \cdot CH_2OH}{|}}{CH} \cdot CH_2OH \end{array} \qquad (II)$$

$$\begin{array}{c} HOCH_2 \cdot \underset{\underset{\displaystyle O}{|}}{CH} \cdot CH_2OH \\ HOCH_2 \cdot CH \cdot CH_2OH \end{array} \qquad (III)$$

[1] Wrigley, Smith, and Stirton, *J. Amer. Oil Chem. Soc.*, 1957, **34**, 39.

If now a "diglycerol" which is a mixture of isomers (I), (II), and (III) is esterified or etherified with an equimolecular proportion of a fatty acid or a fatty alcohol, respectively, isomer (I) can form two isomeric esters (or ethers), (II) can form three, and (III) can form one, though the different reactivities of the different hydroxyl groups should be borne in mind. Apart from the fact that the fatty substituents may not be uniformly distributed among the three diglycerols, there are already six theoretically possible "diglycerol monostearates," for example. When higher polymers of glycerol are involved, the possibilities for the formation of chemical mixtures are obviously enormously increased.

Two general methods have been used for preparing surface-active poly-glycerol derivatives, which again recall the preparation of the poly-ethenoxy agents. The first and most important is illustrated by patents granted to the Emulsol Corporation[1] and to Harris.[2] In these specifications, glycerol was polymerised and then esterified with fatty acids such as those from coconut oil, oleic acid, stearic acid, or mixtures of fatty acids. Alternatively, the polymerisation and esterification steps were combined by heating polyglycerol with a glyceride of the fatty acid, or even by heating glycerol itself with a fatty glyceride so that polymerisation and esterification proceeded simultaneously. B.P. 452,138 emphasised the preparation of polyglyceryl esters which are suitable for incorporation in edible fats, claiming *inter alia* that they can be used to prevent spattering of fats during frying. It has also been proposed partially to esterify the free hydroxyl groups in polyglyceryl fatty esters made in this way: Schou,[3] for example, described the preparation of a polyglycerol which is partially esterified with acetic and stearic acids, the product being claimed as an emulsifying agent.

The condensation of polyglycerols with long-chain alkyl mercaptans, thiophenol, and thionaphthol has also been described.[4]

The second method of preparing polyglycerol derivatives is based on the reaction of glycide

$$HOCH_2 \cdot CH \cdot CH_2$$
$$\diagdown O \diagup$$

with a reactive hydrogen in a substance which is itself not water-soluble.[5] The lists of substances which were stated to be suitable for condensation with at least two molecular proportions of glycide are reminiscent of those in the I.G. patents on condensations with ethylene oxide, including for example fatty acids, fatty alcohols, phenols, amines, and acid amides. The

---

[1] Emulsol, B.P. 452,138.
[2] Harris, U.S.P. 2,022,766 and U.S.P. 2,023,388.
[3] Schou, B.P. 538,717.
[4] I.G., Schütte, Schöller, and Wittwer, U.S.P. 2,205,021.
[5] I.G., B.P. 420,884; B.P. 420,903; U.S.P. 2,089,569.

general formulae for the condensation products of a fatty acid and of a fatty alcohol, each with two molecular proportions of glycide, were given respectively as

$$R \cdot COOCH_2 \cdot \underset{\underset{OH}{|}}{CH} \cdot CH_2OCH_2 \cdot \underset{\underset{OH}{|}}{CH} \cdot CH_2OR_1$$

and

$$ROCH_2 \cdot \underset{\underset{OH}{|}}{CH} \cdot CH_2OCH_2 \cdot \underset{\underset{OH}{|}}{CH} \cdot CH_2OR_1$$

in which R is the long-chain alkyl group and R_1 is hydrogen or a lower alkyl group. These formulae, which take no account of the possible formation of isomers, are almost certainly over-simplified. The products were claimed to be wetting-out agents, dispersing agents, softening agents for textiles, etc., the condensation product of dodecyl alcohol with three molecular proportions of glycide being described as a detergent. It is interesting to note that the condensation product of linoleic acid with approximately 4–5 molecular proportions of glycide, which is not soluble in water, was stated to facilitate the emulsification of linseed oil with a water-soluble surface-active agent, Turkey Red Oil.

The polyglycerol derivatives of B.P. 420,884 and B.P. 420,903 were stated to be capable of further solubilisation by esterification with organic acids, by sulphation, or by condensation with ethylene oxide. The two specifications give the impression, in fact, that such an after-treatment is preferable, and describe for example the sulphation of the condensation products of lauric acid and dodecyl alcohol with three molecular proportions of glycide, and the condensation of dodecyl alcohol with three molecular proportions of glycide and then with approximately forty molecular proportions of ethylene oxide.

Polyglycerol esters have also been described in which the fatty acid residues, which are derived from drying or semi-drying oils, are themselves presumably "polymeric." Thus Schou[1] prepared a polyglycerol by heating glycerol at 260° c. for 72 hours, in an inert atmosphere and in the presence of sodium acetate as a catalyst. The polyglycerol, which was described as "colloidal," was then esterified with soya bean oil, and the ester finally subjected to an oxidising polymerisation in air. This procedure was varied in a later specification[2] in which Schou heat-polymerised soya bean oil, for example, by air-blowing until gelatinisation began, after which it was further condensed with a polyglyceryl palmitate which contained free hydroxyl groups.

The polyglyceryl esters of fatty acids, containing free hydroxyl groups, are usually oily or wax-like substances which contain free glycerol and/or polyglycerol. Lever Brothers, Furness, and Fairbourne[3] have described a

---

[1] Schou, B.P. 494,639.

[2] Schou, B.P. 537,275.

[3] Lever Brothers, Furness, and Fairbourne, B.P. 439,435; U.S.P. 2,154,977; F.P. 795,663.

method for obtaining the coconut oil fatty acid partial ester of polyglycerol, for example, as a powder by the addition of inorganic sulphates and other salts. The purification of similar polyglycerol partial fatty esters from glycerol and polyglycerol, by extraction with concentrated solutions of inorganic salts in which the surface-active material is insoluble, is described in another patent from the same firm.[1]

One of the most important characteristics of the polyglyceryl fatty esters is that many of them are edible and non-toxic, so that they can be used for making margarine and other emulsions which are to be eaten or administered internally. This use is claimed or mentioned in a number of the patent specifications mentioned above, along with claims to general emulsifying, detergent, and wetting-out properties, etc. A number of more specialised or unusual uses are also worth mentioning. The I.G., for example, stated that xylyl polyglyceryl ether, mixed with 10% of butylene glycol, is an effective wetting-out agent for mercerising baths.[2] I.C.I. have described the use of esters such as polyglyceryl oleate or polyglyceryl ricinoleate for improving the fastness to rubbing of wool dyeings,[3] in admixture with cetylpyridinium bromide for improving the dyeing of sheepskins and other soft furs with acid dyestuffs,[4] and for making self-emulsifiable compositions of the medicinal product tetraethylthiuram monosulphide.[5] Finally, an interesting war-time application, described by Kingan and Sadd[6] of the Chemical Defence Research Department of the Ministry of Supply, is the use of partial fatty esters of polyglycerol as anti-dimming agents on the eyepieces of respirators, windscreens, windows, etc. The specification states that thin films of the product of B.P. 439,435, for example, will prevent dimming for longer periods than other devices such as applying glycerine or nicotine. The function of the surface-active agent in this application is to give a low (or vanishing) contact angle for water on the glass surface, so that drops of condensed moisture will spread out into uniformly thin films.

C. Other non-ionic surface-active agents

The fatty esters of unpolymerised ethylene glycol are well known as emulsifying agents. Examples of these agents are glycol dioleate

$$C_{17}H_{33}{\cdot}COOCH_2$$
$$C_{17}H_{33}{\cdot}COOCH_2$$

---

[1] Lever Brothers and Furness, B.P. 442,950.
[2] I.G., German Patent Application I.48725, as laid open to public inspection.
[3] I.C.I., Baldwin, and Woolvin, B.P. 450,868; U.S.P. 2,116,553; F.P. 801,131.
[4] I.C.I. and Burchill, B.P. 542,171.
[5] I.C.I., Collie, Kay, and Moilliet, B.P. 561,838; *cf.* Chapter 6, p. 251.
[6] Kingan and Sadd, B.P. 574,736.

and glycol monostearate

$$C_{17}H_{35} \cdot COOCH_2 \cdot CH_2OH$$

The partial esters of glycerol, for example glycerol monostearate, are also widely used. Both these types of surface-active agents are insoluble in water, but soluble in oils. Their chemistry has been reviewed by Goldsmith,[1] who also gives a useful survey, with references, of the chemistry of the polyglycol and polyglycerol derivatives.

Fatty acid esters of other polyhydroxy compounds are also used, or have been proposed, as non-ionic surface-active agents. Examples are provided by the fatty esters of the hexahydroxyethyl ether of sorbitol or the tetrahydroxyethyl ether of pentaerythritol,[2] and by the fatty esters of anhydro sorbitols and mannitols.[3]

Many of the above-mentioned compounds, especially among those which are water-insoluble, have been used as starting materials for sulphation or for condensation with ethylene oxide.

An interesting type of non-ionic surface-active agent, which is described by Schwartz and Perry,[4] can be represented by the general formula

$$R \cdot CON \Big\langle \begin{matrix} CH_2 \cdot CH_2OH \\ CH_2 \cdot CH_2OH \end{matrix}$$

It is prepared by heating diethanolamine with a fatty acid; when for example RCOOH denotes the fatty acids which are derived from coconut oil, a water-soluble detergent is obtained. The chemistry of this reaction has been studied by Kroll and Nadeau,[5] who confirm that the active agent is in fact the N : N-bis(2-hydroxyethyl)lauramide, though several other reaction products can be and are formed. The diethanolamides, which are chemically identical with the symmetrical version of the type $R \cdot CONH_2$-2EtO, should not be confused with the cationic surface-active agents which are obtained by esterifying one or more of the hydroxyl groups in triethanolamine with a fatty acid (*cf.* Chapter 13, p. 448).

A special class of surface-active agent, which resembles the polyethylene glycol and polyglycerol derivatives in containing polar groups with recurring ether oxygen atoms, has been described in a series of patents issued to the du Pont Company. These are derivatives of polymerised 1 : 3-dioxolanes, which are characterised by the recurrent grouping —$OCH_2 \cdot CH_2OCH_2$—. The polymerised 1 : 3-dioxolanes themselves are stated to be wetting-out agents as long as they are of low molecular weight, the higher polymers (molecular weights over 10,000) to have film-forming

---

[1] Goldsmith, *Chem. Rev.*, 1943, **33**, 257.
[2] I.G., B.P. 375,842; F.P. 716,458; U.S.P. 1,959,930; D.R.P. 544,921 and 628,715.
[3] Atlas Powder and Brown, U.S.P. 2,322,820–1–2.
[4] Schwartz and Perry, *Surface-Active Agents*, Interscience, 1949, p. 212 ff.
[5] Kroll and Nadeau, *J. Amer. Oil Chem. Soc.*, 1957, **34**, 323.

or even fibre-forming properties.[1] The polymerised 1 : 3-dioxolanes which have been substituted with long alkyl chains, for example, are reminiscent of the polyethenoxy compounds, both in their structure and in the properties which have been claimed for them, including high surface-activity in acid media. Examples are afforded by the derivatives based on stearic acid,[2] lauric acid,[3] and dodecyl alcohol,[4] to which the following three general formulae can be assigned:

$$C_{17}H_{35}\cdot CO[OCH_2\cdot CH_2OCH_2]_nOH$$
$$C_{11}H_{23}\cdot CO[OCH_2\cdot CH_2OCH_2]_nOH$$
$$C_{12}H_{25}[OCH_2\cdot CH_2OCH_2]_nOH$$

The polyvinyl alcohols also belong, strictly speaking, to the non-ionic surface-active agents, but it has seemed more convenient to discuss them in Chapter 15, along with other surface-active polymers.

Sucrose is used as a hydrophilic solubilising group in the interesting fatty acid esters ("sugar detergents"), the synthesis of which has been developed by Osipow, Snell, and co-workers.[5] The esters in question are, for example, the monolaurate and the monostearate of sucrose: they have been reported[6] to have good detergent power and to be non-toxic. Unlike many of the polyethenoxy surface-active agents, they exhibit no cloud-point below 100° c. Their critical micelle concentrations (*ca.* 34×10^{-5} *molar* for the monolaurate and 64×10^{-7} *molar* for the monostearate) indicate that they are highly micellar. They form mixed micelles at still lower concentrations with sodium dodecyl sulphate and with a lauric acid-EtO condensate.[7]

A very recent proposal[8] for making surface-active agents based on sugar is to react alkyl (*e.g.*, octadecyl) isocyanates with sugar, giving a urethane link between each fatty chain and the sucrose residue R:

$$C_{18}H_{37}NCO + ROH \rightarrow C_{18}H_{37}NHCOOR$$

In conclusion, the substituted betaines can perhaps be considered to be non-ionic surface-active agents. Examples of this class include N-dodecyl-N : N-dimethylbetaine[9]

$$C_{12}H_{25}\overset{+}{N}(CH_3)_2CH_2\cdot COO^-$$

[1] Du Pont and Gresham, U.S.P. 2,394,910.

[2] Du Pont, Loder, and Gresham, U.S.P. 2,366,737.

[3] Du Pont, Loder, and Gresham, U.S.P. 2,366,738.

[4] Du Pont and Gresham, U.S.P. 2,395,265.

[5] Osipow, Snell, York, and Finchler, *Ind. Eng. Chem.*, 1956, **48,** 1459. See also Hass, *Manufacturing Chemist*, 1958, **29,** 152.

[6] Osipow, Snell, Marra, and York, *Ind. Eng. Chem.*, 1956, **48,** 1462.

[7] Osipow, Snell, and Hickson, *Second Congress*, 1957, **I,** 50.

[8] Bayer, B.P. 827,358.

[9] I.G., F.P. 789,304.

the condensation product of N : N-dimethylglycine with the chloromethyl ether of octadecyl alcohol, which is probably N-octadecyloxymethyl-N : N-dimethylbetaine[1]

$$C_{18}H_{37}OCH_2\overset{+}{N}(CH_3)_2CH_2 \cdot COO^-$$

and the water-proofing agent "Persistol KF," which according to Baird, Brown, and Perdue[2] is N-octadecyloxymethyl-N : N-diethylbetaine.

More recently, sulphobetaines[3] have been described, including quaternised taurine derivatives such as

$$C_{12}H_{25}\!\!-\!\!\left\langle\;\right\rangle\!\!-\!\!CH_2 \!\!\diagdown\!\!\underset{C_{12}H_{25}\!\!-\!\!\left\langle\;\right\rangle\!\!-\!\!CH_2 \;\; CH_3}{\overset{+}{N}}\!\!-\!\!CH_2 \cdot CH_2\!\!-\!\!SO_3{}^-,$$

and quaternary phosphono-ammonium compounds,[4] such as

$$\underset{CH_3}{\overset{+}{\underset{|}{C_{18}H_{37}\!\!-\!\!N}}}\!\!-\!\!CH_2 \cdot CH_2\!\!-\!\!PO_3{}^{--}, \; Na^+$$

(Since the surface-active unit in this last case contains a net negative charge of one, it would perhaps have been more logical to have included this reference in Chapter 12.)

The classification of the substituted betaines as "non-ionic" requires some explanation, in view of the fact that they are in reality "zwitterions," *i.e.*, molecular units containing groups which are ionised cationically and groups which are ionised anionically, both types being present in approximately the same numbers, so that the molecule as a whole is electrically neutral. An internally neutralised molecule of this type will probably differ from a typical non-ionic amphipathic molecule in that it will be more affected by the presence of electrolytes and by changes in the pH, becoming cationic in a sufficiently acidic solution, and that the hydrating effect of the "zwitterionic" grouping will be more like that of an ordinary ionising polar group than that of a single ethenoxy group, for example. As long as it remains a true zwitterion, however, it will probably suffice to consider it as being non-ionic, rather than to set up a new class of "zwitterionic" surface-active agents. The amphoteric properties of this type of agent, to which Schwartz and Perry have drawn attention by including them under "ampholytic" surface-active agents, should nevertheless not be overlooked.

---

[1] I.G., F.P. 851,836; *cf.* U.S.P. 2,217,846.

[2] Baird, Brown, and Perdue, B.I.O.S. Final Report 518, "Textile Auxiliary Products of I.G. Farbenindustrie: Application, Testing, and Miscellaneous Information," p. 9.

[3] California Research Corporation and Stayner, U.S.P. 2,697,116.

[4] General Mills Corporation and Erickson, U.S.P. 2,774,786.

CHAPTER 15

OTHER TYPES OF SURFACE-ACTIVE MATERIALS

In the present final chapter we propose to describe a number of types of surface-active materials, including some special mixtures, which are not readily classifiable under the headings which have already been discussed. Many of these miscellaneous types are chemically ill-defined, but their technical importance is such that the present monograph would not be complete without reference to them.

A. Surface-active macromolecules and polymers

Naturally occurring macromolecular materials, such as the water-soluble proteins and gums, are well known protective colloids, and are still very widely used for stabilising emulsions and other disperse systems. Modern synthetic polymers and specially modified macromolecules are also used for the same purposes, and it is probably a safe generalisation to say that any substance of very high molecular weight which is water-soluble will have protective colloid properties, at least in certain systems. The function of such soluble polymers and macromolecules is therefore essentially steric and "non-dynamic"—*i.e.*, it is to form hydrated sheaths which will interfere with the coalescence or growth of small particles (*cf.* Chapter 4), rather than to promote dynamic processes such as wetting, emulsion formation, and the like. The use of cellulose sodium glycollate in detergent baths (*cf.* Chapter 8, p. 303), which might perhaps appear to be an exception to this statement, appears in fact to be an illustration of protective colloid action, the function of the cellulose derivative being to prevent re-deposition of the suspended dirt rather than to promote the displacement of dirt from the surface of the fibre. The basis for these particular surface-active properties of water-soluble macromolecules is of course that they tend to be strongly and tenaciously adsorbed at solid-liquid and at liquid-liquid interfaces, but nevertheless to be much more slowly adsorbed than are the simpler amphipathic agents, for example.

The structure and physical properties of synthetic polymeric materials is fully dealt with in standard works such as Ellis's textbook[1] and the series of monographs which have been published under the general editorship of Burk, Mark, and Whitby.[2] We propose to confine ourselves here to illustrations of the surface-active properties of some of the better known types.

---

[1] Ellis, *The Chemistry of Synthetic Resins*, Reinhold, 1935.
[2] *High Polymers*, by various authors, published by Interscience, the series to comprise at least nine volumes.

Polyvinyl alcohol, to which can be assigned the general structural formula

$$\ldots \ \underset{\substack{| \\ OH}}{CH \cdot CH_2} \cdot \underset{\substack{| \\ OH}}{CH \cdot CH_2} \cdot \underset{\substack{| \\ OH}}{CH \cdot CH_2} \ \ldots$$

is well known as a protective colloid, in the sols of classical colloid science[1] as well as in technical dispersions of various kinds. Many technical "polyvinyl alcohols" are not fully saponified, but contain an appreciable number of acetylated hydroxyl groups. It has also been claimed that the "dispersing" and emulsifying efficiency of polyvinyl alcohol is improved by reaction, under not too drastic conditions, with aldehydes such as formaldehyde, butyraldehyde, benzaldehyde, etc., giving acetal or substituted acetal groupings of the type[2]

$$\ldots \ \underset{\substack{| \\ O}}{CH \cdot CH_2} \cdot \underset{\substack{| \\ O}}{CH \cdot CH_2} \ \ldots$$

$$O—\underset{\substack{| \\ R}}{CH}—O$$

in which R is hydrogen, methyl, phenyl, etc. Sulphation of the hydroxyl groups by treatment with sulphuric acid in methanol has also been described.[3]

Other examples of the use of vinyl polymers as surface-active agents are provided by the interpolymers of vinyl ethyl ether and acrylonitrile, which are saponified to give emulsifying agents[4] with structures which contain mixtures of the groupings

$$\ldots \ \underset{\substack{| \\ OCH_2 \cdot CH_3}}{CH \cdot CH} \ \ldots \quad \text{and} \quad \ldots \ \underset{\substack{| \\ COOH}}{CH \cdot CH_2} \ \ldots$$

and by the salts of polyacrylic acid

$$\ldots \ \underset{\substack{| \\ COOH}}{CH \cdot CH_2} \cdot \underset{\substack{| \\ COOH}}{CH \cdot CH_2} \cdot \underset{\substack{| \\ COOH}}{CH \cdot CH_2} \ \ldots$$

and of acrylic acid interpolymers.[5] The second of these two references gives an interesting description of the methods of using these surface-active polymers, for example in plastic-milling processes. The polyvinyl esters of polybasic acids such as phthalic acid have been used as emulsifying agents and protective colloids in coating compositions.[6]

The preparation of more highly amphipathic water-soluble polymers by the introduction of aliphatic side chains has been described by American

---

[1] Consortium für Elektrochemische Industrie, Herrmann, and Haehnel, U.S.P. 1,629,161.

[2] I.G., B.P. 356,408.

[3] I.G., B.P. 513,076; F.P. 851,565.

[4] I.G., B.P. 373,643.

[5] I.G., B.P. 369,915.

[6] I.C.I., Tattersall, and Munro, B.P. 552,011.

Cyanamid,[1] who co-polymerise acrylamide with, for example, 10% of its weight of *n*-dodecyl methacrylate. The products are claimed to have wetting-out and emulsifying properties. It has also been proposed to add acrylonitrile-acrylamide co-polymers to ordinary detergents such as sodium oleyl-N-methyltaurine ("Igepon T").[2]

Considerable interest has been displayed in recent years in polyvinyl pyrrolidone

$$\ldots CH \cdot CH_2 \cdot CH \cdot CH_2 \cdot CH \cdot CH_2 \ldots$$

This type of polymer has good general protective colloid properties in aqueous solution, and was even used as a synthetic blood plasma substitute by the Germans during the Second World War. Its use as a stripping agent for leuco vat dyestuffs, sulphur colours, and direct dyestuffs has been described by Bräuer,[3] who reports that it forms more "stable" complexes than do the polyethenoxy dyeing assistants, and suggests that this is due to polyvinyl pyrrolidone having cationic properties in solution. It has been proposed to introduce hydrophobic groups into vinyl pyrrolidone polymers, for example by co-polymerisation with vinyl laurate.[4]

The salts of the alkyd resins (condensation products of polybasic acids such as phthalic acid, with polyhydric alcohols such as glycerol, which may be modified with fatty acids, colophony, and other monobasic acids) have been used as emulsifying agents.[5] The deflocculating or protective colloid action of these alkyd resin salts on dispersed solids such as pigments, is implicit in a patent dealing with the treatment of textiles,[6] while their use specifically for preparing concentrated dispersible powders of phenothiazine has been more recently described.[7]

Synthetic resins of the urea-formaldehyde type have been used as protective colloids in the dispersion of pigments by controlled precipitation;[8] this patent also describes the use of polyacrylic acid salts for the same purpose. Sulphonated derivatives of phenol-formaldehyde,[9] cresol-formaldehyde,[10] and cresol-urea-formaldehyde[11] condensates have also been

[1] American Cyanamid, B.P. 764,409.
[2] Eastman Kodak Co., Touey, and Coover, U.S.P. 2,805,205.
[3] Bräuer, *Textilber.*, 1951, **32**, 53.
[4] Du Pont and Werntz, U.S.P. 2,497,705.
[5] Du Pont, Barrett, and Dorough, U.S.P. 1,967,220.
[6] I.C.I., Baird, and Siddle, B.P. 359,897.
[7] I.C.I., Collie, and Moilliet, B.P. 550,930.
[8] I.G., B.P. 359,643; *cf.* U.S.P. 1,974,510.
[9] Catalin and Riesenfeld, B.P. 523,222.
[10] Bedford, B.P. 399,533.
[11] Bedford, Bedford, and Storey, B.P. 510,515.

claimed to be "dispersing" and emulsifying agents; their use as tanning agents probably goes back to before 1912.* Condensation products of alkylphenols and formaldehyde have also been condensed with ethylene oxide, sulphated, phosphated, and converted to true sulphonic acids or carboxylic acids, to give a range of water-soluble, surface-active polymers.[1]

Cationic polymeric surface-active materials have also been described, such as those prepared by quaternising polymerised 2-vinylpyridine with dodecyl bromide, which have been studied by Strauss and Jackson.[2] Solutions of the quaternised material have lower viscosities than those of the parent polymer, indicating that it has a more compact structure in aqueous solution. Strauss and Jackson suggest that this is due to aggregation of the paraffin chains to form what are in effect micelles distributed along the polymer chain. This is in agreement with the fact that the quaternised polymer solubilises isooctane in water, and does so more powerfully than does dodecylpyridinium bromide. It is also interesting to note that the quaternised polymer has this solubilising action at all concentrations, there being no critical micelle concentration, and that the solubility of isooctane is proportional to the concentration of polymer throughout.

Water-soluble cellulose ethers such as methyl and certain ethyl celluloses, and carboxylic acid derivatives such as cellulose sodium glycollate (carboxymethylcellulose), are well known as emulsion stabilising agents. The emulsifying properties of products of this type have been studied by Morrison and Campbell,[3] who report that methylethylcellulose is particularly effective; it shows some tendency to foam, but this can be reduced by adding carboxymethylcellulose. Fordham[4] has studied the interfacial properties of carboxymethyl cellulose in some detail. The surface tension of water and the interfacial tension between medicinal paraffin and water were both lowered to constant limiting values, at which the total lowerings were 17 and 19 dynes/cm., respectively. The concentration at which the boundary tensions became constant corresponded to the region in which stable emulsions are obtained, suggesting that it is micellar aggregates of carboxymethylcellulose which stabilise the emulsions.

Sulphuric acid esters of cellulose have been claimed as ingredients in detergent compositions,[5] while true sulphonic acid derivatives have been described,[6] in which —OCH$_2$SO$_3$Na groups are attached to the cellulose

---

* See Ellis, *The Chemistry of Synthetic Resins*, Reinhold, 1935, p. 418.
[1] Rohm and Haas, Bock, and Rainey, U.S.P. 2,454,541–2–3–4–5.
[2] Strauss and Jackson, *J. Polymer Sci.*, 1951, **6**, 649.
[3] Morrison and Campbell, *J. Soc. Chem. Ind.*, 1949, **68**, 333.
[4] Fordham, *First Congress*, 1954, 162.
[5] I.G., B.P. 485,649.
[6] Du Pont, Filbert, and Fuller, U.S.P. 2,820,788.

skeleton. The latter materials are stated to be good flocculating agents for dispersions and emulsions, detergent additives, drilling mud additives,* and agents for controlling the rate of setting of cement and plaster of Paris.

B. Lignin sulphonic acids ("Sulphite cellulose lye")

The lignin sulphonic acids, which are obtained in the refining of wood pulp by treatment with sulphites and bisulphites, constitute one of the most important classes of technical deflocculating agents and protective colloids, especially for dispersions of solids in aqueous media. Several illustrations of the use of these agents for this purpose have already been given in Chapter 7.[1] The structure of these agents, which are complicated mixtures containing substances of high molecular weight, has been discussed by Brauns,[2] by Brauns and Brown,[3] and by Erdtman, Lindgren, and Petterson.[4] They are essentially sulphonic acids, obtained by the addition of sulphite to double bonds and/or hydroxyl groups in the lignin. Erdtman, Lindgren, and Petterson conclude that, at least in the later stages of the preparation of highly sulphonated derivatives, it is chiefly the more reactive of the hydroxyl groups which are substituted. These authors also state that the solubility is increased by breaking up the larger molecular complexes of lignin or lignin-carbohydrate.

The states of solution of the lignin sulphonates have been investigated by Gardon and Mason,[5] who fractionated them by dialysis and ultrafiltration. The diffusion coefficients (in the determination of which care was taken to suppress diffusion potentials by swamping with sodium chloride) of the different fractions indicated that the molecular weight of about 30% of the material was in the range between 3,700 and 5,000, and another 30% was between 15,000 and 25,000, the bulk being in the range between 4,000 and 25,000. All the fractions formed complexes with the basic dyestuff Pinacyanol, those of higher molecular weight showing this effect more strongly. The viscosities of the aqueous solutions indicated that these materials are typical polyelectrolytes, with flexible chains which are extended except at high concentrations or in the presence of sodium chloride, when they are coiled. There was some evidence from the conductivity data and the interaction with Pinacyanol that the fractions of lower molecular weight aggregate to form micelles, and Gardon and Mason conclude that

---

* These are essentially deflocculating agents for the aqueous "muds" which are used to lubricate oil well drills.

[1] Further references touching on the use of lignin sulphonic acids in dispersion and emulsification processes will be found in the following British Patents: 258,551; 270,293; 271,550; 286,808; 300,299; 301,549; 402,054.

[2] Brauns, "Lignin and Other Noncarbohydrates," p. 480 ff. in *Cellulose and Cellulose Derivatives*, Vol. V of the "High Polymers" series, Interscience, 2nd edition, 1954.

[3] Brauns and Brown, *Ind. Eng. Chem.*, 1938, **30**, 779.

[4] Erdtman, Lindgren, and Petterson, *Acta Chem. Scand.*, 1950, **4**, 228.

[5] Gardon and Mason, *Canadian Journal of Chemistry*, 1955, **33**, 1477, 1491.

the lignin sulphonates in fact occupy an intermediate position between polyelectrolytes and typical colloidal electrolytes.

According to a British Dyestuffs Corporation patent,[1] improved dispersing agents are obtained by treating lignin sulphonic acids with concentrated aqueous ammonia solutions under pressure, a certain amount of sulphurous acid being split off as ammonium sulphite. This suggests that, at least in some sulphite lyes, the content of sulphonic acid groups may not be at the optimum for surface-activity.

C. Salts of organic bases and anionic surface-active agents

Although the great majority of the anionic surface-active agents which are described in Chapters 10, 11, and 12 are sodium salts, a number of salts of organic bases and anionic agents have been proposed for special uses. In general, the special cation is used in order to make the surface-active agent more soluble in water* or in oils or other organic liquids, but claims have been made that certain amine salts of anionic agents have greater surface-activity than the corresponding sodium salts.

Triethanolamine salts of fatty acids are well-known soap-like products. They were described in an early patent specification of the du Pont Company,[2] which also refers to the triethanolamine salts of sulphated castor oil and sulphated ricinoleic acid. The products are described as having good solubility in water and in alcohol, and as being more efficient dispersing and solubilising agents for organic pigments and other organic substances than are the ordinary soaps. The triethanolamine salts of the alkylated aromatic sulphonic acids of the "Nekal" type were patented soon afterwards by the I.G.[3]

Piperidine salts of sulphated castor oil have been described, improved solubility in organic solvents being claimed.[4] Morpholine and substituted morpholine salts of fatty acids, sulphated castor oil, alkylated aromatic sulphonic acids, and sulphated fatty alcohols have been claimed as stripping agents and dyeing assistants.[5] An example of the last-named type is N-cyclohexylmorpholine cetyl sulphate

$$CH_2\begin{matrix} CH_2-CH_2 \\ CH_2-CH_2 \end{matrix}CHNH^+\begin{matrix} CH_2-CH_2 \\ CH_2-CH_2 \end{matrix}O,\ C_{16}H_{33}OSO_3^-$$

---

* The increase in solubility in aqueous solutions will of course become less the greater the content of other electrolytes such as sodium chloride, calcium bicarbonate, etc.

[1] British Dyestuffs Corporation and Hailwood, B.P. 286,808.
[2] Du Pont, B.P. 295,024.
[3] I.G., B.P. 309,842.
[4] Deutsche Hydrierwerke, B.P. 356,694.
[5] I.G., B.P. 362,060 and 362,061; U.S.P. 1,923,179 and 1,923,243.

Cyclohexylamine salts of anionic surface-active agents appear in a number of patent specifications. Deutsche Hydrierwerke[1] claimed that the cyclohexylamine soap from coconut oil is a better wetting-out agent for textiles than the corresponding sodium soap. The good solubility in oil of the cyclohexylamine salts is apparent from the proposals to make self-emulsifiable oils by the use of the stearate and oleate of dimethylcyclo-hexylamine,[2] or of the diethylcyclohexylamine salts of sulphated dodecyl and octadecyl alcohols.[3] The latter are used in admixture with fatty alcohols such as oleyl or octadecyl alcohol (*cf*. Chapter 6, p. 253). The specification describes the preparation of self-emulsifiable waxes as well as self-emulsi-fiable oils. The specific use of cyclohexylamine soaps for emulsifying fatty acids and fatty glycerides has also been described.[4]

Quaternary ammonium salts of anionic agents have also been described, for example dimethylbenzylphenylammonium dibutylnaphthalene sul-phonate[5] and tetra(β-hydroxyethyl)ammonium stearate.[6]

D. Special mixtures

A very large number of proposals have been made for mixing synthetic surface-active agents with other materials which are claimed to improve their efficiency in use, or to enhance properties such as solubility or physical appearance of dry powders. It is out of the question to attempt a full account of these proposals here, but a few illustrations can be given of three types of mixtures, *viz*., (*i*) surface-active agents which contain solubilised materials, which are probably present in aqueous solutions in complex micelles, (*ii*) mixtures which are intended to give additive or "supra-additive" interfacial effects, and (*iii*) mixtures of surface-active agents with inorganic salts.

Perhaps the oldest example of the addition of a solubilised liquid is provided by the disinfectant soaps which contain phenolic substances; this was followed by Friesenhahn's proposal to add cyclohexanol to soaps,[7] and by the mixtures of anionic surface-active agents and phenolic compounds which are used in mercerising liquors and as emulsifying agents. The following mixtures are taken from the suggestions which have been made in the patent literature, many of them for providing wetting-out agents for mercerising baths:

(1) cresol with methylcyclohexanol or tetrahydronaphthalene;[8]

---

[1] Deutsche Hydrierwerke, B.P. 413,357.
[2] S.C.I., B.P. 469,642; *cf*. U.S.P. 2,155,757.
[3] S.C.I., B.P. 492,742.
[4] Howards and Sons and West, B.P. 501,521.
[5] I.G., B.P. 316,090.
[6] I.G., B.P. 448,251.
[7] Friesenhahn, D.R.P. 365,160 (published 9th December, 1922).
[8] Sandoz, B.P. 279,784; U.S.P. 1,776,052.

(2) cyclohexanol with trichloroethylene and Turkey Red Oil;[1]

(3) cyclohexanone or methylcyclohexanone with soaps or Turkey Red Oil;[2]

(4) perchloroethylene or eucalyptus oil with Turkey Red Oil, potassium ricinoleate, paraffin oil, and alkylated aromatic sulphonates of the "Nekal BX" type;[3]

(5) adipic acid and its esters, with soaps, sulphated castor oils, or agents of the "Nekal BX" type;[4]

(6) terpene alcohols with abietene sulphonates or alkyl aromatic sulphonates;[5]

(7) xylenol and diethylene glycol monobutyl ether, with sulphated castor oil, or cresol and methylcyclohexanol with sulphated ricinoleic acid;[6]

(8) terpineol with phenolic bodies and fatty acids;[7]

(9) butoxyacetic acid with highly sulphated oleic acid;[8]

(10) xylenol with N : N-diisobutylsulphamic acid;[9]

(11) monooxyethylsulphamide and pine oil with sulphated castor oil;[10]

(12) cresol and octylphenol;[11]

(13) phenolic substances with a large number of aliphatic, cycloaliphatic, and arylaliphatic monoamines such as di(β-hydroxyethyl)propylamine.[12]

(14) cyclic ketones, such as camphor, cyclohexanone, isophorone, or 1 : 1 : 3-trimethylcyclohexanone, added to sodium di-*tert.*-butylnaphthalene sulphonate to increase its wetting-out power;[13]

(15) mixtures of "Igepon T" (sodium oleyl-N-methyltaurine), a sequestering agent such as ethylene diamine tetraacetic acid, and a "water-soluble micelle-modifier" such as the butyl ether of diethylene glycol.[14]

A considerable number of commercial products, for example "spot-removers," are mixtures of anionic surface-active agents and grease solvents.

Specific adjuvants for increasing the scouring efficiency of detergents are described in a British Patent of Procter and Gamble.[15] These have formulae such as

[1] Harding Chemical Company, Clutterbuck, and Wooller, B.P. 316,356.
[2] I.G., B.P. 307,944.
[3] I.G., B.P. 298,823.
[4] Böhme, B.P. 307,397.
[5] Newport Chemical Corporation, B.P. 368,351; *cf.* U.S.P. 1,870,251.
[6] Sandoz, B.P. 374,214.
[7] I.C.I., Dunbar, and Todd, B.P. 385,977; U.S.P. 2,000,559.
[8] I.G., B.P. 463,644.
[9] I.G., B.P. 455,893; U.S.P. 2,116,583.
[10] S.C.I., B.P. 449,661.
[11] Deutsche Hydrierwerke, B.P. 454,617.
[12] Sandoz, B.P. 480,837.
[13] Virginia Smelting Co. and Leiserson, U.S.P. 2,453,022.
[14] General Aniline, Ayo, and Gajewski, U.S.P. 2,542,385.
[15] Procter and Gamble and Richardson, B.P. 572,304.

$$R \cdot CONHCH_2 \cdot CH_2OH$$
$$R \cdot CONHCH_2 \cdot \underset{\underset{OH}{|}}{CH} \cdot CH_2OH$$

in which RCO is a fatty acyl radical such as lauryl or myristyl. These agents are added to a number of anionic detergents such as sulphated coconut oil fatty alcohols, sulphated coconut oil monoglyceride, or sulphonated alkyl benzenes.

Other proposals for special additions to detergents, usually for the purpose of improving detergent efficiency and/or foaming power, include the following:

(1) dodecylbenzenesulphonamide, which is added to sulphated fatty alcohols or sulphated fatty monoglycerides;[1]

(2) higher aliphatic glycols, such as 1 : 2-hexadecane-diol, which is added to higher alkylbenzene sulphonates;[2]

(3) N-dodecylacetamide,[3] and substituted betaines, such as C-hexadecyl-N : N : N-trimethylbetaine,[4] which are added to detergents other than those of the cationic type;

(4) ureas substituted with alkyl groups ranging from octyl to hexadecyl, which are added to a variety of detergents, including alkyl sulphates, sulphated fatty monoglycerides, and alkylated aromatic sulphonates.[5]

Mixtures of paraffin-chain cationic agents (*e.g.*, octadecylphenyldimethyl ammonium methosulphate) with the synthetic tanning agents which are obtained by condensing naphthalene-2-sulphonic acid with formaldehyde, have been claimed as levelling and stripping agents for dyestuffs.[6] These mixtures are water-soluble, and presumably form mixed micelles, into which the dyestuff anions become incorporated.

Special mixtures have also been made with the object of obtaining polyethenoxy detergents, many of which are viscous liquids or waxy solids, in solid form. Urea figures prominently as an addition of this type in a number of patents.[7] According to one of the British Specifications, urea (which must be present in stoichiometrical excess) acts by forming "clathrate" compounds with the polyethenoxy agents. It has also been claimed that condensation products of naphthalene sulphonic acids and formaldehyde, in admixture with inorganic salts of the alkali metals, also give dry, stable granules of polyethenoxy surface-active agents.[8]

---

[1] Colgate–Palmolive–Peet and Krems, U.S.P. 2,658,916; *do.*, Gebhart, and Krems, U.S.P. 2,692,235–6–7.

[2] Colgate–Palmolive–Peet and Ross, U.S.P. 2,679,482.

[3] Du Pont, Cupery, and Funderburk, U.S.P. 2,702,278.

[4] Du Pont, Funderburk, and Hurka, U.S.P. 2,702,279.

[5] Colgate–Palmolive–Peet and Ross, U.S.P. 2,708,183.

[6] Geigy, B.P. 610,038.

[7] Atlas Powder Co. and Barker, U.S.P. 2,559,583–4; Anglo-Iranian Oil Co. (subsequently British Petroleum Co.), Birch, Desty, and Harbourn, B.P. 697,315; 748,877–8–9–80–81.

[8] General Aniline and Black, U.S.P. 2,555,285.

A number of special mixtures which are believed to give additive or "supra-additive" emulsifying effects, without necessarily forming mixed micelles, have been described in Chapter 6, and the use of "Tylose" (cellulose sodium glycollate) in detergent mixtures was referred to in Chapter 8. Other examples which may be of interest are the proposals by the S.C.I. to improve the emulsifying power of soap by adding free amines of the "Sapamine" type,[1] and by Neuköllner[2] to use mixtures of "Tylose" and lecithin as emulsifying agents. Further examples of mixed emulsifying agents, which contain fatty alcohols and anionic surface-active agents, will be found in du Pont's[3] proposal to use amine salts of sulphated fatty alcohols (*e.g.*, diethylcyclohexylamine dodecyl sulphate) with oleyl alcohol, and an I.C.I. patent which describes pharmaceutical emulsions containing, for example, octadecyl alcohol, diethylene glycol distearate, and sodium cetyl sulphate.[4] Mixtures of polyethenoxy surface-active agents, such as the "Tweens" (see p. 473), with alkaline earth metal salts of alkylbenzene sulphonic acids, such as the calcium and magnesium salts of dodecylbenzene sulphonic acid, have been described by Sanders, Knaggs, and Nussbaum[5] as being particularly good emulsifiers for pest control emulsions.

A mixture of cationic and anionic agents, such as cetylpyridinium bromide with sodium rosinate, has been used by Courtaulds[6] for pre-treating cellulosic materials in order to increase their affinity for acid wool dyestuffs. The cationic agent is present in excess in these mixtures.

Inorganic salts are present in many commercial surface-active agents, either adventitiously, as stabilisers (*e.g.*, against the hydrolysis of sulphate esters), for standardising the products to a constant effective strength, or for increasing the efficiency of products such as detergents. Examples of these "builders" have been given in Chapter 8.

---

[1] S.C.I., B.P. 361,860.
[2] Neuköllner Oelmühle Lehmann, B.P. 518,641.
[3] Du Pont, B.P. 492,742.
[4] I.C.I., Cockbain, and Timmis, B.P. 546,964.
[5] Sanders, Knaggs, and Nussbaum, U.S.P. 2,696,453.
[6] Courtaulds, Whittaker, and Wilcock, B.P. 501,020.

AUTHOR INDEX*

Patent Specifications in which the patentees include the name of an industrial firm or organisation are indexed only under the name of the firm or organisation

	PAGE
ABBOTT . . . 20, 60, 61	
Abrams 330	
Adam . 4, 7, 26, 27, 66, 67, 91, 96, 126,	
127, 147, 148, 149, 152, 287, 288, 289,	
290, 301, 336, 337, 338	
Adams 327	
Addison . 114, 115, 116, 119, 120	
122, 124, 127, 223	
Adkins 405	
Agthe 309	
Aickin . . . 98, 308, 315	
Albers 260, 261	
Albert 332	
Alexander, A. E. 67, 124, 126, 128, 129,	
130, 202, 253, 334, 352	
Alexander, J. . . . 133	
Alexander, J. C. . . . 299	
Alfrey 342	
Allawala 55	
Alles 456	
Allied Chemical and Dye Corp. . 373,	
385, 387	
Ambler . . . 41, 255	
American Cyanamid and Chemical	
Corp. . 357, 386, 387, 399, 448,	
449, 454, 472, 474, 489	
American Hyalsol Corp. . . 366	
American Viscose Corp. . . 476	
Anacker 39	
Anderson . . . 142, 220	
Andrade 183	
Anglo-Iranian Oil Co. . . 495	
Aniansson . . . 83, 84	
Anode Rubber Co. . . 253, 272	
Anson 254	
Appel 306	
Aranow 89	
Arbiter 337	
Argyle . . 83, 84, 126, 129	
Armstrong 334	
Atkinson 158	
Atlantic Refining Co. . . 349	
Atlas Powder Co. . 453, 473, 484, 495	
Auerbach 222	
Ault 367	
Ayo 357	
BACON 306	

	PAGE
Badische Anilin- und Soda-Fabrik	
(B.A.S.F.) . 41, 277, 278, 356, 357,	
370, 371, 377	
Bagot 119	
Bailey 134, 135	
Baird . 362, 364, 374, 400, 405, 409,	
414, 415, 432, 466, 475, 477, 486	
Baker 327, 328, 332	
Balog 307	
Baltzly 448	
Bann 467	
Barker 307	
Barkman 274	
Barnes 331	
Barrer 157	
Barry 244	
Bartell . 133, 137, 142, 143, 219, 220	
Bartholomé . . . 223, 293	
Bascom 308	
Bass 281	
Bataafsche Petroleum Mij. . 229, 418	
Baumgartner 375	
Baxendale 343	
Baxter, E. F. . . . 359	
Baxter, S. . 140, 141, 142, 151, 216,	
238, 239, 294	
Bayer and Co. 240, 329, 338, 453, 485	
Bayley . . . 98, 301, 304, 310	
Beadell 343	
Beaty 348	
Beaver 313	
Bechhold 325, 326	
Becke 322	
Becker 192	
Bedford 489	
Bell 79	
Benckiser 442	
Bennett 248	
Benson 38, 191	
Benzel 295	
Berch 363, 443	
Bergl 271	
Berkman 248, 250, 253, 256, 264, 265	
Bernett 139	
Berry 184, 276	
Bersworth 444	
Bertsch 302, 303	
Betts 65	

* German modified vowels are classified as unmodified a, o, or u, respectively.

	PAGE
Beyer	172
Bidaux	311
Bikerman	135, 142, 203, 218, 351
Bingham	281
Bird	443
Birkeland	328
Birson	249
Bischof	284
Bistline	410
Biswas	55
Black	359
Blair	118, 250, 266, 267
Blokker	346
Bogan	313
Böhme A. G.	366, 367, 385, 405, 406, 407, 409, 416, 417, 420, 422, 429, 431, 432, 433, 434, 435, 436, 442, 494
Du Bois	329, 332
Born	296
Bovey	343
Bowman	281
Boyd	343
Bradford	342
Brady	80
Brainard	306
Brandner	302, 304, 362, 363, 371, 372, 375, 383, 384, 385, 393, 409, 414, 415, 419, 436, 437, 440, 448, 465, 477, 478
Brass	85, 87
Bräuer	325, 489
Brauns	491
Briscoe	405
British Celanese	372, 376
British Dyestuffs Corp.	272, 274, 275, 280, 283, 369, 371, 372, 492
British Petroleum Co.	495
Brown, C. B.	382, 384, 418, 477, 486
Brown, D. S.	491
Brown, G. L.	26, 58
Browning	327
Bruce	311, 312
Bunbury	14, 41, 176, 279
Bundesmann	246
Burcik	121, 123
Burk	487
Burton	404, 424, 428
Bury	13, 14, 15, 16, 17, 18, 28
Buschmann	293
Büstgens	326
von Buzagh	297
Byrne	428
CABOT	274
Cadle	61, 361
Calco Chemical Corp.	274, 275
Caldwell	364

	PAGE
California Research Corp.	367, 377, 474, 486
Calloway	370
Camp	221
Campbell	490
Carbide and Carbon Chem. Corp.	412, 413, 450
Carmody	240
Carr	342
Carter	74, 316
Caryl	226, 386
Casimir	163
Caspar	315
Cassie	140, 141, 142, 151, 216, 238, 239, 294
Catalin	489
Chaberek	443
Chamberlain	253, 256, 286, 298
Chandler	314
Chapin	340
Chitwood	475
Christison	306
Chwala	10, 171, 221, 230, 231, 236, 241, 273, 285, 306, 318, 322, 380, 381, 388, 398, 405, 434, 450, 477
Ciba	440
Clarkson	224, 226
Clayton	180, 248, 249, 250, 253, 256, 261, 264, 273
Clayton-Cooper	331
Cockbain	74, 79, 87, 88, 107, 249, 253, 254, 255, 256, 259, 260, 264
Coghill	142, 220
Cohen	43
Colgate-Palmolive-Peet	363, 420, 423, 495
Collie	18, 19, 20, 24, 28, 29
Collin	366, 367
Collins	136
Colville	198, 199, 200, 201
Consortium für Elektrochemische Industrie	488
Cooke	136
Coon	442, 443
Cooper	203, 247
Corrin	22, 23, 35, 36, 37, 58, 59, 61, 62, 98
Cottrell	183
Coughlin	310
Courtaulds	279, 323, 463, 496
Cox	337
Craxford	414, 418
Crisp	108
Crowe	306
Cullen	345
Currie	352
Cutillas	207

PAGE

DANIELLI 108
Danielsson 51, 52
Dann 330
Dannenberg 277
Davidson 345
Davies, C. W. 31
Davies, D. G. 16
Davies, G. E. . . 327, 331, 334
Davies, J. T. . 74, 106, 113, 126, 129,
204, 263
Davis 242
Dean 44, 337
Debye 39
Defay 125
Degering 412
Degussa (Deutsche Gold- und Silber-
Scheide-Anstalt) 281
Denman 352
Dennett 244
Derjaguin . 10, 162, 169, 173, 205
Dervichian 121
Desalbres 80
Deutsche Hydrierwerke . 253, 369, 392,
395, 399, 405, 406, 408, 441, 453, 461,
492, 493, 494
Dewey and Almy Co. . . 273, 378
Diamond 307, 308
Dieckhoff 299
Dierkes 326
Diesslin 443
Dintenfass . . . 171, 282
Diserens . 230, 315, 318, 322, 323
Distillers Co. 267
Dixon . . 76, 83, 84, 85, 126, 129
Domagk 327
Donnan 297
Doremus 187
Döring 192
Doscher 296
Doss 126, 127
Dow Chemical Co. . . 396, 474, 475
Draves 224, 226, 227
Dreger 411
Drexler 173
DuBrow 40
Dunbar 303, 308
Duncan 331
Dunn 329
Dunning 348
Du Pont Co. . 235, 241, 246, 272, 284,
352, 363, 368, 369, 375, 376, 384, 413,
415, 416, 418, 420, 440, 441, 442, 447,
448, 460, 463, 484, 485, 489, 490, 492,
495, 496
Durand and Huguenin . . 447
Durham . . . 221, 296, 303
Dvoretskaya 259

PAGE

Dye 24, 25, 28
Dzialoshinskii 163

EASTMAN Kodak Co. . . . 489
Eaton 470
Edelstein 227
Eggenberger 40
Egloff . 248, 250, 253, 256, 264, 265
Ehrenkranz 308
Eichborn 276
Einstein's Electrochemical Co. . . 274
Eirich . . . 108, 110, 178
Ekwall 51, 52
Eley . . . 157, 158, 222
Elliott 119, 159
Ellis 487, 490
Ellis-Foster Co. 459
Elton 138
Emulsol Corp. . . . 329, 481
von Engelhardt 184
Engler 299
Epstein, A. K. 329
Epstein, M. B. . . 77, 79, 80, 86
Erba A. G. 430
Erdtman 491
Erickson 462
Eseltine 326
Evans, A. C. 213
Evans, J. G. . . . 225, 226, 368
Evans, M. G. 343
Evers 26, 58
Ewart 342
Ewers 204
Eyring . 99, 126, 131, 192, 292, 293

FALKENTHAL 313
Färberei A. G. 457
Fava . 99, 126, 131, 292, 293
Feighner 370
Ferencz 250
Feuell 293, 307
Fikentscher 340
Finchler 485
Fineman 291
Flammer 302
Fleming 335
Flengas 87, 126, 129
Flesch 407, 441
Flett 98, 320, 379
Flory 467
Folkers 405
Fong 305
Fordham 124, 490
Fordyce 340
Fortess 244
Foter 328
Fournet 37
Fowkes 205, 228
Fox 139, 245

	PAGE
Frank	187
Franke	173
Frankel	203
Franz	306
Freedlander	329
Freure	475
Frick	242, 243
Fries	98
de Fries	203
Friesenhahn	299, 372, 493
Frilette	340
Frisch	178
Fryling	339
Fuchs	163
Fuerstenau	99
Fulton	299
Fysh	197
GALE	335
Gallily	218, 327
Gardiner	98
Gardner	281
Gardon	491
Gaudin	335
Gavlin	443
Geigy A.G.	378, 380, 381, 385, 390, 397, 399, 400, 434, 454, 462, 495
Gemeson	311
General Aniline and Film Corp.	389, 394, 413, 453, 474, 494, 495
General Mills Corp.	486
Gibbs	91, 187, 188, 189
Giddings	192
Gilbert	436
Gilby	344, 345
Glassman	326, 334
Goldschmidt	468
Goldsmith	484
Goldstein	414, 415, 419
Good	140, 142, 143
Gordon	244, 367
Gotshal	104
Götte	297, 300, 306, 308
Grasselli	372
Graydon	53
Green	45, 47, 48, 49
Greenwood	403
Grieger	26, 58
Griffin	263
Griffiths	233
Grindley	13, 15, 17, 18
Groggins	376
Grün	432
Grünau, Landshoff, and Meyer A. G.	438
Guastalla	120
Guenthner	442, 443
Guggenheim	65, 66, 67, 68, 70, 72, 73, 75, 102

	PAGE
Gündel	473
Gundermann	22
Günther	41, 478
Gurney	93
Gustafson	348
Gutzeit	338
Gyenge	343
HAFFNER	40
Hailwood	90, 190, 287
Hall	414, 418
Hallberg	350
Hamburger	283
Hammerton	313
Hampson	325
Hansen	123
Harding Chem. Co.	494
Hardwick	333
Harisaki	249
Harker	289, 290, 291
Harkins	21, 22, 23, 26, 32, 33, 34, 35, 36, 47, 48, 49, 50, 58, 59, 60, 61, 62, 63, 98, 126, 137, 340, 341
Harper	183
Harrington	339
Harris	454, 481
Hartley	12, 13, 14, 16, 18, 19, 20, 21, 24, 26, 27, 28, 29, 31, 32, 35, 36, 37, 38, 39, 45, 46, 47, 48, 49, 59, 61, 299, 315, 396, 411
Hartmann	447
Harwood	306
Hasan	51
Hass	485
Haugh	331
Hauschild	244, 245
Hauser	343
Hawke	352
Hay	233
Haydon	74, 75, 106, 107
Heidelberger	326
Heidenreich	244
Helin	343
Heller	169, 172
Hemsley	308
Henkel and Cie	309, 363, 366, 383, 392, 394, 395, 408, 413, 419, 438, 441, 474
Hentrich	473
Herbig	224
Hergt	337
Hermanie	168
Hess	22
Heymann	344, 345
Hickson	485
Hiebert	28
Hilditch	366, 367

PAGE

Hill, E. F. 308
Hill, J. A. 349
Hill, T. L. 74
Himelick 329
Hoerr . 14, 20, 24, 26, 27, 28, 29, 57, 62
Hoeve 38
van der Hoff 342
Hoffman 57
Hoffmann 20
Hohenstein . . 338, 339, 340
Holland 306
Holm 414
Holness 347
Hommelen 125
Hoogerheide 329
Horn 358, 362
Horsfall . 221, 230, 318, 320, 321,
322, 323, 324, 435
Hotchkiss . . . 327, 334
Howard and Sons . . 419, 493
Hoyt . 98, 320, 362, 363, 382, 384, 388
Hrenoff 55
Hubbard 44
Huber 330
Hueter 405
Huff 50
Hughes 281, 341
Humphreys . . . 126, 130
Hunsdiecker and Vogt A. G. . 451, 456,
461
Hunter 244
Hutchinson . 24, 45, 80, 83, 116, 119,
120, 124, 223
Huyck 331
Hyatt 467
Hyde 244

I. G. FARBENINDUSTRIE . 42, 230, 231,
250, 251, 276, 309, 338, 351, 357, 363,
364, 365, 366, 369, 371, 372, 373, 374,
375, 378, 379, 381, 382, 383, 384, 385,
387, 388, 389, 390, 391, 392, 393, 394,
396, 397, 398, 399, 400, 401, 405, 406,
407, 408, 413, 416, 418, 419, 421, 422,
423, 428, 431, 432, 433, 435, 437, 438,
439, 440, 442, 447, 448, 449, 450, 452,
454, 455, 456, 459, 462, 468, 469, 470,
471, 472, 473, 476, 478, 481, 483, 484,
485, 486, 488, 489, 490, 492, 493, 494
Imperial Chemical Industries (I.C.I.) 241,
251, 264, 276, 278, 279, 281, 283, 333,
351, 357, 366, 369, 371, 378, 385, 390,
395, 396, 398, 417, 421, 422, 428, 432,
434, 442, 449, 452, 453, 456, 457, 458,
460, 462, 463, 464, 472, 473, 476, 483,
488, 489, 494, 496
Innovations Chimiques . . 359, 423
Inskeep 417

JACKSON 56, 490
Jacobs 326
James 37
Jarrett 281
Jeanson 320
Jebe 308
Jephcott Committee . 311, 312, 313
Jellinek 254
Jensen 298
Jerchel 330
Johansen 348
Johnson, R. E. . . 135, 136
Johnson, R. I. . . . 256
Johnston . . . 24, 25, 28
Jones, E. P. 436
Jones, E. R. . . . 14, 18
Jones, T. G. 304
Joslyn 329
Judson 76, 84, 85

KÄGI 447
Kallé 398
Kamack 184, 276
Karabinos . . . 467, 480
Karassev 173
Karrer 370
Kastens 357, 406
Katchalsky . . . 111, 112
Kauck 443
Kayser 470
Kehren 479
Kelly 246
Kemsley 183
Keps 462
Kern, C. R. 307
Kern, J. G. . 374, 384, 387, 388
Kilhem 343
Killefer 405
Kind 222
Kingan 217, 483
Kinney 267
Kitchener 203
Kivela 327
Klaus 304
Klein 330
Kleinfeldt 271
Klevens . 45, 53, 55, 59, 60, 443
Kline 291
Kling . 79, 159, 295, 306, 405
Kolat 305
Kolloff 329
Kolnig 74, 80
Kolthoff . 46, 47, 48, 49, 51, 53,
342, 343
Konecny 296
Koral 108, 110
Krafft 27
Krais 315

	PAGE
Krämer	. 304
Kramer	. 308
Kraus, C. A. . . .	26, 58
Kraus, W. . . .	325, 326
Krishnamurti . . .	. 22
Krog	. 331
Krokfors	. 52
Kroll	. 484
Kruyt	. 10
Kuhn	329, 330
Kushner	. 44
Kuznetsov . . .	. 183
LACHMANN . . .	. 224
Lambert . . .	306, 310
La Mer . . 74, 218, 237, 345
Lamm	83, 84
Landau. . . .	. 162
Landolt	. 315
Landsberg . . .	. 246
Langbein	. 395
Lange . 79, 89, 157, 159, 223, 295
Langmuir . . .	106, 117
Langstaff . . .	. 347
Lawrence, A. S. C. . .	. 290
Lawrence, C. A. . .	. 326
Lawrie . 221, 230, 246, 318, 320, 321,
322, 323, 324, 435
Layton	. 56
Lederer. . . .	405, 434
Leese	. 159
Lelong	. 361
Lenher . . . 224, 226, 229
Lennard-Jones . . .	. 91
Lerew	. 83
Lesser	. 315
Lever Brothers . 393, 482, 483
Levin . . .	307, 308
Lewis	. 66
Lichtman . . 181, 182, 183
Lifschitz . . .	. 163
Lind	. 98
Lindgren	. 491
Lindner . 253, 306, 309, 359, 383,
405, 428, 433
Lingafelter . . 28, 44, 361
Linhart. . . .	. 436
Linton	. 346
Lipetz	. 336
Lissant	. 50
Liu	. 51
Lloyd	. 299
Lockwood (*see* Brandner)
Loesser	. 137
Logginov . . .	. 181
Long . . . 126, 127
Lottermoser . . 14, 20, 79, 302
Lucchesi . . .	. 193

	PAGE
Luck	. 321
Ludeman . . .	. 307
McBAIN, J. W. . 14, 20, 22, 23, 30,
32, 43, 45, 47, 48, 49, 50, 79, 83, 95,
128, 297, 299
McBain, M. E. L. . 24, 25, 28, 45, 128,
129
McCartney . . .	. 202
McCauley . . .	. 119
McCoy	. 308
McCulloch . . .	. 331
McCutcheon . . .	. 378
Mackor. . . .	. 168
McLaren . . .	98, 301
McLean . . .	. 157
McLeod . . .	366, 367
McMullen . . .	88, 250
McRoberts . . .	249, 254
Maguire . . .	. 443
Maier	. 329
Mallmann . . .	. 327
Malsch	. 26
Manegold . . .	. 203
Mansfield . . .	. 345
Mantele . . .	. 329
March	. 180
Margenau . . .	. 163
Mark . . 338, 339, 340, 487
Marra	. 485
Marsden . . .	. 43
Marsh . . .	366, 367
Marshall . . .	. 331
Martell	. 443
Martin, H. . 213, 214, 215, 219
Martin, H. E. . .	14, 20
Martina . . .	322, 477
Maslennikov . . .	181, 182
Mason	. 491
Matalon . . .	43, 255
Matijevic . . .	. 201
Matthews . . .	. 350
Mattoon . 21, 22, 23, 32, 33, 34, 35,
36, 49, 50
Mauersberger. . .	407, 408
Maurer . . . 367, 409, 410
Mayhew . . .	343, 467
Meader	. 98
Medalia . . .	. 343
Meehan. . . .	342, 343
Melbourne . . .	311, 312
Mercer	. 403
Merrill	. 43
Michaels . 173, 198, 199, 200, 201
Migaki	. 331
Milch (Chem. Fabrik) . .	. 400
Miles, E. M. . . .	. 331
Miles, G. D. . . .	79, 80, 302

PAGE

Miller, B. F. 330
Miller, I. 111, 112
Miller, S. A. 467
Mills 79, 95
Ministry of Fuel and Power . 233, 234
van der Minne 168
Minnesota Manufacturing and Mining
  Co. 443
Mitchell 138
Mittelmann 21, 49, 50
Moghe 55
Moilliet 24
Monsanto Chemical Co. . 206, 252, 344,
  359, 379, 385, 386, 401, 408, 415, 439
  440, 471, 472, 474
Moore 333
Morrison 490
Morrisroe 306
Murray, R. C. . . . 16, 26, 27
Murray, R. L. . 371, 381, 387, 388
Mussard 417
Myatt 313
Mysels 203

NADEAU 484
Nagel (*see* Brandner and Holm)
National Oil Products Co. . 373, 387,
  408, 423
Netter 83
Neugebauer 276
Neuköllner Oelmühle A.G. . . 496
Neville 320
Newhall 306
Newman 121
Newport Chemical Corp. . . 494
Nicholas 350
Nieuwenhuis 304, 305
Nightingale 370
Nilsson 84, 86
Niven 306, 309
Noller 367
Normann 405
Norris 366
Norton 53
Nüsslein 300, 303
Nutting, C. L. 306
Nutting, G. C. 127

OAKESHOTT 476
O'Brien 172
Ockert 267
Ohlenbusch 74
Oliver 477
Ollivier 218
O'Loane 361
Onyx Oil and Chemical Co. . . 462
Oppenheimer . . 26, 47, 48, 50, 340
Oranienburger . . . 230, 400

PAGE

Orthner 395
Osipow . . 249, 250, 307, 308, 485
Osterhof . . 133, 137, 219, 220
Ottewill 201
Overbeek . 10, 162, 163, 164, 166,
  260, 261, 296
Owen 324

PACKTER 193
Padday 136, 213
Padgett 412
Palit 54, 55
Palm 367
Palmer . 288, 297, 307, 308, 315, 316
Pankhurst 26, 27, 108
Parry 28
Passinen 51
Paquette 28, 44
Paquot 408
Paulson 358
Pavlish 350
Peak 157
Peddicord 406
Pepper 157, 158, 222
Perdue 486
Perry, E. 343
Perry, G. S. 310
Perry, J. W. . 37, 128, 129, 195, 363,
  381, 420, 423, 443
Peterson 376
Pethica 65, 74
Petrea 306
Petroff 355
Petrolite Corp. . . . 266, 473
Petterson 491
Phansalkar 99, 303
Phillips, A. P. 448
Phillips, J. N. . . 74, 75, 106
Phillips Petroleum Co. . . . 344
Piccione 40
Pihlblad 276
Pincus 267
Plauson 273
Polder 163
Pope 246
Porter 303, 304
Posner 124
Pott and Co. . 252, 256, 373, 374, 416,
  455
Pound 74
Powney . . 289, 302, 303, 307
Preston, C. 477
Preston, W. C. . . . 14, 316
Price 370, 375
Procter and Gamble . 377, 407, 423,
  472, 494
Pryor 335, 337
Pugh 169, 172

	PAGE
Puplett	374
Purchase	123
Püschel	20, 79
QUINN	467, 480
Quisno	328
RAHN	326, 330
Raison	443
Ralston . 14, 20, 24, 26, 27, 28, 29,	
	40, 57, 62, 404
Ramage	284
Ramsauer	184
Randall	66, 183
Rawlins	329
Ray	143
Rayleigh	114
Rebenfeld	104
Redd	274
Reed, C. F. . . .	358, 362
Reed, R. M. . . .	126, 361
Rehbinder . . 181, 182, 183, 276	
Reichenberg . . .	80, 82
Reid, E. E. . . .	367
Reid, J. D. . . .	242, 243
Reitmeyer . . .	79, 126
Reitstötter . . .	271
Reumuth	300
Reychler . 356, 367, 445, 446, 451,	
	452
Rhodes	306, 308
Richards Chemical Works . .	407
Richardson, R. E. . 374, 384, 387, 388	
Richardson, T. . . .	325
Riddiford	108
Rideal . 87, 106, 108, 120, 126, 129,	
	130, 158, 253, 255, 297
Riegelman	55
Rigg	51
Ring	308
Roberts	187
Robertshaw . . 404, 424, 428	
Robinson . 24, 180, 289, 290, 297,	
	434
Rochow	244
Roe	85, 87
Rogers, B. W. . . .	271
Rogers, J. . . .	337
Roginsky	98
Rohm and Haas Co. . 378, 395, 421,	
	453, 455, 490
Rösch	479
Rose	98
Rosenblum . . .	40
Ross, J. . 77, 79, 80, 86, 302, 411	
Ross, S.	207
Ross, T. K. . . .	347
Röttig	184, 276

	PAGE
Rowe	324
Rubber Producers' Research Assn. .	463
Ruehrwein	194
Ruff	206
Rülke	430
Ruperti	224
Russell (*see* Brandner)	
Ruyssen . . .	84, 333
SACK	20
Sadd	217, 483
Safety in Mines Research Board .	233
St. Denis	430
Sajitz	252, 256
Salley . 76, 83, 84, 85, 126, 129	
Salmon	14
Salonen	52
Salton	332, 333
Samis . 18, 19, 20, 28, 29, 47, 61	
Sanders . . 306, 310, 496	
Sanderson	284
Sandoz . . 230, 407, 439, 493, 494	
Saraga	120
Sata	249
Sawyer, C. N. . . .	313
Sawyer, W. N. . . 205, 341	
Schaefer	117
Schäfer	223
Schenck	405
Schlichtkrull . . .	192
Schlotterbeck . . .	433
Schmidt	405
Schneider	311
Scholberg . . . 442, 443	
Schöller	302
Schönfeldt . . . 466, 479	
Schou 481, 482	
Schrauth . . 253, 369, 405	
Schulman . 43, 87, 98, 250, 253, 254,	
	255, 256, 259, 260, 264
Schuyten . . . 242, 243	
Schwartz, A. M. . 37, 236, 241, 299,	
	335, 363, 381, 420, 423, 443, 459, 484
Schwartz, M.	299
Schwen	223
Scott	13, 24
Scottish Dyes Ltd. . . .	279
Seck 224, 229	
Seddon	349
Segall	239
Segura 307, 314	
Seltzer 277, 431	
Servo	430
Sexsmith	104
Seyferth	224
Shapiro	227
Sharples Solvents Co. . .	374
Sharrah	370

PAGE

Shedlovsky . . . 79, 80, 411
Shelberg 314
Shell Development Co. . 229, 417, 462
Shelton 328
Shepard . . . 142, 143
Sheppard 172
Sherekevsky 74
Sherman . . . 248, 259, 260
Sherrill 307
Shinoda 203
Shirolkar 391
Sholtes 28
Shute 126, 127
Shuttleworth . . 92, 134, 191, 304
Sidgwick 446
Siegrist 315
Silvester 274
Simha 178
Simon . . 26, 47, 48, 50, 340
Simpson, J. E. . . . 247
Simpson, J. R. . . . 313
Singer 112, 113
Sinski 246
Sisley 369, 401
Sivaramakrishnan . . . 99
Sivertz . . 20, 60, 61, 79, 126
Slowinske 246
Smeds 51
Smith, C. E. 308
Smith, E. L. 50
Smith, F. D. 480
Smith, G. H. 364
Smith, J. A. C. . . 126, 130
Smith, J. E. . . 224, 226, 229
Smith, R. L. 443
Smith, W. C. 306
Smith, W. V. 342
Smoluchowski 163
Snell . 249, 250, 306, 307, 314, 485
Snyder 350
Society of Chemical Industry (Basle) . 244,
 276, 280, 372, 376, 380, 387, 392, 397,
 400, 401, 419, 430, 447, 448, 449, 450,
 452, 453, 454, 456, 459, 461, 493, 494,
 496
Somers 215
Sörensen 58
South Metropolitan Gas Co. . . 258
Speakman . . 253, 256, 286, 298
Speer 240
Spink 98
von Stackelberg . . 295, 296
Standard Oil Development Co. . 252,
 366, 418, 442
Stanley, J. S. 295
Stanley, W. M. . . . 327
Stanton 474
Stauff 22, 27

PAGE

Stawitz 304, 305
Stearn 247
Stearns . 21, 26, 32, 33, 34, 35, 46, 47,
 48, 49, 50, 340
Steinhaus 328
Stevenson . . 289, 290, 300, 301
Stewart . . . 41, 176, 279
Sthamer 351
Stickdorn 405
Stigman 314
Stillo 305
Stirton . . 367, 376, 409, 410, 480
Stockhausen . . 428, 430, 431, 433
Stoll 79
Strait 55
Strauss 56, 490
Straw 307
Strecker 366
Stricks . . 46, 47, 48, 49, 51
Stüpel . . . 301, 306, 300
Sudhoff . . 374, 384, 387, 388
Summersgill 443
Sumner . 180, 248, 249, 250, 253, 256,
 261, 262, 264, 273
Sunlicht A. G. . . . 383
Sun Oil Co. 344
Suter 308, 404
Sutherland . 120, 126, 129, 130, 204,
 335, 337, 346
Sweet 329
Sykes 326
Szegvari 272

Taggart 337
Tartar . 13, 14, 20, 24, 26, 27, 28, 44,
 60, 61, 79, 126, 361
Tamaki 99
Tamamushi 99
Tan 305
Tattersfield 323
Taylor, F. H. . . . 106, 107
Taylor, P. A. 91
Taylor, P. W. . . . 245
van den Tempel . . 167, 249
Theimer 185
Thornton 206
Thorpe 252
Thovert 118
Thrower 467
Tideswell . . . 232, 233
Titijevskaya . . 169, 173, 205
Tomlinson, A. J. H. . . 334
Tomlinson, R. W. . . 175, 284
Tordai . 116, 117, 123, 126, 130
Traube 88
Travis 273
Tretolite Co. 266
Trommer 222

	PAGE
Truesdale	311
Trutzer	280
Tunoda	249
Turnbull	187
Turner	327
Twitchell	356
UDYLITE Research Corp.	368
Uehlein	315
Ullman	108, 110
Ullmann	252
Unichem A. G.	399, 419, 422
Unilever	393
Union Carbide	412
Universal Oil Products	359
Uppal	391
Urbain	298
U.S. Rubber Co.	387, 476
Utermohlen	296
VALKO	41, 306, 318, 319, 320, 321, 329, 331, 332, 335, 340, 478
Varley	311
Vaughan (*see* Holm)	
Vaughn, C. R.	121
Vaughn, J. C.	313
Vaughn, T. H.	308
Venkataraman	391
Venkateswarlu	54
Vereinigte Glanzstoff Fabrik	463
Vermilyea	347
Verwey	162, 163, 164, 166, 296
Vetter	28, 40
Vickerstaff	42, 293, 319
Viertel	304
Vinograd	341
Virginia Smelting Co.	494
Vitalis	226
Vlugter	362
Vold, M. J.	102
Vold, R. D.	99, 296
Volmer	186, 188, 192, 196
Volz	300
van der WAALS	168
van der Waarden	168
Wagg	306, 307
Wagner	367
Waldmann	398, 450
Walker	339
Wallace	123
Walling	206
Walter	98, 330
Walton	28
Ward	62, 88, 116, 117, 123, 126, 130, 305
Wark	335, 337

	PAGE
Warwick Chemical Co.	244, 459
Washburn	158
Waterhouse	98
Watt	244
Weatherburn	98, 301, 304, 310
Weaver	242, 243
Webb	233
Weber	192
Weiden	53
Weil	367, 410
von Weimarn	276
Weith	83, 84, 126, 128
Wells	197
Welton	98
Weltzien	244, 245
Wenström	181
Wenzel	139, 142
Weston	44, 241
Westphal	329
Whatmough	253
Wheeler	233
Whetstone	201
Whitby	487
White	104
Whyte	407
Wickert	411
Wiglow	27
Wilcock	323
Wilder	43
Wilke	295
Wilkes	411
Williams, F. V.	194, 331
Williams, R.	339
Wilson, A.	77, 79, 80, 86
Wilson, W. J.	349
Wiltshire	325
Wingfoot	436
Winsor	6, 28, 37, 40, 45, 46, 53
Wisegarver	456
Witten	89
Wolstenholme	98
Wood, L. A.	83
Wood, L. J.	302
Woodman	252
Woody	123
Wool Industries Research Association	463
Wright	14, 20, 26, 27, 60, 61
Wrigley	480
Wyandotte Chemical Corp.	474
Wyss	329
YAMEL Ltd.	435
York	485
Young	207
Zettlemoyer	281
Zisman	139, 245

SUBJECT INDEX

PAGE

ACRYLIC polymers, surface-active . 488, 489

Activation energies of adsorption and desorption 121

Adhesion, work of . 137, 218 ff, 237, 239

Adhesional wetting 137

Adipic acid, effect of surface-active materials on crystal habit . 197 ff

Adsorption . . . . . 64 ff

Adsorption, amphipathic . . 6, 9

Adsorption at solid-liquid interfaces, thermodynamics . . . 89 ff

Adsorption by ion-exchange . 97, 98

Adsorption by solids from non-aqueous media 282

Adsorption, effect of interionic forces. 107

Adsorption kinetics . . 113 ff

Adsorption kinetics at solid-liquid interfaces 131

Adsorption kinetics in non-aqueous media 130, 131

Adsorption maxima at solid-liquid interfaces . . . . 98 ff
  "osmotic machine" corollary . 102
  possible explanations . 103, 104

Adsorption of carboxymethyl cellulose in detergent processes. 304, 305

Adsorption of dyestuffs, effect of levelling agents . . 319 ff

Adsorption of macromolecules. 108 ff, 178

Adsorption of surface-active agents in detergent processes . . 301 ff

Adsorption of surface-active agents in wetting processes . . 213

Adsorption, radio-tracer technique for measuring 77

Adsorption, specific . . 8, 9

Adsorption, thermodynamics of . 64 ff

Adsorption with reversed orientation. 94, 99, 172, 283, 284

"Aerosols" (dialkylsulphosuccinates). 40, 130, 277, 335, 358, 386

Aggregation in solutions of surface-active agents . . . 12 ff

Aliphatic amine-ethylene oxide condensates 470

Alkane sulphonates . 80, 126, 129, 229, 261, 356, 360 ff
  alkylaryl substituted . . 377
  branched . . . 368
  chlorinated . . 366, 367

Alkanolamine esters . . 447, 448

Alkanolamine salts. . . 448

Alkoyl-N-methyltaurines (see also IGEPONS) . . . 300, 313, 319

Alkyd resins as surface-active agents. 280, 489

Alkylamine salts . 29, 48, 57, 85, 322, 337, 344, 350

Alkylbenzene sulphonates . 99, 374, 375

Alkylnaphthalene sulphonates . 370 ff

Alkylphenols, sulphonated . . 379

Alkylpicolinium salts . . . 329

Alkylpiperidinium salts . . . 328

Alkyl sulphamic acids . . 400

Alkyl sulphates . 15, 40, 51, 79, 80, 81, 82, 83, 84, 85, 86, 98, 99, 103, 104, 105, 121, 122, 126, 129, 131, 180, 204, 205, 215, 225, 230, 231, 249, 253, 254, 255, 261, 264, 265, 268, 276, 289, 296, 297, 300, 302, 303, 310, 313, 316, 319, 333, 334, 336, 337, 345, 346, 347, 348, 360, 402 ff, 406, 409, 412, 423, 434 ff

Alkyl sulphosuccinates . 215, 217, 226, 277, 334, 335, 347, 348

Alkyl xanthates . . 336, 337, 338

Alkylated aromatic ethylene oxide condensates . 215, 252, 289, 313, 345, 347

Alkylated aromatic sulphonates . 211, 230, 251, 252, 261, 275, 293, 311, 313, 320, 338, 340, 347, 348, 349, 350, 351, 352, 369 ff, 379 ff

Amagat interfacial equation of state. 106, 118

Amide carboxylates . . . 439

Amide-ethylene oxide condensates . 469

Amide sulphonates . . . 388 ff

Amine salts . . . 446 ff

Amphipathic adsorption . . 6, 9

Amphipathic compounds, solubility . 26, 27
  macromolecules . . . 109

Amphipathy . . . 5, 12

"Amphiphilic" compounds . . 6

Ampholytic surface-active agents . 486

Anhydrosorbitol (see Sorbitan)

Anionic agents, miscellaneous . 427 ff
  salts with organic bases . 492, 493

Anti-dimming agents . 217, 483

Anti-foaming agents . . 351 ff
  mechanism of action . 206, 207
  use with detergents . . 312

"Antonoff's rule" . . . 138

"Aphrosol" . . . 350, 351

507

PAGE

Area of spreading . . . 213, 214
Aromatic hydrocarbons, alkylation . 370
    sulphonation . . . 370, 371
Aromatic sulphonates, chlorinated . 369
Aromatic sulphonates (unalkylated) . 369
Aromatic sulphonic acid-formal-
    dehyde condensates . 109, 272, 273,
        274, 275, 278, 279, 280, 284
Arylalkane sulphonates . . . 376
Arylstearic acids, sulphonated . . 376
Azoic dyestuffs, solubilisation by
    cationic agents 324
    stripping agents for . . 324 ff

BACTERICIDAL action of surface-
    active agents . . . 328 ff
    radio-tracer studies . . . 333
Bactericides, arsonium compounds as 330
    cationic agents as . 327 ff, 456
    micellar solubilising agents in . 334
    mixtures of cationic and non-
        ionic agents as . . . 333
    phosphonium compounds as . 330
    quaternary ammonium com-
        pounds as . . . 327 ff
    sulphonium compounds as . 330
Ball-milling, deflocculating agents in. 272
Ball-milling, foaming in . . . 272
Ball-milling, function of surface-
    active agents in . . . 272, 273
Ball mills . . . 271 ff, 279
Bechhold capillary phenomenon 325 ff
Bedding, cationic agents for steri-
    lising. 331
"Bénard cells" 120
Benziminazole derivatives . 449, 450
Benziminazole derivatives, sulpho-
    nated 380
Benzyl sulphanilates . 276, 278, 398
Betaines, substituted . 454, 485, 486
Bitumen, use of surface-active agents
    to promote adhesion . . . 350
Branched-chain surface-active agents 39,
        411, 412
"Brenthols" 324
Brightening agents, fluorescent . 314
"Builders" in detergents . 308 ff, 358
Building materials, use of surface-
    active agents in . . . 349 ff
Bundesmann test for water-repellency 246
"Burgundy mixture" . . . 215

CALCIUM chloride solutions, wetting-
    out agents for use in . . 233 ff
Calcium-sequestering agents . 302, 338,
        443, 444
"Calgon" 309
"Calsolene Oil HS" . . 233, 428

PAGE

Canvas square test for wetting-out . 227
Capillaries, wetting-out in . 221 ff
Capillary wetting . . 147 ff, 234
    function of surface-active agents
        in . . . . . 149 ff
    kinetics of . . . 157 ff
Carboxylic acids, special . . . 437
Carboxymethylcellulose . 293, 304, 305,
        487
"Card test" for agricultural and hor-
    ticultural sprays 215
Castor oil, sulphated . . 425, 429
Cationic agents for stripping dye-
    stuffs 323, 324
    history 446
Cationic agents, polymeric . 56, 455,
        460, 490
    special uses . . . 463–464
    treatment of pigments with . 284
Cationic surface-active agents . 445 ff
Cellulose derivatives, surface-active. 490
Cellulose ethers . 250, 251, 261, 264,
        326
Cellulose sodium glycollate (see car-
    boxymethyl cellulose)
Cellulose, sulphonic acids from 490, 491
    sulphuric acid esters . . 490
Cement mortars, use of surface-active
    agents in . . . . 349 ff
Chemical potential, effect of micelle
    formation 28
    in adsorbed layers, Fowler's
        expression 107
Chemical potential, increase with
    concentration of pure solute . 102
    regressions in solutions of impure
        surface-active agents . 80 ff
Chemisorption 8
Chemisorption at solid-liquid inter-
    faces . . . . . 94 ff
Citrates, polycondensed . . . 441
"Claying" in dispersions, prevention. 279
"Cloud-point" of polyethenoxy agents 53,
        479
Coal dust, wetting-out of . 232 ff
Coalescence . . . 167, 168
"Colloid mills" . . 249, 257, 273
"Colloidal electrolytes" . . 13, 14
"Colloidal sensitisation" . . . 172
Colloidal state, universality of . . 269
"Comminuters" in milling processes 271 ff
Composite surfaces, effect on wetting. 140,
        141, 148
    in water-proofed fabrics . 238, 239,
        240
Concrete, foamed 350
Concrete, use of surface-active agents
    in . . . . . 349 ff

PAGE

"Condensation" method of preparing dispersions . . 277 ff
Condensed phosphates, addition to detergents . . . . 309 ff
Congo Red, fixing by cationic surface-active agents 322
Constructional materials, use of surface-active agents in . . 349 ff
Contact angle . 134 ff, 217, 218, 236, 238, 240
   advancing . 214, 220, 221, 222, 223, 227, 231, 234, 237
     in wetting-out processes . 213
   as criterion of wetting . 155, 156
   effect of composite surfaces on . 140, 141
   effect of surface roughness 139 ff
   hysteresis . . . 143, 144
   in detergent processes . . 288
   in displacement of underground petroleum 348
   in emulsions stabilised by solids 262
   in flotation . . . 335 ff
   in flushing processes . . 283
   in wetting-out of soils . . 349
   on silicone-treated surfaces . 245
   receding 237
"Contortional energy" in wetting . 142
Controlled precipitation, preparation of dispersions by . . . 277 ff
Corner free energies . . . 91
Corrosion of metals, effect of surface-active agents . . . 347 ff
"Co-solubilisation" 53
Counterions, inclusion in ionic micelles 16, 25 ff, 29, 31
"Creoline" 251
Critical micelle concentration . 16 ff
Critical micelle concentration, determination of . . . 56 ff
   effect of counterion . . . 61
   effect of micelle size . . . 60
   effect of mixed amphipathic electrolytes 62
   effect of molecular structure . 60
   effect of non-electrolytes . . 62
   effect of organic solvents . . 62
   effect of polar group . . 61
   effect of solubilisate . . . 51
   effect of temperature . . 60
   factors influencing . . . 60
Crystal growth . . 192 ff, 199 ff
Crystal growth, thermodynamics of 187 ff
Crystal habit, effect of surface-active agents . . . . 195 ff
Crystals, equilibrium shape . . 190
Crystallisation processes, effect of macromolecules 202

PAGE

Cycloalkylaryl sulphonates . . 377
Cyclohexanol 299
Cyclohexylamine salts of anionic agents 493

Davies's interfacial equation of state 106
"Daxads" 378
Decontamination (from radioactivity) by surface-active agents . . 314
Deflocculating agents, mechanism of action . . . . . 171 ff
Deflocculation . . 160 ff, 234
   degrees of . . . 160, 161
   distinction from wetting . . 177
   in emulsions 250
   in wetting-out processes . 231, 232
Demulsification . . . 264 ff
   by surface-active agents . 265 ff
   in penicillin extraction . . 267
   mechanisms of . . 265 ff
   of oil field emulsions . . 266
   of tar emulsions . . . 267
Demulsifiers, surface films of . . 207
Density of solutions of amphipathic compounds 17
"Detergent builders" . 308 ff, 358
Detergent mixtures . . 494, 495
Detergent phenomena, ancillary (favourable) . . . 297 ff
   ancillary (unfavourable) . 301 ff
   fundamental . . . 286 ff
Detergent power, correlation with states of solution . . 315 ff
Detergent processes . . 285 ff
   "adhesion numbers" in . 296, 297
   carboxymethyl cellulose in 304, 305
   classification 285
   complex formation in 289 ff, 317
Detergent processes, complex micelles in 299
   contact angles in . . . 288
   definition 285
   deflocculation in . . 297, 310
   detachment of solid particles in . . . . . 295 ff
   "dirt-entrainment" in foams . 300
   displacement of liquid dirt in 287 ff
   effect of adsorption in . 292, 293
   effect of composite surfaces in . 294
   effect of condensed phosphates in . . . . . 309 ff
   effect of incomplete displacement of dirt 294
   effect of polarity of dirt . . 290
   effect of substrate . 290, 291, 292, 294
   electrical potentials in . 295, 296, 297, 298, 303, 305

PAGE

Detergent processes—(*contd.*)
emulsification in . . . 297
exhaustion of detergents in 301 ff
fat solvents in 299
foaming in . . . 300, 301
functions of surface-active agents
in . . . . . 287 ff
interfacial tension lowerings in 287 ff
kinetics of 292
lime-soap-dispersing agents in . 302
"myelenic growths" in . 289 ff
oil-soluble amphipathic substances in 298
photographic study of . 288 ff
protective colloids in . 304, 305
Detergent processes, radio-tracer
techniques in study of . . . 304
redeposition in . . 303 ff
"rolling-off" phenomenon in 289 ff
sequestering agents in . 302, 309
solubilisation effect in . 290, 291,
298, 299
spontaneous emulsification in . 290
spreading coefficient in . 287, 294
steric effects in . . . 305
swelling of fibres in . . . 309
van der Waals forces in . 296, 303,
305
work of adhesion in . 288, 291, 292
Young's equation in . 288, 291
Detergent tests, "chopped fibre" technique 307
"Launderometer" . . . 306
mechanical arrangements . 306 ff
radio-tracer techniques . 307 ff
sea water . . . 308 ff
selection of dirt . . . 307
Detergents . . . . 285 ff
addition of condensed phosphates
309 ff
anti-foaming agents for . . 312
biological decomposition of 312 ff
"biologically hard" . . 313 ff
"biologically soft" . . 313 ff
decomposition by bacteria 312 ff
decontamination with . . 314
dynamic service tensions . 121
Detergents, effect on oxygenation of
water . . . . 311 ff
effect on sewage disposal . 311 ff
evaluation . . . 305 ff
"Jephcott Committee" on . 310
precipitants for . . 312 ff
public health aspects of use 310 ff
sales of synthetic in United
Kingdom 313
"Standing Committee" on 313 ff
"Dettol" 332, 334

PAGE

Dialkylsulphosuccinates . 84, 130, 386
387
Diethanolamides, surface-active . 484
Digestion of precipitates, effect of
surface-active agents . . . 195
Diffusion to surfaces, energy barrier 118 ff
Disinfectants (*see* bactericides)
Disperse systems, barrier layers in 162 ff
Brownian motion in . . 170
electrical double layers in . 162 ff
electrokinetic potentials in . 166
inherent thermodynamical in-
stability of 161
solvated layers in . . . 173
stabilisation . . 10, 169, 170
steric stabilising factors in . 168 ff
Dispersed particles, interaction of
charged . . . 162 ff
Dispersible powders . . . 280
"Dispersing agents" . . . 160
Dispersion, by condensation . 277 ff
by controlled precipitation 277 ff
Dispersion by precipitation in mutual
solvent 278
Dispersion of solids . . 269 ff
Dispersion of solids, kinetics of . 185
Dispersion processes, mechanical 179 ff
surface-active agents in . 269 ff
Dispersions, mechanical methods of
preparing . . . . 270 ff
positively charged . . 463, 464
preparation . . . 269 ff
preparation by dry grinding with
solids 276
special characteristics of indus-
trial 270
spray drying of . . . 280
stabilisation . . . 279 ff
"Dispersol" 320
Disruption of solids, effect of surface-
active agents . . . 93, 181 ff
Draves test . . . . 223 ff
Drilling mud additives . . . 491
Drop penetration test . . . 246
Drops, spreading of . . . 214
Dry-cleaning . . . 299, 464
Dry grinding (*see* pulverisation)
Duplex films, effect on evaporation of
water 345
Dust particles, wetting-out . 219 ff
Dyeing assistants . . . 318 ff
Dyeing, pigment-pad . . . 325 ff
Dyestuffs, dispersible powders of . 280
Dyestuffs, dispersion of . 272, 274, 275,
277, 278, 279
fixing agents for . 322 ff, 456
Dyestuffs, micelles of . . . 41
Dyestuffs, stripping agents for 323 ff, 452

PAGE

"Dynamic factor" in wetting-out . 223
Dynamic surface tension. 114 ff, 119,
    121, 213, 214, 223, 224, 228, 229, 231

EDGE free energies 91
Electrical conductivity of amphi-
    pathic compounds . 19 ff, 24 ff, 57
Electrochemical classification of sur-
    face-active agents . . . 10
Electrokinetic potentials . 166, 255,
    259 ff, 295, 297, 298, 305, 446
Electrolysis baths, use of surface-
    active agents in 368
Electrolyte solutions, solubility of
    surface-active agents in . . 234
Electrolytes, amphipathic . 13 ff
Electroplating, effect of surface-
    active agents in . . . 346 ff
"Emulphors" 477
Emulsification by interfacial com-
    plexes . . . . 253 ff
    mayonnaise method . . . 260
    nascent soap principle 251, 253, 260
    processes . . . . 179 ff
    spontaneous 255
Emulsifying agents, effect on emulsion
    type . . . . . 261 ff
    functions of . . . 249 ff
    interfacial films of . . . 249
Emulsifying agents, mixed . 250 ff
    oil-soluble 252
Emulsifying machines . 256, 257, 258
Emulsion polymerisation 338 ff, 366, 436
Emulsion systems, thermodynamical
    stability 180, 252
Emulsion types, effect of surface-
    active agents 181
    factors determining . . . 263
Emulsions, deflocculation of . 250
    interfacial films in . . . 254
    multiple 264
    oil-in-water 254
    petroleum . : . . 266
    preparation . . . 248 ff
    water-in-oil . . 254, 259 ff
"Emulsol" 329
Energy barriers in diffusion to sur-
    faces . . . . . 118 ff
Equations of state, interfacial . 105 ff
Ester sulphonates . . . 381 ff
Esters (partial) of polyhydroxy com-
    pounds 484
Ether sulphonates . . . 394 ff
Ethylene diamine tetraacetic acid
    (and salts) . . 302, 338, 443, 444
Ethylene glycol esters . . 483, 484
Ethylene glycol polyethers (see poly-
    ethenoxy compounds)

PAGE

Evaporation of water, effect of sur-
    face-active materials . . 344 ff
Extraction processes, effect of sur-
    face-active agents . . 345 ff

FABRIC structure, effect on water-
    repellency . . . . 238 ff
Fatty acid salts (see soaps, alkali
    metal, and metal soaps)
Fatty acids 254
    α-substituted 367
Fatty acids, true sulphonates from . 364,
    365
Fatty alcohol-ethylene oxide con-
    densates . . . 255, 325, 470
    sulphated 410
Fatty alcohols . 253, 254, 255, 263,
    298, 345, 346, 405, 406
Fatty alcohols sulphated . . 404 ff
    (see also alkyl sulphates)
    true sulphonates from . . 366
Fermentation, effect of surface-
    active agents 334
"Fibrofix" 323
Fire-fighting foams 351
Fischer-Tropsch process and products 358,
    362, 414 ff, 440
"Fixanol" 322, 446
Flocculation . . . . 160 ff
    by macromolecules . . . 172
    by surface-active agents . 174 ff
    factors determining state of 161 ff
    of dyestuff dispersions . . 278
    of pigment dispersions . . 279
    reversible . 176, 177, 279, 280
Flotation . . . . . 335 ff
Fluorescent brightening agents . 314
"Flushing" process for dispersing
    pigments in non-aqueous media . 284
Foam formation . . . 202 ff
Foamed concrete 350
Foaming agents . 205, 206, 351, 352
Foaming in detergent processes 300, 301
Foams, destruction . . 206, 207
Foams, formation by detergents in
    sewage disposal . . . 311 ff
Foams, stabilising mechanisms in 204 ff
Foliage, spray retention by . . 219
Free energy functions for different
    interfacial processes . . 65
Fundamental interfacial processes 132 ff

GAS-absorption, effect of surface-
    active agents . . . 345 ff
Geophysical applications of surface-
    active agents . . . 348 ff
Gibbs-Duhem equation . . . 68

PAGE

Gibbs's equation . . . 64 ff
and adsorbed macromolecules 110 ff
and hydrolysis of surface-active
solute 76, 77
and "inert components" . . 70
and interfacial complexes . . 87
and micelle formation . 77 ff
and single component phases . 71
and special distribution ratios . 71
and surface-inactive components 71
and surface tension minima . 79
and "swamping" excess of electrolyte 75, 76
application to dynamic surface
tensions 124
at constant temperature and
pressure . . . 68 ff
at solid-liquid interfaces 89 ff, 94 ff
experimental verification . 83 ff
"factor 2" for surface-active
electrolytes . 75, 76, 78, 79, 84
for curved interfaces . . 73
for mutually soluble phases . 72
Gibbs's equation for surface-active
electrolytes . . . 74 ff
Guggenheim's convention . 68 ff
integration . . . 105, 108
prediction of interfacial tension
lowering from . . . 73
validity and applicability . 83
Gibbs free energy (total) of systems
containing interfaces . . . 65
Gibbs-Thomson equation . . 93
Glyceryl esters . 250, 254, 259, 484
Glycol esters 259
Grease solvents, addition to surface-
active agents 494
"Grinding aids" 276
Grinding kinetics 185
"Growth-from-seed" processes in pre-
cipitation 200

Haemolysis by surface-active agents 333
Helmholtz free energy . . . 65
"Hemi-micelles" at solid-liquid inter-
faces 99
Herbig test 224, 391
Highly sulphated oils . . 428, 429
"Highly sulphonated oils" . . 428
"Hostapon" process . . . 364
Hydrophilic-lipophilic (or hydro-
phobic) balance . . 231, 263
Hydrostatic pressure test for water-
repellency 246
"Hydrotropy" . . . 45, 230
Hydroxyamines, esterified . 447, 448

"Igepals" 79, 477

PAGE

"Igepons" . 173, 279, 297, 302, 357,
363, 381 ff, 388, 389, 420, 421, 423, 437,
444, 489, 494
Immersion tests for wetting-out 226, 227
work of 219
Immersional wetting . 137, 219 ff
Impact of spray droplets . 217 ff
Impact penetration test for water-
repellency 246
Impurities in surface-active agents,
effect on boundary tensions . 80, 81, 82
Indicators, use in determining critical
micelle concentration . . . 59
Indole derivatives, sulphonated 380, 381
Inorganic salts in commercial surface-
active products 496
Intensive mixing, preparation of dis-
persions by 277
Interfacial complexes . 87 ff, 253 ff
Interfacial equations of state . 105 ff
Interfacial films in emulsions . . 254
Interfacial free energy . . . 65
Interfacial phases . . . 67 ff
Interfacial processes, fundamental . 132 ff
Interfacial tension . . 4, 64 ff
Interfacial tension, effect of micelle
formation 39
"stretching," at solid interfaces 91 ff
"thermodynamical," at solid
interfaces . . . 92 ff
Interionic forces in adsorbed layers . 106,
107
Ionic antagonism in disperse systems . 280
Ionic micelles (*see* micelles)
Isothiourea derivatives . . . 450
"Izal" 332, 334

"Jephcott Committee" on detergents
310 ff

Kinetics of adsorption . . 113 ff

"Lamepons" 437, 438
Langmuir adsorption . . . 107
Langmuir equation of state . . 106
Launderometer test for detergents . 306
"Leonils" 302, 477
Levelling agents for dyestuffs . 318 ff
Light-scattering by solutions of
amphipathic compounds . . 39
Lignin sulphonates . 272, 274, 275, 276,
277, 278, 279, 280, 346, 491
modified 492
states of solution . . . 491
Lime-soap-dispersing agents . 302, 381,
383, 393, 410, 438, 444
"Lissapols" . 233, 357, 391, 444, 476
"Lissolamines" . . 323, 324, 452

PAGE

London–van der Waals forces between
particles 163
"Lyophobic" sols 10
Lysis of cells by surface-active agents
332 ff

MACROMOLECULES, adsorption of 108 ff,
169, 178
effect on crystallisation . . 202
equations of state of adsorbed . 112,
113
surface-active . . . 487 ff
thermodynamics of adsorption 110 ff
"Mahogany acids" 355
"Marasperse" 277
Mass law, application to micelle
formation . . . . 15 ff
Mass transfer, effect of surface-active
agents on . . . . 344 ff
Mayonnaise method of emulsification
249 ff, 260
Mechanical phase-subdivision pro-
cesses . . . . 179 ff
"Medialans" 437, 438
Mercaptans, oxidation to sulphonic
acids 367, 368
polyethenoxy derivatives . . 470
Mercerising, wetting-out agents for . 230,
231, 493
"Mersolats" . . 358, 362, 363, 368
Mesomorphic phases . . . 52
Metal soaps . 260, 261, 266, 283, 284
Metal-sequestering agents . 443, 444
Metallurgy, uses of surface-active
agents in . . . . 346 ff
Metaphosphates, substituted . . 442
Micelle 11
Micelle, adsorption 85
concentration in solutions of
amphipathic compounds . 17
Micelle, crystalline . . . 22 ff
cylindrical . . . 21, 33, 38
disc-shaped . . . 21, 35
effect of interionic forces on 25, 31
Micelle formation below critical
micelle concentration . . : 26
effect of molecular shape . . 40
effect on chemical potential . 28
effect on osmotic coefficient 27, 28
effect on solubilisation . . 48
effect on solubility . . . 26
Micelle in emulsion polymerisation 340 ff
ionic . . . . . 14 ff
lamellar . 22 ff, 30, 32, 33, 35, 37, 40
possible function in detergent
processes 316
proposed types . . 20 ff
rod-shaped 39

PAGE

Micelle—(contd.)
size, effect of electrolytes on 61, 62
solubility in 47
spherical. 21 ff, 33, 36, 37, 38, 40
types, evidence for and against 24 ff
X-ray evidence on . . 21 ff, 32
Micelles, mixed . 55, 81, 82, 230, 320,
323
"Migration" in textile dyeings . 325 ff
Milling, kinetics of 185
Mine roadways, wetting-out of 232 ff
Miscellaneous types of surface-active
agents . . . 487 ff
"Miscible oils" 251
"Monopol soaps" 433
Morpholine salts of anionic agents . 492
Multilayer adsorption, indications
from surface excesses . . 85
Myelenic growths . . . 52

"NACCONOLS" . . . 207, 320
Naphthalene sulphonates . 357, 369
Naphthalene sulphonic acid-formalde-
hyde condensates . 9, 41, 176, 377, 378
Naphthalene sulphonic acid-formalde-
hyde condensates (alkylated) 378, 379
"Naphthols" 324
Nascent soap in detergent processes . 286
emulsification processes . 251, 253,
260
Negative adsorption and surface
tension minima 80
"Nekals" . . 357, 370 ff, 494
"Neutral colloid" . . 14, 22
Nitrilotriacetic acid . . . 444
Non-aqueous media, flocculating
action of water in . . . 282
preparation of dispersions in 281 ff
stabilising mechanisms in . 281 ff
Non-ionic surface-active agents 465 ff
advantages 465
miscellaneous types . . 483
negative temperature coefficient
of solubility 53
states of solution . . . 42
Nucleation-and-growth processes in
precipitation 200
Nucleation, effect of surface-active
agents . . . 191 ff
thermodynamics of . . 188 ff

"OIL-ABSORPTION" test . . . 232
Oil-in-water emulsions, theory of
stability 167
Oil media (*see* non-aqueous media)
Oils, self-emulsifiable . . 251 ff
Olefins, sulphated . . 345, 415 ff
(*see also* alkyl sulphates)

PAGE

Olefins, true sulphonates from . . 365

Oleyl-*p*-anisidide-2-sulphonate . 197, 280, 302, 319

"Optical bleaches" (*see* fluorescent brightening agents)

Organic bases, salts with anionic agents 492, 493

Osmotic activity of solutions of amphipathic compounds 18, 27, 28

"Oxo" process . 385, 386, 412, 413, 414, 419

Oxygenation of water, effect of surface-active agents . . 311 ff

"PALISADE layer" in ionic micelles . 52

Paraffin-chain salts, solutions of 14 ff

Particle growth, effect of surface-active materials . . . 192 ff

Penetration test for wetting-out agents 222

"Peptising agents" 160

"Peregal" 320, 321

Perfluoro radicals . . 442, 443

Perfluoroalkane sulphonates . . 368

Perfluorocarboxylic acids . . 443

Perfluorosulphonic acids . . 443

"Perminal" 233

"Persistol" 486

Persulphates, substituted . 441

Persulphonates, substituted . 441

Petroleum, displacement from underground layers 348

Petroleum sulphonates, alkylated . 371

Petroleum sulphonates as emulsifiers . 260

Phase-formation processes . 186 ff

"Phemeride" 330

Phenols, solubilisation by surface-active agents 252

Phenothiazine, wetting-out of . 235

Phillips-Rideal interfacial equation of state 106

Phosphated oils . . . 442

Phosphates, substituted . . 442

Phosphono-quaternary ammonium compounds 486

Phthalocyanines, dispersion of. 272, 276, 278, 279, 378

Pigment-pad dyeing . . 325, 435

Pigment-vehicle interface . 281, 282

Pigments, aggregation during drying . 282, 283

　dispersion . 272, 274, 276, 277, 278, 279, 282

　"flushing" process for dispersing in oil media . . . 282 ff

　improvement of oil-dispersibility 282 ff

　improvement of texture . 282, 283

PAGE

Plastic-milling . . . . 273 ff

　antiquity of 274

　function of surface-active agents in 274

　preparation of dispersible powders by 280

　preparation of sub-microscopic dispersions by . . . 275

Plauson mills 273

"Pluronics" 79, 474

Poisoning of nuclei during precipitation processes . . . 194

Polyacrylates 488

Polyethenoxy agents . 42, 215, 252, 289, 313, 320, 323, 325, 352, 466 ff

　critical micelle concentration . 479

　detergent power . . 479, 480

　distribution of molecular weights 467, 468

　effect of number of polyether groups on properties . . 478

　emulsifying power . . 479

　foaming power . . . 479

　for washing fuel oil tanks . 476, 477

　from alkyl phenols . . 471

　hydration mechanism . 173, 174

　in self-emulsifiable oils . 252

Polyethenoxy agents in wetting-out processes 235

　negative temperature coefficient of solubility . . . 43, 477

　preparation . . . 466 ff

　starting materials for . 469 ff

　summary of B.I.O.S. information 477 ff

　uses of . . . 468, 475 ff

　versatility of . . 475, 476

　wetting-out properties . 479

Polyether carboxylates . . 439

Polyethylene glycols (*see* polyethenoxy agents)

Polyglycerol derivatives . . 480 ff

　esters . . . 217, 278

Polyglycol esters . . . 259

Polymer sulphonates . . 250

Polymerised dioxolane derivatives . 484, 485

Polymers, adsorption of . . 109 ff

　surface-active . . 487 ff

Polypropylene oxide-polyethenoxy compounds . . 474, 475

Polysiloxanes (silicones) . . 244 ff

"Polysoaps" 56

Polyvinyl acetals . . . 488

Polyvinyl alcohol . 8, 264, 305, 488

　sulphated . . . 488

Polyvinyl pyrrolidone . 305, 489

PAGE

Porous masses, wetting-out of . 151 ff,
222 ff

Potential energy curves for disperse
particles 164, 165

Powders, dispersible . . . 280

Powders, wetting and wetting-out of . 158,
231 ff, 275

Precipitates, effect of surface-active
agents on fineness . . 193 ff

Precipitation processes . . 186 ff

Protective colloid action . 10, 117 ff

Prussian Blue, flocculation and deflocculation by cationic agents . 175

Pulverisation. . . 184, 275, 276

Public health aspects of detergents 310 ff

Purity of surface-active agents, surface tension minima as criterion . 82

Pyridinium compounds, surface-
active . 26, 29, 45, 48, 58, 99, 122,
126, 215, 225, 251, 297, 322, 328, 329,
332, 336, 347, 348, 350, 445, 447, 456 ff,
463, 464

QUATERNARY ammonium compounds 19,
30, 39, 126, 130, 175, 197, 249, 253, 267,
284, 323, 324, 325, 326, 328, 329, 332,
335, 336, 343, 347, 348, 445, 447, 451 ff,
460, 463

Quaternary arsonium compounds . 462,
463

Quaternary phosphonium compounds 284,
445, 462, 463

Quaternary stibonium compounds . 462,
463

RADIOACTIVE contamination, removal
by surface-active agents . . 314

Radiotracer technique, application
to adsorption measurements . 83 ff,
99, 129

Rain, increasing wetting-out power
for soils 349
penetration into water-proofed
fabrics . . . 237 ff

Rain test (du Pont) for water-
repellency 246

Rebound of spray droplets . 218 ff

Redeposition of dirt in detergent
processes . . . . 303 ff

Reed reaction . 358, 362 ff, 368,
376, 408, 440

Rehbinder effect . . 181 ff, 276

Restraining agents for dyestuffs 318 ff

"Retrograde dissociation" . . 31

Reversible flocculation by surface-
active agents . . . 176, 177

"Re-wetting". 217

PAGE

Road-building, use of surface-active
agents in 350

Roller mills 273

Roughness of surfaces, effect on
wetting . . . . 139 ff

SALICYLATES, substituted . . 440

"Sand-milling" . . . 272

"Santomerse" 340

"Sapamines" . 322, 446, 447, 452, 453, 496

Sarcosine derivatives . . . 437

Schultze-Hardy rule . 162, 167, 298

Screw dislocations in crystal growth . 187

"Second critical micelle concentration". 52

"Sedimentation paradox" . . 171

Sedimentation volume . 170, 171, 175

Self-emulsifiable oils . 180, 251 ff

Sewage disposal, effect of surface-
active agents in . . . 311 ff

Silane-substituted carboxylic acids . 443

Silicone oils as anti-foaming agents . 352

Silicones, surface properties . . 245

Silicones, water-proofing with . 244 ff

Silver halide sols, effect of surface-
active agents 201

Sinking of porous masses . 221 ff

Sinking tests for wetting-out . 222, 226,
227, 228

"Sinking" wetting . . 147 ff, 159

Soaps, alkali metal. 34, 36, 48, 52, 80, 85,
121, 205, 249, 253, 254, 261, 265, 268,
280, 284, 298, 302, 304, 309, 314, 336,
338, 339, 341, 342

Sodium cellulose glycollate (*see* carboxymethyl cellulose)

Sodium hexametaphosphate . 302, 309,
314

Soils, water-proofing of . . 348
wetting-out of . . . 349

Solid-liquid interfaces, Gibbs's
equation for . . . 89 ff, 94 ff

Solid-liquid interfaces, kinetics of
adsorption 131
mobility in . . . 93, 94

Solid-liquid interfacial tension . 90 ff

Solids, boundary tensions of . . 138

Solids, dispersion of . . 269 ff

Solubilisation . . 4, 26, 37, 44 ff
effect of ordinary electrolytes . 52
lipophilic and hydrophilic affinities in 54
mechanism of . . . 47 ff, 55
of surface-active agents in oils . 251,
252
of water in non-aqueous solvents 54

Solubility, differential . . . 49
effect of particle size on . 189 ff

PAGE

Solubility—(*contd.*)
of amphipathic compounds   26, 27
of surface-active agents in concentrated electrolytes   .   . 234
"Solution Salts"   .   .   . 398
Sorbitan esters   .   .   259, 473
condensed with ethylene oxide . 252, 473
"Spans"   473
(*see also* sorbitan esters)
Spontaneous emulsification   .   . 180
Spray retention   .   .   215, 219
Sprays, effect of surface-active agents
in   .   .   .   .   . 217 ff
Spreading, areas of.   .   . 213, 214
Spreading coefficient   .   133, 212, 213
calculation from dimensions of
single drops 137
for finite contact angle   .   . 136
Spreading of drops 214
Spreading wetting .   .   133 ff, 212
Spreading, work of.   .   . 214, 216
Stabilisation of dispersions   .   279 ff
"Standing Committee on Detergents,"
reports   .   .   .   . 313 ff
States of solution of surface-active
agents   .   .   .   . 12 ff
correlation with detergent action 315 ff
Static surface tension in wetting
processes   .   .   .   213, 214
Stearamidomethylpyridinium chlor-
ide   .   .   .   241, 242, 243
(*see also* "Velan" and "Zelan")
Stearyloxymethylpyridinium chloride 241, 244
Steric effects in stabilisation of
emulsions 266
in non-aqueous media   .   . 281
Stokes's law, application to ionic
micelles   .   .   14, 25, 26
Stripping agents for dyestuffs .323 ff, 452
Succinates, substituted   .   .   . 439
Sucrose derivatives   .   250, 485
"Sugar detergents"   .   .   . 485
Sulphamic acids, acyl   .   .   . 391
Sulphated abietyl alcohols   .   . 420
Sulphated carbohydrates   .   . 436
castor oil   .   425, 429, 430
fatty acids   .   .   424 ff
fatty alcohol-ethylene oxide condensates   421
fatty alcohols   .   .   404 ff
(*see also* alkyl sulphates)
branched-chain .   .   410 ff
chlorinated   .   .   . 409
Sulphated fatty alcohols, modified   . 408
secondary   .   .   . 410 ff
tertiary .   .   .   . 410 ff

PAGE

Sulphated fatty condensation products.   .   .   .   . 420 ff
esters   .   .   .   . 424 ff, 431
glycerides   .   .   . 424 ff
Sulphated glucosides   .   .   . 422
glycerol esters .   .   . 422, 423
glycerol ethers.   .   .   . 422
glycol esters   .   .   422, 423
oils   .   230, 265, 325, 424 ff
oils, as additives to soaps .   . 435
as dyeing assistants   .   . 435
as wool-felting assistants   . 435
by-products in .   .   426, 427
esterified .   .   .   431 ff
modern   429
polymerised   .   .   . 433
reactions in preparation   424 ff
Sulphated olefinic telomers   .   . 418
Sulphated olefins, halogenated .   . 418
Sulphated squalene   .   .   . 417
tallow alcohols   .   409, 410
unsaturated amines .   .   . 417
Sulphating agents   .   .   405 ff, 430
Sulphation, chemistry of.   403, 404, 430
Sulphation in mutual solvents .   . 413
Sulphation processes, catalysts for   . 430
continuous   .   .   407, 408
Sulphinates, substituted .   .   . 442
"Sulphite cellulose lye" (*see* lignin
sulphonates)
Sulphoacetates, alkyl   .   .   . 385
Sulphoacyl compounds   .   385 ff
Sulphoacylamide compounds   .   392, 393
Sulphoamide compounds.   .   388, 389
Sulphobetaines, substituted   .   . 486
Sulphocarboxylic acid esters   .   . 387
Sulphochlorination process   .   362, 363, 393
Sulphoesters 382
Sulphonamide sulphonates   .   393, 394
Sulphonated amines   .   .   398 ff
Sulphonated benzoin condensation
products   .   .   .   400, 401
Sulphonated castor oil   .   .   . 360
esters   .   .   .   380 ff
fatty acids   .   338, 364, 365, 367
formaldehyde-based resins   489, 490
ketones   .   .   .   400, 401
"Sulphonated oils" (*see* sulphated oils)
Sulphonated sulphones   .   .   . 401
sulphur-containing compounds   . 401
Sulphonates, miscellaneous types   394 ff
Sulphonates, perfluoroalkane   .   . 368
Sulphonates (true) in sulphated oils . 427
Sulphonating agents   .   358, 359, 364 ff, 377, 381, 383, 396, 397
Sulphonic acids, classification   . 359, 360
Sulphosuccinate esters   .   .   . 357

PAGE

Sulphosuccinates, polymeric esters . 387
"Superficial tension" . . 91, 92
Surface activity, fundamental pheno-
mena 3
Surface-ageing, diffusion phenomena
in . . . . . 116 ff
    effect of hydrolysis . . . 122
    effect of micelle formation in . 122
    energy barriers in . . . 122
    (rapid) . . . 114 ff
        effect of volatility of solute . 125
        factors in . . . 124, 125
    (slow) . . . . 126 ff
        effect of electrolytes . . 127
        effect of micelles . . 127
        effect of trace impurities . 129,
                                130
        steric barriers in . . 129
    transition state kinetic theory . 123
Surface excesses . . . 64 ff
    contradictory results on . . 86
    conventions for expressing . 66, 67
    direct determination . . 83 ff
    possible effect of impurities on . 87
    very high 85
"Surface pellicles" . . . 85, 128
Surface tension, dynamic (*see*
    dynamic surface tension)
Surface tension lowering as criterion
    of wetting power . . . 155
    minima as criterion of purity . 82
Synthetic fibres, spinning additives
    for 463

"TEEPOL" . 202, 233, 363, 417, 418
Ternary sulphonium compounds . 284,
                            445, 462, 463
Textile oils, emulsifiable . . . 434
Textiles, water-proofing of . 236 ff
    wetting-out of . . 151, 221 ff
Thiosulphates, substituted . . 441
Transport numbers of amphipathic
    compounds . . . 28 ff
"Traube's rule" . . . 88, 89
Triethanolamine . 252, 348, 448, 492
"Tritons" 44, 329
Turkey Red Oil . 339, 347, 348, 355,
    406, 427, 429, 430, 433, 435, 494
"Tweens" . . . 122, 192, 473
Twitchell process . . . 356
Twitchell reagents . . 356, 375, 376
"Tylose" 496

UREA, addition to polyethenoxy
    agents 495
Urea-formaldehyde resins as surface-
    active agents . . . 489

PAGE

VALVE homogenisers . . . 249
"Vantropol" 333
Vat dyestuffs, stripping agents for 323 ff
"Velan" . 184, 241 ff, 440, 451, 457,
                            459, 463
Vibrating jet technique . 114 ff, 120, 123
Volmer-Frumkin equation of state . 107,
                            293
Volumes, partial specific, of amphi-
    pathic compounds . 13, 17, 28

VAN DER WAALS, forces in adsorbed
    layers 106
Water-in-oil emulsions . 254, 259 ff
Water-proofing agents . 450, 457 ff
Water-proofing, mechanism of action
    of "Velan PF" . . . 241 ff
Water-proofing of soils . . . 348
Water-proofing processes . 211 ff, 236 ff
Water-repellency, break-down of . 239
    tests for . . . 245 ff
Waxes, use in water-proofing . . 240
Wettability of solids, reduction by
    surface-active agents . . 146
Wetting . . . . 132 ff
Wetting, adhesional . . 137
Wetting-back processes . . 235 ff
Wetting, capillary . . . 234
    distinction from deflocculation . 177
    dynamic boundary tensions in 156 ff
    effect of adsorption of surface-
        active agents in . 144, 145
    effect of composite surfaces 140, 141
    effect of surface roughness 139 ff
Wetting, hysteresis in . 143, 144
Wetting in capillary systems . 147 ff
    kinetics of . . 157 ff
Wetting, immersional . 137, 219 ff
Wetting in tapering capillaries 148 ff
"Wetting index" . . . 225
"Wetting inertia" . . 157, 159
Wetting, kinetics of . . 156 ff
Wetting of composite and rough sur-
    faces, thermodynamics . 141, 142
    porous masses . . 147 ff
    powders . . . 158
    textile yarns . . . 151
Wetting, spreading . . . 212
    thermodynamics of . . 132 ff
    types of . . . 133
Wetting-out . . 5, 211 ff
Wetting-out agents, horticultural 213 ff
    in calcium chloride solutions 233 ff
    mercerising . . 230, 231
Wetting-out, canvas square test for . 227
    capillary . . . 221 ff
    deflocculation in . . 231

PAGE

Wetting-out—(*contd.*)
 depletion of surface-active agent
  in 228
 dynamic factor in . . . 223
 immersion tests for . . 226, 227
 in concentrated electrolytes . 229
 in detergent processes . . 286
Wetting-out of coal dust. . 232 ff
 dust particles . . . 219 ff
 mine roadways . . 232 ff
 phenothiazine 280
 porous masses . . . 221 ff
 powders . . . . 231 ff
 textiles . . . . 221 ff
Wetting-out power, equilibrium surface tension as a guide . 229
Wetting-out processes . . 211 ff
 significance of contact angle in . 213
 spreading of bulk liquid phases in 212
Wetting-out, sinking . . 221 ff
 sinking tests for . . 226, 227

PAGE

Wetting-out tests . . . 224 ff
"White dyes" (*see* fluorescent brighten-
 ing agents)
Work of adhesion . 137, 218 ff, 237, 239
Work of immersion . . . 219
Work of spreading . . . 214, 216

Xanthates . . 336, 337, 338, 441
X-ray data on solutions of amphipathic compounds . 21 ff, 32 ff

YOUNG's equation . 134 ff, 228, 229
Young's equation in detergent processes 288, 291

"Zelan" (*see* also VELAN) . 241, 247
"Zephiran" . . . 329, 331
"Zephirol" 329
Zeta potentials (*see* electrokinetic
 potential)
Zwitterions, surface-active . . 486